KU-465-972

The Migrations of Birds

The Migrations of Birds

by

JEAN DORST
(of the National Museum of Natural History, Paris)

TRANSLATED BY
CONSTANCE D. SHERMAN

WITH A FOREWORD BY
ROGER TORY PETERSON

HEINEMANN

LONDON MELBOURNE TORONTO

William Heinemann Ltd
LONDON MELBOURNE TORONTO
CAPE TOWN AUCKLAND
THE HAGUE

First published in Great Britain 1962

First published in the French language under the title
Les Migrations des Oiseaux

Printed in Great Britain
by The Windmill Press Ltd
Kingswood, Surrey

Contents

Foreword vii
Introduction xi
1. Old Explanations of Bird Migrations 1
2. Methods of Studying Migrations 12
3. Migrations in Europe and Northern Asia 37
4. Migrations in North America 97
5. Migrations in the Southern Hemisphere 140
6. Migrations in Intertropical Regions 155
7. Sea-bird Migrations 171
8. Modes of Migration 207
9. Bird Invasions 263
10. The Hibernation of Birds 278
11. The Physiological Stimulus of Migration 282
12. Orientation of Migratory Birds 320
13. The Origin and Evolution of Migrations 371
Conclusion 387
Bibliography 389
Index 443

Foreword

BIRDS HAVE WINGS; they travel. That is undoubtedly the key to their popularity, for of all living things no other class of animals has such immediate appeal.

Were it not for this mobility bird-watching would lose half its glamour. It is the unexpected bird, the rare wanderer, that delights the field-glass fraternity. But, by and large, the sweep of birds northward in the spring, southward in the autumn, follows an orderly, almost predictable pattern. Predictable perhaps, but nonetheless puzzling and mysterious.

Through the activities of the birders, who during our century have multiplied from mere thousands to hundreds of thousands, we know a great deal about the obvious or visible aspects of migration, particularly the dates of arrival and departure. By means of bird-banding, which now has many thousands of devotees in at least a score of countries, we know approximately the paths taken by a majority of the birds of the northern hemisphere. Less well-known are the mechanics and aerodynamics of their flight and just how they are affected by winds and the other meteorological conditions they encounter; but we know far more of the facts than we did twenty years ago.

The frontiers of investigation lie mostly in the sphere of navigation. Just how does a bird find its way? What is the nature of its built-in mechanism of orientation? We cannot as yet give a clean-cut answer. However, both the existence and the physical basis of bird navigation have been established, though they are not well understood. Since the end of World War II there has been a renascence of research along these lines. A number of provocative theories have been advanced; some have been discarded.

At the post-war International Ornithological Congresses held in Uppsala, Basel, and Helsinki and attended by scientists of thirty or forty countries, the most sensational papers—the show stoppers—

have usually dealt with migration. How thrilling it was in 1950 to hear Gustav Kramer tell of his controlled experiments with starlings, indicating that the ultimate source of their orientation was the sun. However, he did not account for the ability of night migrants to find their way. At the meetings in 1958 Franz Sauer of Germany explained how he used a model planetarium to prove that nocturnal migrants derive their orientation from the stars. At the same session, Ernst Sutter, of Basel, opened a whole new vista of exploration by showing movies of night migration as revealed by the radar screen.

It might seem, then, that to study migration properly, a pair of binoculars has little use today; one must use a radar screen, a planetarium, or some other highly technical and prohibitively expensive apparatus. This, of course, is far from true. There is much to be learned simply by looking at live birds. It might be pointed out that radar-watching, which is becoming popular, often produces data quite at variance with the field data turned in by the local bird-watchers who scout the countryside the following morning. The reasons for the disparity should be sought; neither technique should be discredited. All data, to have value, must be correctly interpreted.

The advantages of migration are obvious. By summering in one area and wintering in another, many birds acquire a flexibility denied more sedentary animals; they can exploit two different parts of the world. Food would seem to be the key factor. But though the advantages are easy to see, they do not explain the complicated evolution of such a habit. We can only speculate about this, and advance theories; the origin are lost in the past.

Observation and experiment must concern themselves mostly with the actual process of migration as it occurs today. And yet it takes clever detective work to arrive at some of the facts—particularly the obscure activities of night migrants. Nocturnal airborne movements may seem to contradict what we see close to the earth in the daytime. Moon-watching, by means of small telescopes and now the radar screen, is revealing some of the massive movements of the night travellers. But to know precisely what the individual bird does, to know how it takes its direction, how it compensates for the wind that bears it effortlessly like a swimmer in a strong current, how it reacts when confronted by fog or storm, what it does should it overshoot its mark—to know these things accurately one would have to *be* a bird.

The pleasure in most things is in the quest. I wonder whether we shall ever arrive at the ultimate answer to the riddle of migration. But it will be fun trying.

Because the study of migration is so many-sided and because recent advances have added so much to our knowledge there is need for such a book as this to bring things up to date and summarize them clearly.

There is no provincialism, no regional slant to this work; nor should there be, for migration is a world-wide phenomenon. The European or the North American bird student with a sophisticated knowledge of his own continent may well have his eyes opened when he reads about migration and migration studies on the other side of the ocean. Bird-ringing, or bird-banding, call it what you will, involves many countries, thousands of ornithologists, and millions of birds (in fact more than 1,000,000 birds are ringed annually, over 600,000 in the United States and Canada alone). Among the thousands of interesting facts that fill this book, we are given an up-to-date breakdown of bird-banding activity and methods, country by country.

Those who already have the earlier books on migration on their shelves will find many of the post-war advances presented here for the first time in an all-inclusive volume. No one can claim 'migration literacy' unless he knows some of the details about Professor Yeagley's theory of orientation in relation to the earth's magnetic field; Lowery and Newman's ambitious moon-watching project; Kramer's diurnal migration experiments with starlings; Sauer's experiments with nocturnal migrants using a planetarium; and the radar work that is now being conducted on two continents. These exciting developments are explained clearly and with a generous use of illustration.

We are grateful for the number of maps and diagrams that Dr Dorst has selected for our pleasure. There are more than 130 of them, some of which have been published elsewhere, while many others are new. A schematic diagram often explains an experiment or an idea much more clearly than words.

European ornithologists need no introduction to Jean Pierre Dorst. No one is better qualified to speak with authority about the involved problems of bird migration and to take the whole world in his stride. Since receiving his Docteur ès Sciences at the Sorbonne in 1949, he has had a brilliant career and is now a member, officer, or committee member of 25 scientific societies of France, Spain, Great Britain, the United States, Germany, and the Netherlands. He has three books and 160 scientific papers to his credit and, in addition, is deeply involved in international wildlife conservation—an extraordinary record for a man who is only thirty-seven.

Ornithologists, like the birds they study, have a way of travelling. With wings on their heels, they chafe at the confinement of the office or the classroom. Although the Muséum National d'Histoire Naturelle in Paris is Dr Dorst's base of operations—his chosen habitat, if we may call it that—he loses no opportunity to investigate such faraway places as the Peruvian altiplano, desert islands of the Pacific, or the forests of tropical Africa. I, myself, have watched birds and talked birds with Dr Dorst in such farflung parts of the world as the Swiss Alps, the Finnish forests, the Kafue Flats in Northern Rhodesia, and at my home in rural Connecticut. As the author of a book such as this he is eminently qualified, for no scholar can fully comprehend the sweep of migration and its various ramifications unless he himself has travelled.

ROGER TORY PETERSON

Introduction

One of the fundamental characteristics of animals is their ability to move about. Although this trait varies considerably from one zoölogical group to another, no animal is chained fast to its environment; and all travel about in at least one stage of their development.

This capacity to move is used primarily to seek improved living conditions. These journeys are, however, of two different types: some are non-cyclical, with individuals or whole populations covering long distances, yet never going back to their place of departure; others, on the contrary, are much more regular, occurring at definite intervals in the animal's life cycle, and always including a return trip to the region where they began.

Many authors have combined these two types of movement, cyclical and 'one-way', under the name *migration*. Thus the term 'human migration' is used to designate the wanderings of men who have come in successive 'one way' waves to settle in various parts of our globe. The same type of migratory movement is found in various animals, for example, mammals which settle or attempt to settle in new territories, and which have no impulse to return to their former abodes.

It is true that, etymologically, the term *migration*, derived from the Latin *migrare*, 'to go from one place to another,' applies to all such movements. In our opinion, however, it would be well to make a sharp distinction between these two types of animal mobility, and to reserve the word *migration* for cyclic or periodic movements. This usage, customarily applied to birds, should, of course, be extended to several other zoölogical groups. The other types of movement may be termed emigration, immigration, invasion, extension or dispersal as the case may be.

Let us note, however, that even true migration may be linked to non-cyclical movements, at least in its remote origin. The annual rhythm of movements, particularly of birds, may be conceived as resulting from an extension of their original habitat towards regions which they did not occupy earlier. Certain animal populations, moreover, still perform massive migrations which are easily confused with seasonal movements [i.e. migrations]. But there is a basic distinction. We shall therefore define the term 'migration' as a series of periodic 'round-trips' – usually annual – in the course of an animal's life cycle between a breeding area – called 'home' – and a region where the animal spends a period of varying length outside the reproductive area and which it then leaves to go back to its 'home'.

Movements of this kind are very common throughout the whole animal kingdom. Among invertebrates, numerous crustaceans move periodically from one marine zone to another; the common crab, for example, *Cancer pagurus*, leaves the intertidal zone at regular intervals to go into deeper waters; certain species adapted to life in the air, like the land crabs of tropical regions (*Geocarcinus* of the West Indies, for instance), reproduce in the sea and then return to land. Insects make much more generalized migratory movements, but they are not always truly cyclic. The brevity of their life span prevents most insects from performing real migrations like those of birds, that is, making a round trip. Populations and their progeny seem to migrate, rather than individuals. The monarch butterflies (*Danaus plexippus*) of North America leave the Great Lakes to winter as far south as the Gulf of Mexico. They move in groups and spread on rather constant axes along the Atlantic Coast and through the Mississippi Valley. We do not know, however, whether any individuals survive long enough to travel from the north to Florida or whether successive generations give the impression of migration. There is no need to recall the famous periodic movements of migratory locusts, which occur in continental areas, both in the Old and the New World.

Vertebrates probably perform the most specialized migrations. Innumerable fishes are great travellers, coming to specific places to spawn but spending the rest of the time in regions that are often very remote. Among them sardines, herring, codfish and tuna often cover long distances during the course of the year in their search for optimal conditions (particularly water temperature). Certain fishes, notably salmon, make even longer migrations, which include movements from fresh to salt water and back again.

Among the mammals, the caribou, the North American bison, a

large number of African antelopes and the elephants perform periodic movements of varying distance which are probably explained by grazing requirements that cannot be satisfied in any one region during the whole year. Certain cetaceans (such as the hump-back whale [*Megaptera*]) leave the antarctic seas every year, travelling north to spend the southern winter in equatorial waters. Certain species of bats of both the Old and New World also make long seasonal flights.

Migratory phenomena are thus very common throughout the whole animal kingdom, but they are most conspicuous among birds, which have the best developed faculties for swift, long travels. Gifted with exceptional mobility, remarkable facilities for adaptation, they are, however, extremely dependent on their surroundings in spite of an excellent adjustment to changing temperatures. Because of their high rate of metabolism, most species require a rich, abundant supply of food at frequent intervals; this is often unobtainable throughout the year in any given region. Furthermore, the oviparous reproduction of birds makes them exceptionally sensitive to their environment. This is because the egg and the young bird require very special conditions, especially in the many species in which the young hatch at a very early stage of development (altricial species) and thus require a long period of nest care.

These factors suggest why birds perform the most numerous and best defined migrations. Innumerable varieties of birds reproduce in a territory called their *home* but which, when the young are grown, they forsake for a different and often very distant area (winter quarters), where they spend most of the year outside of their reproductive period. There are thus two early journeys, the first, the postnuptial, towards the winter quarters, and the second, the prenuptial return flight, to the breeding area.[1]

1. For a long time it was believed that certain migrants breed in a fixed locality, then migrate towards another where they raise a second brood. This would imply that a migration occurred between two zones of reproduction. That, however, is false and, with rare exceptions, difficult to imagine from a physiological point of view. Only a few tropical birds whose internal rhythm is not well regulated might perform movements of this kind, as seems to be the case with some Mexican humming-birds, which nest near Mexico City in April and May, then migrate six months later a distance of 75—112 miles to the eastern Sierras, where they raise a new brood (Wagner *in* Schüz, 1952). Such a movement is, however, very exceptional among migrants.

We should note that some birds which raise two broods a year may make a rather long flight between the two nesting grounds. According to Peiponen (1957), the redpoll (*Carduelis flammea*) does this in Finland. Redpolls are believed

It is important to state that these names are arbitrary and often improper. The purely conventional idea of *home* does not imply that the species came originally from the part of the world where it is nesting at the present time. The latter is by no means its fixed centre of differentiation and dispersion. The terms winter zones and winter quarters are also improper when the species goes into the opposite hemisphere; a boreal bird which goes into the austral hemisphere to avoid our winter does not 'winter' in the literal sense of the term because it is in a region of 'summer.'

Some birds, moreover, leave their nesting grounds not to winter but to *pass the summer* in a different place. H. and T. Heim de Balsac (1949–51) pointed this out in the case of some Sahara birds. The cream-coloured courser (*Cursorius cursor*) and the bar-tailed desert lark (*Ammomanes cinctura*), for example, nest in the northern Sahara in early spring, then go farther *north* to the Barbary Coast to spend the summer. The desert regions where they breed have become uninhabitable because of the high temperature and ensuing drought. These birds therefore make their postnuptial flights in a northerly direction, in contrast to what is usually the case among Palearctic birds. Instances of this kind seem exceptional but may be more common than we now suppose. Therefore, in such circumstances it seems better to substitute the phrase 'rest area' for the term 'winter quarters'. Rest area would apply to the inactive sexual period of the bird.

As the bird's breeding cycle is annual in the vast majority of cases, migrations generally have a yearly rhythm, and only a few species, which breed every second year, have migrations extending over a longer period. Also young birds which have not attained sexual maturity are sometimes not subjected to as rigorous a calendar as their elders; yet all this applies but to special cases.[1]

---

to nest early in the spring in the coniferous forest zone, and then to go north into the *fjeld* region (barren plateaus) for their second brood. In view of the short distance involved, this seems to be really only a change of habitat; but, as there is a journey between the two broods, it fits, to a certain degree, into the migratory picture.

1. There are also some birds whose cycle lasts less than a year. This is especially true of the wide-awake tern (*Sterna fuscata*) nesting on Ascension Island, about which Chapin and Wing have furnished remarkable details (*Auk* 71:1–15, 1954 and 76:153–158, 1959). These terns nest on an average every 9.6 calendar or 10 lunar months, which means that they begin to nest five times

One might think that migratory would differ radically from sedentary birds. But it would be a mistake to attempt to draw a clear line of demarcation between the two categories because of many intermediate types that exist. A glance at the birds comprising the European avifauna will prove this.

During the breeding period, all birds are tied down to specific areas, their *territories*; there the nest is usually placed and the area is defended jealously against intrusion by other individuals of the same species. Apart from the breeding period, however, there is much less attachment to a given spot. Numerous birds, European tits, for example, wander through an area of varying size but they do not leave the general region where they were hatched, or where they raised their young. During the winter season the so-called sedentary species often keep to very small areas of a few square miles in extent.

Others, like black-headed gulls, go much farther and spread widely over a vast region. This we call *winter dispersion.* Intermediary stages range from simple wandering or nomadism on a larger scale to occasional flights in a particular direction.

Next come the better defined *migrations* which take birds to definite territories. In general, winter quarters usually have less sharply defined boundaries than do the breeding territories, apparently because birds do not seem to feel the same attachment for the former. Yet this notion must be revised, in some instances at least, as more and more observations reveal migrants that return every year to the same winter quarters. Salim Ali (*Journ. Bombay Nat. Hist. Soc.*, 47:161, 1947) noted that a grey wagtail (*Motacilla cinerea*) came back to his garden in Bombay to spend every winter from 1942 to 1946. In the New World P. Schwartz (*in litt.*) found during the course of studies devoted to the northern waterthrush (*Seiurus noveboracensis*) that several individuals returned to occupy the same winter territory in the botanical gardens of Caracas, Venezuela, in which they had been banded the previous year. In Bent's classic *Life Histories* the volume on the wood warblers records that a myrtle warbler (*Dendroica c. coronata*), banded in its winter quarters at Thomasville, Georgia, in February, 1917, was captured again in March, 1920, and on

---

instead of four in every four-year period. Such periodicity is probably correlated with absence of climatic variation on this oceanic island. These terns thus have a functional cycle whose rhythm is not understood. Similar cases will be found among birds living in equatorial zones where there are no seasonal changes.

several occasions in March, 1921; this bird was then at least five years old and meanwhile it had gone back four times to its northern nesting territory. In tropical Africa F. Roux (*personal communication*), while studying the biology of Palearctic migrants in Senegal, found insectivorous passerines in the very places where they had been banded the year before.

These cases reveal a hitherto unsuspected fidelity to winter quarters. Although experiments with winter homing have indicated a certain attachment to this area (see p. 326), it should not be concluded that all migratory birds return to occupy exactly the same winter quarters.

Every transitional form may be manifested in one species or even in a single local population. Cases of *partial migration* are rather numerous where certain individuals in a given region carry out their whole annual cycle in one spot, while others of the same species, even of the same brood, may migrate.

The respective geographic positions of breeding grounds and winter quarters also vary tremendously. Sometimes the two regions partially overlap and again they are widely separated by regions in which the species is known only as a transient. The same wide diversity occurs in migration routes, migratory behaviour, the determinism of migrations and the physiology of the migrants, so it is futile to try to set up sharply separated divisions.

These facts should be borne in mind while studying avian migrations. Our information on the subject is still very inadequate in spite of the great number of recent observations and experiments, which, when combined, furnish excellent documentation. Many authors have thought they could draw general conclusions from partial results pertaining to a certain species in one area and under special conditions. Often whole theories are based on such observations, but these are errors to be avoided. Certainly no fact should be neglected, no matter how slight, but great care must be taken in applying conclusions to all migrants, for what is true of one does not necessarily apply to others. Solutions suggested for various specific problems cannot be considered generally applicable at the present time.

Furthermore, there is not a 'single,' there are 'many' migrations, whose circumstances, infinite in variety, change from species to species, region to region, or from one set of conditions to another. Migrations may be regarded as variable adaptations of birds to their environment, and they constitute a series of special conditions which bear witness to the astonishing flexibility that has been and still is displayed by these vertebrates. In no case can they be reduced to mathematical formulas.

We may add that 'migrations' occur in all systematic groups. Only flightless land-birds, such as the ratites (ostriches, rheas, cassowaries) do not perform regular seasonal movements because of their inability to make long journeys. Yet inability to fly does not prevent penguins (*Sphenisciformes*) from migrating for considerable distances by swimming through austral seas.

Migrations are particularly well developed in the cold and temperate regions of the northern hemisphere, where strongly-marked seasonal climatic changes force most birds to seek refuge during the winter in more hospitable regions. The migrants which travel the greatest distances are those that breed in that part of the world.

The temperate and cold regions of the southern hemisphere also witness regular migrations but with marked differences. These migrations are shorter, and no migrant (except among sea-birds) 'winters' in the northern hemisphere beyond the intertropical zone.

But the cold regions of the globe do not have a monopoly on migrations, for seasonal movements occur among the avifauna of tropical regions in a more constant climate. Birds of equatorial zones are almost unique in not displaying the slightest tendency to migrate, a circumstance explained by uniform climatic conditions in the environment where they spend the whole year. Sedentarism also occurs in higher latitudes, for even in the most barren arctic regions the ptarmigan (*Lagopus mutus*) winters among the snows and shows no impulse to leave the inhospitable home which has been abandoned by countless other winged guests that come there in summer to nest.

This brief glimpse may suffice to show the diversity of migratory behaviour among birds. Detailed study reveals still more clearly the multiplicity of solutions open to these vertebrates for making the best use of our globe and avoiding the inconveniences of winter, the deadliest enemy of living things. The necessity of fleeing the cold is so imperative that most migrants are forced to make long, hazardous flights. Dangers along the way are countless: storms, ocean and desert crossings, artificial obstacles created by mankind, particularly maritime and aeronautical beacons and ceilometers, against which blinded migrants often crash in great numbers, high buildings and radio and television transmitters, and electric wires which cover the civilized world with a tight network that traps countless winged travellers.[1] Despite disasters that wipe out countless numbers of birds, migrants would encounter far heavier losses if they attempted to remain in their 'homes' throughout the whole year.[2]

This book is the American adaptation of a volume published by Editions Payot, Paris, in 1956 and entitled *Les migrations des oiseaux*. Since that time numerous studies have been made in various parts of the world, some of them of vital importance to an understanding of avian migrations. From many points of view more has been learned during the last few years than during preceding decades. This knowledge necessitated a complete recasting of the book. Most chapters have been revised to incorporate the new results; those on North America and the austral regions were entirely rewritten; those dealing with the orientation and physiology of migration were developed in accordance with recent discoveries.

We have tried, as in the French edition, to remain as objective as possible, and our aim was to present the sum of current knowledge rather than to defend certain theories. We believe that the migrations of birds constitute an extremely complex system of biological facts, and that at times they seem contradictory; this explains why writers working on different material or under different conditions may get apparently totally different results.

It is a pleasure to thank all those who have helped in the preparation of this book.

Mr George Dock, Jr., suggested this translation. We are deeply indebted to him for his advice and for his careful editing of the text.

Dr E. Thomas Gilliard, Dr Robert Cushman Murphy and Dr Charles Vaurie read the whole text and Dr William Dock the chapter

1. Such mass mortality sometimes goes far beyond what is easily imaginable. Reitz (1954) reported that from 500 to 1,000 migratory Passerines (chiefly warblers) were killed between 11.30 p.m. and 12.30 a.m. by flying against the doors of airplane hangars, shiny because of fog condensation. Kemper (1958) estimated at 20,000 the number of migrants (especially warblers) which perished in a single night during autumn migration by striking a television tower 1,000 feet high, 50 miles from the Mississippi River in Wisconsin. Many similar examples are also mentioned by Tordoff and Mengel (1956).

2. Enormous flocks of migrants, such as starlings, may cause serious accidents to aviation when they collide with airplanes or are sucked up by jets.

on the physiology of migrations. Dr R. A. Falla and Dr D. L. Serventy supplied original documents for the chapter on migrations in Australia and New Zealand. Their criticism was always helpful, and we are grateful for their suggestions.

We also wish to thank Dr J. W. Aldrich, Washington; Dr Salim Ali, Bombay; Prof. F. Bourlière, Paris; Dr James Chapin, New York; Prof. G. P. Dementiev, Moscow; Prof. A. N. Formosov, Moscow; Dr F. Goethe, Wilhelmshafen; Dr K. A. Hindwood, Sydney; Dr A. Keast, Sydney; Dr R. Kühk, Radolfzell; Prof. G. H. Lowery, Baton Rouge; Dr P. Paulian, Paris; Dr A. C. Perdeck, Leiden; W. H. Phelps, Jr., Caracas; Dr F. Sauer, Hamburg; Dr A. Schifferli, Sempach; P. Schwarz, Caracas, for their advice and for making a number of documents available to us. We are also grateful to the numerous authors and editors who have given permission to reproduce the figures. Miss Odile Jachiet prepared the manuscripts and the bibliography with great care. We are indebted to Dr Kenneth Scott for reading the galley proofs.

Finally, we express our appreciation to Dr Constance D. Sherman, who translated the book. We are deeply grateful for her ornithological knowledge, linguistic ability and her exact rendition of the original text.

JEAN DORST

Paris, August 1960.

CHAPTER 1

Old Explanations of Bird Migrations

Birds and their migrations seem to have attracted the attention of men ever since the most remote antiquity; the gathering of birds, their disappearance in the autumn and their return in fine weather are part of the annual cycle which impressed primitive man to such an extent that he regarded them as a divine manifestation. Accordingly we find very ancient testimony about migratory birds. People were quick to observe the direction of these seasonal flights which were southbound during the autumn and which brought the birds back at the beginning of good weather in the spring.

But men had also observed that many animals become torpid during the winter; frogs bury themselves in marsh mud, curtailing their activities and literally 'hibernating.' The same is true of all the batrachians, reptiles and certain mammals (marmots and dormice, for example). It was a great temptation to explain the birds' disappearance in the same fashion.

These two theories, 'migrationism' and 'hibernation', conflicted with one another for almost twenty-three centuries before it was realized that migration is the only possible explanation for the birds' disappearance in the autumn. We must admit that it took a long time to refute a series of flagrant errors!

Certain passages in the Bible show that in ancient times seasonal flights were observed; in the Book of Job, for example (XXXIX, 29), it is written:

> 'Is it by thy wisdom that the hawk soareth
> And stretcheth her wings towards the south?'

And in Jeremiah (VIII, 7):

'Yea, the stork in the heavens knoweth her appointed times; and the turtle-dove and the swallow and the crane observe the time of their coming.'

Homer, in the third book of the *Iliad*, describes how the Trojans marched against their enemies with shouting 'like unto birds, even as when there goeth up before heaven a clamour of cranes which flee from the coming of winter and sudden rain, and fly with clamour towards the streams of ocean, bearing slaughter and fate to the Pygmy men. . . .' Similar quotations could be drawn from the works of Anacreon, Hesiod (*Works and Days*) and Aristophanes (*The Birds*).

Men in early times had a tendency to deify all natural phenomena, or at least to consider them as divine manifestations. Migratory phenomena, which are so astonishing in themselves, did not escape this interpretation, and numerous are the legends which accompany the migrants on their journeys. Furthermore, these flights played an important rôle in divination, as migratory birds were often regarded as messengers from Olympus or other sacred places.

Aristotle was the first to make a 'scientific' contribution in his monumental *History of Animals*, in spite of the fact that it bears no resemblance to a modern scientific treatise. This author is very prudent when he discusses bird migrations, and he seems to keep a balance between migration and hibernation. In his opinion, certain birds are migratory: 'All animals have an instinctive perception of the changes of temperature, and, just as men seek shelter in houses in winter, or as men of great possessions spend their summer in cool places and their winter in sunny ones, so also all animals that can do so shift their habitat at various seasons. Some creatures can make provision against change without stirring from their ordinary haunts; others migrate . . . as in the case of the crane; for these birds migrate from the steppes of Scythia to the marshlands south of Egypt where the Nile has its source. . . . Pelicans also migrate, and fly from the Strymon to the Ister, and breed on the banks of this river' (Book VIII, Chapter 12, translated by Thompson, 1910).

Aristotle therefore admits that a certain number of birds at least do migrate. It is he too who first mentions altitudinal migration: 'Weakly birds in winter and in frosty weather come down to the plains for warmth, and in summer migrate to the hills for coolness . . .' (*Ibid.*)

But he does not believe that all birds migrate; some of them stay on their native heath during bad weather and become lethargic: 'A great number of birds also go into hiding; they do not all migrate, as is generally supposed, to warmer countries. Thus, certain birds (as the kite and the swallow), when they are not far off from places of this kind, in which they have their permanent abode, betake themselves thither; others, that are at a distance from such places, decline the trouble of migration and simply hide themselves where they are. Swallows, for instance, have been often found in holes, quite denuded of their feathers, and the kite on its first emergence from torpidity has been seen to fly from out some such hiding place . . . the stork, the ouzel, the turtle-dove, and the lark, all go into hiding.'

Aristotle also had quite a different theory for certain species which, he declared, experienced a real transmutation: 'The erithacus [robin] and the so-called redstart change into one another; the former is a winter bird, the latter a summer one.'

Aside from this fantasy, Aristotle thus explains the autumnal disappearance of birds by hibernation, as well as by migration. During succeeding centuries, and especially during the Middle Ages, his text was subjected to various interpretations which only amplified the errors it contained.

After Aristotle, the outstanding classical author on natural history is, of course, Pliny the Elder, the celebrated Latin naturalist who wrote a *Natural History* in thirty-seven volumes. By no means critical, he adopted all the opinions that came his way without examining them, and he borrows at length from his illustrious Greek predecessor. Like Aristotle, he admits that cranes make migratory flights: 'The tracts over which they travel must be immense, if we only consider that they come all the way from the Eastern Sea. These birds agree by common consent at what moment they shall set out, fly aloft to look out afar, select a leader for them to follow, and have sentinels duly posted in the rear, which relieve each other by turns, utter loud cries, and with their voice keep the whole flight in proper array. During the night, also, they place sentinels on guard, each of which holds a little stone in its claw; if the bird should happen to fall asleep, the claw becomes relaxed, and the stone falls to the ground, and so convicts it of neglect.' Storks have the same habits.

He believes, as Aristotle did, that swallows spend the winter in a torpid state, after seeking 'sunny retreats there on the mountain sides; sometimes they have been found in such spots bare and quite unfledged' (XXXIX). 'It is, however, a well-ascertained fact that the turtle-dove conceals itself, and loses its feathers' (XXXV, trans. by Bostock and Riley).[1]

The two greatest naturalists of antiquity agreed therefore in dividing birds which vanish in autumn into migrants and hibernators; the latter, they claim, withdraw into 'retreats' as soon as cold weather begins and become torpid after moulting. When spring comes they emerge as soon as their new feathers are grown.

These statements were regarded as law during the Middle Ages. Medieval scholars merely paraphrased them without attempting to observe the birds themselves. Nature, moreover, was not considered important by scholastic philosophers, who were more concerned with unprofitable discussions about the exegesis of ancient texts than with acquiring first-hand knowledge.

There were some exceptions, especially Emperor Frederick II of Hohenstaufen (1194–1250), who was certainly the greatest zoölogist of the Middle Ages and who has been called the 'first modern man upon a throne.' His *De Arte venandi cum Avibus* was first published in Latin in Augsburg in 1596, but several manuscript copies of the thirteenth century survive. Although this work deals chiefly with birds of prey, it contains other valuable information, particularly notes on the seasonal flights of raptores, herons, etc.

Towards the close of the fifteenth century a book called *Gart der Gesundheit* was published by the German Johann Wonnecke von Caub. This went through fifteen successive editions, the first appearing in 1485. It was translated into Latin under the title *Ortus sanitatis*. (It is worth noting that this book – a classic in its time – contained the first bird drawings ever printed.) This work gives a detailed résumé of contemporary natural history information. Much of the text deals with bird migration, particularly that of geese which 'seek and require high places and fly, as do the cranes, in order one after another and direct and pursue their flights according to the movement of the winds . . .' (*Ortus sanitatis*, translated from Latin into French, *Des Oyseaux*, Paris, 1501, Chapter V). Storks do the same: 'The stork heralds the

1. Pliny also makes a statement showing that in ancient times people were aware of the ease with which swallows can find their nests. He says: 'A man of knightly rank at Volterra, Caecina, who owned a racing four-in-hand, used to catch swallows and take them with him to Rome and despatch them to take the news of a win to his friends, as they returned to the same nest; they had the winning colour painted on them' (XXXIII). That is a modern homing experiment long before the tests were invented!

spring and loves to be with human beings. They travel across the sea and fly in large numbers into Asia and warm regions.' The swallow, on the other hand, 'seeks mountain peaks when it leaves for the winter, and there it is found all bare and without feathers.'

In 1549 G. Agricola states about the same thing in *De animantibus subterraneis*.

He was followed by Conrad Gesner, one of the greatest scientists of his era. Born in Zürich, Gesner wandered around Europe for a long time, especially France, according to a custom which seems to have prevailed among all the learned men of his century. After studying the humanities, science and medicine, he returned to his native city, where he wrote numerous treatises, the most important of which is doubtless the *History of Animals*, published in five volumes between 1551 and 1587 (in Latin). In Book III, which deals with birds, he repeats the assertions of earlier writers, declaring: 'Some birds are resident, such as doves; others, like swallows, stay for only six months. We have watched them arrive in March and leave in August. Swallows go to more temperate places for the winter if they are near by; but if they are distant, they hide in the localities where they are' (*Conradi Gesneri Tigurini medici et philosophiae professoris Schola Tigurina, Historiae animalium Liber III qui est de Avium natura*).

All authors agree that swallows hibernate in holes as soon as winter comes. But that is not all! In 1555, Olaus Magnus, Archbishop of Upsala, published a little book which was translated into French in 1561 as a *Histoire des pays septentrionaux*. This slender volume contains some delightful details pertaining to the biology of swallows: 'Several authors who have written at length about the inestimable facts of nature have described how swallows often fly from one country to another, travelling to a warm climate for the winter months; but they have not mentioned the denizens of northern regions which are often pulled from the water by fishermen in a large ball. They cling beak to beak, wing to wing, foot to foot, having bound themselves together in the first days of autumn in order to hide amid canes and reeds. It has been observed that when spring comes they return joyously to their old nests or build new ones, according to the dictates of nature. Occasionally young fishermen, unfamiliar with these birds, will bring up a large ball and carry it to a stove, where heat dissolves it into swallows. They fly, but only briefly, since they were separated forcibly rather than of their own volition. Old fishermen, who are wiser, put these balls back into the water whenever they find them.' This text is accompanied by a drawing showing fishermen raising a net which contains a mixture of fish and swallows.

This fable, which was repeated by authors quite devoid of critical sense, represents the most absurd aspect of the antimigration theories. One can perhaps admit the likelihood that a bird could hibernate in hiding places, but how could anyone believe that it would be able to spend long months under the surface of the water, living an anaerobic existence? Yet opinions of this kind were voiced by ornithologists as famous as Ulysses Aldrovandi, author of a notable *Ornithology*, published between 1559 and 1603, and by J. J. Wagner in his *Curious Natural History of Switzerland*, which appeared in 1680.

All these authors were thinking in terms of European birds. Since Herodotus and Aristotle people had agreed that birds in tropical countries were resident. As discovery of new parts of the globe and ornithological exploration had always gone hand in hand, it is rather surprising to discover that good observers of this period fell into the same errors in discussing the biology of tropical birds. Jean Baptiste Dutertre, for example, the West Indian explorer, states in his *General History of the Isles of Christopher, Guadeloupe, Martinique and others in America*, which was published in 1654 in Paris: 'My personal opinion is contrary to the generally accepted one, according to which all swallows migrate and spend the six winter months in tropical regions: I consider that pure fantasy, since it is known that in tropical regions they hide in the same way.'

We now arrive at the threshold of the eighteenth century, which will witness a revolution in scientific thinking. Despite the credulity of certain authors, the scientific spirit will come to the fore. But was no voice raised in earlier centuries to defend migration of the birds, which so many authors relegated to marsh bottoms during the winter months? The leading 'migrationist' was certainly the ornithologist Pierre Belon, born in 1517 in the Sarthe. During the course of his peregrinations through the Eastern Mediterranean and Asia Minor – which was quite an exploit for that era! – Belon had an opportunity to observe in migratory flight the birds we are accustomed to see during the summer, and he therefore defends avian migrations. In his *History of the Nature of Birds with their Descriptions and Naive Portraits from Nature*, Paris, 1555, he writes, for example: 'It is definite that they [the storks] spend the winter in Egypt and Africa, for we have seen the

Egyptian plains white with them in September and October, so numerous they were' (Book IV, Chapter 10). 'Quails are migratory. When we were on the Mediterranean in autumn and in the spring-time, the weary birds used to alight on our ship to rest from their out-bound and homing flights. And when we crossed from Rhodes to Alexandria, we ate some of those we had captured. Their crops were full of wheat, an indication that they cross the sea in almost unbroken flight' (Book V, Chapter 20).

'. . . . Not wanting to hide anything of what we have observed, we shall say frankly that, although some people have believed that turtle-doves hide and lose their plumage in the winter, we have seen them at this season when they are away from us' (Book VI, Chapter 20). '. . . As swallows cannot spend the winter in Europe both because of the great cold and because they would not find food, they go to Africa, Egypt and Arabia, where, since winter resembles our summer, they have no lack of nourishment.'

Belon also tells about an experiment which he regarded as conclusive: if you put 'migratory' birds in an aviary where there are facilities for hiding, you should be able to observe the hibernation of the captives. But that is not so at all! With remarkable scientific acumen, Belon therefore rejects the idea of a winter torpor for all those birds which disappear from our part of the world, including the swallows, kites and storks, which were the chief subjects of controversy. We could expect no less from this ornithologist, who, in the midst of flagrant errors and somewhat ridiculous legends, which are quite excusable in that era, makes exact observations of a number of details in a language free from scholastic rubbish. His *Ornithology* is, incidentally, the first treatise in France on this subject.

The first American naturalist was Oviedo, whose *Historia general y natural de las Indias, islas y tierre-firme del mar oceano* was published in 1526–1535. He gives numerous details about the behaviour of animals in the New World and, as Baughman noted (1947), he speaks particularly of the migrations of birds of prey. The translation, in the racy English of the time, states: 'Every yeare there pass from the end of Cuba infinite numbers of divers sorts of Birds, which come from the North of the firme Land, and cross over the Alacrain Ilands and Cuba, and flye over the Gulfe Southwards. I have seen them passe over Darien and Nombre de Dios and Panama in divers yeares, in the Firme Land; so many that they cover the Skie; and this passage or march continueth a moneth or more about the moneth of March.' As he did not see a return flight, Oviedo assumed that the birds continued their flight around the world.

During the next century Willughby, in the famous *Ornithology* published in 1678, likewise defended the migrations of birds, especially swallows.

We might suppose that by the beginning of the eighteenth century the absurd ideas about hibernation would be rejected once and for all as an explanation of the birds' disappearance in the autumn. This was by no means the case, and the whole century was devoted to passionate discussions on the subject.

In 1703 an essay of some fifty pages was published anonymously in England.[1] The writer, who signed himself simply as 'a person of learning and piety,' had an entirely new theory on the subject. As a practical joker or a fierce adversary of the 'migrationists' whom he wanted to ridicule, he declares that 'migratory' birds take refuge on the moon in cold weather. Sixty days are required for the trip; on leaving the earth the birds head straight for the moon, which they find in the same place, even though it has completed two lunar cycles during this interval. The author gives a long explanation about how the birds, not being able to find nourishment, live on their reserves like hibernating bears. Furthermore, he tells us that, while in the interstellar ether, they are in a torpid state, which reduces their requirements for energy. We may note that the author himself is not convinced about this fantastic theory, for he closes his memoir by saying that if people refuse to accept the moon as a hibernating area, they will have to find some other place for the birds!

More serious authors also came out in favour of antimigration. J. T. Klein, the author of a rather confused scientific memorandum on this subject, which was published in the *Memoirs of the Natural History Society of Dantzig* in 1747, is a partisan of hibernation for storks and swallows. The same is true of Gmelin, the famous ornithologist to whom we owe so many scientific bird names, and of Pontopiddan, a celebrated Scandinavian authority.

It is quite surprising to discover that the great Linnaeus, father of our modern zoölogical nomenclature, upheld the same theory; in his *Systema naturae* he writes that the swallow: '*Hirundo urbica* . . . lives

1. According to R. Gladstone (*British Birds*, 22, p. 195, 1928), the author may have been Charles Morton.

under the roof in European houses; it is immersed during the winter but comes out in the spring.' He develops his ideas in the *Ammoenitates academicae* (1749). His friends tried in vain to make him discard this theory, which people were beginning to realize was completely false. Linnaeus declined to budge, and his prestige caused a number of contemporary ornithologists to stand with him.

Other authors, however, were acquiring more sensible ideas. The English anatomist, John Hunter, showed that it is physiologically impossible for swallows to dive beneath the water. Spallanzani repeated the same experiments a little later. Travelling naturalists observed the birds in exotic countries and recognized a number of European migrants. In Senegal, for example, Adanson saw swallows and other birds which leave Europe as cold weather begins (*Voyage au Sénégal*, Paris, 1770).

Little by little, therefore scientists joined the migrationist party. Buffon deserves special mention, as he exerted great influence on contemporary thinking. In the first volume of his *Natural History of Birds*, published in 1770, he declares himself a partisan of migration, especially in the case of swallows; he tells how he put some birds inside an ice-box, where, despite the cold and the bad environment, the subjects made no attempt to hibernate but promptly died.

In spite of a certain amount of opposition, especially from an Englishman named Barrington who replied point by point to his observations, Buffon stuck to his guns and, in the following volumes of the *Natural History of Birds*, developed his ideas still further. He shows how diving under water is completely contrary to avian physiology, how all previous observations were bristling with errors, and he declares there is no definite proof of the hibernation of swallows or of any other species of birds. In his conclusion Buffon attributes the disappearance of the swallows to alimentary rather than thermometric causes: 'If, therefore, swallows (I might say the same of all birds of passage) can never obtain under water an asylum congruous to their nature, we must return to the most ancient opinion, and the most consonant to observation and experience. When the proper insects begin to fail, these birds remove into milder climates, which still afford that prey, so necessary to their subsistence' (Volume VI).

Certain scientists, however, remained partisans of hibernation, even Georges Cuvier, who, in 1817, wrote in the 'Swallow chapter' of his *Animal Kingdom*: 'It seems that it becomes torpid in winter and even spends this time at the bottom of the marshes.'[1]

Migration was, however, accepted by numerous authors, including J. J. Audubon. In his gigantic work this writer described the flights of many North American migrants. He gives excellent details concerning the avian migrations he observed, and these are of particular interest, as they cast light on seasonal movements of the American avifauna before the country was transformed by man. He recorded the arrival dates of various migrants such as the purple martin, which comes from New Orleans to Philadelphia in the spring. Audubon was one of the first to use bands to mark birds, but we shall come back to that later.

Although mistakes were still made on this controversial subject, the principle of migration was universally accepted, and discussion now involved methods. But it took a long time to refute the errors of which even a number of celebrated ornithologists were guilty.

These erroneous theories are, of course, explained by analogies with certain other animals, marmots, dormice, reptiles, frogs and toads. Like birds, these animals follow a rhythm which makes them disappear at the beginning of winter and return with the spring. We might assume *a priori* that birds obeyed the same natural law.

Moreover, a number of migrants are often surprised by sudden cold which forces them to seek refuge in hollow trees or amid rocks, where persistent low temperatures prove fatal to them; bodies of migrants that have perished in this way are found fairly frequently. It is only a step farther to assume that the birds withdrew into these places for the winter, especially as certain observers have noted that when some birds were taken into a warm place they came back to life if they were merely numbed by cold.

Among the swallows we observe that it was chiefly the bank swallow or sand martin (*Riparia riparia*), which was considered a hibernator. It is known that this bird leads a rather peculiar life, laying its eggs and raising its young in holes dug in river banks. It is evidently this species which can put people on the wrong track, making them think that it spends the winter there.[2]

1. 'So prevalent, even still, is the notion that swallows take spontaneously to the beds of rivers or pass the winter in a torpid state, that the re-recital of these experiments, and matter of fact to refute them, is not, as yet, needless' (London, 1829).

2. Migrating swifts sometimes assemble in enormous roosts. Thousands of chimney swifts (5,000 to 10,000) have been observed massing in chimneys in the eastern United States (Groskin, 1945), and this too may start a rumour that the birds are getting ready to spend the winter in compact masses.

We shall see, moreover, that a real instance of avian hibernation occurs in North America. This bird, which was evidently not suspected of hibernating by ornithologists of former centuries, is the only confirmation of ancient theories which reveal the errors caused by hasty and poorly interpreted observations.

CHAPTER 2

Methods of Studying Migrations

A study of migration involves fairly simple techniques, based primarily on careful observation of birds in the wild, and on banding or 'ringing.' Beyond this, by means of experimental devices, the physiology and orientation of migrants are studied. Some branches of research require very specialized techniques, but the two principal methods, field observation and banding, are paramount as well as complementary. The former gives a general idea of the migrations of birds in a certain region, and of the influence of various geographical, climatic and other factors on migratory behaviour. Banding supplies information on two precise moments in the bird's life: when it is banded and when it is found or recaptured. By the accumulation and collation of such facts, information is obtained about the movements of a population or of a species of bird. Whereas observation concerns a whole species, banding isolates an individual.

Observation in the Field

Careful observation of birds in the wild is the essential basis of all studies of migration, provided it is fitted to a well-established plan. Studies of visible migration, that is 'migration actually in progress, under conditions allowing its performance to be observed' (Thomson, 1953 c), have developed considerably during recent years and have led the way to discoveries, especially with regard to the sequences involved in migratory flights, which could not have been obtained by other methods. In most cases, the observer must work from a fixed point, and at a definite time of day in order to get comparable results.

From his chosen location, he carefully records the identity of the birds he sees, together with their approximate number, the direction of their flight, their behaviour. Altitude is often difficult to determine, but this information may be obtained from known landmarks or by other more or less ingenious devices. Optical instruments used in anti-aircraft defence and detection are very useful for precise measurements. The speed of migratory flights is also important, and often difficult to determine.

Time of day is a very important factor. As many species of birds fly only at certain hours, best results are obtained by a team of ornithologists, working in relays.

Nocturnal migrations are, of course, the most difficult of all to study; they are, however, very common, particularly among insectivorous Passerines, most of which migrate mainly at night. A really scientific study of these birds was not even attempted until a short time ago. At first, people were satisfied with simply noting the flight-calls uttered by migrants. This method, which was used by Ball (1952) while studying migration on the Gaspé Peninsula, consists of counting the number of calls of the various species in a given interval of time and noting their direction. Recognition of the call of any species is necessary for identification, and some types of birds can easily be recognized, *Hylocichla* for example.

Graber and Cochran recently perfected the technique (1959), using a microphone placed in the centre of a parabolic reflector, an amplifier and a tape recorder. The sound gathering device is arranged so that you can determine exactly in what space dimensions the flight calls are registered (they are detected as high as two miles aloft, i.e., more than five times the range of the unaided ear). This method makes it possible to study the recordings without interruption, and later they can be analysed and the calls counted in the laboratory. This method may revolutionize studies of nocturnal migration.

But until now this aural method has given only an approximate idea of the importance of nocturnal migrations. Many flights are made at such high altitude that it is impossible to hear the calls. So Lowery (1951) and Lowery and Newman (1955) developed another method, consisting of observing and counting migrants at the moment when they cross the lunar disc in the observer's field of vision. These observations are made with the aid of telescopes focused on the moon, and the watcher mentally divides the disc into sectors to determine the direction of flight. The estimated number of birds flying in profile across the moon has to be corrected, however, since, because of the moon's elevation, the number of birds observed may vary greatly, as a little plane geometry reveals (Fig. 1). This method, which has enabled

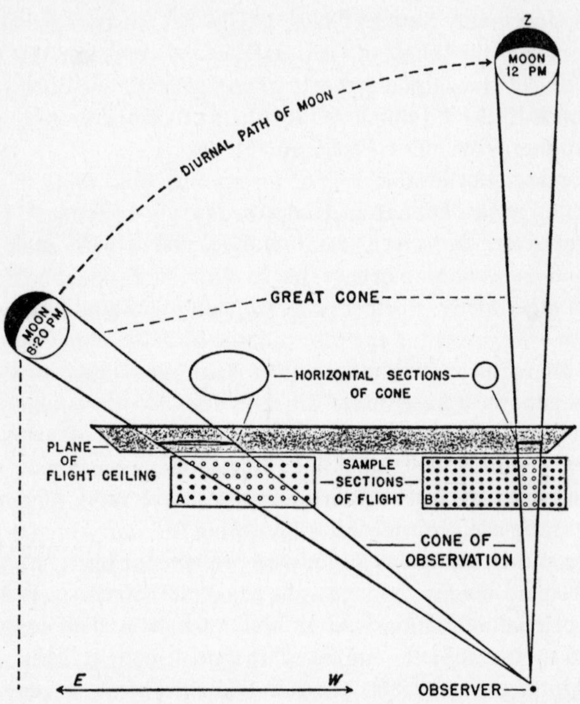

Fig. 1. A tally of the migrants flying across the lunar disc. The number has to be corrected according to the moon's elevation. Sample sections A and B represent densities of flight at 8.20 and 12.00 p.m. With twice as many birds in the air at midnight, when the moon is at the zenith (Z) as there were at the earlier hour, only half as many are visible because of the decrease in size of the cone of observation. From Lowery, 1951.

Lowery and his collaborators to obtain very interesting results, cannot be used unless the lunar disc is of sufficient size (Lowery restricts the observation period to the five days when the moon is full). Furthermore, the sky must be clear, and this is not always the case during migration periods.

That is why a new method, using radar, has been developed to supplement Lowery's. This equipment, which was commonly used during and after the war, produced bizarre observations, which could not be interpreted for a time. Clouds of small responses, called 'angels,' appeared on the screen. They were studied in different countries, and finally Sutter (1957a, 1957b) demonstrated that these spots are merely the 'blips' of birds in flight. What Sutter saw on the radar screen of the Zürich airport, where he made his observations (Surveillance Radar Equipment), was the trail of nocturnal migrants within a radius of ten miles (Figs. 2 and 3).

This seemed unbelievable at first, for no one could think that little birds would provide enough surface to send back an echo. At certain times, moreover, the screen was literally covered with such 'flight points,' and it was hard to believe that so many birds could be flying in so limited a perimeter. Furthermore, isolated individual birds do not provide an echo, except in the case of large birds, so whole groups of migrants are required to produce one. It is thus not surprising that the first explanations were entirely different (dealing particularly with atmospheric phenomena, echos on the contact surfaces of layers of air of different temperatures, humidity and electrical constants).

The possibility of birds registering themselves on radar screens had, of course, long been considered, even during the war years (Bonham and Blake, 1956), but it was Sutter who proved that birds, even small ones, can create an echo, and it was he who first used this technique to study nocturnal migrations. After him Lack, who had long been interested in the subject, employed the new method with several collaborators (Lack, 1958b; Tedd and Lack, 1958; Harper, 1959; Lack, 1959).

Location and environment are highly important in making observations. We shall see that there are occasionally narrow migration routes, outside of which migrants are scarce. Birds often follow the major lines of local topography, mountain chains, passes, river valleys, lake shores and seashores. It is clear that a complete knowledge of the terrain is essential for making observations.

Lighthouses are usually excellent observatories, especially for studying nocturnal migrants, as their powerful beams attract migrants, affording an opportunity to observe them and determine the exact composition of the flights. Unfortunately, many birds, blinded by rays, crash against lanterns or towers, unless the latter are equipped with safety devices. Study of these casualties has furnished interesting data on the specific composition of a wave of migrants.

Other studies deal with the relationship between migration and

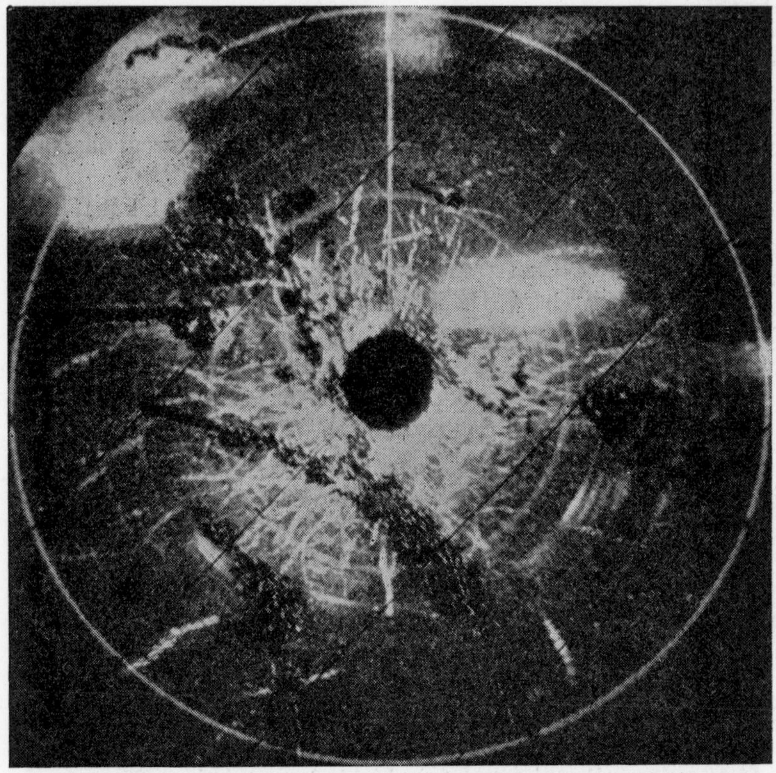

Fig. 2. Radar observation of nocturnal migrations. Very small flights in bad weather (note patches caused by rain). The few birds migrating scatter in all directions. Photo taken on the radar screen of the Zürich airport (Kloten) 24 September, 1958, at 11.39 p.m. Exposure: 4 minutes. The vertical line indicates north, the large outer circle, the limit of 10 nautical miles; the concentric circles, which are less visible, are a nautical mile apart. Courtesy of Dr Ernst Sutter, Basel.

local and general meteorological conditions. It has long been known that bird flights depend to a large degree on weather. One of the current problems is examination of these reports, so every observation should be accompanied by as detailed a meteorological statement as possible, including cloud conditions, barometric pressure, and direction and force of the wind.

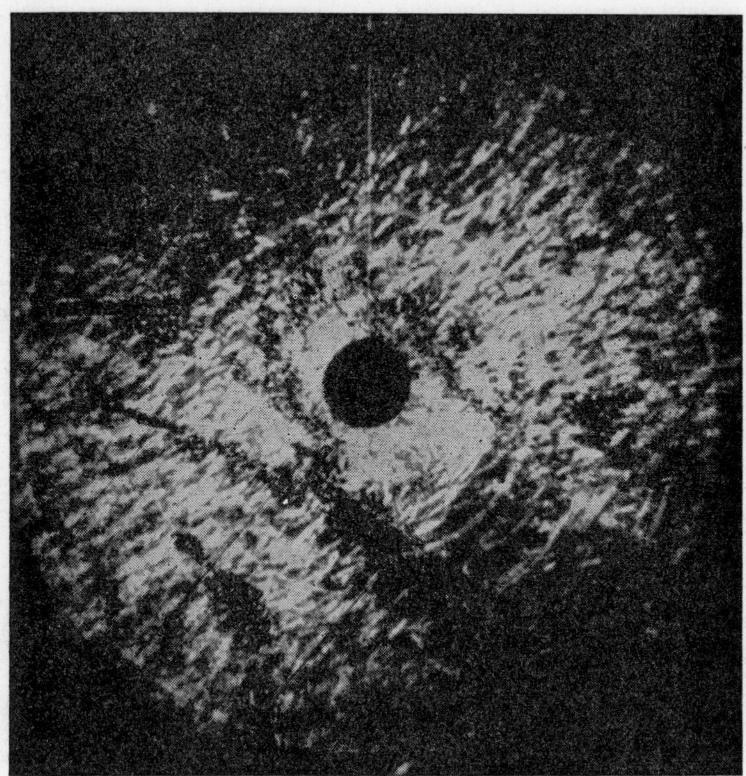

Fig. 3. Radar observation of nocturnal migrations. Normal migration in good weather. Note the density of the migrants moving from north-east to south-west. Photo taken on the radar screen of the Zürich airport (Kloten) 24 October, 1957, at 7.30 p.m. Exposure: 1 minute. Courtesy of Dr Ernst Sutter, Basel.

Along with these relatively simple observation methods, there are more advanced techniques. Some observers have used aeroplanes, particularly at low speed, to follow bands of diurnal migrants and study their behaviour in flight (for example, some of Griffin's homing experiments). These approaches, however, are still only used occasionally, and no general method has so far supplemented direct observation.

Although on the whole elementary and requiring only a good pair of binoculars, methods of studying visible migration will generally fail to get results unless they are the product of well co-ordinated teamwork. That is why certain observations, carefully prepared in advance, have enlisted several hundred observers, as in a recent study of migrating swifts (*Apus apus*) in Great Britain. By far the best results are obtained from simultaneous observations by ornithologists stationed at various points to collaborate on a research programme. One of the best instances was 'Operation recovery' (Baird, Robbins, Bagg and Dennis, 1959), in which American ornithologists all along the Atlantic coast participated in 1957. A systematic banding campaign linked with observations revealed what migration study can accomplish by teamwork.

BANDING

Yet attentive observation of migrations in a specific place is insufficient, for it is important to follow the individual bird in its flight, and to know exactly where a bird nesting in a given region will spend the winter. Recognition of the bird requires marking, by placing a ring of light metal on its leg, with numbers which make possible a precise identification. This method was pioneered by H. C. C. Mortensen, a Danish ornithologist who developed the technique towards the close of the last century.

Attempts at banding had been made before, some of them centuries ago. People had attached messages to birds' legs, indicating where they had been captured. According to Rydzewski (1951), who has made an excellent compilation of the most important experiments, birds of prey used for hunting and bearing their master's name were occasionally taken at great distances from their customary haunts. The same is true of some wild 'quarry' birds. Herons, for example, were marked at different times with metallic rings – occasionally gold or silver! – bearing the name of the 'bander,' and some were found far from the scene of their capture. A peregrine falcon (*Falco peregrinus*), bearing the mark of Henry IV, King of France, escaped from Fontainebleau and was recovered twenty-four hours later in Malta, 1,350 miles away. More nearly at hand is the story of the Danish stork marked with a medallion bearing a message; the following year it returned with a reply from Benares, India. Twelve months later the same manœuvre was repeated, and the story ended in a romantic way – by the marriage of the Dane to the young Englishwoman with whom he had corresponded through the intermediary of the migrating stork! This anecdote was certainly made up of whole cloth, but it is known that during World War II soldiers in Africa attached messages to the legs of wintering European migratory birds in the hope that they would be carried to their distant homeland.

Some of these banding accounts are more or less fanciful, but a few early ornithologists tried to mark birds scientifically. J. J. Audubon was surely the first in the New World to band birds in such a way that they could be recognized individually. He described his experiments several times, especially those on the 'pewee' [eastern phoebe] (*Sayornis phoebe*) which were undertaken at Mill Grove, near Norristown, Pennsylvania. He wrote: 'I attached light threads to their legs; these they invariably removed, either with their bills, or with the assistance of their parents. I renewed them, however, until I found the little fellows habituated to them; and at last, when they were about to leave the nest, I fixed a light silver thread to the leg of each, loose enough not to hurt the part, but so fastened that no exertions of theirs could remove it. . . . At the season when the pewee [eastern phoebe] returns to Pennsylvania, I had the satisfaction to observe those of the cave in and about it. . . . Having caught several of these birds on the nest, I had the pleasure of finding two of them had the little ring on the leg.'

Much later, in 1909, Jack Miner, of Kingsville, Ontario, Canada, marked ducks with rings bearing simply 'Box 48, Kingsville, Ontario,' which did not, of course, permit individual identification. The first capture was reported 14 January, 1910, near Anderson, South Carolina.[1]

But it was in Europe, about the end of the nineteenth century, that the initial scientific banding attempts were made by H. Christian C.

1. This ornithologist later founded the Jack Miner Migratory Foundation, a refuge where migrants continue to be protected and banded. Tens of thousands of birds, chiefly ducks and geese, have been captured there since Jack Miner used his first band in 1909.

Mortensen. About 1890, this Danish ornithologist first fastened a zinc ring bearing the locality (Viborg, Denmark) and the year to the leg of the starlings he had trapped. Later, he used aluminium bands, much better suited to the purpose, and this metal has been employed ever since. At the same time Lord William Percy began to band woodcock in England, but the honour of using numbers, which permits individual recognition, belongs to Mortensen.

The first really scientific banding in America seems to have been done by P. Bartsch (1952), who, in 1902, banded black-crowned night herons (*Nycticorax nycticorax hoactli*) in colonies south-east of Benning, D.C. These bands bore the legend 'Return to Smithsonian Institution,' together with the year and a serial number. That year only twenty-three birds were banded, one of which was recaptured in Abington, Maryland. These efforts were renewed in 1903 and in 1910, and some of the herons thus marked were later recaptured, one near Toronto, Canada, another in Cuba.

These banding techniques soon spread all over the world even to Antarctica! L. Gain, a zoölogist of the Second French Antarctic Expedition, was the first to work with penguins. On 28 December 1908, he put green celluloid bands around the tarsi of fifty gentoo penguins (*Pygoscelis papua*) on islands off the Palmer Peninsula. Gain visited the same colonies during the next breeding season and found a good proportion of the adults but not a single young bird. He concluded that the latter do not return immediately and do not reproduce until they are two years old (Gain, 1914, *in* Austin, 1957), a theory which has since been corroborated.

The bands in use today are metallic rings of an aluminium alloy, each bearing a legend giving in condensed form the name of the organization responsible for the banding and its location; next comes a serial letter and a numeral which make it possible to identify the bird. The size of the bands varies, of course, in accordance with the size of the bird; the largest have a special fastening, designed to prevent the bird from removing the band with its bill (some birds with a strong bill, like herons and storks, will remove the bands if they are not securely fastened); the smaller ones, made for medium-size or small birds, are plain metallic bands closed by fitting the ends together (Figs. 4 and 5). All these bands are fastened around the bird's leg; they can slip up and down the tarsus, but will not slip over the toes or interfere with the joints. Aluminium alloys are light, inexpensive, and easily shaped to fit the bird's leg, but they are all affected by salt water, and burrowing birds (like petrels) soon wear out this soft metal. For such species bands are made of monel, a copper-base alloy more resistant to wear and to corrosion by salt water.

Fig. 4. Some of the bands used by the U.S. Fish and Wildlife Service for bird banding operations. They contain a serial number and directions for returning them to the banding organization, Washington, D.C. Photo by R. G. Schmidt; courtesy of U.S. Fish and Wildlife Service.

Fig. 5. Two types of bands used by the British Trust for Ornithology. Courtesy of Mr R. Spencer, London.

Other methods of identification for large birds have been tried in a number of countries, especially small, light, metal plates set on the bird's wing in the patagial membranes. This system has been successful with ducks and flamingos, but a few attempts with penguins made it apparent that the conformation of their legs and the shortness of their tarsi do not permit the use of a standard band, for it can slip, immobilize the joint, and cause a fatal stiffening and swelling. Sladen (1952) therefore tried a new type of banding, using flipper-rings that have several advantages (Fig. 6); they do not immobilize any joint, last longer, and can easily be read in the field with binoculars. The same type of band was used in Adélie Land by biologists of the Paul

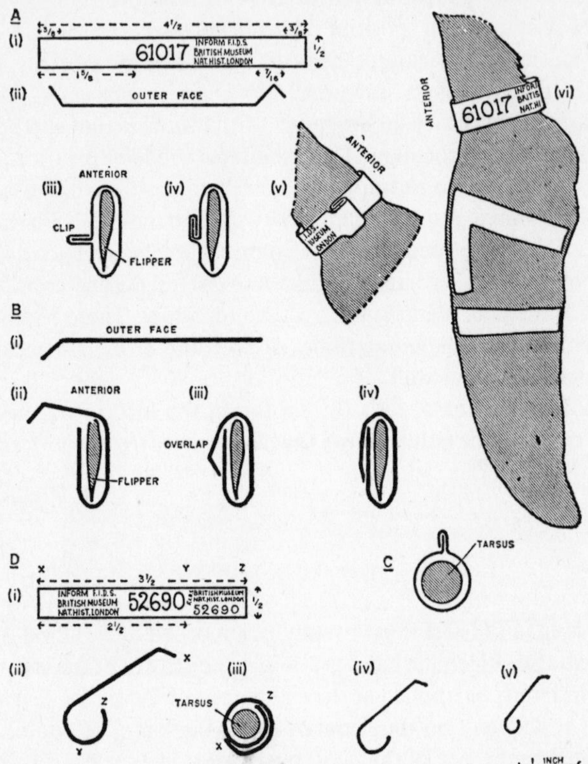

Fig. 6. Some bands used by the Falkland Islands Dependencies Survey (FIDS).

A. (I–VI) 1953 design flipper bands for penguins. (I) strip as supplied. (II) first shaping. (III) shaping around flipper. (IV–VI) final position, VI showing the left flipper as held to the side of the body. The number (17) is painted on the flipper for temporary identification.

B. (I–IV) 1955 design flipper bands for penguins. (I–III) stages in shaping. (IV) final position.

C. 1947. Design leg bands for penguins.

D. Double inscription bands. (I–III) for giant petrel, III showing the final position. (IV–V) bands of the same type but of smaller size. All measurements are given in inches. From Sladen and Tickell, 1958.

Emile Victor Expeditions (J. Sapin-Jaloustre, J. Cendron, J. Prévost). But this flipper-ring has to be put on very carefully, as the catch can hurt the bird in the axillary region. The ring must be tight enough not to slide, yet not tight enough to interfere with the penguin's swimming.

These rings permit positive identification of the bird once it is captured, but they cannot be read on a free bird in the wild, so German ornithologists have recently tried to place on big birds, especially storks, much larger bands, with numbers that can be read at a distance with binoculars. This facilitates the identification of birds which do not have to be trapped, a delicate operation that disturbs the animal. A similar result is obtained by using bands with characteristic features that can be detected at a distance with glasses, such as notches in various shapes, or bands in distinctive sequences of colour, which permit immediate identification of an individual. These bands, which serve chiefly for behaviour studies of breeding birds, are occasionally used for migrants as well.

Banding, of course, calls for capturing the bird in the first place, which can be done either before the fledgling leaves the nest, or else by trapping the adult.

Banding in the Nest

Banding in the nest must usually be preceded by a period of observation during which the bander watches the growth of the young birds. The band must be applied at the right stage of the bird's development so that it will stay on the fledgling's leg (the band, of course, is proportioned to the size of the *adult* bird's leg). The location and date of the operation are carefully recorded, together with the identification of the bird and any other biological data that can be obtained. The ideal time for banding is several days before the flight of the fledgling.

If the latter is too young, it will lose the band, which is still too large; if it is too old, fright makes it escape from the nest, and the parents soon lose interest in the offspring. Arnhem (1957) has also recently called attention to another danger menacing banded young birds: their parents, goaded by the same stimulus which makes them remove all strange bodies from the nest, try to remove the band. And if the fledgling is too young, it may be tossed out too! In any case, whether banding fledglings in the nest or adults, the bander must protect the birds. It is of paramount importance to safeguard our avifauna and, on a purely scientific plane, it is extremely ill-advised to band birds whose survival is endangered by the operator's negligence.

Banding adults

The individuals must first be captured, and any method is good provided the bird is neither hurt nor excessively frightened by the trap or the subsequent handling incident to banding it. Amateur banders

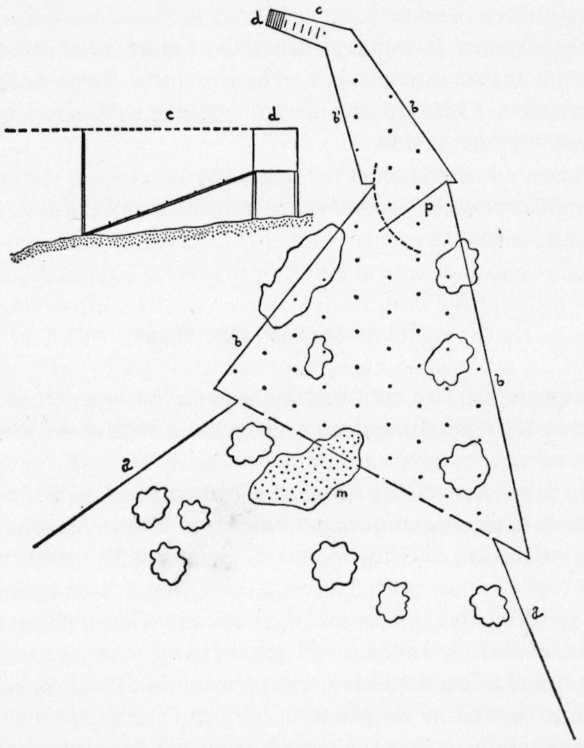

Fig. 7. Heligoland trap, ground plan; above, at the left, side elevation of the rear: a. guide walls bound an assembly area; in the front bushes and (m) water b. catchment area bounded and covered by wire netting b^1 lock up closed by a swinging door (p) c. ramp d. catching box.

use a wide variety of traps, designed in many ways. In some banding stations, trapping is done on a large scale and is more standardized. Among the most common are the 'Heligoland traps,' so called because they were first developed on that island in the North Sea. This trap is a large, open funnel of fine wire netting, leading into a corridor that curves slightly as it narrows (Fig. 7). At the far end, a ramp leads to a box with a glass back, from which the birds can be removed through a side opening. This trap is set up in the favourite feeding area or drinking place of the birds the bander wishes to capture (generally Passerines). At its entrance are shelters where the birds come to rest. An extra attraction is afforded by food and shrubbery placed at the opening of the funnel.

Birds alighting in front of the trap are gently driven towards the rear, and, once they have sought refuge in the box at the end, it is easy to catch them. Each type of bird requires a slightly different technique: *Sylviidae* (garden and leaf warblers), for example, are easily driven, but finches are often harder to lure and trap.

A similar principle is used in the construction of decoys and traps for water-birds, particularly ducks; curving canals covered with grating run from a central pond, or nets form a tunnel three or four yards wide at the entrance, which gradually narrows to a small pocket at the far end (Fig. 8). The sides of the canals are flanked by screens, to prevent the birds from seeing observers while permitting the latter to watch them. Birds alighting on the central pond – often attracted by semi-domesticated decoys – are directed towards the canals by various means (often by a spaniel trained for the purpose) and then driven to the end where they are easily captured.[1]

Other trapping techniques use nets in which the birds are caught, or which are thrown over them. Peter Scott, in the British Severn Wildfowl Trust, has modernized an ancient method. Nets are cast over the birds to be banded, by means of electrically controlled rockets. The net is prepared and rolled to the edge of the terrain where the birds – chiefly geese of many species – are accustomed to feed. Rockets at the sides can be fired by electric push buttons. The geese alight on their favourite terrain, and, when their number is judged sufficient, rockets

1. Many banding techniques and decoys, such as those used at Heligoland, are similar to devices formerly employed by hunters. Decoys of this kind are still found in various countries, chiefly England and the Netherlands, where they are used to capture birds, especially water-fowl.

carry the net over them, lowering it on the birds, which can then be easily and harmlessly captured.

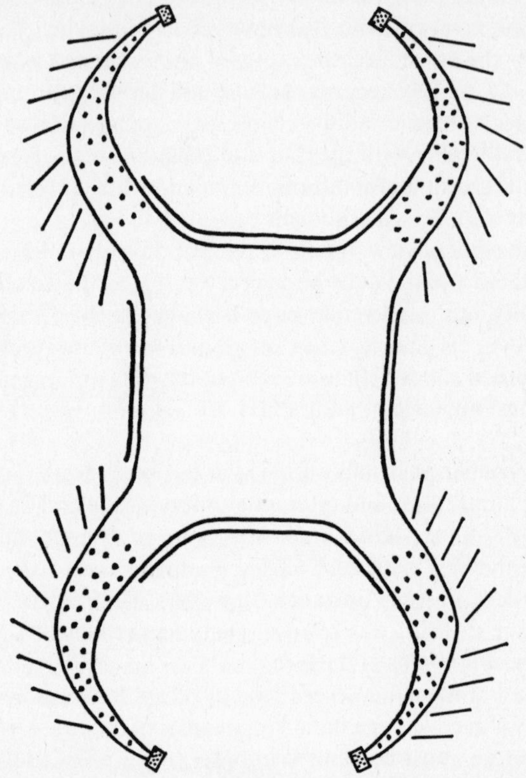

Fig. 8. Duck decoy, ground plan. Semi-circular canals run out from a collecting pool. They are covered with grating and bordered by screens placed in such a way that the ducks can be slowly driven toward the narrow end of the canals where the catching boxes are located.

Another method consists of surrounding colonies of birds too young to fly, and driving them like so many sheep towards nets, which form a corral. This gives excellent results with birds like flamingos and geese, where the young remain incapable of flight until long after attaining almost adult size. This method enabled Peter Scott and James Fisher to band over 9,000 pink-footed geese (*Anser brachyrhynchus*) during a single breeding season in Iceland.

Finally, there is the use of hypnotic drugs which, when mixed with bait, make birds drowsy for a time, and permit their capture for banding. Among these products glucoral or chloralose are the most common, but great care must be observed in employing them.

Whatever the procedure, the captured bird is banded at once. Next the observer carefully records all its characteristics, noting species, sex, plumage (juvenile, adult, eclipse or nuptial), size and weight. These facts, together with the date and exact location of the banding station, will furnish useful information if and when the bird is caught again. Birds are released as soon as they are banded.

From the point of view of returns, the banding of adults is generally more satisfactory than young birds because, during the first few weeks, the mortality rate of juvenile birds is high, which, of course, very greatly reduces the chance of recovery. Since adults are more resistant, there is more likelihood of recovery, but the data are less precise, for the exact nesting place of adult birds banded on migration is seldom known.

Recovery of bands usually occurs after the bird's death, whether it is killed by a hunter or found after a natural or accidental death. Some recoveries do occur, however, in the traps of banding stations, in which case the bird is released after the information on the band has been recorded. In every instance these data are transmitted to the station where the bird was banded, enabling the bander to plot and study the various flights of the bird.

Since most of them are never found or recaptured, it is evident that the chances of recovering a banded bird are slim indeed. A great many birds, therefore, must be banded in order to get a few useful results. According to Spencer (1959), the percentage of recoveries of different species of birds in Great Britain, based on a very large number of bands (approximately 2,000,000), is recorded in the files of the British bird-ringing scheme as follows:

	Percentage
Grey Lag goose (*Anser anser*)	24.3
Cormorant (*Phalacrocorax carbo*)	23.2
Tufted duck (*Aythya fuligula*)	20.0
Shoveler (*Spatula clypeata*)	19.8
White-fronted goose (*Anser albifrons*)	19.0
Pintail (*Anas acuta*)	17.2
Wigeon (*Mareca penelope*)	16.7

Teal (*Anas crecca*)	16.1
Pochard (*Aythya ferina*)	15.8
Sparrow hawk (*Accipiter nisus*)	15.0
Pink-fronted goose (*Anser brachyrhynchus*)	14.7
Heron (*Ardea cinerea*)	14.7
Merlin (*Falco columbarius*)	14.6
Hen harrier (*Circus cyaneus*)	14.0
Barn owl (*Tyto alba*)	12.6
Kestrel (*Falco tinnunculus*)	11.5
Mallard (*Anas platyrhynchus*)	10.6
Shag (*Phalacrocorax aristotelis*)	10.5
European coot (*Fulica atra*)	9.5
European woodcock (*Scolopax rusticola*)	7.6
Jay (*Garrulus glandarius*)	6.8
Wood pigeon (*Columba palumbus*)	6.4
Stock dove (*Columba oenas*)	6.3
Rook (*Corvus frugilegus*)	5.6
Hooded crow (*Corvus cornix*)	5.6
Eider (*Somateria mollissima*)	5.2
Jackdaw (*Corvus monedula*)	5.1
Great black-backed gull (*Larus marinus*)	5.1
Buzzard (*Buteo buteo*)	4.7
Black-headed gull (*Larus ridibundus*)	4.7
European oystercatcher (*Haematopus ostralegus*)	4.7
Snipe (*Capella gallinago*)	4.5
Lesser black-backed gull (*Larus fuscus*)	4.1
Great spotted woodpecker (*Dendrocopus major*)	4.1
Magpie (*Pica pica*)	4.0
Common gull (*Larus canus*)	4.0
Curlew (*Numenius arquata*)	3.9
Gannet (*Morus bassanus*)	3.8
Herring gull (*Larus argentatus*)	3.7
Starling (*Sturnus vulgaris*)	3.6
Guillemot or common murre (*Uria aalge*)	3.5
Turtle dove (*Streptopelia turtur*)	3.3
Blackbird (*Turdus merula*)	3.2
Redshank (*Totanus totanus*)	2.8
Razorbill (*Alca torda*)	2.7
Mistle thrush (*Turdus viscivorus*)	2.5

Cuckoo (*Cuculus canorus*)	2.4
European robin (*Erithacus rubecula*)	2.3
Lapwing (*Vanellus vanellus*)	2.0
Common tern (*Sterna hirundo*)	2.0
Blue tit (*Parus caeruleus*)	1.7
Kittiwake (*Rissa tridactyla*)	1.7
Sandwich tern (*Thalasseus sandvicensis*)	1.6
Pied white wagtail (*Motacilla alba*)	1.6
Swift (*Apus apus*)	1.6
Great tit (*Parus major*)	1.5
Bullfinch (*Pyrrhula pyrrhula*)	1.5
Dunnock (*Prunella modularis*)	1.3
Arctic tern (*Sterna paradisaea*)	1.3
House or English sparrow (*Passer domesticus*)	1.3
Ringed plover (*Charadrius hiaticula*)	1.3
Manx shearwater (*Puffinus puffinus*)	1.2
Chaffinch (*Fringilla coelebs*)	1.1
Fulmar (*Fulmarus glacialis*)	1.1
Yellowhammer (*Emberiza citrinella*)	0.8
Meadow pipit (*Anthus pratensis*)	0.8
House martin (*Delichon urbica*)	0.7
Yellow wagtail (*Motacilla flava*)	0.7
Swallow (*Hirundo rustica*)	0.7
Spotted flycatcher (*Muscicapa striata*)	0.7
Linnet (*Carduelis cannabina*)	0.7
Skylark (*Alauda arvensis*)	0.6
Puffin (*Fratercula arctica*)	0.5
Wheatear (*Oenanthe oenanthe*)	0.4
Reed bunting (*Emberiza schoeniclus*)	0.4
Whitethroat (*Sylvia communis*)	0.4
Bank swallow or sand martin (*Riparia riparia*)	0.2
Leaf warbler (*Phylloscopus trochilus*)	0.2

It is clear that the proportion of recoveries varies widely with the species.[1]

1. Even lower percentages of recoveries are recorded. According to figures published in a study of the migrations of European Sylviidae by Brickenstein-Stockhammer and Drost (1956), 16,203 garden warblers (*Sylvia borin*) were banded between 1910 and 1955 by the Vogelwarte Heligoland; but only 15, or 0.09 per cent were ever recovered!

It is high for water-fowl, but Passerines, especially the little ones, are seldom recovered. Such recoveries are, of course, usually a matter of purest chance, whereas game birds, like woodcock or ducks, or birds that are reputed to be harmful, like herons, are often shot or trapped.

In addition to the 'natural' attrition which makes it possible to recover only a small number of birds, innumerable bands are lost because of carelessness on the part of persons who find them and do not bother to notify the authorities. Some of these people imagine that the band indicates ownership, and fear that the banding organization will punish them for shooting or capturing the bird, so they destroy the compromising evidence of the metallic band. They have no idea that they are depriving an ornithological station of valuable information.

Bird banding can have significant results only if efforts are co-ordinated, and it is rare indeed for an isolated bander to obtain useful data. What is needed are well-laid plans for banding, plus networks of observers and banders whose simultaneous studies will provide an overall picture of migratory phenomena. This necessitates the formation of large central organizations to give directives and co-ordinate the efforts of volunteer banders. The function of such organizations is to stamp the bands, distribute them and keep files on banding and recovery. The oldest is certainly the 'Vogelwarte Rossitten,' founded in 1901 by Joh. Thienemann. It is on the shore of the Baltic Sea, on a curious tongue of land, only about sixty miles long and in places no more than a few hundred yards wide, which forms the Kurische Nehrung. Thienemann had noted that this geographical feature provided a very popular migration route for Scandinavian, Russian and Siberian birds moving in autumn towards the West and Southwest of Europe. According to some observers, up to 500,000 birds can be counted there. Unfortunately, after World War II, this ornithological station was obliged to move from its original site, and it was taken to the shores of Lake Constance at Radolfzell, where it is now installed in Schloss Möggingen (*Vogelwarte Radolfzell der Max-Planck-Gesellschaft*). This location seems much less favourable than Rossitten for study of migration, but the shores of Lake Constance are, nevertheless, important migration routes and flocking areas for great numbers of migrants.

Figures communicated by R. Kühk (*personal communication*) reveal that the activity of this station has resumed its pre-war level;

whereas only 4,893 birds were banded in 1947 by *Vogelwarte Radolfzell*, the number in 1957 was 110,688, and 544,835 birds were banded there during that decade. Between 1903 and 1945, more than a million bands were applied at this ornithological station, and so it is a great blow to science that all of the station's records were destroyed during the war. In 1956 Russian scientific authorities began work at Rossitten. Now in Soviet territory and called Rybatschi, this station is directed by the Zoölogical Institute of the Academy of Sciences of the U.S.S.R. in Leningrad, and 33,500 birds were banded there in 1958 alone.

The second German ornithological station is established on the island of Heligoland in the North Sea, off the German and Danish coasts. This area is an important crossroads for studying autumn migrations of birds from Scandinavia and eastern Europe. The scientific importance of the island was revealed long ago by the original founder of the ornithological station, Heinrich Gätke. Some of his observations were summarized in his classic *Die Vogelwarte Helgoland* which appeared in 1891, and was translated into English in 1895 under the title *Heligoland as an Ornithological Observatory*. In 1910 this station was officially established in its present form, with Hugo Weigold as ornithologist. It was badly damaged during World War I and during World War II it was entirely destroyed, as a result of Heligoland's having been converted into a German military and naval base. Moved to Wilhelmshaven on the mainland, its operations were resumed in 1947, as mentioned earlier.

The intense activity of this station has led to very significant results. Between 1910 and 1957, 2,085,080 birds were banded there, about 143,000 in 1958 alone (F. Goethe, *personal communication*). These figures show better than words the efforts of the ornithologists who have succeeded one another at Heligoland, one of the best places in western Europe to study migration.

Ornithology is held in high repute in Britain, which is fortunate because the British Isles are a crossroads, where migration routes converge from northern and eastern Europe (England provides winter quarters for many birds of these regions), and where migrants from Greenland and Iceland are also observed. The British Isles are bordered with small coastal islets that form ready-made observatories for studying migration. Famous stations have been set up at Fair Isle, between the Shetlands and Scotland, on the Isle of May and Spurn

Head on the coast of the North Sea, on Saint Kilda off the Hebrides (where James Fisher has done remarkable work), Skokholm, off the coast of Wales (made famous by R. M. Lockley), not to mention Slimbridge in England, where Peter Scott and the Wildfowl Trust are observing migratory ducks and geese.

In 1909 two banding projects were founded simultaneously in Great Britain, one by A. L. Thomson at the University of Aberdeen, the other by H. F. Witherby, in connection with the review *British Birds*. The former collapsed, but in 1937 the latter was made part of the British Trust for Ornithology, which now centralizes banding and its results for the whole country. Up to 1959, approximately 2,000,000 bands were used in Great Britain, half of this total since 1950; about 20,000 are applied every year. By the end of 1957, 47,465 recoveries had been reported.

In the Netherlands the Dutch Central Organization for Bird Ringing was founded in 1911, under the aegis of the *Rijksmuseum van Natuurlijke Historie* of Leiden, and directed since 1958 by the Vogel-trekstation in that city. About 650,000 birds were banded there between 1911 and 1956, and some 50,000 birds are now banded every year, with 25,000 recoveries reported so far.

In Switzerland the *Station ornithologique suisse de Sempach* (*Schweizerische Vogelwarte Sempach*) is in charge of all research on migration and the distribution of Swiss bands. Since 1911, 450,786 birds have been banded in this country. The activity of this station has increased considerably during recent years, and nearly 36,000 birds were banded in 1958.

In each Scandinavian country there is a growing ornithological centre. Sweden has a magnificent station at Ottenby, at the southern tip of the island of Öland, in the Baltic. This is an excellent place to study autumn migrants from Scandinavia because of the dense concentration of migration routes.

In the U.S.S.R. banding was begun in 1913, but efforts were not coördinated until 1924; in 1951 the 'Bird-ringing Bureau' was made an official organization under the Academy of Sciences of the U.S.S.R. Between 1934 and 1947, about 100,000 bands were applied. While this figure naturally dropped during World War II, the activities of this organization have been considerably developed since 1945, and 678,550 birds were banded between 1925 and 1954. More than 200,000 birds are now banded annually in Russia, especially in the reservations (Black Sea; Volga Delta, Oka, Ryazan region; Kandalaksha [Murmansk region]). It is noteworthy that bird protection and banding are very closely associated in the U.S.S.R., as the banding organization is under the direction of the Commission for Nature Protection of the Academy of Sciences of the U.S.S.R.

After several attempts in France, A. Chappellier organized a banding service for birds of agricultural importance (*Institut National de Recherches agronomiques de Versailles*). In 1930 E. Bourdelle established a Central Service for Research on Bird and Mammal Migration at the *Muséum National d'Histoire Naturelle* (now *Centre de recherches sur les migrations des Mammifères et des Oiseaux*). During the first twenty-four years of its existence, 176,000 bands were applied, a large number in view of the modest means available, and there have been 1,686 recoveries, or one per cent. This service has been completely reorganized, and about 100,000 bands are now used every year. Unfortunately, France does not yet have a network of ornithological stations. One is set up at certain times of the year at Ouessant, an island off the coast of Finistère, Brittany, where many migrants from England and eastern and northern Europe can be observed. The only permanent station at present is the Biological Station at Tour du Valat, in the Camargue, which belongs to its director, Dr L. Hoffmann. His work and the work of his staff have led to fruitful discoveries, which are to a considerable degree responsible for revival of French interest in bird migration. Formerly a banding centre was operated with great success at Cap Bon, in Tunisia, but for political reasons it had to be closed.

Europe, however, is by no means the only part of the globe where banding projects have been well developed. We have already noted that Paul Bartsch of the Smithsonian Institution was the first to band birds scientifically in the U.S.A. After several individual attempts, including that of P. A. Taverner in 1904, the American Bird Banding Association was founded in December, 1909. This was carried on until 1920, when, because of the growing importance of banding, the task was taken over by the U.S. Bureau of Biological Survey, now the Fish and Wildlife Service of the U.S. Department of the Interior. At first, most banding was in the hands of amateurs, but because of its importance in connection with the protection of migratory birds and wildfowl management, government biologists developed a banding service within the framework of the wildlife research programmes. These programmes have been considerably enlarged during recent years, especially since the second world war. All administrative work is now concentrated in the Central Bird Banding Office, at the Patuxent Wildlife Research Refuge of the Bureau of Sport Fisheries and Wildlife, near Laurel, Maryland, where about twenty-five U.S. Government employees are engaged in various banding operations. Microfilm copies of all records are sent to the Canadian Wildlife Service in Ottawa, Canada, with which the U.S. Fish and Wildlife Service cooperates. The two countries use the same series of bands, to facilitate operations on the entire North American continent and to avoid confusion and duplication.

Fourteen band-sizes (all of aluminium, and of the split-ring type) are used in North America, ranging from 0.083 inch to 0.875 inch in diameter. Each bears a number and an address ('Notify F and Wildlife Service – Write Washington, D.C. USA' for the largest; 'Write F and W Serv. – Wash D.C. USA' for the smallest). According to information received from John W. Aldrich, Fish and Wildlife Service, Washington, D.C. (*personal communication*) approximately 11,000,000 birds, of about 600 species, have been banded since the programme was set up, with 600,000 birds now being banded every year. Of this number, there have been some 900,000 recoveries, from 40,000 to 50,000 being made annually.

Banding migratory game birds is chiefly within the province of professional biologists, whereas most of the work with Passerines is done by amateurs under the direction of government biologists. There are some 2,000 such banders in North America, each of whom must have a federal permit and usually a local state permit, both requiring investigation.

In Australia, the first attempts at banding were made in 1912, when the Bird Observers' Club of Melbourne and the Royal Australasian Ornithologists' Union banded short-tailed shearwaters (*Puffinus tenuirostris*) and white-faced storm-petrels (*Pelagodroma marina*). After praiseworthy but somewhat scattered efforts, an Australian Bird-banding Scheme was founded in 1953, under the direction of the Wildlife Survey of the Commonwealth Scientific and Industrial Research Organization (C.S.I.R.O.), which is now nation-wide. Between October, 1953, and June, 1958, nearly 70,000 birds were banded by this organization, more than half of them in 1958. There have been remarkable recoveries both among land migrants and sea-birds, which make enormous seasonal flights over the Antarctic and the Pacific Ocean.

New Zealand, too, has had a banding programme since 1950, under the direction of the Ornithological Society of New Zealand.

In Japan, Dr Nagamichi Kuroda began to band night herons (*Nycticorax nycticorax*) in the vicinity of Tokyo in 1924. By the year 1948, 418,825 birds had been banded, and there were 15,924 recoveries.

This is, of course, only a partial list of the countries which maintain or encourage bird banding organizations. A number of others, including Belgium, Czechoslovakia, Italy, Poland, Portugal and Spain, have kept up with recent ornithological research. Banding has also been developed in several intertropical countries, which will yield extremely useful information about bird migration there, and, also, about movements of boreal migrants in their winter quarters. However, bands applied in temperate regions to migrants that winter in tropical areas have little opportunity for recovery because these birds scatter over vast territories where there are few trained ornithologists. On the other hand, bands applied in tropical regions have a much better chance of being picked up in Europe or in North America, because of the large number of ornithologists and well-organized banding stations in these countries. It must be remembered, too, that relatively few persons are needed for banding, whereas recovery is a collective operation requiring the co-operation of a very large number of well-informed volunteers, particularly sportsmen, fishermen, and farmers. That is why the French Research Centre on Migration has undertaken to band birds wintering in Senegal, where there are hundreds of thousands of European Passerines and shore-birds. Efforts of this kind have also been started in the Congo (under the direction of IRSAC), and recently in Nigeria and Ghana. South Africa also has an excellent banding organization, which is already doing fine work.

A modern banding centre is a highly complex organization, because banding requires a large number of operations. Registers and files must be carefully kept, as the smallest mistake can have disastrous consequences, spoiling the results of hard work and misleading the research worker. Filing recovery records is an even more complicated task. Most stations have punch cards that make it possible to analyse results quickly. The U.S.A. and Canada have an electronic card index, and they recently adopted a new American Bird banding Recovery card, a standard IBM card, with eighty columns, all written in code. This is the only system permitting rapid analysis of a large number of cards and study of the data they furnish. Not long ago the Netherlands took advantage of the reorganization of their Banding Centre to adopt the same system.

These banding organizations are not content to band birds and keep track of recoveries. Each one has set up an enormous research project on migration, of which banding constitutes only one phase. This programme deals particularly with study of visible migration, types of migration and orientation, with connected research on terrain, bird protection, without which all research is futile, and with basic studies to put hunting on a practical basis of conservation.

A vast banding programme incorporating standardizing methods was recently instituted in Europe, setting a pattern for co-ordinated international research. It is noteworthy that this was accomplished on a continent so politically subdivided. The co-operative enterprise has taken the form of the International Committee for Bird Ringing, whose organ, *The Ring*, is edited by Dr Rydzewski, in Poland. It is impossible to overestimate the importance of this international organization in its bearing on the study of the vast and challenging problems of bird migration.

In addition to bird banding, other techniques are used in certain cases. Sometimes bird plumage is dyed, to obtain restricted but precise migration data. This is one way of identifying and following a bird without having to capture it. Rüppell dyed hooded crows red, and Dutch ornithologists recently spread yellow paint on the wings of starlings. These methods, of course, are purely temporary but they help in specialized experiments. The study of the orientation and physiology of some migrants requires distinct techniques, which will be discussed later.

CHAPTER 3

Migrations in Europe and Northern Asia

Europe is one of the areas where much is known about migration because of wide interest in birds. Every year the arrival of winter causes a large proportion of the feathered world to depart, its disappearance depending upon the country and species involved. But part of this avifauna remains or winters over in its breeding grounds, particularly in the milder regions of the Mediterranean and Atlantic coasts. The warmer parts of Europe also serve as winter quarters for various birds which are driven out of eastern and northern countries by the severe climate. Other migrants, still more sensitive to cold or food shortages, leave even the mild parts of Europe to go to tropical Africa, the favourite wintering ground for occidental Palearctic birds. Migration carries them through unfavourable zones such as the sea, the desert and mountain ranges – obstacles which the travellers overcome in many different ways.

Europe constitutes, of course, only part of the vast Eurasiatic land mass, inhabited by a relatively homogeneous fauna (Palearctic). In analyzing migration among European birds, therefore, it must be remembered that they usually represent only the western populations of species that are widespread over Asia.

A study of European birds and their seasonal flights makes it possible to distinguish several migratory patterns and to define certain aspects of this migration, which, on that continent, is characterized by astonishing diversity. It is needless to emphasize that we shall speak of only a few species chosen for their distinctive migratory behaviour. A detailed study of all European migrants would entail much repetition.

MIGRATIONS OF SOME TYPES OF EUROPEAN BIRDS

1. GULLS AND OTHER COASTAL BIRDS

It may seem surprising to see gulls placed among land birds, but they are not strictly bound to the sea. They inhabit only the littoral and, as a rule, never leave the continental shelf, while certain species, like the black-headed gull (*Larus ridibundus*), dwell far inland as well as along the coast. The migrations of gulls have, therefore, nothing in common with those of true sea-birds, particularly shearwaters and fulmars.

It should be noted, however, that a few species of gulls, like the kittiwake (*Rissa tridactyla*), are better adapted to marine life. In this study the migrations of the distinctly pelagic kittiwake will therefore be considered with those of sea-birds.

The winter behaviour of some gulls is characterized by simple dispersal rather than migration. This is especially true of the black-headed gull, a very abundant bird, which nests throughout most of Europe except in the Mediterranean countries. In general, black-headed gulls do not leave Europe (or at least the Palearctic region), but a few of these birds, banded in Europe, have been captured in tropical Africa. Although the population of a single locality will disperse in winter all around its nesting area, a preference for flight in a north-east–south-west direction is occasionally shown (Fig. 9). Recoveries on Swiss lakes, for example, have revealed that a large proportion of the winter-resident gulls have come from eastern Europe, from as far as Lake Ladoga in Russia. But birds coming from other directions also converge in the same wintering area: black-headed gulls come to Berlin from the north-west (Schleswig), from the south-east (Saxony, Silesia), as well as from the east and north-east. Some of these birds, banded in the Camargue, on the Rhône Delta, have been recovered in winter all along the French Mediterranean coast, in Italy, Spain, and on the Algerian coast.

Occasionally these gulls follow river systems, but they are by no means dependent on water and can cross easily from one drainage basin to another. As is often the case, young birds are more venturesome than adults or perhaps have a stronger migratory impulse, for they undertake longer flights in autumn.

Black-headed gulls show little attachment for their winter quarters, and some of them merely wander from one place to another. One such gull, banded in Berlin in December, was recovered six days later in Geneva, and another, banded in Berlin at the end of November, was

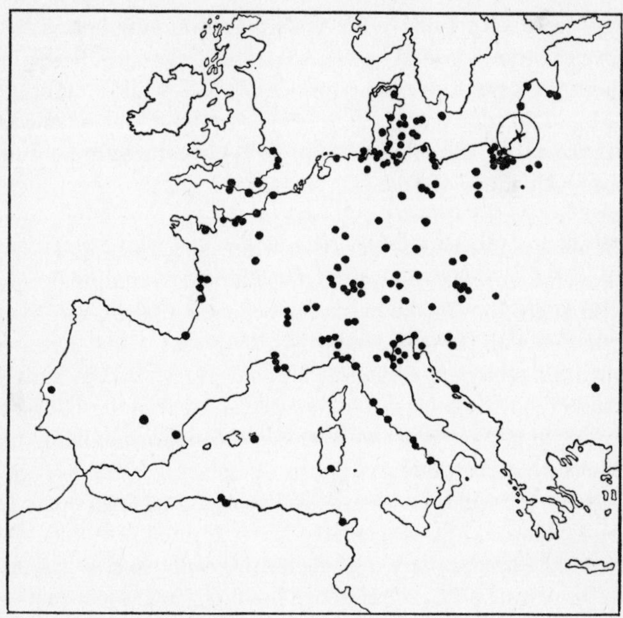

Fig. 9. Winter dispersal of the black-headed gull (*Larus ridibundus*). All the birds were banded at Rossitten (the site is marked by a cross inside a circle). Each dot represents a recovery. After Schüz and Weigold, 1931.

captured in January in southern Italy. As observations of this kind have been made repeatedly in other wintering places, it is clear that gulls from many populations mingle, and this doubtless prevents geographical segregation.

Certain gulls, taken from their winter quarters during homing experiments, came back, strangely enough, to the place where they had been captured. But the proportion of such returns was low and may reflect the fact that many of these birds have little or no attachment for their winter quarters, aside from its feeding and climatic merit.

The black-headed gull does not 'migrate.' Instead, there is a vast dispersal when this bird, often fed by man, or eating the waste of cities, spreads over most of Europe in winter. Other species of gulls behave in a different fashion and, although their migrations often resemble dispersals, they are more or less 'oriented' towards the south and south-west. The herring gull (*Larus argentatus*), a common gull along European shores, wanders casually in winter. Some individuals do not even leave their nesting areas, while others scatter farther about – with perhaps a slight preference for a south or south-westerly direction – for distances from 200 to 300 miles. Some herring gulls from Britain winter along the French coast.

The lesser black-backed gull (*Larus fuscus*), a related species, is however, a true migrant. Only a few individuals which breed in Great Britain (*L.f. graellsi*) remain there during the winter; the majority fly down the coast of France and Spain, and a few individuals even reach West Africa, as recoveries have been made as far south as Senegal. Most of the German populations (belonging to the typical race [*L.f. fuscus*]) winter on the shores of the Baltic Sea and in Denmark, but some of them cross Central Europe to the eastern Mediterranean and then move along the Red Sea coast, or follow the valley of the Nile southwards to winter in East Africa, as far as Lakes Victoria and Nyassa (Schüz, 1934), and even to Sierra Leone, Ghana and the Congo – flights equal to those covered by any of the classic migrants. The winter behaviour of the lesser black-backed gull presents some physiological problems, for within a single population there are notable differences in the hormonal balance between true migrants and nomadic birds. We shall consider this problem in dealing with 'partial migration.'

While the species of gulls whose migrations we have just considered make seasonal flights, usually in a north-south direction, others, like the Mediterranean gull (*Larus melanocephalus*), migrate along an east-west axis. This was proved by Russian banders working with gull colonies on Orlov Island, in the Black Sea (Mayaud, 1954, 1956a; Schevareva, 1955); some 34,440 young birds had been banded by 1955, 627 of which were later found in various winter ranges. These recoveries, together with many observations throughout the whole Mediterranean region, show that in autumn the main wave of migrants flows west and south-south-west. Most of these gulls winter in the central Mediterranean, between Italy and Tunisia. A small number move on even to the western Mediterranean. A few winter on lakes in Hungary (Balaton), Austria (Neusiedler) and Switzerland, apparently after following the Danube and then reaching the Upper Rhine. Still others go up to the Baltic, probably by way of the Dnieper.

The migratory behaviour of the slender-billed gull (*Larus genei*), which nests along the shores of the Black Sea and the Caspian, is similar. In southern Russia 65,127 birds were banded on Orlov Island between 1947 and 1954, and 809 recoveries have revealed their migration routes and winter quarters. As the studies of Semenov and Sabinevskii (1957), and of Erard (1958) disclose, the breeding populations of southern Russia winter in the central and eastern Mediterranean in great numbers, while a smaller contingent reaches the Persian Gulf. As in the case of the Mediterranean gull, however, the chief wintering zone is over the seas that wash southern Italy and northern Tunisia, where the birds remain from November to April. By flying across Transcaucasia and Mesopotamia, some of these migrants reach another, less important zone in Egypt, the Persian Gulf and the Sea of Oman.

Other families of birds, which live off the seacoasts, make more or less extensive migrations. Some seem to be simple dispersals, but others may be considered real migrations, like the razorbills (*Alca torda*), for which Thomson (1953a) has supplied data on the populations of Great Britain. Here again there are important variations in behaviour. Some of these birds spend the whole winter in British territorial waters or over the English Channel, whereas others go much farther south, to the Gulf of Gascony and off the Iberian Peninsula. Others even cross the Mediterranean to the Gulf of Genoa and to the North African coast. Some of these auks cross the North Sea to southern Norway and Denmark. The young are usually more inclined to make true migrations, while the adults are more apt to remain in the vicinity of their breeding grounds.

The winter migrations of guillemots (*Uria*), puffins (*Fratercula arctica*), and gannets (*Morus bassanus*) are of much the same type (Fig. 10). The gannets of the large summer colonies in the British Isles spread in winter along the Atlantic coast of Europe and Africa to Senegal and the western Mediterranean (Thomson, 1939). It should be noted again that young birds are bolder than adults. They even visit Africa, while most of their elders remain off the coast of western Europe.

A certain number of birds from European littoral zones doubtless travel to Morocco, where they find an abundance of food in and about the cool currents that extend along the shores of Morocco and Mauritania to Senegal, currents which support an abundance of marine life that provides food for wintering birds.

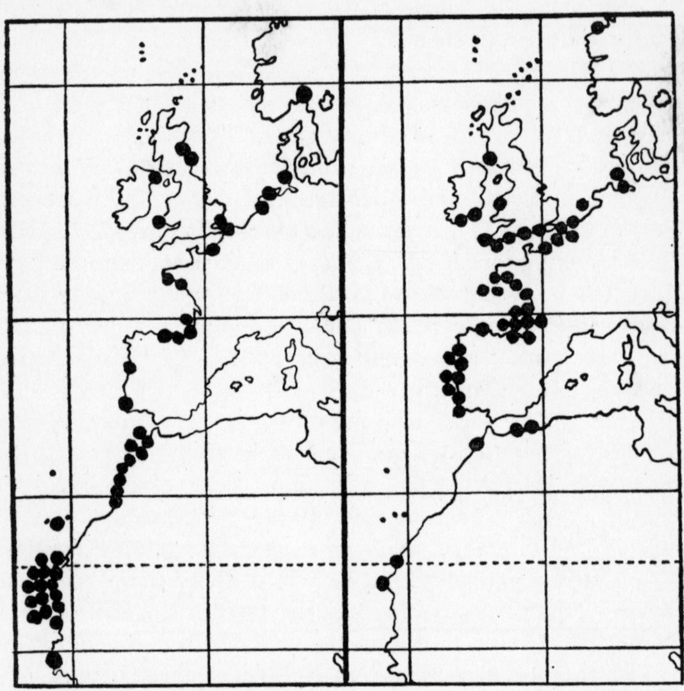

Fig. 10. Winter recoveries (November-February) of gannets (*Morus bassanus*) banded in Great Britain. Left: recoveries of first year birds. Right: recoveries of adults. Note that the young birds usually frequent the African coasts (Morocco and western Africa), whereas adults restrict their flights to the European littoral. After A. L. Thomson, 1939, completed by recent records.

2. DUCKS AND OTHER WEB-FOOTED BIRDS

Duck migration is familiar to all hunters who shoot these web-footed birds during their seasonal flights, as well as in their winter quarters. Most migratory ducks travel from north-east to south-west across Europe, and a few species even reach tropical Africa.

We may take as an example the teal (*Anas crecca*), familiar to all hunters in the Old World. Holarctic in distribution, its nesting area covers most of Europe except the extreme south and northern Asia. (Much of this material is taken from Lebret's study of the migrations of this bird [1947].)

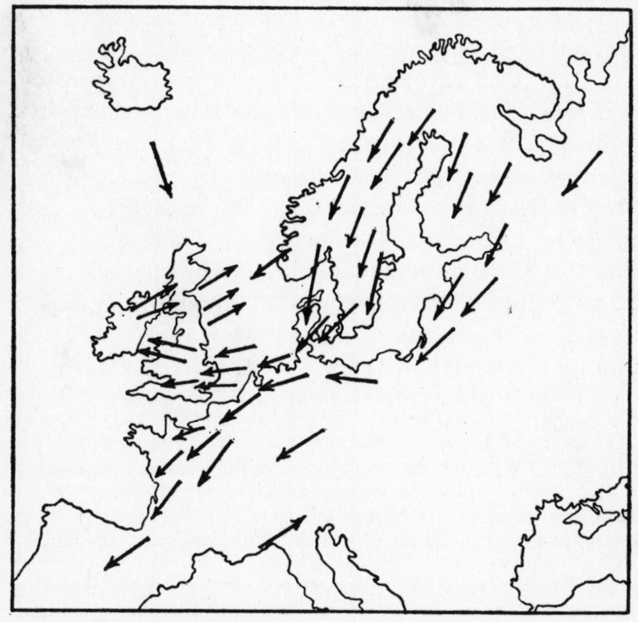

Fig. 11. General directions of autumn movements of the European teal (*Anas crecca*) in northern and western Europe. After Lebret, 1947.

The breeding territories of teal which winter in western Europe include Iceland, northern Europe (Scandinavia) and eastern Europe (the Baltic countries and Russia). The postnuptial migration of the latter populations is of particular interest, for, although there are direct flights between Scandinavia and the British Isles, and also across central Europe and Germany, the majority of the migrants seem at first to be concentrated between Denmark and Holland, where they arrive at the end of August and in September (Fig. 11). There they remain until October or November, after which they leave for their actual winter quarters in the British Isles, France, the Iberian

Peninsula, and northern Italy. In mild winters, the birds stay even farther north, in the Netherlands. As in the case of many other web-footed birds, the northern border of the winter range depends a great deal on local weather conditions, especially the frost line. Mild winters in central Europe permit water-fowl to winter farther north and to cancel their flights to southern France and Spain.

Teal thus make a stop-over during their migration. At first glance it seems that this might be related to the *moult migration* of certain ducks (see page 282)[1] which leave the nesting territories to moult their flight feathers in zones where they are not molested (many ducks lose all the flight feathers at once and thus for a time are unable to fly and at the mercy of predators). After replacing the flight feathers, they go to their final winter quarters. In the present case, however, most teal arrive in the Danish-Dutch zone after growing their new wing-quills; they are thus quite able to fly, so from that point of view this zone cannot be regarded as a refuge. They then moult the contour feathers, acquiring nuptial plumage. It is probable that an abundant supply of food is needed during this phase of the annual cycle. This the birds apparently

1. Another very curious type of migration, known so far only among ducks, is what Thomson (1931) has called *abmigration*. Individuals which nested one summer in one place have been found breeding the following year in a wholly different area. British ducks were thus found breeding in Scandinavia, Scottish teal in Poland and Russia, and Danish teal near Archangelsk. Wigeons banded in Iceland have been captured in the U.S.S.R. (Donker, 1959). These birds obviously had no nostalgia for their native land!

Several explanations have been suggested. One is that migratory ducks which winter where the native population of their species is sedentary may mate with individuals of that country. Since it is known that waterfowl acquire their nuptial plumage and form pairs during the winter, it is presumed that such a pair would display and be influenced by the migratory behaviour of the individual duck sensing the stronger migratory impulse; thus the migrant would lead the sedentary member of the pair to his or her homeland.

It is also possible that sedentary birds, unpaired or 'single,' because of their gregarious instincts, so well developed among ducks, may be lured away from their true homes by passing migrants. They will then become part of the same population that 'captured' them and will breed in the new nesting area.

Again, birds belonging to two distinct regional breeding populations may mate in a common wintering area, and one of the pair would then follow the other to the latter's breeding area.

These explanations are all valid, each covering certain specific cases. The last may explain the behaviour of ducks, derived from different regions, which winter in Great Britain, where the native population is practically sedentary.

Abmigration, a phenomenon apparently peculiar to the duck family, is evidently possible only among species which pair in the winter and which, unlike most migrants, arrive mated on their breeding grounds.

find in the immediate region, where they linger until cold temperatures drive them to milder areas.

The concentration of teal in a relatively small zone is accompanied by a mingling of different populations, which then migrate south-west by various routes, as teal populations have no narrow flyway. The return flight in the spring is more direct, and does not cross a limited zone of Europe. While the majority of teal appear to return to their 'homeland,' others go elsewhere. One contingent winters in tropical Africa, where this bird has been found in Somaliland, the (Anglo-Egyptian) Sudan, Kenya and Nigeria. Birds which nest in Siberia winter in southern Asia, Iraq, Baluchistan, India, Ceylon, Burma, and even in the Philippines.

Many other ducks have similar behaviour, differing somewhat, of course, according to species.[1] The mallard (*Anas platyrhynchus*), another Holarctic species, is also partially migratory, for birds from the northern and eastern parts of the range migrate far south-west in winter. Some individuals even go to tropical Africa, as far south as Abyssinia and Senegambia. As with all ducks, climatic variations during the winter have a great influence on dispersion. Other Anatidae do not, however, go so far south. The golden eye (*Bucephala clangula*) winters in southern France and the northern side of the Mediterranean basin (Italy, Greece). In Asia the same species migrates only to northern India, so its winter area, like its nesting area, is farther north than that of allied species.

Geese and swans which nest in extreme northern Europe and Siberia and migrate to Europe during the winter behave in much the same fashion. The grey lag goose (*Anser anser*), for example, reaches the Mediterranean and even North Africa on its winter flights, and swans, especially the whooper swan (*Cygnus cygnus*), reach western and southern Europe. Climatic conditions play an even more important rôle in their winter distribution than in the case of ducks. They are numerous in France only in rigorous winters. Cold waves sweeping

1. Donker (1959) recently devoted an excellent study to the migrations of European wigeons (*Anas* [*Mareca*] *penelope*). He showed that the population of Iceland migrates chiefly south-east towards Great Britain, but that a certain number of birds go west, to the Atlantic coast of North America. Most wigeons that winter in western Europe come from northern Russia and western Siberia and describe a vast curve of migration across Europe; they fly west and south in autumn along the shores of the Baltic and the North Sea, but return in the spring to their breeding area by more direct 'land' routes, across central Europe. This seems true of other web-footed birds, even geese.

over the more northern countries where they generally winter – England, Netherlands, Germany – drive them far south, where their arrival heralds the approach of cold weather.

It should be noted that these birds, like many ducks, are especially abundant in western France. Some Anatidae become frankly maritime during the winter, frequenting estuaries and the sea-shore. The freezing over of expanses of water on which they are accustomed to feed in their homeland forces them to migrate to open water, along the coast and at sea. Thus birds which are clearly fresh-water species in their nesting areas become 'oceanic' in winter quarters.

Aside from ducks, a classic example is furnished by loons, the best known being the black-throated diver or Arctic loon (*Gavia arctica*) (Bodenstein and Schüz, 1944). This bird is dependent on open water for food and also for security, as it cannot take off from the ground because of its heavy body and the rearward position of its feet. These factors determine its migrations. Arctic loons from northern Russia migrate in autumn to the Black Sea, then south and south-west, but in the spring they leave their winter range in a north-west and north-north-west direction, towards eastern Prussia and the Baltic Sea. A little later, they fly north-east and east, thus completing a necessary loop in their migration because Russian lakes and ponds are ice-bound at the beginning of their spring flight, so the birds have to follow a more western route.

Another part of the black-throated diver population winters in western Europe, particularly France. These birds, which are strictly limited to fresh water in their nesting territories, become almost exclusively maritime in France, illustrating to what an extent behaviour can vary according to the conditions in which migrants are placed. The search for open water causes even some fresh-water birds, like the kingfisher, to become occasionally marine species during the winter.

3. HERONS

European herons provide a very interesting example of seasonal migration, for, even within a single species, they present every form from the sedentary bird to the migrant. The migrational tendency differs greatly amongst local populations in various parts of Europe. This group of birds shows, possibly more than any other, how migration is a local, even at times an individual, phenomenon, rather than a universal species characteristic.

Quite apart from any tendency to migrate, young herons have a very marked inclination to wander. As soon as they are able to fly, they 'explode' over a vast area, not following any specific direction other than that imposed by topography and favourable hunting areas. Common herons (*Ardea cinerea*), which are banded in May in Pas-de-Calais, French Flanders, are captured in July and August, not only throughout northern France, but also in Normandy, Lorraine, western Germany, Belgium (in large numbers), Holland, and even in England. Purple herons (*Ardea purpurea*) and night herons (*Nycticorax nycticorax*) banded on the nest in May in the Camargue, in the Rhône Delta, have been recovered in July in the Jura, the Saône valley and westward even to the Loire. This post-juvenile wandering, found in varying degrees among all species of Ardeidae,[1] has nothing to do with real migration; the phenomenon, which German authors have named *Zwischenzug*, may be caused by feeding conditions. Many herons nest in large, congested colonies (heronries), and their nearby fishing grounds would soon become depleted if the young did not scatter over a vast area as soon as they can fly. But that fact alone does not explain a behaviour pattern which herons share with several other birds.[2]

The common heron (*Ardea cinerea*), a large species similar to the great blue heron of the Americas, is widely distributed throughout most of Europe and Asia but also nests in some parts of Africa and in Madagascar. Its migrations in Europe have been recently studied by Rydzewski (1956).

1. Identical migratory behaviour has been observed among several North American herons and egrets, where the young scatter widely and even fly north of their breeding grounds. This is particularly true of the little blue heron (*Florida caerula*) and the black-crowned night heron (*Nycticorax n. hoactli*).

2. Later we shall see that starlings also scatter in the postjuvenile period. Movements of this type have also been noted among birds of prey, particularly bald eagles (*Haliaeëtus l. leucocephalus*), which Broley (1947) has thoroughly studied. The records of this author show that young bald eagles banded in Florida scatter at once over the eastern half of the U.S.A. and into south-eastern Canada, flying far north in a very short time. A young bird, banded on its nest in Tampa, in February, 1942, and ready to fly about 15 April, was found a month later at Leger Brook, New Brunswick, about 1,600 miles to the north. Similarly the young of the tawny owl (*Strix aluco*) scatter widely on leaving the nest (Olsson, 1958), and many gulls do so (in varying degree). Postjuvenile dispersion, which is doubtless fundamentally distinct from migration – as is shown from the fact that it is observed among such completely sedentary birds as the tawny owl – must be a very important factor in the spread of species.

That common herons are remarkably sedentary in Great Britain (Ticehurst, 1939) is clear from many recoveries which show that they scarcely travel save into the interior of the British Isles, where they spend the winter. A few birds banded in Sussex have been recovered in France, one even in Spain, but these are isolated cases. The sedentarism of English bird populations is a rather common phenomenon.

Common herons of northern Europe are much more migratory, and numerous recoveries of birds banded in southern Sweden reveal that they radiate in winter throughout western Europe, particularly France. Herons of eastern Prussia are also migratory, as shown by Knabe (1938). The majority of these birds appear to leave the nesting area between mid-July and mid-September to fly south and south-west, without following any well-defined routes, and to winter in southern France, Portugal, Spain and the Balkan Peninsula, but chiefly in North Africa, where a great many recoveries have been reported. The overseas journey does not seem to cause herons serious difficulty, as their flapping flight is perfectly adapted for long over-water travels. Some of them go even farther south, crossing the vast Sahara, to winter in tropical Africa. Individuals banded in eastern Prussia have been recovered at the inundation zone of the Niger, at the mouth of that river, and also in Ubangi-Shari. Young birds go the farthest, since, as is often the case, they are impelled by a stronger migratory impulse than adults. They start the return trip towards their breeding range in March, or earlier.

French herons are much more 'hesitant,' and it is curious to note that individuals from the same heronry have winter behaviour patterns which differ in a most disconcerting way (Fig. 12). Banding records in Clairmarais, near Saint-Omer, Pas-de-Calais, reveal that some birds winter in that general region, as shown by December recoveries. Others fly towards more northern latitudes, into Belgium, Holland, Germany and even to England. Numerous recoveries also indicate a 'slipping' towards the west and south-west of France, particularly Normandy, Brittany, Vendée and Charentes. Other individuals, however, perform a real migration, which takes them by a similar route into the western part of the Iberian Peninsula, especially Portugal, where many recoveries are made near the estuaries of Portuguese rivers. Still others go on, not only to North Africa (Morocco), but even to tropical Africa. A heron banded in May at Clairmarais was

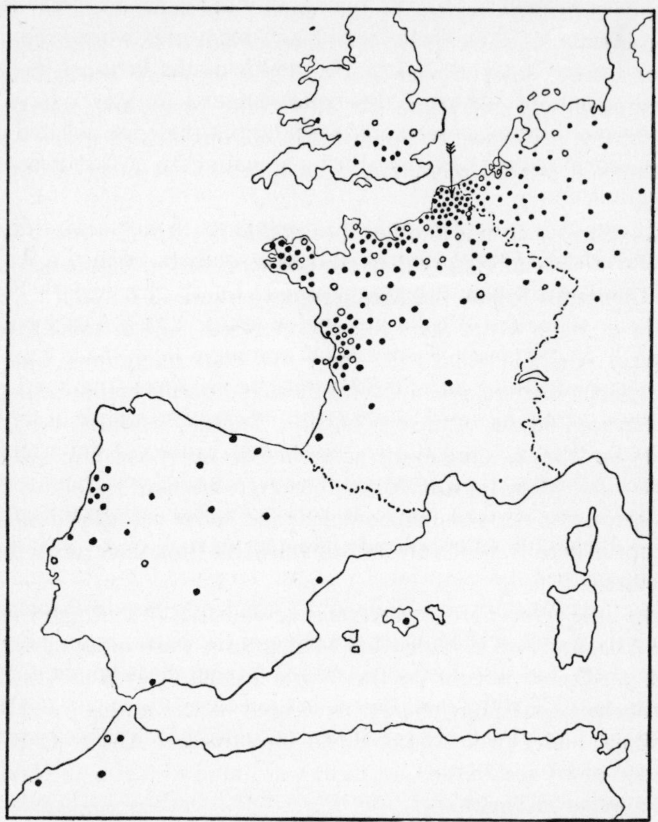

Fig. 12. Winter dispersal of European herons (*Ardea cinerea*) of the Clairmarais heronries, Pas de Calais, northern France (the arrow indicates the banding site). Dots represent the recoveries of first year birds, circles the recoveries of older individuals. The map does not show several recoveries of young birds in the Azores, Cape Verde Islands, Mauritania and southern Italy. The number of recoveries in the region near the banding area is actually larger than indicated.

recovered in September on the bridge of a vessel off the Cape Verde Islands.[1]

1. This recovery near an island remote from the mainland is comparable to the capture of common herons banded in Europe and recovered in the Azores and even in the West Indies, where they have been carried by strong winds (see p. 204). It shows how easily herons fly over the ocean.

Belgian herons scatter in the same fashion during the winter (Verheyen and Le Grelle, 1952). The behaviour of European common herons thus varies tremendously. There is every stage between sedentarism and migration, the latter being principally, though not exclusively, performed by young birds. Herons thus furnish a typical example of *partial migration*, which occurs in other groups of birds.

The purple heron is another species that nests in Europe, but it is more distinctly migratory than the common heron. Purple herons of the Camargue follow the Mediterranean shore in autumn towards Spain or Italy. From there they fly to North Africa, some even to tropical Africa. Occasionally there are huge migrations, like one Gurtchich observed, when several thousand purple herons settled on the terraced houses of the city of Sfax, Tunisia, in March 1933. The weary birds rested until dawn, sometimes as many as a hundred on a single roof. Migrations in Africa, however, are hard to follow, since this heron also nests on that continent and native herons and migrant European herons, which are indistinguishable from them, are mingled together.

The little egret (*Egretta garzetta*) likewise nests in southern Europe and Asia, and also in Africa and Madagascar, while other races have populated most parts of the Old World, extending even to Australia. European populations migrate to various winter ranges from Italy, Sardinia, and North Africa, down into tropical Africa. One bird banded on its nest in the Camargue was found wintering in Gambia, and another in Timbuktu.

The squacco heron (*Ardeola ralloides*), the night heron (*Nycticorax nycticorax*), the little bittern (*Ixobrychus minutus*), the European bittern (*Botaurus stellaris*), and the great white heron (*Egretta alba*) are all widely distributed species, nesting over a fairly large part of Europe. Their migratory behaviour patterns are much the same, as they spread during the winter through North Africa and occasionally go deep into tropical Africa. Generally speaking, they are more highly migratory than the common heron, which is a more northern species.

4. STORKS

The white stork (*Ciconia ciconia*), one of the most popular European birds, nests along a broad strip extending from the Netherlands and

Alsace across Germany to western Russia, as well as in part of Spain and North Africa, where the population is very large, especially in Morocco. A race related to the European and North African stork nests in the region of Bukhara, Turkestan and Yarkand (*C.c. asiatica*), and a third, more clearly distinguished, nests in eastern Asia, from the Ussuri River south to Korea and Japan (*C.c. boyciana*).

Our knowledge of stork migrations rests on hundreds of banding recoveries and countless observations. Strange circumstances have produced some of this information; while the Mohammedans respect the stork, for religious reasons, the same is not true of animist tribes that occupy a large part of Africa. These people sometimes hunt storks both for meat and for ornamental plumes. Thus, in various parts of Europe, storks have been found with African native arrows lodged in their flesh without crippling the birds. These arrows, characteristic in shape, permit fairly close identification of the locality where the bird was shot, and incidentally they indicate the regions the migrants must have crossed.

European storks have been the subject of many controversies pertaining both to their migration routes and to their wintering quarters in Africa. The European population is divided, for migration purposes, into two very distinct parts, one of which takes an eastern route, over the Bosphorus, Turkey and Palestine to East Africa, whereas the other passes through France, Spain, the Strait of Gibraltar and reaches the Dark Continent by way of West Africa (Fig. 13). These two migratory currents are very unequal in importance. They are divided by a line crossing the Netherlands and West Germany (the *Zugscheide*), which is not, of course, exact. From certain points of view it would be better to speak of a dividing zone (*Zugscheidenmischgebiet*), through the midst of which passes a virtual line where the division is fifty per cent. We can, however, speak of this line without attributing any precise value to it. Formerly it was said to be near the Weser, but, according to recent studies, especially those of Haverschmidt (1950), Schüz (1953) and Wichert (1956), it should be drawn through Leiden, the Osnabrück region, Minden on the Weser, Marburg, Schweinfurt and through the Lech valley. Only the populations of southern Holland, extreme western Germany and Alsace migrate over the Gibraltar route. This fraction is estimated at about 4,000 individuals (there are now only from 100 to 130 nesting pairs in Alsace, according to the latest figures of Schierer, which go back to 1956), without counting of course some 110,000 Spanish birds, whereas some 170,000 storks from eastern Europe take the Near East route. The

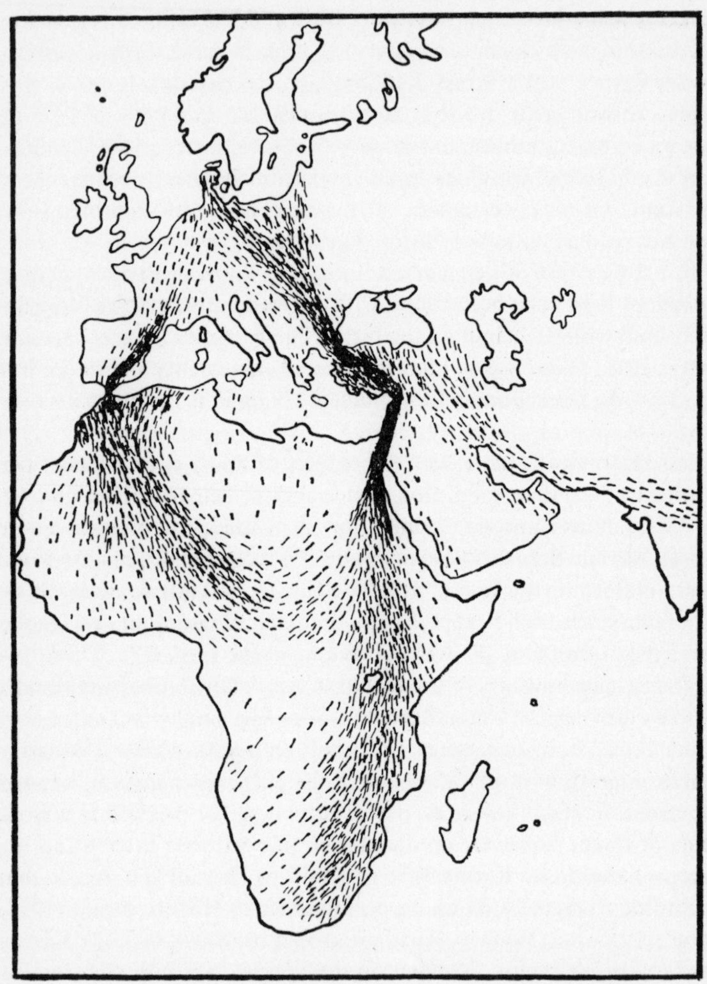

Fig. 13. General directions taken by European white storks (*Ciconia ciconia*). After Rüppell, modified by Verheyen, 1950 a.

separation between the 'western' and 'eastern' migrants occurs in a curious way; it has been observed that some of the young from the same nest near the dividing line migrate west, the others eastward (Kühk, Skovgaard).[1]

These separate migration routes are probably explained by the storks' aversion to long, over-water flights. These birds thus avoid the Mediterranean by using the two routes providing the shortest possible 'water carries' – the Strait of Gibraltar, and the Bosphorus (with a short crossing over the Red Sea through the Gulf of Suez on the eastern route). Granting that storks can be seen in other Mediterranean regions, notably Italy, as well as in the eastern Mediterranean, especially Crete, nevertheless, all these areas are outside of the two normal, regular flyways of European storks.

The storks' fear of flying across great expanses of water was demonstrated by Schüz (1938). Storks carried to the southern part of England (an island which is wholly outside the normal habitat of the species),[2] and released about the middle of August, made great efforts to migrate southwards; they followed the English Channel in all directions, not daring to venture out to sea. A stork will not risk itself over water unless the opposite shore is in plain sight. The narrow Channel thus constituted what seemed an insurmountable barrier to these exiled birds. That crossing is, however, much shorter than many of the storks' normal flights. The repugnance for over-water flights is doubtless explained by the storks' flying style, which is gliding, rather than a steady flapping, and which takes advantage of rising and falling air currents, prevalent over land but lacking above the sea.

The eastern itinerary of European storks is very interesting because it is so clear-cut; although in places it appears nearly 500 miles wide, elsewhere it narrows down considerably (the *Schmalfront*). European storks migrating along this route gather in large flocks, numbering hundreds, or even thousands of individuals. In 1955 Schüz reported a flight of storks passing from north-east to south-west over the Gulf of Suez in a skein only about 100 feet wide, but extending about twenty-five miles in length, and numbering at least 40,000 birds! Similar flocks

1. It should be noted (*a*) that some recoveries of bands have been made in northern Italy, especially of birds coming from regions where the migratory flow is divided; (*b*) that storks used to nest in Italy, and (*c*) that today it is very unusual to observe a stork migration along the Italian peninsula or at Malta.

2. Although storks are occasionally captured in England (especially in Norfolk and Suffolk), and even at times in Ireland, the British Isles are not on the normal migration routes of this bird. Most storks appear between March and June, although occasionally one is taken in autumn. A stork banded on its nest in Denmark was found in Sussex in October.

have also been observed in North Africa, and Panouse (1949) noted some at Séfrou and Ifrane, Morocco, at the end of August. In Alsace and Holland the flocks are much smaller because there are not nearly so many birds. Numerous legends are related about these flocks, which are said to constitute clans, with chieftains and a military hierarchy from which the unfit are eliminated. If there is any truth in these stories, the observations have been poorly interpreted and they are coloured by imagination.

Storks converge in autumn around Romania (notably the Dobruja), follow the coast of the Black Sea and cross the Bosphorus in serried battalions from about 20 August to 20 September. They go on to Turkey, Syria and Palestine, cross the Gulf of Suez near Sinai, and reach the Nile about latitude 25° N. They follow that river valley towards the Sudan in groups widely separated at many points.

According to Malbrant (1949), numerous flights of storks have been observed at Lake Chad and in Ubangi-Shari, especially in the eastern part of these territories. Birds banded in eastern Germany (Rossitten), in Lithuania and Poland have been recovered, chiefly between October and February. A fraction of the host migrating along the 'eastern' route thus passes through French Central Africa. Some of them stay there for the winter, and thousands can be observed in certain districts, especially from November through January on Lake Fitri, a huge expanse of water and marsh east of Lake Chad (but they may also include some 'western' storks).

While the migratory flights of a few storks reach all the way to the Cape of Good Hope, the wintering area really begins much farther north, in the (Anglo-Egyptian) Sudan, and even in Upper Egypt. The main zone extends from Kenya and Uganda to South Africa. Storks do not penetrate the equatorial rain forest, a barrier they seldom even fly across. No stork has been seen in Gabon or the Central Congo; the most southerly record in this region is the recovery at Dchang, in the Cameroons, outside the forest, of a bird banded at Viborg, Denmark. This distribution is apparently determined by both feeding and aerodynamic factors (the ascending currents, marked over open regions, are absent in the forest). The return migration follows roughly similar routes, with some local differences for topographical reasons.[1]

1. Whereas the black stork nests occasionally in South Africa, only an infinitesimal number of white storks have been known to breed in their winter range. The only definite record, indeed, is that of Austin Roberts (*Ostrich*, 11:24,

The migration pattern of the 'western' population of European and North African storks is quite different from that of their eastern relatives, which keep to a narrow path. Western storks follow several routes, so their migration is much more 'widespread.' European storks belonging to this group leave their northern 'homeland' during the first fortnight of August, at about the same time as storks migrating to the east. They then cross France, Spain and the Strait of Gibraltar to join their relatives native to North Africa. The latter are far more numerous. In Morocco alone, Bouet counted 48,000. They are less abundant in Algeria (13,000), and much rarer in Tunisia (200), where they occur in only a very small district. Panouse (1949) undertook a census of Moroccan storks, which yielded a much lower figure, about 24,000. He did not, however, count all the nests, so his estimate is doubtless too low. There are also the storks of the Iberian peninsula, which form the largest western contingent of all, with some 110,000 individuals.

The migrations of western storks have been studied by Bouet (1935, 38 a, b, 50), who banded a number of birds in North Africa (more than 4,000 since 1934), and recently by Bernis (1959). On the basis of recoveries and many observations made in the oases of the Sahara, Bouet believes that North African storks migrate along fairly definite paths. He postulates two migration routes: the first, or 'northern' route, is used by storks nesting in Tunisia and most of Algeria, except the western part. It follows roughly the Irharhar wadi, which comes from the Ahaggar Mountains, and is dotted by a series of watering places providing favourable conditions for storks. The second of these roads, called 'the western route,' used by birds nesting in Morocco and western Algeria, is said to drain through the valley of the Guir and the Zousfara wadis. These storks then take the Saoura valley to go much farther south-east and pick up the northern route again at Tamanrasset. This would make Ahaggar an important turning point for stork migration, as the birds would have to fly from there in an east-south-easterly direction through Borku and Ennedi to meet their eastern relatives at Chad and in East Africa. This hypothesis seems

1940; *ibid*, 12:34, 1941), who reports that a nesting pair was followed for several years to the same spot, and each time it raised a brood. This, of course, indicates a complete reversal of the physiological cycle of the Palearctic species in the southern hemisphere. (Murphy observed the same in the Zoölogical Garden of Lima, where a stork bred in November; see *Bird Islands of Peru*, 1925.)

to be substantiated by the recovery at Chad of a certain number of bands of North African storks. One bird, however, was captured near Sevilla, Spain, bearing an arrow from an East African tribe, which proved that it had spent a winter in that part of tropical Africa.

It seems impossible, however, to reduce the migration of North African storks to a simple diagram like Bouet's migration routes. Observations made throughout the Sahara show that, while these routes are followed by numerous storks, there are many others. The migration of 'western' storks is widely deployed and not *concentrated*, as in East Africa, as is apparent from the recent studies of Jespersen, Panouse, Heim de Balsac, and, above all, Bernis, the most important writer on this subject.

The existence of many more 'western' routes has now been demonstrated; Jespersen showed that numerous storks were observed in oases of the western Sahara in December, whereas the still more easterly ones, especially Ahaggar, had not yet been visited. These birds were probably on their way to nesting territories in Morocco, where vast numbers of storks arrive in December and January. It is only later, about the first of February, that records become more frequent in the eastern Sahara, particularly at Ahaggar, where the number of storks increases until March. These are birds which are going to nest in Algeria, where they arrive later than in Morocco. The observations of Heim de Balsac and Panouse in south-western Morocco have confirmed Jespersen's hypotheses. In any case, the storks which are in Morocco in December and January cannot be the same ones seen in March at Ahaggar!

Some European birds take the identical route on their return or prenuptial migration. They have been sighted flying north in the spring, long after the North African storks, which are already rearing young by this time. Their prenuptial migration is also later, for they do not reach the nesting areas until March and April. This small number of individuals corresponds to the lesser density of the populations, in contrast to those in Africa.

These 'Atlantic' migration routes are also used for the southward migration. On 20 August, 1950, Panouse, (1951) found in south-west Morocco (in the Aït-Baha circle) a stork banded 21 June, 1950, near Neustadt on the Hardt, Germany. This Atlantic route is also important.

According to Panouse, Moroccan storks on prenuptial migration do not follow the coastal region, where the low altitude would apparently provide easy flight; the majority, on the contrary, pass the Tizi-n-Test, a pass rising to a height of about 7,400 feet between Jjebel Tichka and Toubkal in the High Atlas. From there they go northwards in a straight line.

A few years ago Kullenberg (1956) published a new map showing migrations of the white stork across Africa. This points to two favourite routes through the western and central Sahara: the one through Mauritania would drain off all European storks migrating along the 'western route' and Moroccan birds (this route is the more important, according to Bernis); the second crosses the central Sahara through the Saoura valley, Tademaït and Ahaggar. It now seems clear that these itineraries are the most popular of all that cross the western and central Sahara because ecological conditions are more favourable for storks and, in a general way, for other migrants. But these routes should not be taken too seriously, for the white stork is known all over the Sahara, and it has been seen in even the most barren regions, such as Tanezrouft. There are, furthermore, changes from year to year, as local conditions, particularly humidity, vary.

The problem of winter quarters for these populations remains, since it is impossible for Moroccan storks to winter in East Africa. Leaving their nesting sites in August and September, they return in December and January, and this would not give them nearly enough time for such a long journey. We now know that these birds winter in certain parts of West Africa. Several authors, including Rousselot, have found very large flocks (more than 1,000 individuals) wintering there, especially in the inundation zone of the River Niger. After lengthy studies, Bernis states that, generally speaking, the winter quarters of western storks extend over the West African savannahs between the 12° and 18° north parallels. These birds usually reach the central African basin but seldom go farther east. The winter quarters of the eastern and western storks thus overlap slightly in Central Africa (Chad) but they are nevertheless quite distinct.

Several factors complicate a study of the winter quarters of these storks. First of all, the birds are by no means bound to any definite region. They are, on the contrary, quite nomadic, their movements within the winter range being largely determined by the local abundance of the migratory locusts (*Schistocerca*), which are one of their chief winter sources of food. Storks, moreover, are not in breeding condition until they are about three years old. Since immature birds wander about Africa in flocks of various sizes, only recoveries of adult birds should be counted, for the young storks found in Africa at all seasons of the year confuse observers.

The vast majority of storks winter in Africa, but a small number go to Arabia, especially the southern part, where there have been recoveries of birds banded in Bulgaria, Hungary, Schleswig and eastern Prussia. Occasionally, European storks seem to go even to India, as witness the recovery in Rajputana of a stork banded in Brunswick, Germany (this was a young bird, and consequently nomadic).

India, is, however, the regular wintering area for storks from Turkestan and Yarkand (*C.c. asiatica*) and perhaps also from the populations of *C.c. ciconia* of Mesopotamia and Persia, but very little is known about these migrations. The stork is not an uncommon visitor in north-west India and, more rarely, in the Deccan and Ceylon.

The more eastern race, *C.c. boyciana*, which nests from the Ussuri to Korea and Japan, seems less migratory in certain respects, although some individuals winter south to Assam and Burma. Others remain in their nesting territories, like those which feed on dead, coarse fish dumped on the ice of the Ussuri. The Japanese and Korean stork populations are also sedentary (Hemmingsen, 1951a).

We shall say only a word about the migrations of the black stork (*Ciconia nigra*), a relative of the white stork which nests from southern Sweden and Denmark across Asia to northern China. The migrations of the European population are quite similar to those of white storks; there are two migration routes, although the dividing line lies farther east than in the case of the white stork (thus the black storks of Jutland migrate to the west). The wintering zone is essentially the same.

5. CRANES

In Europe cranes (*Grus grus*) nest in a strip extending across northern Germany and Scandinavia to Lapland, and from there eastward across Russia, as well as locally farther south.

Since remote antiquity, these birds have been seen making the long autumn migrations to their winter range, which is chiefly in Spain (Estremadura and eastern Andalucía), North Africa, the Sudan (formerly Anglo-Egyptian), and Abyssinia (as far as Addis Ababa).

These flights are quite unlike those of storks. Cranes have, in fact, a very different type of flight, one which is much more 'flapping,' more even, and more rapid. They barely use the ascending air currents and are therefore much less dependent on atmospheric conditions. Moreover, although they do not migrate exclusively by night, they can fly at night, and even throughout the night, whereas storks are diurnal migrants. Cranes are thus able to fly over vast bodies of water, and are not obliged to 'go around' the Mediterranean, which, in fact, they cross at its widest part, notably in the eastern basin. Finally, their measured wing-beat enables cranes to fly in the familiar V-formation, whereas storks travel in scattered, patternless flocks. The differences between storks and cranes are explained by relatively small variations, which, nevertheless, determine their distinct types of migration.

Seasonal flights of these large birds follow narrowly defined paths, outside of which they are seldom seen. The migration routes differ from one European population to another. Three principal migratory currents are distinguishable in the European part of the area where cranes breed (Fig. 14). In Scandinavia and Germany flocks begin to assemble in September and continue to grow through October and even into November. Some have been seen at the end of August, but these were doubtless immature birds, which, although not nesting, had come to spend the summer in the breeding territory of the species. Occasionally these flocks are numbered in thousands, and Libbert (1957) reports that in the Müritz region of northern Germany flocks of some 11,000 cranes were sighted in October, 1951 and 1955. The birds had probably been driven from Scandinavia by a cold wave.

Norwegian and Swedish cranes, together with birds from part of Finland, converge near the Schonen in Germany, where they meet their Teutonic relatives. The migration route then cuts across Germany from north-east to south-west across Holland, Belgium and as far east as Strasbourg. The birds then move over Champagne and Lorraine south-westward, then to Sologne and western France (Vendée) to the Lower Pyrenees, where the flocks enter Spain. The birds never follow the Alsatian plain but, towards the east, the left flank of the migration skein drops towards Doubs and Burgundy, although few birds are observed in the Rhône valley and the Camargue. Flights of cranes are especially common over France in October.

Spain is spanned for its full length, chiefly in November. The birds do not stop in Castile (Valverde, 1952); they begin to find winter grounds in Andalucía and in several parts of Portugal (Bernis, 1960), but the main wave spreads out over North Africa.

Another, more eastern route, draining part of the cranes from Finland and western Russia, leads across Galicia, Hungary, Yugoslavia, southern Italy and Sicily before spreading out in Tunisia. A third, still more easterly route, leads another portion of the cranes from western Russia towards the Ukraine, the coasts of the Black Sea (in the Dobrudja they are observed in large flocks every year). Then the cranes leap the Mediterranean, off the coast of Asia Minor, to enter Egypt west of Alexandria. Therefore these birds do not fly over the Bosphorus as the storks do. They winter instead in the region of the White Nile, where endless swamps provide a favourable environ-

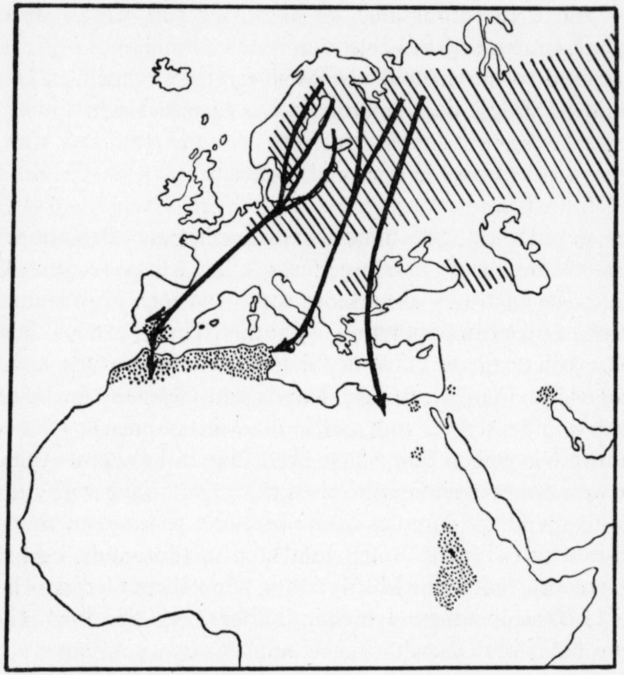

Fig. 14. General directions taken by migratory European cranes (*Grus grus*). Hatched: nesting zone; dotted: winter zone. The arrows indicate the principal itineraries followed during migrations. From Libbert, 1936, modified after Bernis, 1960.

ment. Finally, other Russian cranes cross the Caucasus to Mesopotamia.

Although the date of arrival in the wintering area of North Africa is not fixed, the birds reach the region of the White Nile about the middle of October. The return flight begins in February and continues into March, when many birds are observed flying through the Mediterranean region, from Tunisia to Gibraltar. The cranes which go to Scandinavia to nest usually do not arrive at their breeding sites until April or even May. Prenuptial migration is generally swift.

6. BIRDS OF PREY

Birds of prey are by no means all sedentary, as might at first be supposed. Some are real migrants, which perform periodic flights as long as those of other seasonal European visitors. A tendency to migrate is most prevalent among the Raptores of northern Europe. This is particularly true of the common buzzard (*Buteo buteo*). Scandinavian buzzards belonging to the form *vulpinus* (*B.b. vulpinus*) winter in southern Asia and Africa; Russian populations cross the Bosphorus and Asia Minor. These great migrants avoid the Mediterranean, somewhat like the storks, and this is in keeping with the soaring, circling flight of these Raptores.

Buzzards of the typical 'broad-winged' form (the common buzzard, *Buteo buteo*) are less definitely migratory. After nesting in Scandinavia, they fly south-west along the shores of the Baltic, then over the plains of northern Germany, the Netherlands and Belgium, avoiding mountain ranges. Great numbers winter in northern France, but only a few reach the south of France and Spain, as Mayaud (1955) showed on the basis of recoveries of birds banded in different countries of northern Europe. The populations of buzzards nesting in northern and eastern Germany also migrate south-west in winter (Burr, 1936), some flying short distances, about sixty miles, many others going to west Germany, Belgium and France (Fig. 15); a German buzzard was even found wintering in southern Spain. A study of the age of migrants recovered in France indicates that Scandinavian buzzards wintering in western France include both adults and young, as the latter do not seem more inclined to migrate than their elders. Buzzards do not appear to vary in behaviour pattern as they grow older, whereas other birds, particularly partial migrants, certainly do.

The fact that the buzzards of Great Britain are sedentary, wandering in winter over distances up to a hundred miles at most, was shown by Thomson (1958a) on the basis of banding results in England.

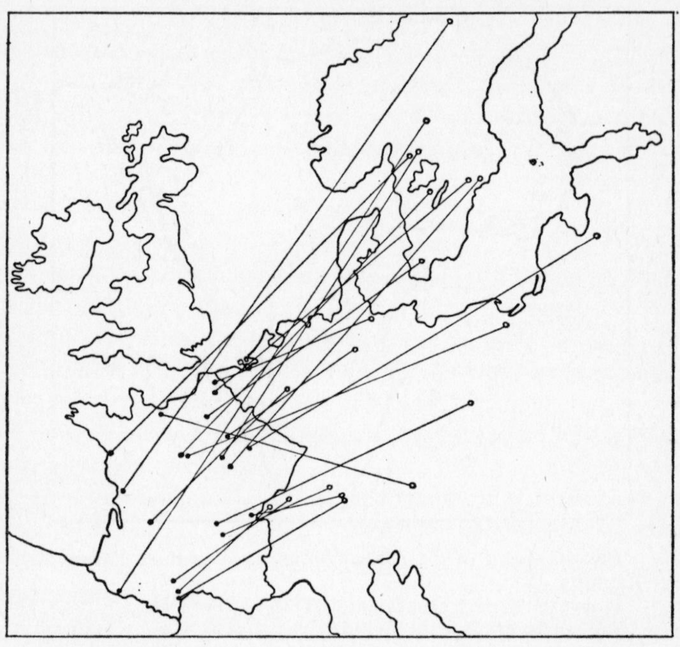

Fig. 15. Several winter recoveries of the common buzzard (*Buteo buteo*) in France, a wintering ground for birds coming from Scandinavia, the Baltic Countries, Germany and Switzerland. As on the following maps, circles indicate the banding areas, dots the recovery points.

Ospreys (*Pandion haliaeëtus*), which are very widely distributed throughout the world, are migratory in a good part of Europe. Their flights are longer than those of the buzzards, for part of the osprey population winters in tropical Africa. The migration routes pass over western Europe or the Dardanelles and Asia Minor, and also cross the Mediterranean at its widest point. The factors determining the migration of this bird of prey are linked to its diet, which consists almost entirely of large fish. Since winter lakes and rivers are frozen in northern and eastern Europe, where the bird is particularly abundant in summer, it is forced to seek open water for its prey far to the south.

The kestrel (*Falco tinnunculus*) is sedentary or nomadic throughout most of Europe but migratory in the north-east, from which it flies

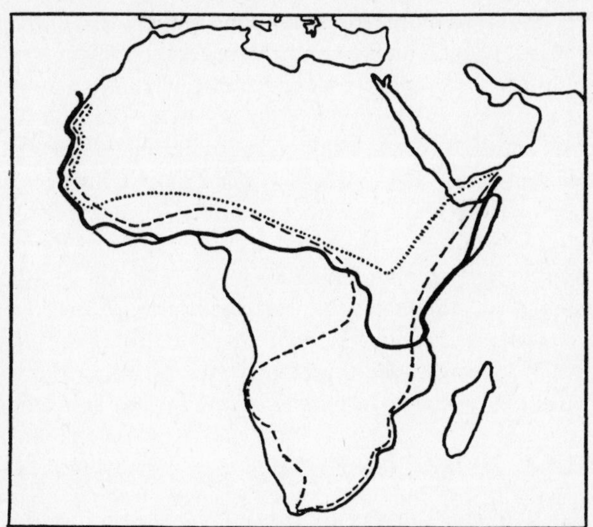

Fig. 16. Limit of the African winter area of three Palearctic Raptores.
Unbroken lines: European kestrel (*Falco tinnunculus*)
Broken lines: Lesser kestrel (*Falco naumanni*)
Dotted lines: Scops owl (*Otus scops*)
From Chapin, 1932.

south-west or south-south-west, so the wintering areas of kestrels from north-eastern Germany extend to France, Italy and Spain. Some European birds even winter in tropical Africa, as far as Nigeria and Tanganyika.

The lesser kestrel (*Falco naumanni*), a close relative of the kestrel with which it is often confused, is even more migratory. Nesting in colonies in Spain, Morocco, southern France, Italy and generally along the whole northern shore of the Mediterranean, it winters widely in tropical Africa, and even reaches South Africa. As this bird eats insects almost exclusively, it is forced to seek more favourable conditions by forsaking its breeding area, where few arthropods are found in winter. Similar factors probably impel honey buzzards (*Pernis apivorus*) to winter in tropical Africa, where they occur both in the south and east. This bird of prey often migrates in large flocks, which is surprising in view of its great size. Drost (1940) described a flight to Heligoland on which nearly 200 birds could be seen at a glance, and there were doubtless more than a thousand in the flock.

The hobby (*Falco subbuteo*) and the red-footed falcon (*F. vespertinus*) are insectivorous Raptores which also winter in South Africa. The latter performs, as Mayaud (1957) has shown, a definite migration loop across both ends of the Mediterranean during its seasonal flights to Central and West Africa. The autumn flight is only accidental in western Europe, especially in France and Italy, where the main flow of migrants moves through Greece, Asia Minor, Sinai and Egypt. In the spring, however, its prenuptial migration spans a much broader area, including Algeria, Italy and south-eastern France, so the routes shift west and cover a wide front. Mayaud thinks that this shift is due, in part at least, to the westward wandering in the African winter grounds of the red-footed falcons, in pursuit of the locusts and termites on which they feed.

The black kite (*Milvus migrans*) is definitely more migratory than its relative, the kite (*M. milvus*), whose northern populations simply migrate towards the Mediterranean region. Black kites make very long migratory flights, with almost all the European birds moving to Africa, some even to South Africa. Their migration, or at least that of the birds in western Europe and North Africa, usually follows the western Sahara. These Raptores migrate in enormous flocks, which sometimes fill the whole sky with their evolutions.

Other migratory Raptores include the short-toed eagle (*Circaetus gallicus*), which winters in Africa as far as Abyssinia in the east, Togo and Senegal in the west, and the marsh harrier (*Circus aeruginosus*), which has been recovered in Tanganyika and Angola.

European and North African populations of Egyptian vultures (*Neophron percnopterus*), a relatively small species with a vast distribution throughout the Old World, also go to tropical Africa for the winter.

Some other European birds of prey lead a non-migratory, nomadic existence in the winter, although their flights may cover long distances.

7. SWALLOWS AND SWIFTS[1]

Swallows are certainly the most common European migrants and, as they live close to man, they are easy to watch. The disappearance of these birds in autumn and their reappearance in spring have, since time immemorial, been interpreted as seasonal harbingers. Numerous proverbs allude to them.

Swallows require aerial insects – a kind of flying plankton – and, with the approach of winter, they must go southward for their prey, which vanishes in cold weather. Their remarkable flying ability enables them to perform long migrations in quest of a favourable environment.

Of the four species of swallows breeding in Europe the two most common are the barn swallow (*Hirundo rustica*) and the house martin (*Delichon urbica*). That all of them winter in Africa has been proved by a large number of recoveries of banded birds and their complete absence from Europe in the cold months. Migrations of European swallows have been thoroughly studied by Drost and Schüz (1952) and by Verheyen (1952a).

European swallows do not leave at a definite date. By the end of July some individuals are beginning to migrate, at least those that have not raised a second brood. Migration increases in volume during August and by the end of September it is almost over, although belated individuals are often seen. The date of their disappearance does not depend on temperature but rather on the abundance or scarcity of the insects which form the birds' diet.

The autumn migration is performed by day in large flocks, which may number many hundreds of individuals. Part of the day is devoted to hunting insects, for swallows can easily pursue their favourite prey during migration. At sundown they often stop in marshy regions, where bulrushes and reeds furnish a welcome cover.

The advance guard of barn swallows arrives in Abyssinia about mid-August (10–12 August, Friedmann), about the middle of September at Lake Chad (19 September, Grote), the Cameroons (12, 13 September, Young), Gabon (17, 20 September, Malbrant and Maclatchy),

1. We have grouped together two types of birds belonging to different orders: Passeriformes and Apodiformes, because of similarities in their mode of life. Both are swift, skillful fliers, and both depend on aerial insects for food.

and in Nigeria (15 September, Serle). These are, of course, only forerunners, for numerous barn swallows remain in Europe. In Rhodesia and South Africa the arrival takes place about the middle of October.

The barn swallow usually winters in Africa south from the 20° parallel N. But that vast zone is very unequally inhabited by these winter residents, most of which are concentrated in South Africa, in the Congo, and in certain coastal regions of West Africa. These swallows avoid the equatorial forests. The bird is a very common winter resident in Africa and much more abundant than native African swallows.

The sand martin or bank swallow (*Riparia riparia*) and the house martin likewise winter chiefly in West Africa (Gambia, Ivory Coast, Ghana, N. Nigeria) and in East Africa from the north-eastern Congo to South Africa.

Although it is impossible to assign to each local European population a definite winter territory, swallows seem to have some preference (Fig. 17). The swallows of Great Britain like to winter in South Africa, as recoveries of banded birds have revealed. Birds nesting in northern and central Europe, on the contrary, go to West and Central Africa, and swallows nesting in western Europe cross Arabia and Egypt to East Africa. Bont (1960) discovered that all the swallows which winter in the eastern Congo (Katanga) nest in the U.S.S.R., Poland, Hungary, Czechoslovakia, etc.

Prenuptial migration is performed in the reverse of the autumn flight. It begins about 10 January in various parts of Africa (Katanga, Kenya, Nigeria). All swallows have left Cape Province before the end of April, and flights across the Mediterranean are observed by the end of March, but continue over a period of several weeks.

Most North African swallows come back to their nesting sites at an earlier date. Heim de Balsac records barn swallows in southern Morocco at the end of January. It is probable that some of these birds are even sedentary in southern coastal Morocco.

The return of swallows to Europe in the spring has been studied by several authors, particularly Southern (1938a), who showed that the migratory front of this Passerine follows the isotherm of 8.9° C. (=49° F.) northward until 1 April, then passes it, to move north more rapidly. It should be observed that swallows return to western Europe earlier than to the east, so barn swallows are in England even before they reach the Crimea. This is explained by climatic conditions, indicated by the remarkable parallelism between the isotherms and the advance of the migratory front of the barn swallow (see p. 234).

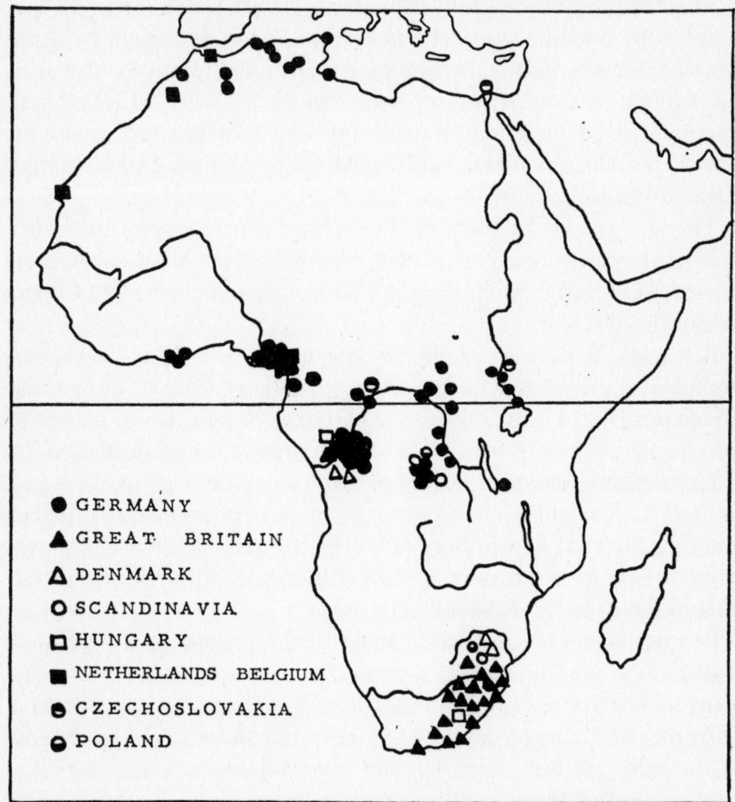

Fig. 17. Recoveries of swallows (*Hirundo r. rustica*) in Africa. This map shows that swallows retain a geographical grouping and that each population has favourite wintering grounds. From Drost and Schüz, 1952.

The behaviour of the house martin is similar, although this bird arrives a little later. Prevailing meteorological conditions also cause some variation from year to year.

Spring migration is likewise performed by day, but flocks are smaller, as swallows go north to nest in little groups. Only a few individuals have been observed in winter territories during the northern summer months, especially in July, and these birds are probably weaklings or very old specimens, unable to migrate.

Both the autumn migration and the return flight are accomplished in the brief compass of five or six weeks. Although swallows are powerful fliers, they occasionally encounter serious difficulties, when unfavourable atmospheric conditions kill off the aerial insects upon which they depend for food. This causes appalling mortality among the birds, which have pushed close together, and it was this custom which gave birth to the old legend of the hibernation of swallows.

Desert country seems highly unfavourable for birds that feed on aerial insects. The house martin crosses the Sahara on a non-stop flight, using all its energy to return as quickly as possible to an area where food supplies are abundant. The bird flies high, so it is hard to see. The barn swallow, on the other hand, stops much more frequently, to waste time hunting non-existent food. Flying insects are rare in the Sahara, especially in windy weather so common in these desert regions, and, as the bird often fails to cross the desolate expanses, bodies of these migrants are found there at times in great numbers.

The tropical climate is much less favourable to swallows than that of Europe. Frequent tornadoes cause great losses in avian populations. Verheyen (1952a) tells how a flock of barn swallows wintering in Upemba, in the Congo, was surprised by a tornado accompanied by hard rain. After the storm a third of the birds had vanished, and the survivors had a hard time drying their rain-soaked plumage. Almost every bank swallow had perished. Verheyen thinks that half the swallows which leave their European nesting territories will never see them again.

Finally, we should note that the crag martin (*Riparia rupestris*), which also migrates to cold regions, is more or less sedentary in the south of France and in other parts of its Mediterranean habitat.

The swift (*Apus apus*), like the swallows, performs long migrations, which take it to Africa, where it is observed all the way from West Africa to the Cape. This is one of the first birds to leave the temperate regions of Europe. In August a few of them are already found in West Africa (Timbuktu, Niger). They are also very late in returning to Europe, the date depending, of course, to a large degree on what part of the continent is involved.[1] In the Parisian region the last week of April may be considered the average spring date of arrival.

Swifts are strong, rapid fliers, which do not hesitate to cross deserts and vast expanses of water. Their migration routes follow many lanes. It should be added that it is difficult to obtain information about their migrations and behaviour in winter quarters, as these birds are easily confused with related species native to Africa.[2]

6. STARLINGS

Among the most sociable and gregarious of birds, starlings (*Sturnus vulgaris*) nest throughout most of Europe, as well as in a large area over western Siberia, Turkestan and the Iranian region. In Europe they demonstrate every phase between sedentary, nomadic and migratory forms.

Most of the populations of western Europe are sedentary. Those nesting in Great Britain scarcely ever leave the British Isles, within whose boundaries they make erratic flights, no farther than to Ireland. Dutch starlings also travel only within a very circumscribed area. In central Germany some of the population winters on the nesting grounds, but the eastern and northern birds are more migratory.

Unlike black-headed gulls and teal, starlings seem to migrate as a population, and they retain a certain individuality in winter quarters;

1. Swifts illustrate how widely birds systematically closely related, living under the same conditions and having the same diet, may differ in their life cycle. According to Heim de Balsac (*Alauda*, 17–18: 108–112, 1949–1950) the swift (*Apus apus*) and the pallid swift (*Apus pallidus*), species which are very closely related, have a cycle differing by about a month and a half, both as to their arrival in the breeding areas of North Africa and the laying of eggs, the swift being later than the pallid swift. These factors reveal a distinct physiological difference.

2. The black swift on which Koskimies (*Ann. Acad. Sci. Fenn.* A. IV 15: 151 pp., 1950) has collected a great deal of information, and probably other species of Apodiformes, especially the spine-tailed swift (*Hirundapus caudacutus*), which nests in eastern Siberia and south-eastern Asia and winters in Australia and Tasmania among other places (see H. Stuart Dove, *Ibis*: 748–751, 1911), and the American black swift (*Cypseloïdes niger*), studied by M. D. F. Udvardy (*Condor*, 56:261–267, 1954), also perform unusual flights, quite distinct from migrations. These birds require flying 'plankton' for food, but the supply of flying insects depends on meteorological conditions and may be temporarily wiped out by rain or cold. Bad weather and an absence of insects may thus cause swifts to make long flights, usually south, and often in large flocks, to avoid the centre of an approaching cyclone and to find more favourable regions (weather flight movements). These swifts return to their original quarters as soon as the atmospheric disturbances have subsided.

birds nesting in one particular area migrate in the same direction (although not necessarily all together) and spend their winter in the same region (Fig. 18). Thus, starlings nesting in northern Germany

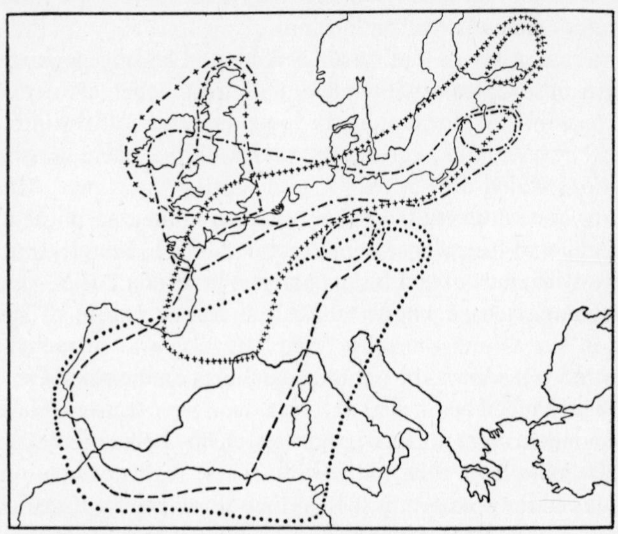

Fig. 18. Winter dispersal of starlings (*Sturnus vulgaris*) in western and southern Europe.

Crosses: Starlings from southern Finland
Dots and dashes: Starlings from Latvia
Broken line: Starlings from central Germany
Dotted line: Starlings from Saxony, Silesia and Bohemia
Dashes – crosses: Starlings from Great Britain

The smaller zone indicates the breeding area of the population, the larger zone, its winter territory. Note that the starlings of Great Britain are practically sedentary, although some of them go to Ireland. From Schüz and Weigold, 1931.

and the Baltic plains migrate westward in autumn to winter in Great Britain. They arrive between September and November, by way of Belgium and Holland. The winter range of Scandinavian starlings extends down through Belgium and northern France as far as the Loire.

Starlings from central and southern Germany, on the other hand, like those of central Europe, migrate south-westward. They spread in winter over western Europe, especially southern France, the Iberian Peninsula, Italy, and the Balearics, as well as North Africa, where they arrive in very large flocks, and do a good deal of damage, especially to olive groves. For this reason they are hunted relentlessly. They illustrate how a bird, useful in the region where it nests (the starling destroys enormous numbers of insects while feeding its young), can become a costly nuisance elsewhere. Such cases reveal the futility of classifying a bird as 'useful' or 'harmful.'

In any case, it seems that starlings remain in homogeneous flocks, and have little contact with individuals from other districts. This would explain the formation and maintenance of distinct geographical races, since segregation preserves the characteristics of populations which do not mingle even during the winter. This behaviour is quite different from that observed in the case of the black-headed gull and teal, whose winter populations do mingle, thus preventing any character from becoming fixed in certain flocks.

Ornithologists have known about the unique nature of starling migration for a long time, but their attention was attracted only recently to what seem to be paradoxical flights on the part of some of them. Birds banded on the nest in Switzerland were recovered later the same summer in more northern countries, chiefly Belgium, at distances up to 300 miles from their native land. These flights, which indicate that young starlings scatter as soon as they are able to fly, have nothing to do with real migration, but resemble the scattering flights of herons after the nesting season. An analogous, although more restricted, dispersion has been cited in other countries, notably Germany. It is evident, therefore, that in some starling populations there is a *post-juvenile dispersion* distinct from, but often preceding, migration.

The behaviour of Swiss starlings explains what has long been observed among migratory starling populations of eastern Prussia (Fig. 19). Juvenile birds hatched in that part of Europe leave their breeding areas in June and migrate west to Pomerania and Schleswig-Holstein, occasionally even farther; a later migration takes them to England, Holland, Belgium and northern France (Schüz, 1932; Kratzig, 1936a, b). This tendency is not noticeable among birds from far eastern Europe. There is, then, a true migration at two periods, with a pause at an intermediary station, a little like that of teal. These movements have a slight relationship to the post-juvenile dispersion observed among Swiss starlings, but they involve the whole population and doubtless have a different meaning. Again, Swiss starlings scatter widely, but this has no connection with their migration, whereas starlings of eastern Europe all go in the direction of their eventual

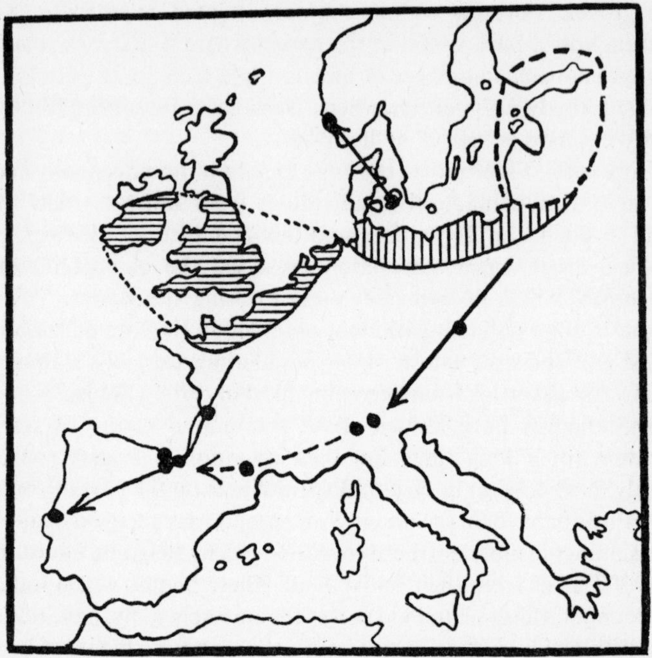

Fig. 19. Winter dispersal of starlings from the Baltic Countries. The nesting zone is marked by a broken line. Vertical hatching shows the intermediate zone (*Frühsommerzuggebiet*); horizontal hatching the winter quarters. Arrows and dots indicate recoveries outside the normal migratory routes of the population. From Krätzig, 1936 b.

autumn migration. It is possible that food factors influence these flights.[1]

1. The European starling was first introduced into the United States in Central Park, New York City, in 1890. From there it has spread over southern Canada, the whole of the U.S.A. and north-eastern Mexico. It nests in great numbers in the northern and eastern part of this vast region, performing flights comparable to those observed in Europe. Kessell (1953) showed that the behaviour of this bird is particularly interesting, since it reveals how a migratory bird adapts itself to a new continent. As in Europe, starling migrations in North America are only partial, the proportion of migrants varying with the populations. This bird has adapted its migration routes to those of native birds. It flies along the Atlantic coast on a north-south axis or follows the Mississippi Valley. Young birds, as in Europe, have a stronger urge to migrate, and they travel in a highly irregular fashion; their behaviour is doubtless one of the most important factors in the spread of the starling in America.

9. CORVIDAE

Crows and carrion crows, which are highly developed, omnivorous Passerines with a gift for adaptability, show a marked tendency to make seasonal migrations. The rook (*Corvus frugilegus*), which nests almost everywhere in Europe, save in the Mediterranean region,[1] the extreme north of Russia and Scandinavia – and in part of western Siberia – performs true migrations which a number of authors have studied because of the importance of these birds to agriculture. Giban (1947) compiled some highly significant data on the biology of rooks in Europe. French rooks are sedentary on the whole and, in any case, they do not perform real migrations. At most, there is a westward and south-westward movement in winter, and no flight observed has exceeded 230 miles. Only part of the rook population, and mainly the young, participate in these movements, which mingle the populations of various rookeries.

During the winter western Europe receives a very large contingent of eastern rooks, which come to the plains of France (except around the Mediterranean), Germany, Belgium, Holland and the southern half of England. The general direction of this migration is east-west, occasionally north-east–south-west. (Fig. 20). Within the framework of this vast movement several population groups can be distinguished, characterized by slightly differing regions and migration routes. Rooks from the northern part of the Russian plain migrate across the large flat expanses of northern Europe into northern France. Rooks of the Baltic countries cross northern France but winter mostly in Belgium and England. The rooks of the Ukraine, southern Poland, Silesia, Franconia and Austria also follow an east-west direction, but their path is definitely farther to the south, to Switzerland, France and northern Italy. Occasional recoveries are made in Spain or North Africa, but there is nothing to indicate that many of the birds winter regularly in this southern region.

Some of these migratory rook populations appear biologically distinct, but there is no morphological character to separate them. Giban distinguishes four groups of European rooks: a Baltic group; a

1. Valverde discovered in the Orbigo Valley, Province of Leon, Spain, several large colonies which had apparently been in the region for a long time without being observed (*Nos Oiseaux* XXII: 78–82, 1953).

Russian group (the north of the Russian plain); a southern group (Ukraine, Poland, Silesia, Franconia, Bohemia, Austria); a western group (England, Belgium, France). The fourth population group is the only one where the birds are sedentary, or make only short seasonal flights. There is, of course, no strict barrier between these groups, which merely represent a general tendency to be observed in a specific population.

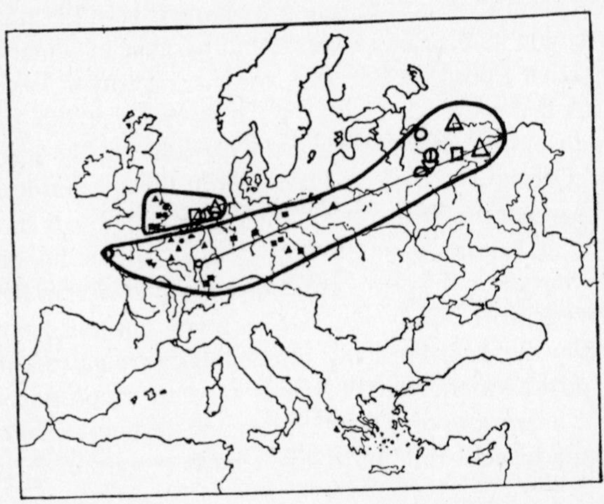

Fig. 20. Migrations of rooks (*Corvus frugilegus*) from the northern Russian plain and the Baltic Countries. Hollow signs show the banding places, solid signs the recovery places in winter. The broken line shows the movement of a rook banded in winter quarters and recovered in its nesting territory. From Giban, 1947.

During the autumn migration most eastern rooks enter France through the Belfort Gap to avoid the Vosges and Jura Mountains. This invasion generally occurs during October. The birds travel in flocks, which often number from 1,500 to 2,000 but may run from several hundred to more than 8,000 individuals. Rooks fly quite rapidly in a more or less open crescent, and they alight with the utmost care to feed or roost for the night, being always surrounded by scouts or sentinels. A remarkable social instinct characterizes the behaviour of these birds, which are certainly among the most intelligent to be found. Migratory rooks never mingle with native birds but preserve separate flocks.

During the nesting season rooks are considered useful because they destroy great numbers of insects and larvae (including white worms) which they feed to their young. But during the winter they are 'harmful,' as they systematically pull up the young shoots of cereals with their long beaks, that are bare at the base in the adult bird, as if designed to dig more easily into the soil. Migratory rooks are much more numerous than native birds, and, since they visit western Europe only in winter, they do not compensate for their destructiveness by consuming harmful insects during the summer. Like the starling, the rook is useful in its breeding territory but harmful in winter quarters.

Among other European Corvidae, the carrion crow (*Corvus corone*) and the hooded crow (*C. cornix*) are both more or less migratory, especially the latter, which replaces the carrion crow in Scandinavia, Denmark, Germany east of the Elbe, central Europe and Russia, and in several parts of the British Isles. The general migratory direction of these birds in autumn is south-westward. In winter hooded crows frequently appear on the plains of northern France west to Brittany.

Jackdaws (*Corvus monedula*) also travel in autumn from east to west. Jackdaws and carrion crows often migrate in small numbers with flocks of rooks (Waterhouse [1949] indicates that the proportion is one to ten). The migrations of carrion crows and jackdaws are only partial, as the young travel, while most adult birds remain in their nesting area.

10. OTHER PASSERINES

Passerine birds nesting in Europe range from sedentary to migratory forms. The northern and eastern populations of many species have pronounced migratory tendencies, whereas populations of western Europe are more sedentary. Some Passerines, moreover, offer examples of partial migration. In general, the young are more migratory than the less enterprising adults, which tend to winter in the nesting area. As a general rule, it should be observed that most grain-eating birds are sedentary or, at the most, nomadic, while the majority of insectivorous birds migrate.

Tits are usually sedentary in western Europe, especially in France, where they winter in small flocks that often settle near human dwellings. They are definitely more migratory in northern Europe, where their flights often resemble a short migration. Adult birds, as well as young, perform seasonal flights, which are particularly characteristic of the great tit (*Parus major*) (Drost, 1932). On the whole, however, tits are nomadic, rather than migratory.

This is also true of the European goldfinch (*Carduelis carduelis*). Although this Fringillid winters in the nesting territory in most European countries, its winter dispersion is characterized by a short,

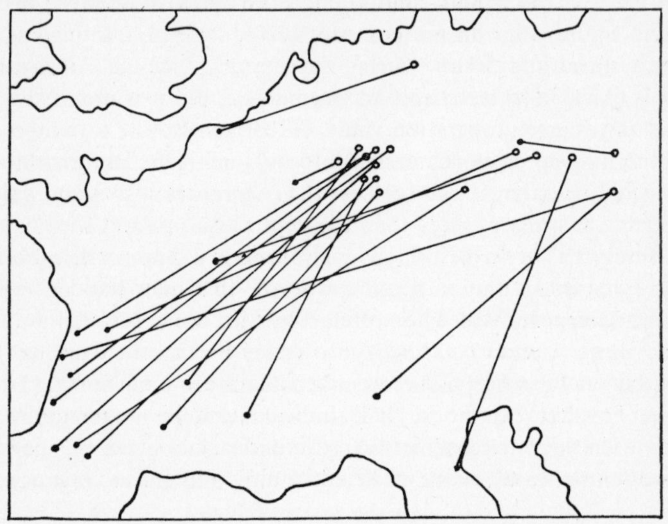

Fig. 21. Migration of European blackbirds (*Turdus m. merula*) banded in Germany and recovered in their winter quarters in France and Italy. From Drost, 1930 a.

irregular movement towards the south-west. Goldfinches banded in Germany are recovered a little farther west and south-west, chiefly in Belgium. A few recoveries have been made in southern France and Spain (Grittner, 1941). French goldfinches seem much more sedentary, and their flights purely local.

The blackbird (*Turdus merula*), one of the best known of all European birds, is a somewhat similar case. French blackbirds are more or less sedentary; so are most German ones, but a fraction may be considered migratory, as banding records have proved. Drost (1930a) thinks that a third of the German blackbirds have a migratory tendency which takes them south-westward. These birds winter in Belgium, France and Italy (Fig. 21). Scandinavian blackbirds take the same route, but some of these northern populations also winter in the breeding area.

A large number of Passerines are far more migratory, and particularly among the Sylviidae, Turdidae and Fringillidae there are seemingly weak travellers which cover great distances, crossing regions as perilous as the seas and the Sahara. They often journey at night and spend the day resting and feeding.

In general, the winter zone of these European migrants extends around the Mediterranean and into tropical Africa, although some reach Central and South Africa. There are several large migration routes, chiefly a western and an eastern one, but it is impossible to speak of a narrow migration route, for the birds take a number of paths that do not go systematically around the Mediterranean but run now south-west and now south-east. The routes also vary widely according to species.

Among the Passerines whose migrations are only partial, though clearly defined, is the European robin (*Erithacus rubecula*), which winters in France, where it is often seen near human dwellings. The much more migratory German robins leave in the autumn for countries as far south as Persia, Egypt, and parts of North Africa. Some, however, winter in their homeland, showing no desire to migrate, so there are considerable differences among individuals and, as is often the case among birds performing only partial migrations, males are definitely more sedentary than females.

The chaffinch (*Fringilla coelebs*) is also partially migratory in Europe (Figs. 22 and 23). French populations are generally sedentary, although some individuals have a tendency to make short flights. Scandinavian chaffinches and those of north-east Europe and Germany make true migrations (Tinbergen, 1941), spreading over western Europe (England, the Netherlands, Belgium, France, Spain, Italy) and even North Africa. Dutch ornithologists have made a series of studies of these birds to which we shall refer later (see p. 228).

Among the Turdidae, the song thrush (*Turdus philomelos*), which nests throughout northern Europe to about 60° Lat. N., is an even better instance of migration (Eichler, 1934). Song thrushes nesting in the British Isles are the only ones that are partly sedentary. Since the birds generally migrate in a south-westerly direction (Fig. 24), thrushes banded in Germany are recovered in France, chiefly in the Garonne and Rhône basins, where these birds are common in winter, the Iberian Peninsula, the Balearic Isles and North Africa (especially the coastal regions of Algeria and Tunisia, but they go as far as the Draa

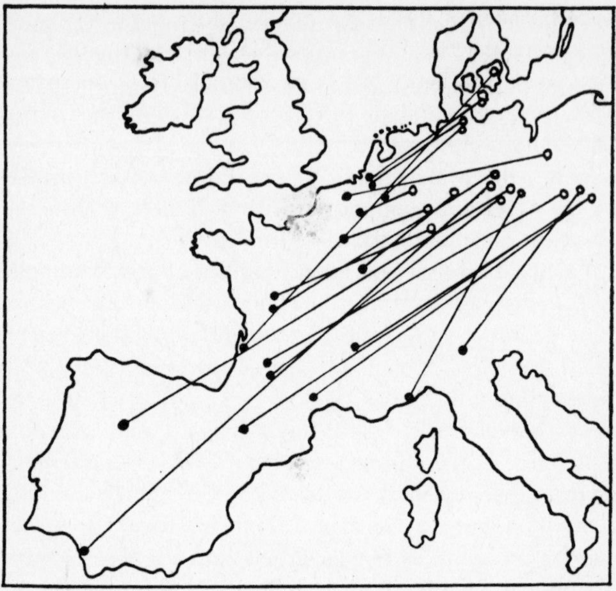

Fig. 22. Recoveries of chaffinches (*Fringilla coelebs*) banded in Germany and Denmark. From Tinbergen, 1941.

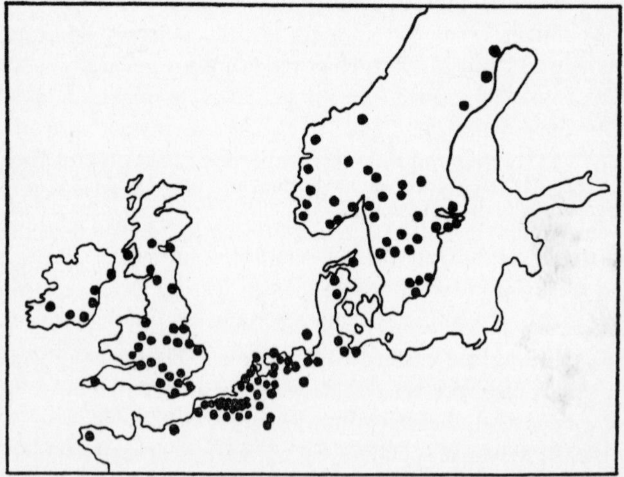

Fig. 23. Winter range of Scandinavian chaffinches (*Fringilla coelebs,*) which includes their nesting areas (partial migration). After Tinbergen, 1941, completed by Deelder, 1949.

Valley in Morocco). German thrushes reach France in September.

Much more spectacular migrants are wheatears (*Oenanthe oenanthe*) which winter both in West and in East Africa (Hempel, 1957). These

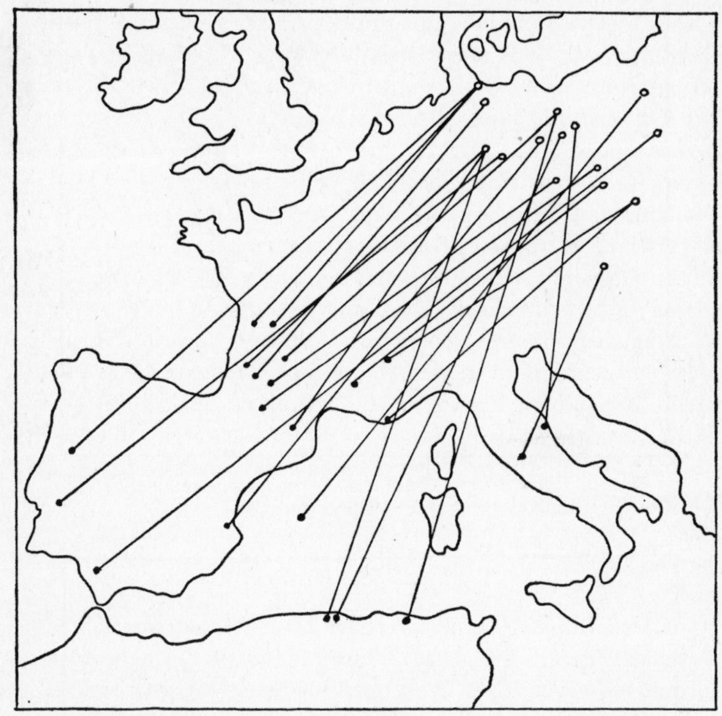

Fig. 24. Recoveries of song thrushes (*Turdus philomelos*) banded in eastern Germany. These birds migrate southwest to winter in France, Spain, Italy and North Africa. Note the breadth of the migratory front. After Eichler, 1934, simplified.

migrants seem to follow a north-east–south-west direction in the autumn, avoiding the eastern Mediterranean. Large numbers cross France, which also receives populations from Greenland (*leucorhoa*), Iceland (*schiöleri*) and eastern Europe.

Most of the Sylviidae spend the winter in tropical regions; blackcaps (*Sylvia atricapilla*), which nest throughout most of Europe and North Africa, go to tropical Africa, to Sierra Leone on the West and Tanganyika in the East. But large numbers of these birds also winter around the Mediterranean in southern Europe and on the Barbary Coast.

The garden warbler (*S. borin*), that spends the summer in western Europe, is much more migratory than the preceding species. It winters in tropical Africa from the equator to Natal, as well as in West Africa, where, however, it is rare. The whitethroat (*S. communis*) nests all through Europe and winters in tropical Africa, chiefly in the western part. Even the subalpine warbler (*S. cantillans*), a bird that nests in the Mediterranean area, migrates in winter to tropical Africa, crossing the Sahara in many places, particularly in the west.

Icterine and melodious warblers (*Hypolais icterina* and *H. polyglotta*) winter in tropical Africa, the former reaching the north of Cape Province in South Africa, the latter remaining in West Africa.

Leaf-warblers also seek refuge in Africa during the winter (Drost and Stanislaus, 1938). Their winter territory, however, varies considerably according to species; the chiff-chaff (*Phylloscopus collybita*) winters in southern France, in the Mediterranean countries and in North Africa (as far as 12° lat. N. in West Africa); the willow-warbler (*Ph. trochilus*), on the other hand, while occasionally wintering on the Mediterranean coast and a little more frequently in North Africa, goes chiefly to tropical Africa, where it ranges from Senegal to Cape Province, South Africa. It is thus a great migrant, unlike the chiff-chaff.

The Muscicapidae family also have some great migrants. The pied flycatcher (*Ficedula hypoleuca*), a bird widespread throughout most of Europe, winters chiefly in West but also in East Africa, from Egypt to Kenya (Drost and Schilling, 1940b). Large flocks of these flycatchers cross France in the autumn, especially in the far west. In the spring, however, the bird is more abundant in eastern than western France. It seems that pied flycatchers usually take a western route for their postnuptial migration but return in the spring by a more eastern lane, through Italy and south-eastern France. Their migration thus forms a loop (the German *Schleifenzug*). This curve is, however, barely evident in Africa, for the bend occurs in the Mediterranean region (Mayaud, Heim de Balsac).

Most of the European migrants we have discussed go chiefly through western Europe, towards West Africa, although some follow a number of different routes across the Mediterranean at numerous points, and others take a more eastern route. Such is the case with the spotted flycatcher (*Muscicapa striata*), which nests throughout most of Europe and winters in tropical and subtropical Africa as far as the Cape (Creutz, 1941). This bird migrates along two distinct routes, the population nesting west of 12° Long. E. going west across France, the Iberian Peninsula, and the western Sahara, the population nesting east of that meridian migrating south-east, through southern Italy, Greece, and possibly Libya and Egypt, to East Africa (Fig. 25). This

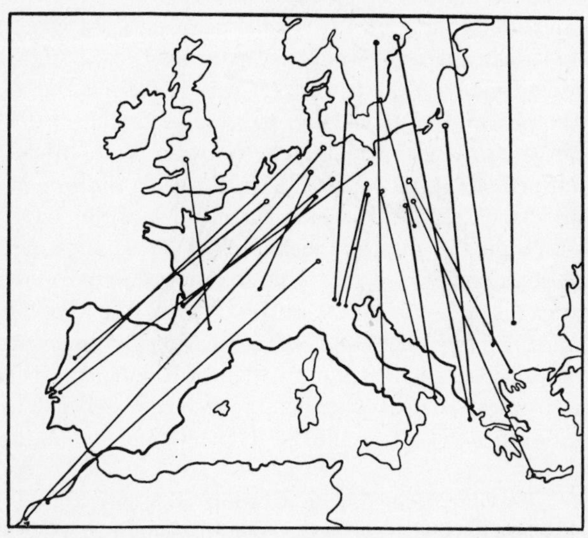

Fig. 25. Recoveries of the spotted flycatcher (*Muscicapa s. striata*) *en route* toward its African winter quarters. This Passerine migrates toward western Europe as well as over the central and eastern Mediterranean. After Creutz, 1941, simplified.

separation of populations is, of course, only approximate. The migration of the spotted flycatcher thus differs from that of the pied flycatcher, which usually migrates south-west.

Brickenstein-Stockhammer and Drost (1956) showed that a similar situation prevails among several European warblers (Sylviidae). Some blackcaps (*Sylvia atricapilla*) and garden warblers (*Sylvia borin*) migrate along western routes towards France and Spain, whereas others take eastern lanes, towards the Near East. Individuals from the same region have been seen flying in directions which form an angle of 75°. This proves that the separation is not absolute, and that it never has the weight of the line that divides the two white stork populations.

The majority of the black redstarts (*Phoenicurus ochruros gibraltariensis*), even those in central (Hempel and Reetz, 1957) and northern Europe (Sweden: Rendahl and Vestergren, 1958), migrate along

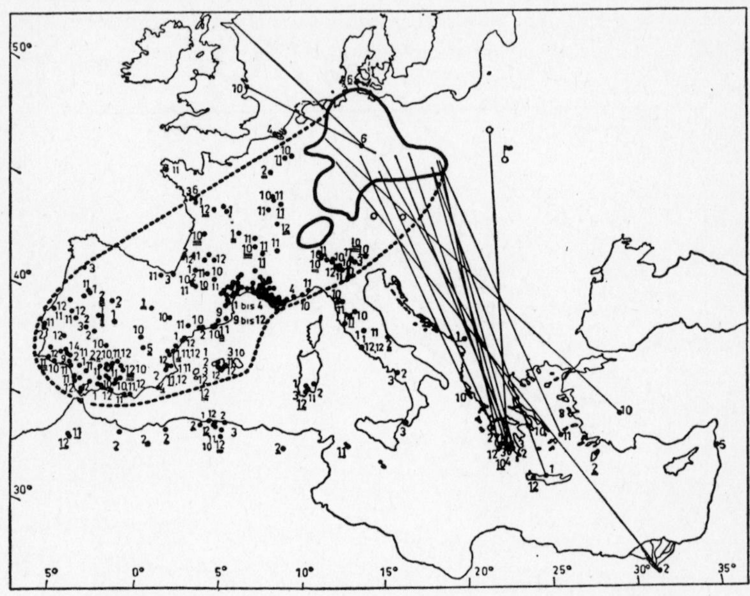

Fig. 26. Recoveries of black redstarts (*Phoenicurus ochruros gibraltariensis*) banded in central Europe (Germany and Switzerland). The banding zones are surrounded by a heavy line (except for some places marked with a hollow dot). Recovery sites are marked by dots; broken lines link the banding and recovery sites only when birds are migrating south-east. Numbers indicate the recovery months; the broken lines under them indicate the number of years between banding and recovery. From Hempel and Reetz, 1957.

western lanes to France and Spain and then to winter quarters in North Africa (Fig. 26). But recoveries in Greece, Turkey, Syria and Egypt reveal that a small group of individuals from central Europe migrates south-east. This pattern contrasts with that of the redstart (*Phoenicurus phoenicurus*), all of whose populations, even those in the North and East of Europe, seem to fly south-westward on their postnuptial migration (Fig. 27).

The typical race of the white wagtail (*Motacilla alba*) inhabits the whole European continent, with a neighbouring race in the British Isles (pied wagtail, *M.a. yarrellii*). Although some of these birds winter in part of Germany, even occasionally in Scandinavia, and some in

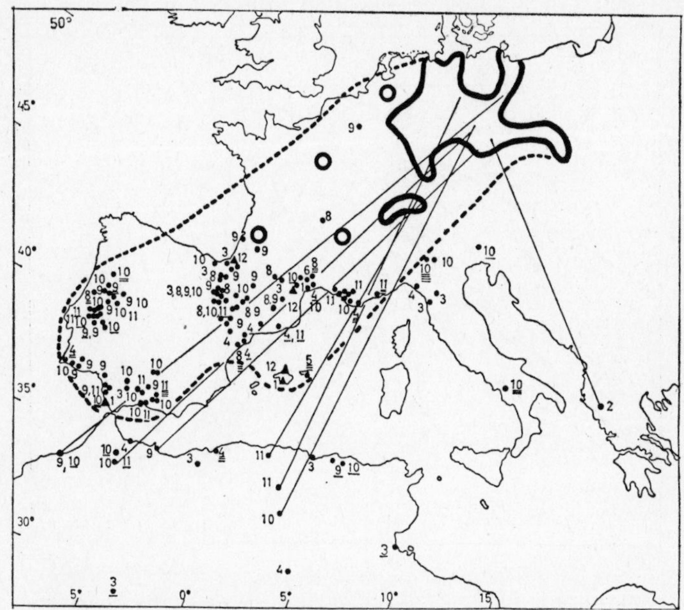

Fig. 27. Recoveries of redstarts (*Phoenicurus phoenicurus*) banded in central Europe (zones surrounded by a heavy line). Same legend as in figure 26. From Hempel and Reetz, 1957.

Great Britain, their most common winter quarters are southern Europe and North Africa, Egypt, and tropical Africa as far south as Kenya (Fig. 28).

Most European white wagtails migrate in a south-westerly direction through France and the Iberian Peninsula. Populations nesting in Finland, the Baltic countries and possibly Prussia migrate south-east towards Asia Minor, Egypt and the Sudan (Anglo-Egyptian). The separation is thus analogous to that among the species we have already cited. These facts recall the stork, but the little Passerines differ from these big birds by flying easily over vast stretches of water.

Finally certain Passerines migrate almost exclusively south-eastward. The golden oriole (*Oriolus oriolus*) winters in East Africa, chiefly in Kenya and Tanganyika. Postnuptial migration takes western and central European orioles across Greece, the Aegean Sea and Egypt towards East Africa (Fig. 29). In the spring the prenuptial migration route crosses Tripolitania and Tunisia towards Italy. These birds thus make a migration loop (Stresemann, 1948). Orioles of

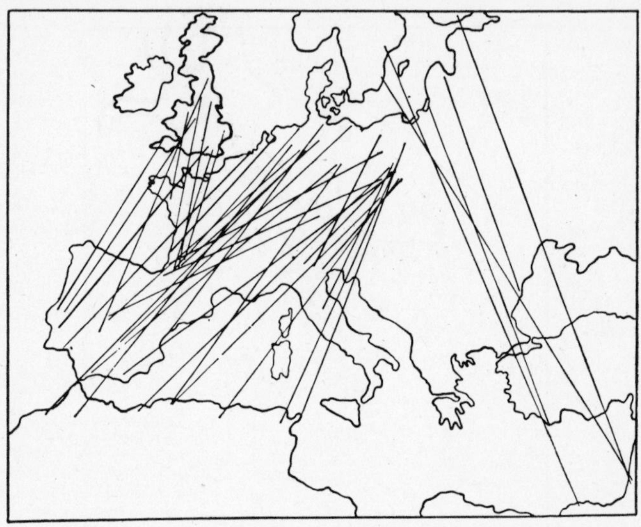

Fig. 28. Migration of European white wagtails (*Motacilla alba*) according to recoveries of banded birds. The majority go south-west but a few fly south-east. After Drost and Schüz, 1940, simplified.

Spain and Morocco, where the species is spreading, migrate south over the western Sahara. Some, at least, of the Spanish and Moroccan orioles very probably winter in West Africa.

Similar migratory behaviour is observed in the European roller (*Coracias garrulus*), a bird that winters in East Africa, chiefly from Kenya to South Africa, which it reaches by eastern lanes. Rollers nesting in North Africa go to the same winter quarters by crossing the Sahara in a north-west–south-east diagonal. We should note that this nomadic bird takes a very long time to reach winter quarters; leaving Europe in August and September, it does not arrive in Kenya until early November, and it is December before the roller arrives in South Africa. Spring migration seems to be more rapid (Stresemann, 1944c).

Another Passerine migrating through eastern Europe is the red-backed shrike (*Lanius collurio*), which has been the subject of numerous studies, particularly by Verheyen (1951b). These shrikes, which nest throughout most of Europe, western Siberia, and part of Asia Minor, converge in autumn near Greece. They then traverse the eastern part of the Mediterranean, flying towards Egypt. Their winter quarters

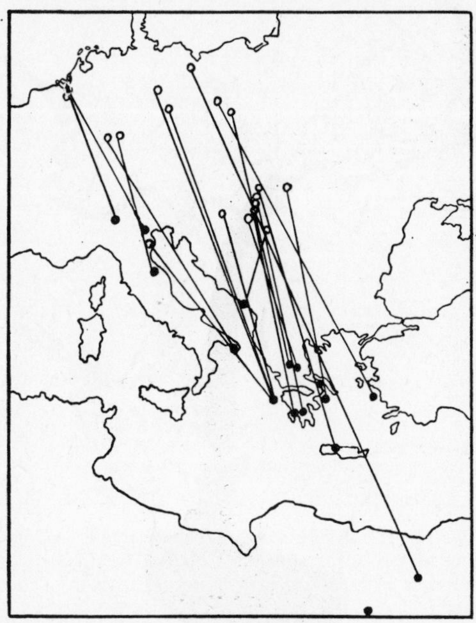

Fig. 29. Autumn migration of the golden oriole (*Oriolus oriolus*) according to recoveries of banded birds. Note that this bird moves south-east. From Stresemann, 1948.

extend from the north-eastern Congo to South Africa; the red-backed shrike inhabits the savannahs and semi-arid habitats often found in this part of Africa, but avoids dense forest (Fig. 30).

The return trip is by a still more easterly route through Syria, the Near East and Asia Minor. The birds then spread out like a fan across Europe as they go to their breeding areas. These Passerines thus make a definite *migration loop* over the eastern Mediterranean. Verheyen believes that meteorological factors play a large part in the selection of different migration routes in autumn and spring. The species apparently flies before the wind. As the general meteorological situation

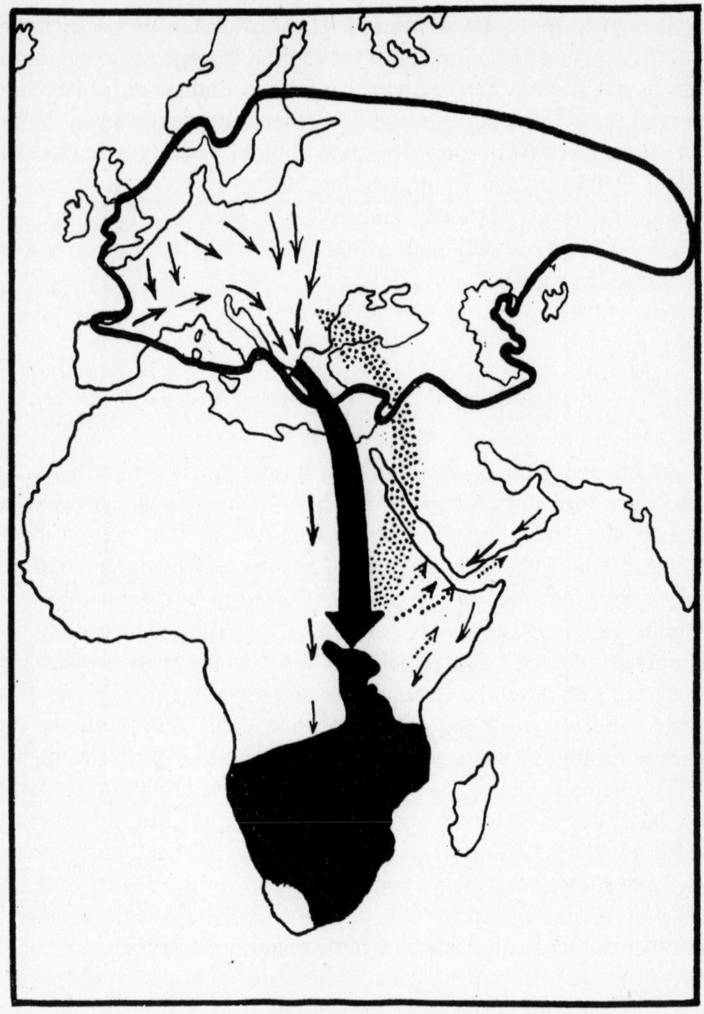

Fig. 30. Migrations of the red-backed shrike (*Lanius collurio*). The heavy line surrounds the breeding area, the black zone indicates winter quarters. Black arrow: autumn migration; dotted arrow: spring migration. After Verheyen, 1951 b.

prevailing in the eastern Mediterranean at migration periods and the division of warm and cold winds are constant from year to year, the choice of migration routes is clear.

Some European Passerines cross the Mediterranean at various points, others display a marked inclination for one route or another, but in no case are there 'narrow routes.' A number of ornithologists believe these lanes indicate the primitive roads followed by birds in their invasion of Europe. Migration routes would thus be the paths taken by the species in populating European territories, and they might also reveal traces of Quaternary glaciations. Although these questions are extremely interesting, the theories are not always corroborated by fact.

The Principal Migration Routes in Europe and Northern Asia

As European birds reveal infinite variety in their migrations, they also show how difficult it is to classify migrants by categories. Every intermediate stage between the sedentary and the migrant bird is found in the European avifauna. Despite severe winter conditions prevailing over most of the continent – except in the Mediterranean region and along the coasts warmed by the Atlantic Ocean – a good proportion of the avian population is sedentary in its nesting areas. We have seen several examples showing how birds nesting in north-eastern Europe are more migratory than their relatives of the same species nesting in western Europe. Some types of birds are more or less nomadic in winter, whereas others make real migrations. Among the latter are those which simply retire to the Mediterranean region, either to southern Europe or to North Africa. Others, more exacting in their requirements, leave for Africa south of the Sahara and reach the most southerly part of that continent. Moreau (1952) has listed the number of European Passerines in these various categories:

Wintering in the Palearctic region	89
Wintering partly in the Palearctic region, partly in the Ethiopian region	13
Wintering in the Ethiopian region	43
Wintering in the eastern region (Indian)[1]	3
	148

1. These three species are: the greenish warbler (*Phylloscopus trochiloides*),

The African continent, lying as a southern prolongation of Europe, offers migrants a fine winter territory by reason of its size and resources. To reach it, the birds have to solve the problems presented by the Mediterranean and the large desert girdle that bar their route from the Atlantic to Arabia. Even Europe has a certain number of difficulties because of its mountain chains, most of which run from west to east (Pyrenees, the Alps). This configuration has shaped the several routes followed by a large number of migrants. Migration routes, however, are diverse, and they cover Europe with a dense network which varies according to conditions such as the weather and the species involved. It is possible, nevertheless, to distinguish several main axes around which routes are grouped.

The coasts provide well-marked lanes that permit migrants from the arctic regions to 'descend' towards the south. Innumerable Passerines and shore-birds take them, as one can see by visiting coastal districts or spending a night in one of the lighthouses dotting the shore. These migration routes follow the Scandinavian coasts, then most of them cross the North Sea towards the British Isles, where they follow both the west and east coasts. Most of the British ornithological stations, in fact, are located on islets off the mainland. The British Isles also receive migrants from Greenland (a small number) and from Iceland. The French coasts prolong these migration routes, and they too are dotted with places famous for bird flights: Somme Bay, Ouessant Island (Ushant Island), Cotentin, Aiguillon Bay, Landes.

In considering the whole western Palearctic region, as Rudebeck (1956) and others have done, it is apparent that the principal migratory routes go south-west or south-east, doubtless because of the very configuration of Europe, where the Alps constitute an important barrier, although their rôle has been exaggerated. It should be noted that, while most migrants travel from north to south in North America because of the configuration of the continent (see p. 124), this is not the case in Europe. (Fig. 31). Some flights are definitely from east to west, like those of the Mediterranean gull (see page 40) and the slender-billed curlew (*Numenius tenuirostris*), which breeds in western Siberia and

---

the arctic warbler (*Ph. borealis*), and the red-breasted flycatcher (*Muscicapa parva*). These Passerines, now nesting in the most eastern part of Europe, east Germany, Poland, the Baltic countries, Russia and Finland, recently came from the East; like their relatives which remain in the original home of the species, they migrate eastward to reach their winter range.

winters in the Mediterranean region, as far west as North Africa and Spain. Its migration is thus much more latitudinal than longitudinal.

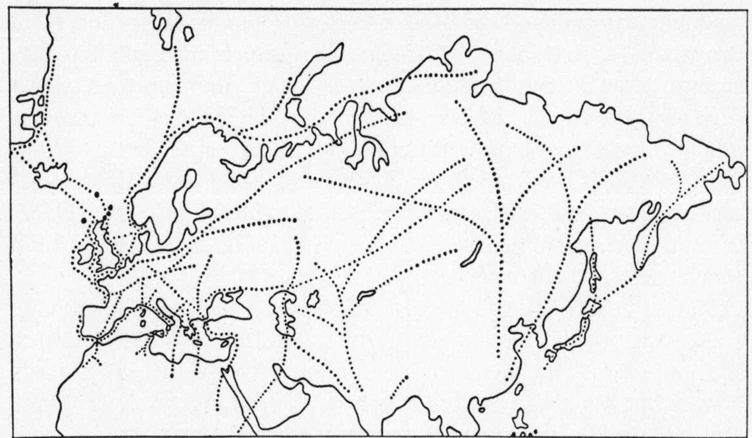

Fig. 31. Principal migration routes in Europe and northern Asia. These are approximate, of course, but they show the general tendencies of migrants which take a number of paths extending over broad strips of terrain.

But the most important routes, on the basis of the number of species using them, are those to the west and south-west. According to Rudebeck, there are about 150 species of migrants travelling in this manner, at least thirty-five of which reach tropical Africa, while the others stay in Atlantic Europe and the Mediterranean region. The great plains of northern Europe and the littoral of the Baltic Sea and the North Sea witness the passage of countless migrants from Scandinavia, Poland and Russia. These migrational axes take travellers towards England (a wintering zone for some continental populations) or France, which serves as a winter asylum for many species from the north or east of Europe, while others simply cross it on their way to the Mediterranean and Africa.

Other routes take migrants south-east, and these lanes are used by at least twenty-five species, of which fourteen have their winter quarters in East and South Africa. Three of them winter in India, as we shall see (page 90). (Fig. 32).

There is evidently nothing mathematical about this division, which often separates populations of a single species by a migratory dividing line that is not fixed (*Zugscheidenmischgebiet*), so the same species may thus include both 'western' and 'eastern' migrants.

Whatever the route chosen, western migrants must leap the Medi-

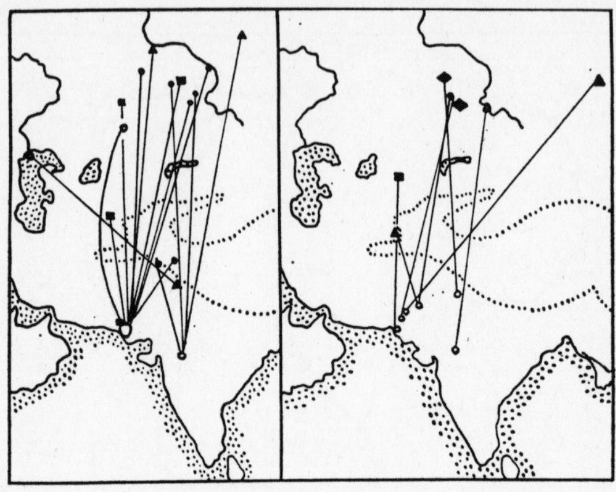

Fig. 32. Migrations of ducks from Central Asia toward India.
LEFT: *Dots:* Wigeon (*Anas penelope*)
Triangles: Pintail (*Anas acuta*)
Squares: Gadwall (*Anas strepera*)
RIGHT: *Dots:* Pochard (*Aythya ferina*)
Triangles: Red-crested pochard (*Netta rufina*)
Squares: Ferruginous duck (*Aythya nyroca*)
Diamonds: Shoveler (*Anas clypeata*)
The dotted line marks regions above 10,000 feet. From records published by Salim and Abdulali, map published by Böhringer, *Vogelwarte*, 1951.

terranean to reach any part of Africa. This inland sea does not present serious difficulties. Some soaring birds – storks and large birds of prey – avoid flying over water, so they go around the Mediterranean, either to the west (Gibraltar) or to the east (Bosphorus, Asia Minor), and these are excellent points from which to observe migration. Cap Bon, in Tunisia, also witnesses the flight of many birds from Sicily and Italy. But, as Moreau (1953) very wisely remarked, the Mediterranean is crossed almost everywhere, even in the Ionian Sea, where it is widest. Only the western basin, between France and North Africa, seems to have fewer birds.

Because of its desert climate, northern Africa is rather unsuitable for migrants. The Sahara is, however, crossed nearly everywhere, both west and east. Various observers have tried to plot migration routes across the Sahara. Kullenberg (1956) suggested several, but they are not entirely satisfactory. (Figs. 33 and 34). On the whole, two great

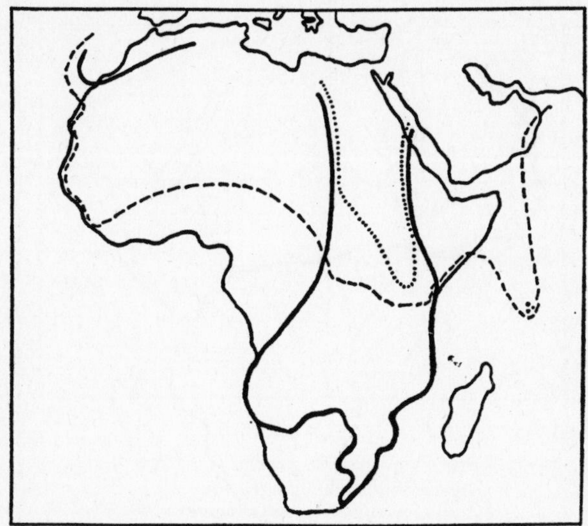

Fig. 33. Migrations in Africa of three Palearctic snipes
Solid line: Great snipe (*Capella media*)
Broken line: European snipe (*Capella gallinago*)
Dotted line: Jack snipe (*Limnocryptes minima*)
From Chapin, 1932.

migratory axes may be distinguished, one across the most western part of the Sahara, chiefly Mauritania, the other across the central Sahara, linking Algeria and the Ahaggar. Ecological factors – food and water – doubtless set these vast corridors. But it is wise not to generalize, for it seems that the whole Sahara is crossed by birds whose behaviour varies according to species and circumstances. To the east, the Nile Valley affords favourable conditions, so many migrants take this route, although it is by no means the only one used. Moreau reports that numerous birds actually leave the Nile, to fly over desert regions.

Europe is, however, only the projecting peninsula of the huge continental Eurasiatic land mass, whose northern regions see most of their avifauna disappear during the bitter winter. The systematic groups to which these migrants belong are usually the same as those found in Europe (Palearctic fauna). The migration routes of these birds are still quite inadequately known, in spite of recent Russian studies, but they, too, depend on various geographical factors,

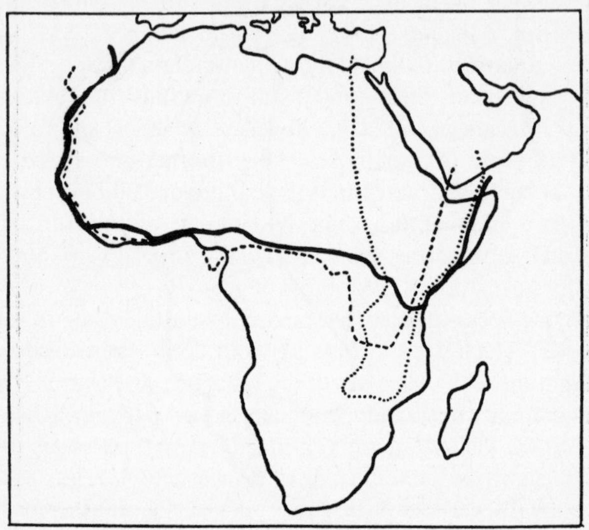

Fig. 34. Migrations in Africa of three Palearctic Turdidae
Solid line: Nightingale (*Luscinia megarhynchus*)
Dotted line: Thrush nightingale (*Luscinia luscinia*)
Broken line: Whinchat (*Saxicola rubetra*)
Note that, as among snipes, these Passerines avoid the equatorial rain forest.
From Chapin, 1932.

especially the large mountain ranges of central Asia. They do not constitute an obstacle to some migrants, which fly easily over the Himalayas.

Russian Asia – for this is the part with which we are chiefly concerned here – may be divided at the Yenissei into two parts, from the point of view of migrations and fauna. One region includes western Siberia and the Palearctic territories to the south (Moreau's 'Central Palearctic'); the other is the eastern region – eastern Siberia, Mongolia, northern China, etc. ('Far Eastern Palearctic').

The western part, thus defined, has some mountains on its southern border which are especially difficult to cross. Beyond it, however, India constitutes the favourite wintering area for birds capable of crossing the roof of the world, and ducks and shore-birds come there regularly.

Another part of the avifauna is concentrated in winter around the Caspian Sea. Misonne (1953, 1955) and Schüz (1959a) state that countless aquatic birds spend the winter on the southern shores of this inland sea, in Iran. There are tens of thousands of ducks, especially mallards, garganeys and teals, shovellers, wigeons, and tufted ducks, as well as geese (especially the white-fronted goose and the bean goose). Misonne estimated that several hundred thousand coots also winter there, and that shore-birds and innumerable bustards are found in the plains bordering the coast. This extraordinary bird concentration in turn attracts many birds of prey.

This zone does not, however, offer a favourable winter residence for Passerines, which are more sensitive to cold. These birds continue their flight through the passes of the Elburz chain towards India. That they migrate in considerable numbers is evident from Schüz's report (1956) on the yellow wagtails (*Motacilla flava*). He states that in the Pahlevi region, on the south side of the Caspian Sea, he once counted 2,250 wagtails between 9.20 and 9.50 a.m. On another occasion he noted 1,800 migrants between 8.31 and 8.46 a.m. As the flight went on for hours, Schüz believes that at least 80,000 wagtails a day fly over this area!

Tropical Africa is the favourite winter area for many birds that nest in western Siberia; Moreau (1952) found thirty-seven wintering in India, thirty-three going to Africa, and ten others divided between the two zones. (Figs. 35 and 36). This is remarkable in view of the relative distances separating these two regions from the breeding territories, India being much closer than Africa. Routes to the Dark Continent cross the Caspian Sea and then lead south-west past the Black Sea.

The most easterly portion of the Palearctic world finds its autumn migrants travelling south-east, towards the warm areas of Asia, southern China, Indochina, Malaysia, and even, in some cases, the South Sea archipelagos. The great migration routes pass over the continent as well as along the seas bordering eastern Asia. Many Siberian migrants cross Japan and then head towards South-east Asia and Malaya. The same diversity in winter behaviour is found in Asia as in Europe. Furthermore, the rigour of the winter climate in northern

Asia forces many birds, sedentary in Europe, to migrate every year to the most eastern part of their habitat.

We should not conclude that all birds nesting in this region migrate

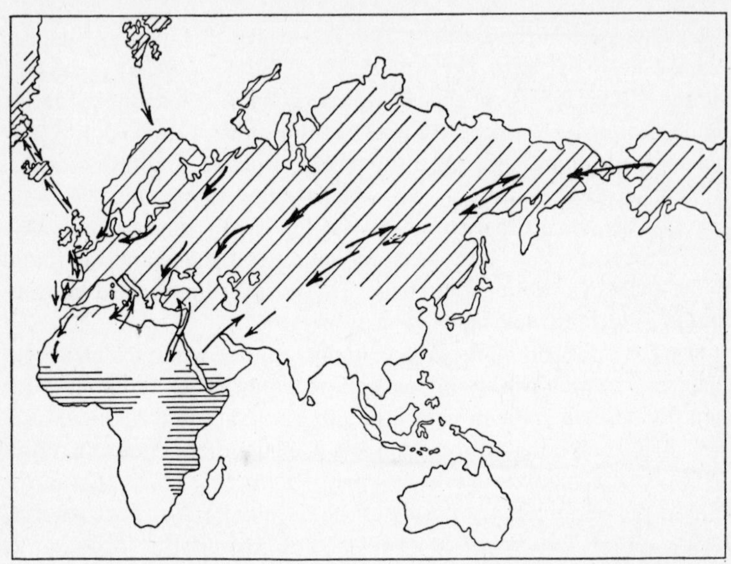

Fig. 35. Migrations of the wheatear (*Oenanthe oenanthe*). Nearly all populations, even the one that colonized Alaska, migrate toward African winter quarters. Arrows indicate the chief migratory currents.

south-eastward. Although this seems very strange, some migrants start south-west in autumn and go from Bering Strait and Manchuria to African winter quarters, whereas logic would direct them to the much closer South-east Asia. These birds include many non-Passerines (*Falco amurensis* [it winters as far as the Cape of Good Hope], *Falco naumanni*, *Grus grus*, *Caprimulgus europaeus*), as well as Passerines (*Oenanthe oenanthe*, *Monticola saxatilis*, *Phoenicurus phoenicurus*, *Phylloscopus trochilus*). Thus the migration routes of these birds cross all of northern Asia before reaching their winter quarters.

It is true that the greenish warbler, the Arctic warbler, and the red-breasted flycatcher, which we have already mentioned, migrate in the opposite direction, traversing this vast part of the world to winter in the Asiatic south-east. These examples illustrate to what extent migration routes may criss-cross. In any case, the breeding fauna spreads out over the largest winter territory, from Siberia, to three continents: Africa, Asia and Australia.

The large migration axes we have considered reflect general

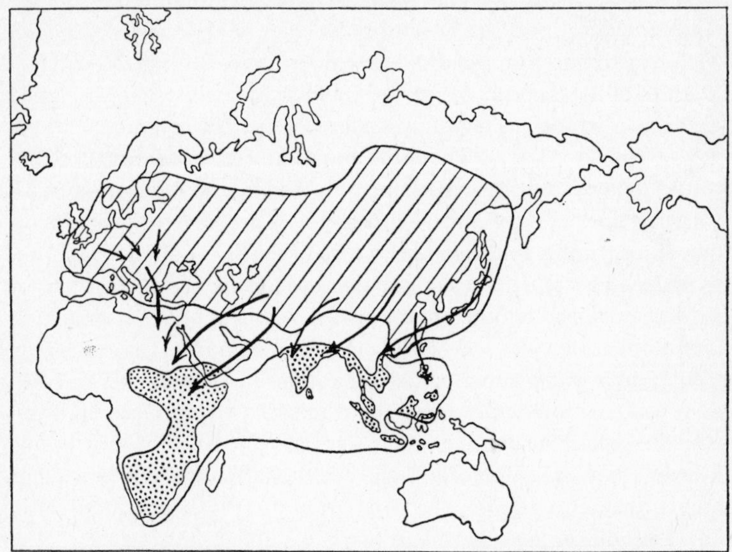

Fig. 36. Migrations of shrikes of the *Lanius cristatus-collurio* group. Note that there are wintering zones in Africa as well as in India and Malaysia. Arrows indicate the chief migratory currents. From Stresemann and other authors.

directions rather than precise lanes. Instead of speaking of a network of routes, which implies a rigid framework, it would be better to refer to a number of advantageous spots: swampy areas, sea-shores, mountain passes, straits where numerous lanes meet but from which the migrants follow paths that often diverge. Such a system of 'knots' would be closer to the truth.

A study of the migrations of the Palearctic fauna of Eurasia also reveals that Africa constitutes the principal winter range. There has been much discussion about the winter quarters of Palearctic migrants to the Sahara. Some authors, especially H. and T. Heim de Balsac (1949–1951), have never found any winter residents in the oases of the western and central Sahara, save for a few North African birds which go to the northern edge of the desert: *Monticola solitarius*, *Diploötocus moussieri*, *Sylvia deserticola* (reported also by Jany [1959]), *S. con-*

spicillata, S. melanocephala. But that is not so general as one might think, for Niethammer and Laenen (1954) found in the central Sahara quite a large variety of birds, including the tawny pipit (*Anthus campestris*), the white wagtail (*Motacilla alba*), the chiff-chaff (*Phylloscopus collybita*) and the Sardinian warbler (*Sylvia melanocephala*), which were obviously spending the winter there. Ethiopian Africa, to the south of the Sahara, is, however, a favourite wintering ground for Palearctic migrants, as it contains a large variety of habitats, scattered over a tremendous area. The birds apparently seek regions similar to those in their nesting area, avoiding only the large equatorial forest.[1]

Winter quarters are thus distributed rather diversely in Africa. Some birds fly only to the southern edge of the Sahara in the Sahel and the Sudan. This is true of many Passerines, some of which remain in the Mediterranean region. Others always winter south of the equator; for example, the river warbler (*Locustella fluviatilis*), the lesser grey shrike (*Lanius minor*) and the red-backed shrike (*Lanius collurio*). Still others scatter more widely over the whole Dark Continent, like very many Passerines, including some warblers and swallows. It seems, however, that geographical origin occasionally determines a segregation of winter residents; one population will prefer a certain region, while a neighbouring one will go to quite a different destination. This is especially true of barn swallows, although there is never any definite segregation.

There are a few more species wintering in East than in West Africa, because of the supplementary influx of birds from eastern Europe and Siberia which have not penetrated western Europe and whose winter quarters are restricted to East Africa. In spite of the fact that these migrants reside in Africa from October to March, which is the breeding period for many African birds, there does not seem to be enough competition between winter birds and native ones to disturb the breeding of the latter in the austral hemisphere.

1. As the great forest disappears, the avifauna tends to change in districts which are modified by clearing and cultivation. Palearctic migrants, in particular, keep increasing, so the bee-eater has become abundant in certain parts of Gabon, where it was unknown before the forest disappeared. This is one more proof of the plasticity of birds.

CHAPTER 4

Migrations in North America

North American birds have to contend with much the same difficulties as European species. Since nature fails to provide sufficient food during the winter for many birds, it is not surprising that a large part of the Nearctic avifauna is migratory to at least some degree.

Some species, however, are sedentary, even in the sub-arctic part of the continent. The ruffed grouse (*Bonasa umbellus*), for example, remains in winter in the most northerly parts of its range, in Labrador and south of James Bay, Canada. It seeks shelter in dense woods, where it finds 'insulated' hiding places by diving a foot or two into the snow for the night. This bird stays all year in the same area, in spite of a range in temperature from +95° F to –40° F. Yet such total sedentarism is rare, and most North American birds perform migrations of varying length in the spring and autumn.[1] There are, of course, all forms, ranging from the sedentary, the vagrant (nomadism), and the partial to real migrants, whose winter quarters extend from the Gulf States all the way to Patagonia and whose northern breeding areas reach to the Arctic Ocean.

The situation, however, does not exactly parallel that of Europe, since the two continents are very different and their geographical conditions totally unlike.

Temperate Europe is separated from the tropics by the wide marine barrier of the Mediterranean, and by the desert barrier of the Sahara, both of which pose serious obstacles for migrants. In the New World, however, there is no barrier between the temperate and tropical regions except the Gulf of Mexico, which birds can easily avoid, if they

1. The only authentic case of bird hibernation yet known, that of Nuttall's poor-will (see page 279), was found in western North America.

wish, by flying either west, along the Mexican coast, or south-east, over the West Indies island-chain. Moreover, the great mountain ranges, the Alps and the Pyrenees, run like ramparts from west to east in Europe, whereas in America the Appalachians, the Rockies, and the Sierra and Coast ranges all lie mainly north and south, so that, far from being obstacles, they actually guide migrants.

Tropical regions in Central and South America are thus easily accessible to autumn migrants. Furthermore, the more hardy migrants find a favourable winter environment in many parts of North America. California and the Gulf States offer a subtropical winter climate to many birds, and the Gulf States, particularly, provide a favourable cold weather retreat across most of the continent.

After studying several species, we shall consider the over-all problem of migration in North America, paying special attention to the major migration routes and different winter areas. We shall reserve the Anatidae to the end, together with an examination of the east-west and north-south trans-continental migration routes which have been clearly confirmed by thousands of seasonal records of banded wildfowl.

The biogeography and origins of the North American fauna explain why the Nearctic avifauna includes a large proportion of migrants. As North America is wide open to spring travellers from tropical regions, it was occupied in part, ages ago, by birds with clearly tropical affinities. Such is the case with the tanagers (*Thraupidae*), of which one genus (and four species) has reached Canada in the spring, while the sixty-one other genera are strictly tropical, and the Icteridae, of which ten out of thirty-four genera have moved deep into North America to nest. This is also true of humming-birds (*Trochilidae*), a typically tropical family, of which two species migrate even to the far north of North America. It is not surprising that these birds of tropical origin, whose counter-parts are few in the Old World, are forced to return to the intertropical regions at the end of the northern summer.

A large number of studies have been devoted to migration in North America. Among the significant books are those by Cooke, who has made remarkable discoveries, by Wetmore and by Lincoln. It was Lincoln who described the flyways – the main arterial routes followed by migrants in the New World. We have borrowed much from him, and from the classic monographs of Bent, which are a mine of information on the biology of American birds.

1. SHORE-BIRDS

North American Charadriidae (*sensu lato*) are great migrants like their counter-parts in the Old World and winter in the warm zones of the western hemisphere. Some remain along the North American coasts, but a number go to the tropical West Indies and Central America, and a few travel much farther, deep into South America. Philippi (1940) and Bullock (1949) record twenty-three species in Chile, among which nearly half are regular migrants. These shore-birds are found on high Andean plateaus as well as along both South American coasts. During the northern winter the Andean lake shores and coasts of Peru and Chile are inhabited by large numbers of lesser and greater yellow-legs (*Totanus flavipes*, and *T. melanoleuca*) and by various sandpipers.

The most interesting migrations of any North American shore-birds are, however, those of the American golden plover (*Pluvialis dominica dominica*), which makes an enormous loop over much of the New World. With the adults, at least, the autumn and spring itineraries are notably different. After nesting in the tundras of northern Canada and Alaska, these plovers assemble in Labrador, and then fly to the Brazilian coast over an oceanic route about 2,400 miles long, which barely touches Bermuda and the Lesser Antilles, where most of these birds do not even pause. (Fig. 37.) They journey on through southern Brazil and Uruguay, to live from September to March on the Argentine pampas. The birds thus inscribe a vast semi-circular arc over the terrestrial globe as they take the shortest route to their winter quarters. Their return flight, however, follows a much more western course, as they cross South America to Central America and the Gulf of Mexico, to reach the Texas and Louisiana coasts, and then fly north by way of the Mississippi Valley to sub-arctic breeding grounds, some 8,000 miles distant from their winter quarters. There is as yet no explanation of the origin of this enormous ellipse, all the stranger because young golden plovers, which leave the breeding grounds after the adults, keep to the land route on both flights.

The Eskimo curlew (*Numenius borealis*), now probably extinct, used to make seasonal migrations quite similar to those of the American golden plover (Greenway, 1958). After nesting in the Canadian and Alaskan tundras, the birds gathered in the north-eastern part of North America, from Labrador to the vicinity of Long Island. From there they flew straight to South America, sometimes

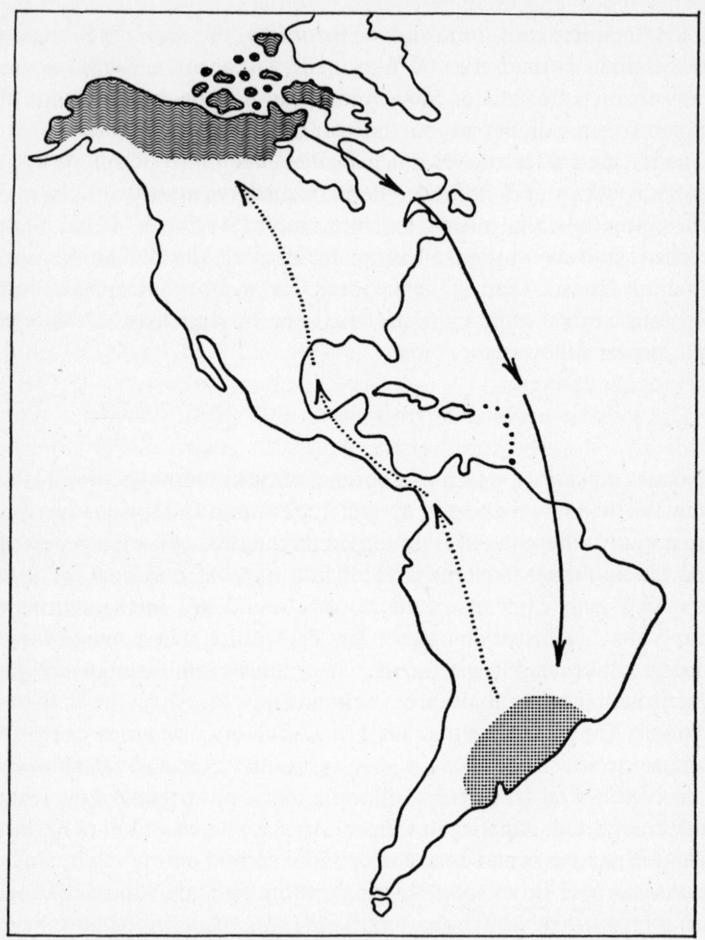

Fig. 37. Migrations of the American golden plover (*Pluvialis d. dominica*). The autumn migration route is in a solid line, the spring migration route is dotted. After Lincoln, 1935. b.

touching Bermuda and the Windward Islands of the West Indies. The curlews spent the northern winter on the plains of the Gran Chaco and Argentina, then started north, by the continental route, early in March. In the spring they flew up the Mississippi Valley and on to their breeding grounds, with their migrations thus forming the same vast loop as that of the golden plovers.

Other shore- and water-birds also take the oceanic route from the eastern Canadian coast to Brazil, with possible stop-overs in Bermuda and the chain of the Lesser Antilles. It is, of course, very difficult to follow the exact routes of these birds; they have been seen both in flight and resting on the sea, but many of them prefer a non-stop flight.

The Pacific golden plover (*Pluvialis dominica fulva*), which nests in western Alaska and eastern Siberia, makes an enormous trans-oceanic flight before reaching south-eastern Asia and Malaysia. It has been recorded in New Zealand, Tasmania, most of the Pacific Islands, including Hawaii, and in Micronesia as well as Melanesia and Polynesia. Several other migrants nesting in the American North-west make similar flights (see p. 195).

2. PIGEONS

No description of avian migrations in North America would be complete without evoking the extinct passenger pigeon (*Ectopistes migratorius*), whose flocks once darkened the sky. This pigeon nested in deciduous forests from the Great Plains to the Atlantic coast of New Brunswick, and wintered in a relatively small area in the southern Ohio valley. Because of the countless birds taking part, these migrations were highly spectacular until man exterminated one of the most flourishing species of birds in the world.

Some of the Columbidae surviving in North America perform migrations. The band-tailed pigeon (*Columba fasciata*), which nests in the North-west to British Columbia, winters farther south, from California to Guatemala. This pigeon used to be very abundant, but its numbers have been considerably reduced by hunting (fortunately the bird is now protected). It, too, made a very impressive picture during migrations, and flocks numbering millions of birds have been described in Santa Barbara County, California, where a large part of the populations nesting north of that area was concentrated in winter.

The mourning dove (*Zenaidura macroura*), which breeds throughout most of North America, goes in winter to the southern states and Central America though a few remain in the North.

3. CUCKOOS

In North America, as in other parts of the world, cuckoos are highly migratory, as their insect diet is not available in northern regions during the winter.

Although their migrations are long, the birds are difficult to observe, for they are wary. The yellow-billed cuckoo (*Coccyzus americanus*), which nests in most regions of the U.S.A., spends the winter in South America, especially in Colombia and Venezuela; the black-billed cuckoo (*Coccyzus erythrophthalmus*), with a more restricted breeding area, also goes to South America, where its winter quarters include Colombia, Ecuador and northern Peru. Both species have also been recorded in relatively large numbers in western Europe, where they are carried by west winds sweeping across the North Atlantic.

4. HUMMING-BIRDS

The humming-birds (*Trochilidae*) of North America are a perfect example of a group of birds from intertropical regions, some species of which have been coming north in the spring, even as far as Canada and Alaska, during the warm period which followed the last Ice Age. Since these birds feed chiefly on insects and the nectar of flowers, which are unobtainable in winter, they are obliged to make long semi-annual flights, which seem out of all proportion to their diminutive size and apparent fragility.

The ruby-throated humming-bird (*Archilochus colubris*), the only species found in the eastern U.S.A., is one of the most northern of all the Trochilidae, as its breeding grounds extend to New Brunswick, Nova Scotia, and, in general, to the borderline of Canadian farm-lands. In autumn some birds fly to Central America, from Central Mexico to Panama. Many of them are found in southern Mexico and Guatemala, and a few go to south-eastern Texas and Florida. To reach Central America some fly non-stop across the Gulf of Mexico, crossing the open sea as easily as many birds of much larger size. A few individuals, however, reach Central America through Florida and Cuba.

The earliest departures occur in July in the most northern portion of the birds' habitat; the males leave first, while the females are still busy rearing the young. Southern populations leave their breeding territories at later dates. It has often been stated that the return of these humming-birds in the spring is timed to coincide with the blossoming of their favourite flowers.

Because of their early arrival, these little migrants are often the victims of sudden cold snaps, which occur after a period of warm weather, but their death is due to lack of food rather than to low temperatures. Males are the first to reach the breeding territory, as is the case among many other species. The earliest recorded dates of their appearance in Canada (Manitoba, Saskatchewan) are in late May.

The rufous humming-bird (*Selasphorus rufus*), which nests in western North America up into Alaska, is also highly migratory. Its chief winter quarters is Mexico, where most of these birds are concentrated in the states of Zacatecas, Jalisco, Mexico and Michoacan. Observers agree that this is one of the most characteristic humming-birds of the high Mexican plateaux in winter. Although it does not have to cross such large expanses of water as those traversed by the ruby-throats, it is capable of such performances, for it has been seen far off the Alaskan coasts. That it is an excellent flier is evident, since it crosses glaciers in the Rocky Mountains at altitudes up to 9,000 and even 12,000 feet. In the spring it follows the Pacific slope of the Rocky Mountains, avoiding their eastern side.

Other North American humming-birds are also fairly migratory, especially the black-chinned humming-bird (*Archilochus alexandri*), which nests north to British Columbia, and winters in southern California and Mexico. The calliope humming-bird (*Stellula calliope*), one of the smallest species known, breeds in British Columbia but winters in Mexico (Michoacan, Mexico, Guerrero).

Certain others make only irregular flights which resemble rather large-scale nomadism. Some California humming-birds wander merely in altitude, to follow the blossoms of plants. Anna's humming-bird (*Calypte anna*) abandons only the most northerly parts of California in winter and is sedentary in the southern parts of its breeding range.

5. AMERICAN FLYCATCHERS

The Tyrannidae, American flycatchers, or tyrants, feed almost entirely on insects, so it is not surprising that they are migratory. The group, moreover, is essentially native to warmer regions; a few of its members come north to nest, but must return to tropical areas for the winter.

The migratory tendency differs in strength among North American Tyrannidae. Some species find their northern boundary in the southern U.S.A. The black phoebe (*Sayornis nigricans*), for example, occurs south to northern Argentina, north to California and Texas. On the whole, this bird is sedentary in the northern portion of its habitat, and its seasonal flights seem basically nomadic.[1] This behaviour differs from that of its relative, Say's phoebe (*Sayornis saya*), which goes north-west of the Great Plains as far as western Canada and Alaska. In winter the bird occurs from California to Mexico. Coues's flycatcher (*Contopus pertinax*) breeds in the far south of the U.S.A. (Arizona) and winters on the Mexican plateaus.

The eastern phoebe (*Sayornis phoebe*) is common in summer throughout the eastern U.S.A. and Canada, where it breeds as far north as the Mackenzie and Nova Scotia. This is a true migrant, for it leaves the northern part of its nesting territory to spend the winter in the Gulf States and northern Mexico.[2] However, during very mild winters eastern phoebes are found in southern Illinois, Ohio and even New Hampshire. This bird is quite hardy, it does not have such rigorous feeding requirements as many other flycatchers, and it comes north early in the spring with the hatching of the first insects in sheltered spots, where they appear on the first warm days. The phoebe's migratory behaviour is somewhat reminiscent of the European chiffchaff, which is also one of the first birds to come north.

The yellow-bellied flycatcher (*Empidonax flaviventris*) is more migratory, breeding in the coniferous regions of the northern states and wintering from Tamaulipas in Mexico to Panama. It is difficult to observe this wary flycatcher, which seeks inaccessible, swampy spots both on migration and during the breeding period.

The western flycatcher (*Empidonax difficilis*), which nests in the western part of North America, from Alaska to north-western Mexico, also spends the winter in central Mexico.

Central America and Mexico are thus the chief winter quarters for a

1. The vermilion flycatcher (*Pyrocephalus rubinus*), another tropical species which goes north in the breeding season to California and Utah, is also only partially migratory. It is an all-year resident of Nevada and California.

2. This was first shown by J. J. Audubon, who banded a few phoebes and discovered that they returned to the same area the next spring.

number of species of North American flycatchers. Certain others, however, spend the winter in South America, especially in the north-western part of that continent. The eastern wood pewee (*Contopus virens*), for example, one of the most common flycatchers in the eastern U.S.A. and southern Canada, winters in tropical America from Costa Rica and Panama through Colombia and Ecuador to central Peru. The ecological requirements of this flycatcher must be rather exacting, because the bird is fairly late in reaching its breeding territories. In general, it is the last of the migrants to arrive in the spring, and it starts south early in the autumn.

Another highly migratory member of the Tyrannidae is the eastern kingbird (*Tyrannus tyrannus*), which breeds from British Columbia and central Canada to the southern U.S.A., and winters from Costa Rica to southern Bolivia and Peru. Always active and exuberant, this bird hunts in open country, so it is one of the easiest migrants to observe. Furthermore, it migrates by day, flying chiefly in the morning and late afternoon in flocks that may number a hundred. Many authors, including Skutch in Central America, have noted that during migration the eastern kingbird is often one of the most conspicuous of all birds.

The Arkansas or western kingbird (*Tyrannus verticalis*), which replaces *T. tyrannus* in western North America, is also a migrant, but goes only as far south as Mexico, Guatemala and Salvador.

6. SWALLOWS AND MARTINS

Most swallows, like their counter-parts in the Old World, make long migrations. North America has more species than Europe, as no less than eight occur within the limits of the U.S.A., each with its distinctive migratory behaviour.

The tree swallow (*Iridoprocne bicolor*), which nests in North America up to northern Alaska and throughout most of Canada, is a hardy bird. During the winter it withdraws from the northern part of its breeding territory, but remains in all the southern states from California to North Carolina. Common in winter in all the Gulf States, it sometimes remains much further north. Elliot (1939) saw a small group on Long Island, N.Y., during the winter of 1937–38. Some of these birds, however, go to Mexico, Guatemala, and others to Cuba. Always the first of the swallows to reach its breeding area, the tree swallow seems, indeed, to follow close on the heels of early spring.

The violet-green swallow (*Tachycineta thalassina*), a very abundant species in the West, where it more or less replaces the tree swallow, is

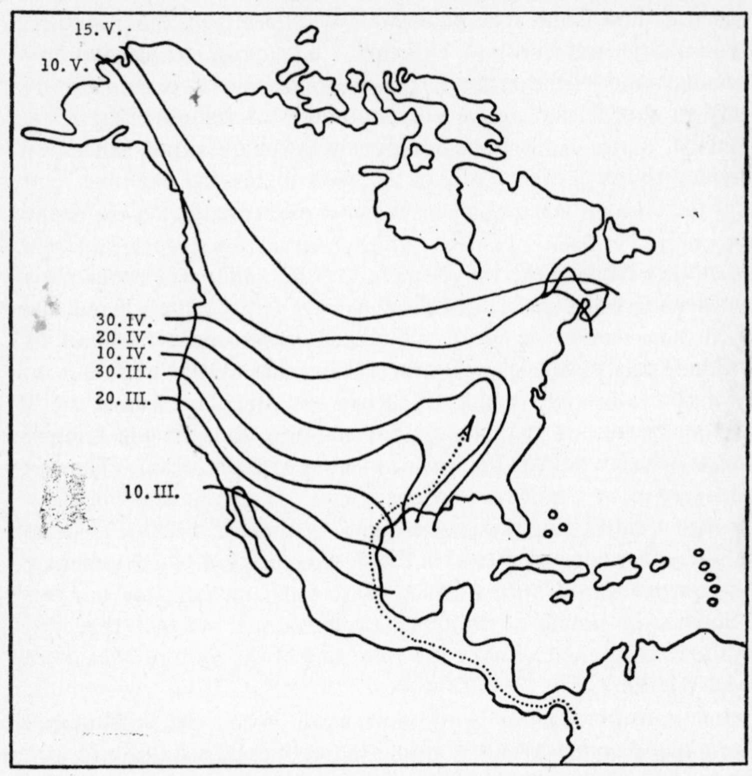

Fig. 38. Isochronal lines of the cliff swallow (*Petrochelidon pyrrhonota*), a diurnal migrant which follows the coast of the Gulf of Mexico but does not cross it. After Lincoln, 1935 b.

not very migratory. A few birds even winter in California, but the majority fly to Mexico, Guatemala, and Costa Rica.

The purple martin (*Progne subis*), a bird which is closely attached to man, nests throughout North America and winters in South America, principally in the Amazon Basin. It returns in January over the Gulf of Mexico to the Gulf States, and moves slowly northward with the advance of spring.

The barn swallow (*Hirundo rustica erythrogaster*), a close relative of the European swallow, also makes very long seasonal flights. Although its breeding territory extends to Alaska and northern Canada, this swallow winters in South America, chiefly from Colombia to central Argentina and Chile. The barn swallow differs from other species, especially the tree swallow, by being a late spring arrival and, apparently, a more delicate creature. The advance guard reaches Florida early in April, and migration continues throughout May. The principal routes of the barn swallow are through Central America – the land routes – and by way of the West Indies, the Bahamas, and over the Gulf of Mexico. These birds are often seen flying above the sea.

Another North American species, the cliff swallow (*Petrochelidon pyrrhonata*), which nests throughout most of North America and part of Mexico, winters in Brazil and Argentina. According to various ornithologists, particularly Lincoln (1935b), this swallow differs from the barn swallow by keeping strictly over the land. This is assumed by Lincoln because it migrates by day in short stages while hunting insects, which would be impossible over the Gulf of Mexico. The first birds arrive in northern Mexico in late March, having come up through Central America. From there on there is a sharp contrast between their dates of arrival in the west and east of North America. The northward advance is much more rapid in the west, but this difference in timing is doubtless explained by the fact that cliff swallows continue to follow the coast-line of the Gulf of Mexico to reach the East (Fig. 38). This greatly lengthens their travel route. Populations breeding in Nova Scotia must fly an extra 2,000 miles! From many points of view it is interesting to compare this bird with the barn swallow and various other migrants, including the blackpoll warbler.

On the whole, North American swallows are highly migratory. A few species actually fly from Alaska to the Argentine, or almost the whole span of the western hemisphere.

Among North American swifts (*Apodidae*), the chimney swift (*Chaetura pelagica*) is another notable migrant. Lincoln (1944) has banding records of birds wintering in South America, chiefly in the Amazonian basin. Others go to Central America, whereas the white-throated swift (*Aëronautes saxatilis*), which breeds in the West, spends the winter in California and Mexico.

7. THRUSHES AND THEIR ALLIES

The family Turdidae also includes some highly migratory birds, although certain species are quite sedentary. Townsend's solitaire (*Myadestes townsendi*), for example, which breeds in western North America, from Alaska to central Mexico, scarcely budges in winter,

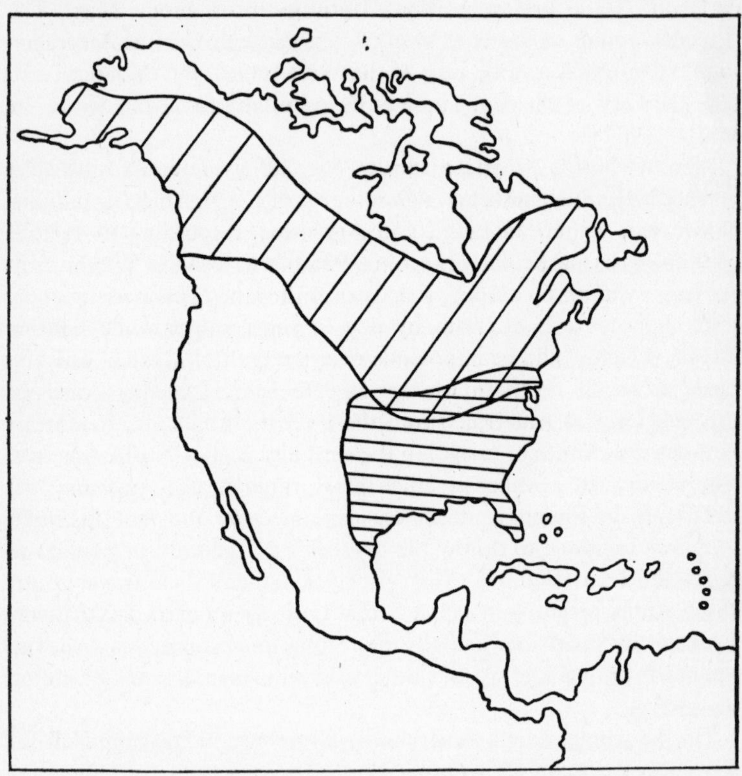

Fig. 39. Migrations of the American robin (*Turdus m. migratorius*). Diagonal lines show the breeding territory, horizontal lines the winter quarters.

though some of the more northern birds move south or drop from high elevations into valleys. The very low winter temperatures in Montana, Idaho, and British Columbia seem to have no effect on this bird, which occasionally moves about in a somewhat erratic manner when there is a shortage of the berries on which it feeds.

The North American robin (*Turdus migratorius*), one of the most popular birds in North America, is only partially migratory (Fig. 39). It nests throughout the whole continent from the northern tree line to southern Mexico (Vera Cruz), and is split into a number of local races whose migratory behaviour varies considerably. The bird is sedentary in the southern portion of its habitat. Most robins that nest in the northern U.S.A. and Canada go south, while the majority winter in the Gulf States. Winter residents have, however, been recorded at latitudes as far north as British Columbia and the most northern states. The chief winter area is the south-eastern U.S.A., where, especially in Florida, flocks numbering up to 50,000 birds assemble in roosts. (Fig. 40).

Like the robin, the eastern bluebird (*Sialia sialis sialis*) leaves the northern part of its breeding territory to winter in the south-east of the U.S.A. with its northern limit being, roughly, the Ohio Valley. This limit depends, however, on the winter climate, for birds have been seen at this season in the north-eastern states, and even in Ontario.

Turdidae of the genus *Hylocichla* are far more migratory. The veery (*Hylocichla fuscescens*), for example, breeds in Canada and the northern U.S.A. but winters in South America; it appears both in Colombia and Venezuela, but the bird's chief winter quarters seem to be southern Brazil. Little is known about migration routes of the veery, which moves somewhat furtively through Central America.

The grey-cheeked thrush (*Hylocichla m. minima*) and Bicknell's thrush (*H.m. bicknelli*) both breed in the extreme northern part of the American continent and winter in tropical America, the former in South America, chiefly Colombia and Venezuela, but also casually in Ecuador and Peru, while the latter has been recorded only on the island of Hispaniola (Haiti and the Dominican Republic), and in Venezuela.

The breeding range of the grey-cheeked thrush has spread from Alaska to north-east Siberia. But the Siberian birds return to America and do not follow the flocks of Siberian migrants, which traverse eastern Asia towards the warm regions of that continent and the Malay Peninsula, while American thrushes cross the whole North American continent, travelling south-east, and then turn southward.

In similar fashion, but in the opposite direction, north-western America was settled by another member of the Turdidae from Asia, the wheatear (*Oenanthe oenanthe oenanthe*). We have seen (p. 94) that the Alaskan populations migrate south-west to reach winter quarters in East Africa.

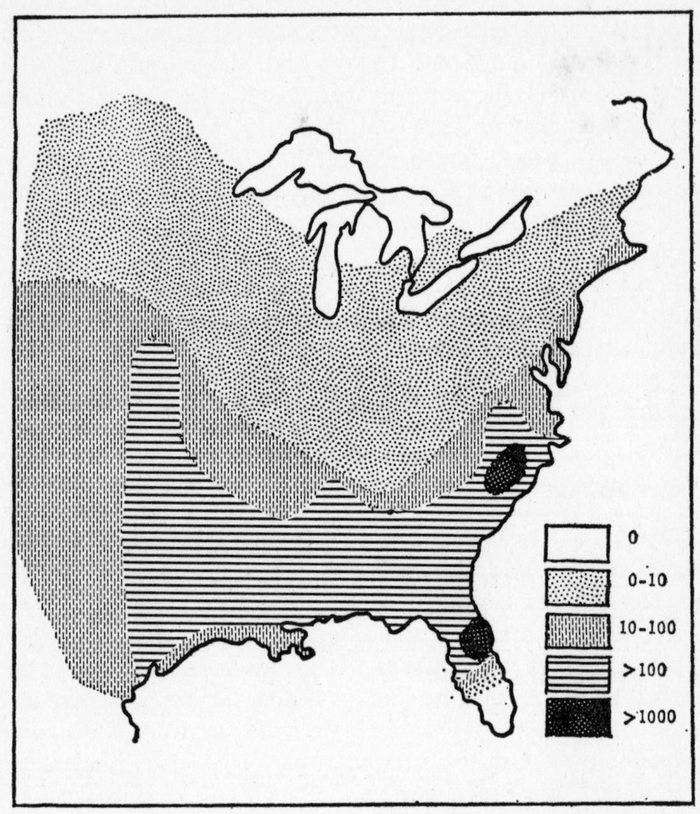

Fig. 40. Relative density of robins (*Turdus migratorius*) in late December, as indicated by Christmas Censuses taken in 1938, 1939 and 1940. The numbers show how many robins were observed by each Census party. This map may give the impression that the robin's distribution is static. In reality, as among many birds, populations are constantly moving in accordance with variations in temperature and the quantities of food available. From Speirs, 1953.

These two examples suggest again how certain migrants take ancient trails broken during the dispersion of the species from its original range. This is true of other birds that nest in Alaska, like the yellow wagtail (*Motacilla flava tschutschensis* (= *alascensis*) and the arctic warbler (*Phylloscopus borealis kennicotti* (see p. 377), both of which came from Asia.[1]

Among the other migratory species of *Hylocichla* is the familiar wood thrush (*H. mustelina*), which nests in eastern and central North America from South Dakota and Maine south to the Gulf States, and spends the winter in Mexico (as well as in Florida and the most southern part of Texas) and in Central America as far south as Panama. The hermit thrush (*H. guttata*), which nests from central Alaska to south-eastern Canada in the east and to California in the west, winters in part of its breeding range but also reaches Guatemala during its southerly movements. The russet-backed thrush (*H.u. ustulata*), breeding from Alaska to California, does not migrate farther south than Guatemala, but its relative, the olive-backed thrush (*H.u. swainsoni*), which nests from Alaska eastward to the Atlantic in the north-eastern United States, winters as far south as South America (Peru and even Argentina).

8. TANAGERS

These birds, like humming-birds, represent a tropical group, several species of which now breed in North America, so it is not surprising that they should migrate in autumn to intertropical regions.

The western tanager (*Piranga ludoviciana*) is a characteristic species of western North America that now breeds as far north as southern Alaska. In mid-August the southbound movement begins gradually in the northern part of the habitat. The winter territory of this tanager includes Lower California, a large part of Mexico, and Central America to Costa Rica (Fig. 41).

In the autumn this tanager migrates by two routes – one along the Pacific coast, the other over the plains to the east of the Rocky Mountains. It then follows the high Mexican plateaus to its tropical winter range. In the spring the same routes are used for the northward flight, but Lincoln (1939) has shown that there are differences in the speed of the northward movement. Up to the end of April the waves of migrants progress at approximately the same rate both east and west of the Rocky Mountains, through New Mexico, Arizona and southern

1. The migratory behaviour of these two birds is all the more interesting because they have been breeding in Alaska for a long time, as evidenced by the development of separate races.

California. But at that time the northward movement surges ahead in the West, for only three weeks later the tanagers reach Vancouver Island and central Alberta, while to the east they are still in northern

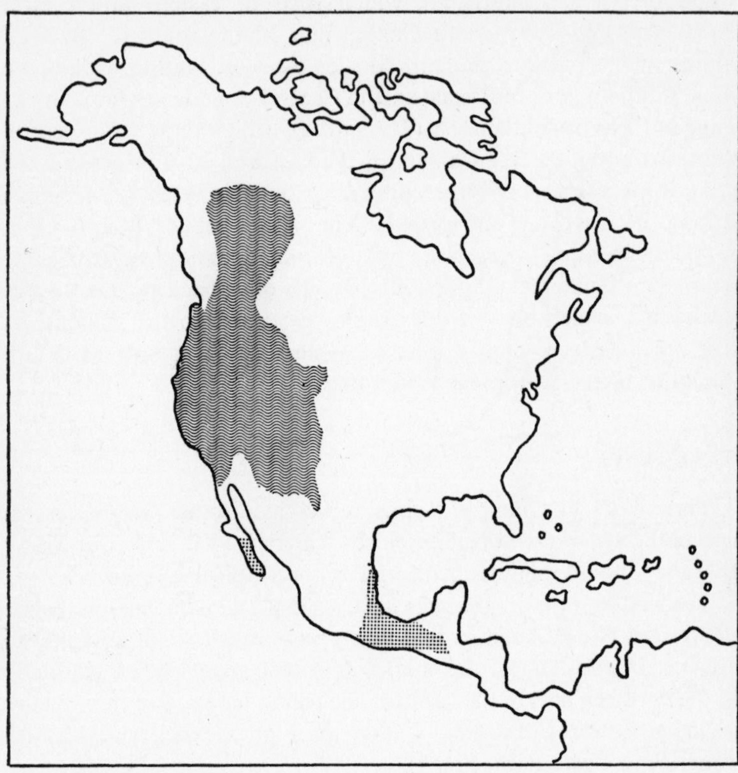

Fig. 41. Migrations of the western tanager (*Piranga ludoviciana*). After Lincoln, 1935 b.

Colorado. The birds seen at that time in Alberta must therefore take a western route through inland California, Oregon and Washington to British Columbia, where they cross peaks and passes still covered with snow, instead of the more favourable eastern route. This anomaly may be explained by climatic considerations, which are responsible for the fact that the most northern portion of the summer habitat is settled before the south-eastern area, which the birds reach by a more direct route (Fig. 42).

The scarlet tanager (*Piranga olivacea*) is another great migrant, whose seasonal flights are much longer than those of the western tanager. This bird breeds in the eastern U.S.A. and Canada, and winters in north-western South America – Colombia, Ecuador, central

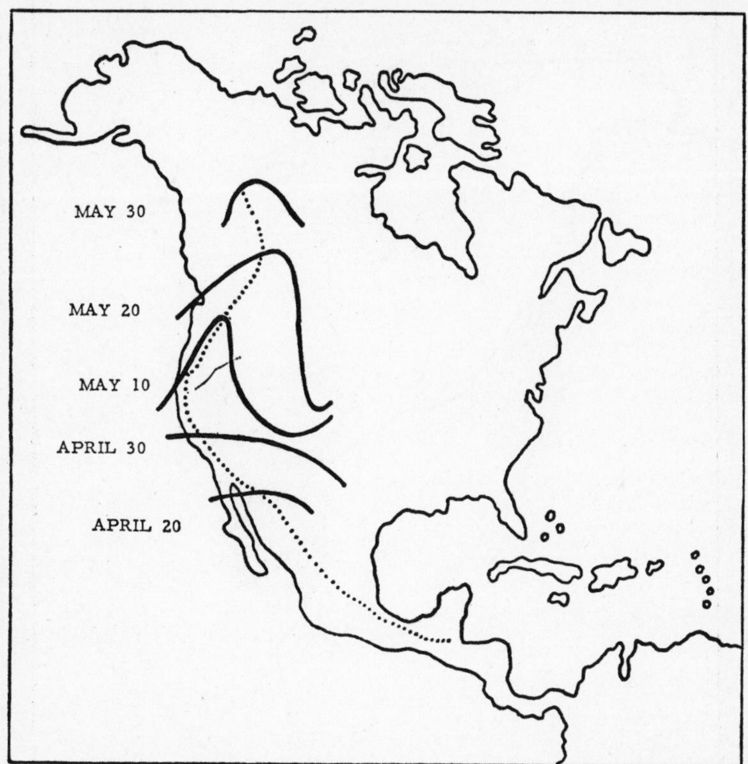

Fig. 42. Isochronal lines of the western tanager (*Piranga ludoviciana*). After Lincoln, 1935 b.

Peru, and even Bolivia (Yungas). The scarlet tanager is one of the best examples of migrants travelling along a narrow front. While the breeding area is some 2,000 miles in width, the birds travel south in a sort of funnel, converging near the Gulf Coast from eastern Texas to the tip of Florida – a space of only about 600 miles. The scarlet tanager then flies south across the Gulf of Mexico, on a front scarcely 100 miles wide, to Honduras and Costa Rica (Fig. 43).

The eastern summer tanager (*Piranga r. rubra*) breeds farther south than the last two species. It winters in southern Mexico (from

Michoacan to Yucatan), Central America, and even in Bolivia and Brazil. In Central America it is one of the most common winter

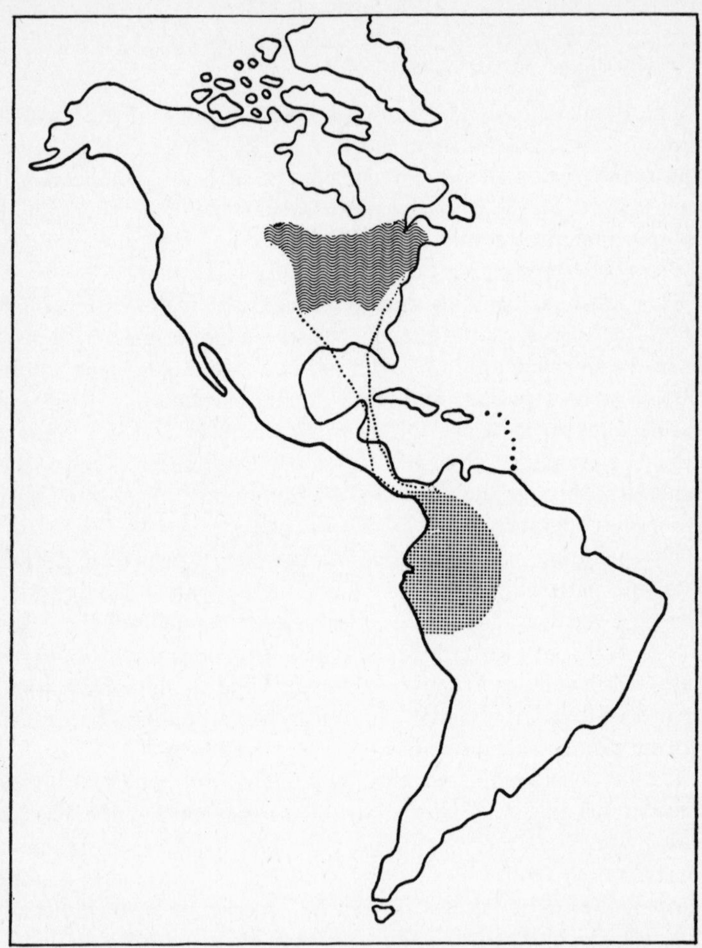

Fig. 43. Migrations of the scarlet tanager (*Piranga olivacea*). Note the narrow migratory front in the Gulf of Mexico. After Lincoln, 1935 b.

residents from Guatemala to Panama, although never gathering in flocks like some other wintering species.[1] The western race of this

1. Skutch (1950) states that these tanagers seem to defend a sort of feeding area, like other insectivorous birds, water-thrushes, for example.

tanager (Cooper's summer tanager, *P. rubra cooperi*) does not seem to go south of Mexico on migration.

9. AMERICAN WOOD WARBLERS

The Parulidae, with fifty-seven species, are one of the most important Passerine families in North America, where their position is equivalent to that of the Sylviidae in Europe. As American wood warblers are, on the whole, insectivorous, some of them entirely so, they must migrate to intertropical regions to find food in winter. Most of them perform their long flights by night.

Their seasonal flights are among the most exciting spectacles offered by North American ornithology. The spring migration, which occurs when the warblers are in full nuptial plumage, takes place within a relatively short period. In certain areas, particularly in the East, warblers appear in 'waves' of incredible numbers. Roger T. Peterson and J. Fisher (1955) described in striking fashion the flight of these small birds through the Great Smoky Mountains, where some thirty-five species migrate, usually in mixed flocks.

The migrations of these warblers vary widely, however, in distance, date, and pattern. A very few species migrate only a short distance. The pine warbler (*Dendroica pinus*) breeds throughout the eastern U.S.A. and south-eastern Canada, and winters in the south-eastern states, north as far as Arkansas, Mississippi and Virginia. Occasionally it has been found as far north as Massachusetts, doubtless because this bird supplements its insect diet with berries and seeds.

The black-and-white warbler (*Mniotilta varia*), which occupies a considerable part of eastern North America during the breeding season, travels farther north and west than the previous species. It winters in the Gulf States, in the West Indies (where it is common except in the Lesser Antilles), in Central America, and even in Ecuador (Fig. 44). The bird arrives in the north in early spring and remains until late autumn, behaviour which is without doubt correlated with its manner of hunting, for it seeks insects hidden in the crevices of bark, and such insects survive much later in the autumn than less sheltered species.

The hardiest member of the wood warbler family is the myrtle warbler (*Dendroica coronata*), which breeds in the coniferous belt of eastern and central Canada and in the north-eastern U.S.A. It winters as far north as Maine but most commonly in the South-east, Mexico and Central America. It is the only warbler that can withstand the ice and snow of winter, and one of the few whose regular diet consists of

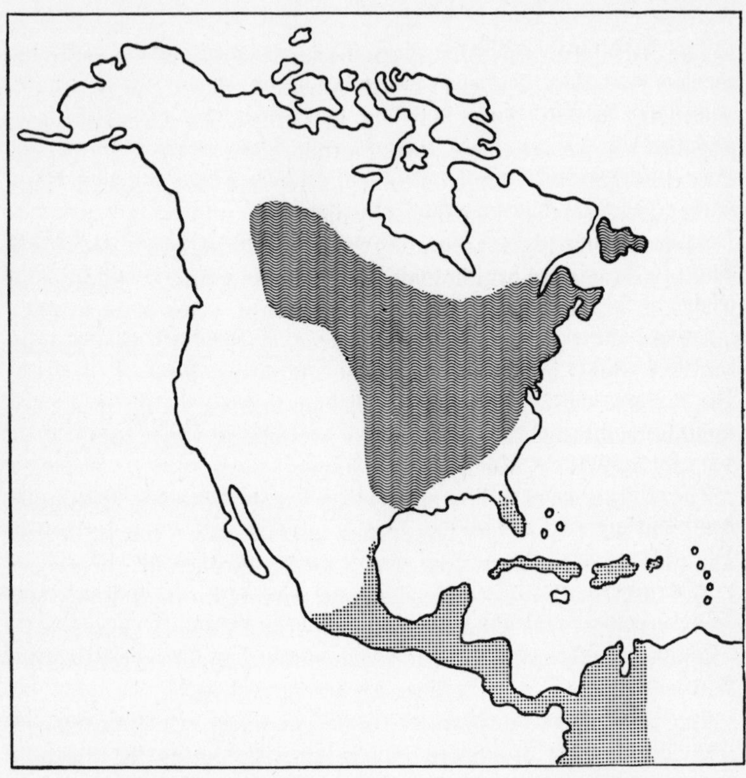

Fig. 44. Migrations of the black-and-white warbler (*Mniotilta varia*). After Lincoln, 1935 b.

berries, even seeds, available in winter. This is one more example of the extent to which diet is related to migratory tendencies.

One of the most common warblers in the East and Centre of North America is the ovenbird (*Seiurus aurocapillus*). It nests in deciduous forests but performs much longer migrations than the myrtle warbler, for it winters from the southern part of the Gulf States to Central America, the West Indies (it is abundant in the Greater Antilles and the Bahamas) and even to northern Venezuela.

Parulidae differ not only in the length of their seasonal flights, but in the fact that their travel routes vary considerably. Many birds which go to Central and South America cross the Gulf of Mexico, thus linking the Gulf States with Yucatan. A number of North American warblers cross the Gulf of Mexico at its widest point – a real challenge to such little birds. While the whole list is too long to give, it suffices to mention one of the best-known species, the yellow warbler (*Dendroica petechia*). The bird breeds over an enormous area, including Alaska and northern Canada, and winters from Mexico south to Brazil and Peru. In the spring a small number of yellow warblers come by way of Cuba to Florida, but the main wave crosses the Gulf from Yucatan to Louisiana, and a few others follow the Mexican and Texan coast. Early in autumn yellow warblers leave for the south, flying over the centre of the Gulf of Mexico.

Other warblers, for example the blackpoll (*Dendroica striata*), cross the West Indies island chain. One of the most abundant of all the North American Parulidae, this bird also has one of the longest migratory routes (Sprunt *in* Griscom and Sprunt [1957] called it the 'Arctic tern of the warbler tribe'). It breeds in the most northern part of the continent, especially in Canada, to the tree line, and also in the north-eastern U.S.A. (Maine, New Hampshire, Massachusetts, New York). It winters from northern South America to Guiana, Brazil, and northern Peru (one of these migrants has even been captured in Chile). To return to its breeding area, the blackpoll migrates from Venezuela through the West Indies and across Cuba to Florida. On arriving in North America, it goes north, then north-west, travelling more and more rapidly as it advances. Even birds that nest in Alaska take this roundabout route (the species is unknown in Central America), indicating that their presence in extreme north-west North America represents a recent extension of range, and a total flight of some 5,000 miles (Fig. 45).

Not all warblers take such narrow paths, and some of them follow a number of separate lanes, across a very broad front. The American redstart (*Setophaga ruticilla*), another very abundant warbler throughout most of Canada and in northern and central U.S.A., winters in Mexico, the West Indies (especially the Greater Antilles), and South America from Ecuador to Guiana. The paths of this migrant cross part of Mexico, the whole Gulf of Mexico and the Antilles, but no single route seems to be favoured above the others. Indeed, it seems that the most western birds tend to go straight south from California, thus 'creating' a new route for the species which, theoretically, still assembles in the south-eastern U.S.A. before flying to tropical America.

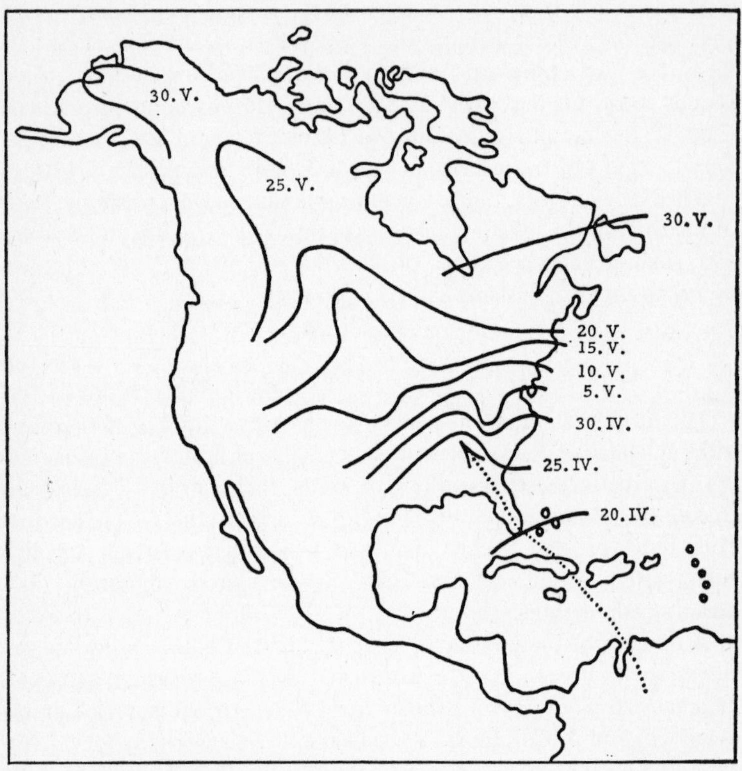

Fig. 45. Isochronal lines of the blackpoll warbler (*Dendroica striata*). After Lincoln, 1935 b.

One of the most rarely observed of all the wood warblers, the Connecticut warbler (*Oporornis agilis*), breeds in a narrow strip of southern Canada and the north-central U.S.A., but winters in South America, chiefly in Brazil, but doubtless also in Colombia and Venezuela. Its migration routes are particularly interesting, as they describe a vast semi-annual 'loop' inside the U.S.A. In autumn as in spring, the Connecticut warbler migrates across Florida and the West

Indies; in the autumn it travels straight east from its breeding territory to the Atlantic coast and then south to Florida, but in the spring it takes a much more western route, from Florida to the Mississippi Valley and then north. This is unusual migratory behaviour among North American Passerines.

The winter habitats of American warblers thus vary widely over a vast territory, which includes the West Indies. In the case of certain birds, the Cape May warbler (*Dendroica tigrina*) for example, these islands constitute the *only* winter quarters. After breeding in southern Canada, this bird winters in the West Indies from the Bahamas to St. Lucia; it is most common in the Bahamas and Greater Antilles (particularly in Hispaniola), where its abundance is surprising in view of its rarity in the breeding territories. Bond (*in* Griscom and Sprunt, 1957) lists nineteen species of warblers that migrate to the West Indies, of which ten are transients and six vagrants.

10. GROSBEAKS, BUNTINGS AND SPARROWS

This large and important group also contains a number of migrants, although most of them make only short flights or nomadic movements. As their diet consists essentially of seeds, they can find ample food during the winter in the northern U.S.A. and southern Canada. It is true, however, that finches, like their Old World relatives, are also insect-eaters, which explains why they are more migratory than strictly grain-eating birds.

A number of these birds, indeed, are great migrants, spending the northern winter in South America. The rose-breasted grosbeak (*Pheucticus ludovicianus*) winters from southern Mexico to Central America, and in Colombia, Venezuela and Ecuador (Fig. 46). Likewise, the dickcissel (*Spiza americana*), a somewhat erratic bird in its breeding territory, winters from Guatemala to Guiana.

Other finches do not go beyond Central America. The blue grosbeak (*Guiraca caerulea*) winters in Mexico and Guatemala; the indigo bunting (*Passerina cyanea*), lazuli bunting (*P. amoena*), and painted bunting (*P. ciris*) winter in Central America from Mexico to Panama, whereas the black-headed grosbeak (*Pheucticus melanocephalus*) goes only as far as Mexico, like many other birds of the western U.S.A.

The Gulf States constitute the principal winter quarters for certain Fringillidae, such as the eastern purple finch (*Carpodacus p. pur-*

pureus), which breeds in Canada and the northern U.S.A.[1] (the western populations, *californicus*, winter in the southern part of their breeding

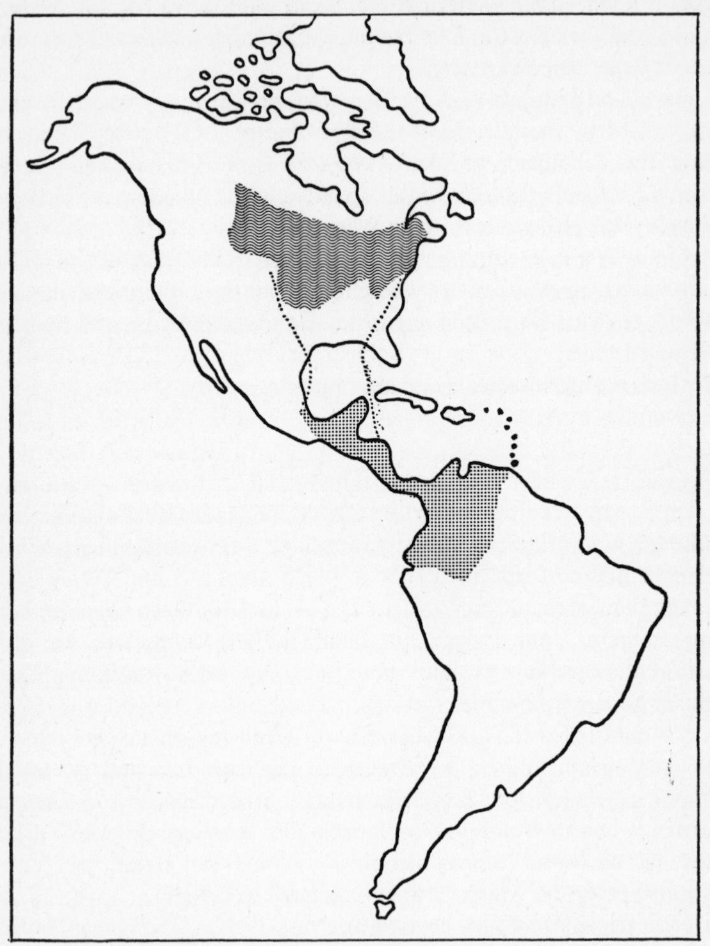

Fig. 46. Migrations of the rose-breasted grosbeak (*Pheucticus ludovicianus*). After Lincoln, 1935 b.

territory), the American goldfinch (*Spinus tristis*), and the rufous-sided towhee (*Pipilo erythrophthalmus*).

Many other Fringillidae, including a number of 'partial' migrants,

1. These birds make southern invasions in certain winters (Weaver, 1940).

merely leave the most northern portions of their breeding territory. In this category are the majority of the 'sparrows,' such as the slate-coloured junco (*Junco hyemalis*), which migrates from as far north as Alaska and western Canada to winter in the eastern states .This is also true of the white-throated sparrow (*Zonotrichia albicollis*), which winters in large numbers in North and South Carolina. Among finches that breed in the West and migrate south to spend the winter in California are the Oregon junco (*Junco oreganus*), the white-crowned sparrow (*Zonotrichia leucophrys*), and the golden-crowned sparrow (*Zonotrichia atricapilla* [= *coronata*]).

Some of these Passerines, like the song sparrow (*Melospiza melodia*) and the fox sparrow (*Passerella iliaca*), breed throughout the whole of North America, and their migrations cover the entire continent, both East and West.

Migratory behaviour, of course, varies considerably. Some species take multiple paths covering an enormous area, while others follow narrower routes. Harris's sparrow (*Zonotrichia querula*) breeds in Canada, at the edge of the Hudsonian zone, and migrates through a narrow strip, avoiding both the once-wooded land in the East and the short-grass prairies in the West, towards the winter area, a narrow belt from Kansas to Texas.

Many of these Passerines are only partially migratory, and all intermediates from migrants to sedentary birds can be observed even within a limited population. Nice (1937) showed how this applies to the song sparrow, but the most striking phenomenon in many instances is the existence of races that are distinctly characterized from a morphological point of view, some being highly migratory, others wholly sedentary. The breeding territory of the former is, of course, farther north than that of the latter. This is especially clear among western sparrows, whose races are spread all along the North American Pacific coast. These birds provide excellent material for studying the physiology of migration.

11. BLACKBIRDS AND ORIOLES

Although obviously of tropical origin, the Icteridae are well represented in summer in North America, especially in the U.S.A., and they display every migratory tendency.

The bronzed grackle (*Quiscalus quiscula versicolor*), one of the most common American birds, nests from British Columbia and northern Canada to the south-western U.S.A.; during the migration period it retreats only from the northern part of its habitat, and some birds winter as far north as Minnesota or even New Brunswick. Always highly gregarious, grackles gather during the winter in flocks of thousands, even tens of thousands of individuals, mostly in marshy areas.

The purple grackle (*Quiscalus quiscula stonei*) usually winters in the south-eastern states where it breeds. The chief winter quarters are between North Carolina and the Gulf Coast, where the birds assemble in enormous flocks, in which several other species of Icteridae, including red-winged blackbirds and cowbirds, may mingle.

The eastern meadow-lark (*Sturnella magna*), which is so characteristic of open country in the U.S.A., breeds as far as the Great Lakes and New Brunswick, but in September and October it leaves the northern part of this territory to fly farther south. It occurs in winter, however, even in southern Canada (Ontario), Michigan and Maine. Meadow-larks also assemble in flocks during the winter, but they are much smaller than those of grackles.

The south-western states, particularly the Gulf States, are thus the chief wintering grounds of many Icteridae. Notable among the species is the red-winged blackbird (*Agelaius phoeniceus*), which masses in these regions in preparation for returning to its breeding area at the first breath of spring. Here too we find the brown-headed cowbird (*Molothrus ater*), whose normal winter territory extends south from Kentucky and Virginia. The northern limit of its winter area varies to a certain degree according to the weather, and a number of individuals may winter much farther north than the bulk of the population. Such species are only partially migratory.

Other Icteridae are more highly migratory. After returning at a fairly late date to its breeding territory (about the middle of May in the North-east), the Baltimore oriole (*Icterus galbula*) leaves quite early in autumn for southern Mexico (Vera Cruz), Central America, and even Colombia and Venezuela. The orchard oriole (*Icterus spurius*), which nests in the central and eastern U.S.A., also winters from southern Mexico to Colombia and Venezuela. Its migration routes in spring lead over at least part of the Gulf of Mexico. In autumn its routes seem to be farther west, along both coasts of Central America.

But the greatest migrant of the Icteridae is the bobolink (*Dolichonyx oryzivorus*) (the *goglu* of the French Canadians), a very common field bird which nests in northern Canada, and throughout much of the

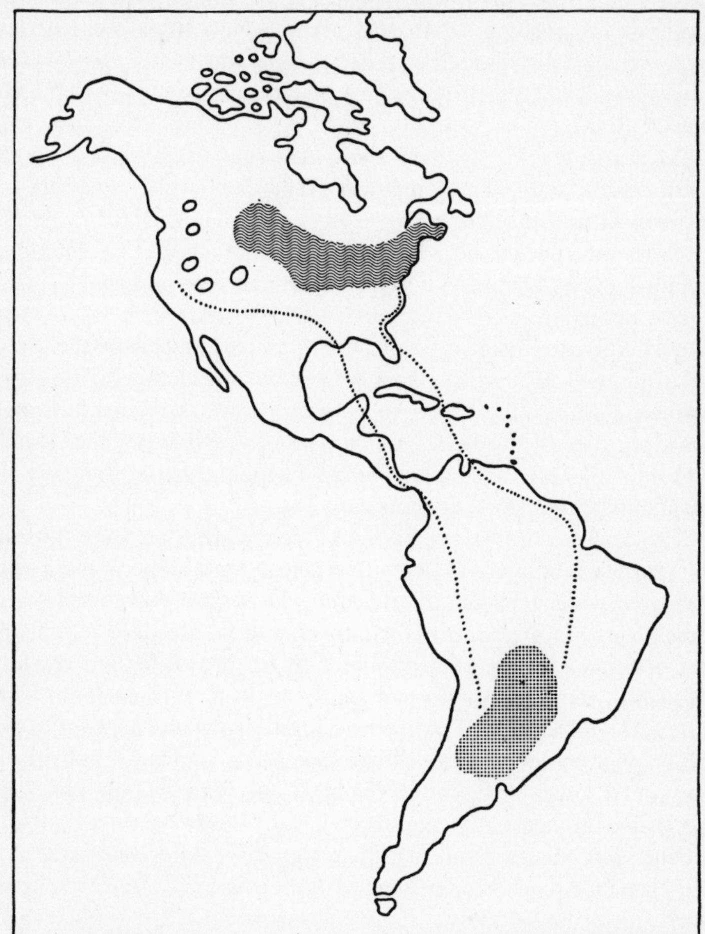

Fig. 47. Migrations of the bobolink (*Dolichonyx oryzivorus*). Most of them go directly from Jamaica to northern South America. After Lincoln, 1935 b.

northern and central U.S.A. The bobolink winters in swampy regions, like the Chaco of eastern Bolivia, southern Brazil and northern Argentina, after making an enormous flight across the Americas (Fig. 47). Its route, which Lincoln named the 'Bobolink route,' leads up and down the eastern states, and populations 'recently' established in the West have to travel across the continent, along the 'road' built as the breeding area was gradually extended. Very few individuals migrate south along more western lanes, such as the Mississippi Valley. The wave of migrating bobolinks cuts across Florida, with most of the birds going on to Cuba, Jamaica, and then to South America. A few also cross the Gulf of Mexico to Yucatan, and then migrate south through Central America. In the spring, bobolinks take the same route in reverse or cross the Gulf of Mexico.

The Great North American Migration Routes

That migrations in North America differ very considerably both as to their length and pattern is due in large part to the geographical arrangement of the continent. The gradual geographic climatic change from temperate to subtropical and tropical zones, without marine or mountain barriers, and the general north-south orientation not only of the mountain chains, but of the largest river basin, the Mississippi and, of course, of the sea-coasts, have a profound influence on migration. On the whole, birds travel along north-south axes correlated with these geographical factors.

In the northern part of the continent, however, many migrants fly mainly from west to east. The white-winged scoter (*Melanitta deglandi*) breeds near lakes in eastern and central Canada but winters on both the Pacific and Atlantic coasts. The birds that come to the Atlantic coast make a loop migration. When these scoters reach Labrador in autumn, they cross the Gulf of St Lawrence and turn south, as the majority winter along the shores of Maine and Massachusetts; but in the spring they fly west to the Great Lakes before returning to their breeding area.

Both water- and land-birds migrate from west to east in the autumn. The evening grosbeak (*Hesperiphona vespertina*), for example, travels from Michigan to winter in the eastern states, and several other Passerines do the same (McGee, 1934). From the region of the Great Lakes, and to the north of them, many ducks, like the canvasback and the redhead, fly east in autumn to the Atlantic states before going south.

Yet in the central and southern states migrations are, on the whole, oriented from north to south. The geographical arrangement has determined routes which are stable and well defined for a population or even a species, but many species migrate along widely separated lanes. The American redstart (*Setophaga ruticilla*) migrates along a broad front, even in the vicinity of the Gulf of Mexico. Generally, however, the routes come closer together in the southern states, and even more so, of course, in Central America, which forms a kind of funnel, open on the north side and narrow in the south. Migration routes thus tend to converge in southern Mexico and Guatemala.

Because of this geographical configuration, migratory routes are grouped in several large lanes. F. C. Lincoln first called attention to this in 1935 after he had recovered thousands of banded Anatidae in the U.S.A. and Canada. Lincoln named these large lanes *flyways* and defined them (1952) as 'a vast geographic region with extensive breeding grounds and wintering grounds connected with each other by a more or less complicated system of migration routes.' (Fig. 48). The flyways include a network of migratory routes which may be parallel, convergent or divergent, depending on local factors. While dealing primarily with Anatidae, in practice they apply to all other birds, including the Passerines, and serve for both the postnuptial and spring migrations, since, with a few remarkable exceptions, such as the golden plover, the same itinerary is used for both. These flyways are enormously important for wildlife management and hunting regulations, because they provide a check on the numbers of Anatidae available to gunners and adequate to conserve the breeding stock.

ATLANTIC OCEANIC ROUTE

This route was mentioned in connection with the golden plover, which flies directly from north-eastern Canada – Labrador, Nova Scotia – down the Atlantic Ocean to the Brazilian coast, barely brushing Bermuda and the Lesser Antilles (Fig. 37). A number of water- and shore-birds, in addition to the golden plover, take this path, but no land-bird uses it regularly because of the dangers inherent in flying long distances non-stop over the sea.

ATLANTIC COAST ROUTE

In autumn this flyway drains a number of birds from the East and

North-east as it follows the Atlantic coast south from Greenland and north-eastern Canada; but most of these migrants have crossed the continent on a south-eastward diagonal from the North and North-west. Many Anatidae from the plains of northern central Canada

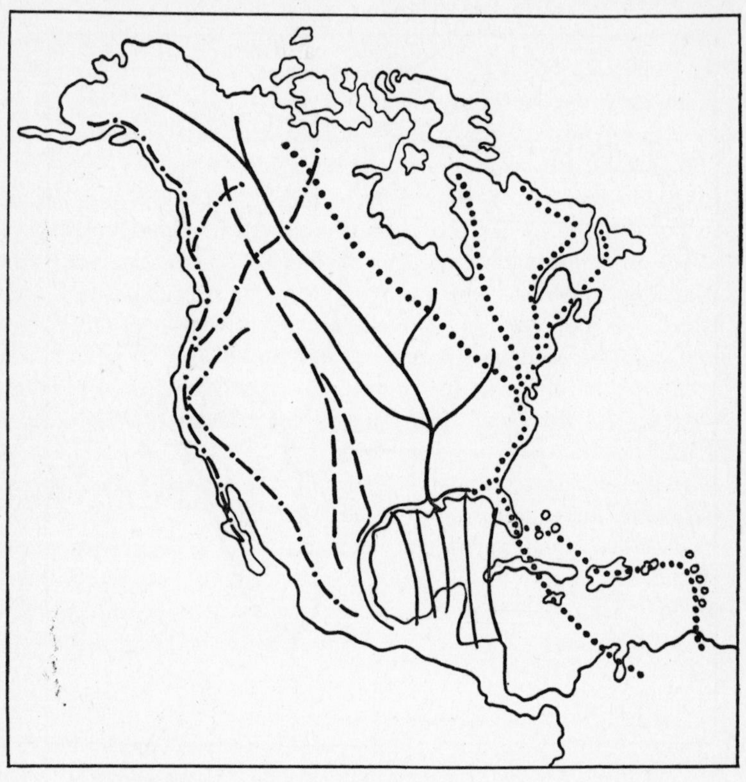

Fig. 48. Flyways in North America, as they were plotted by F. C. Lincoln.

Dotted line: Atlantic Coast Flyway
Solid line: Mississippi Flyway
Broken line: Central Flyway
Dots and dashes: Pacific Flyway

These great migration routes continue across the West Indies, the Gulf of Mexico and Central America.

traverse the Great Lakes area, fly to Pennsylvania and then towards the Atlantic. They winter along the coasts, chiefly on Delaware and Chesapeake Bays, which are famous for their hosts of wildfowl. These birds include the canvasback (*Aythya valisineria*), which breeds in the Far West and North-west, and winters in large numbers along the Atlantic coasts, especially in Virginia and North Carolina; the redhead (*Aythya americana*), the greater scaup (*Aythya marila*), and the lesser

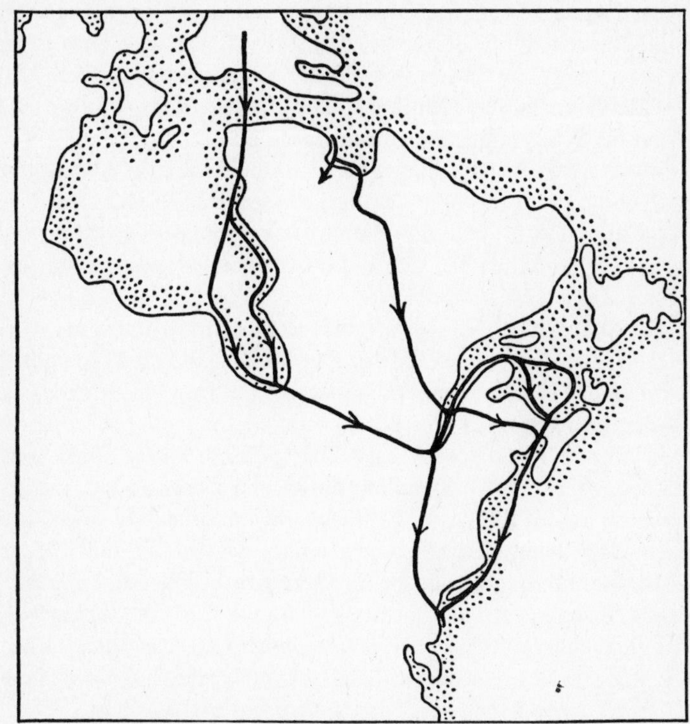

Fig. 49. Autumn migration routes of brants (*Branta bernicla hrota*). After Lewis, 1937.

scaup (*Aythya affinis*). Other ducks take the same route, and so do some Canada geese and brant (*Branta bernicla hrota*). The races of eastern Canada follow certain definite lanes (Lewis, 1937). Brant skirt the eastern shores of Hudson Bay in the autumn, or come down the continent from Ungava. After gathering in the Gulf of St Lawrence, they follow the coast or fly south, overland, to reach it. Then they continue along the shore to New Jersey, where a large number spend the winter. Some go on to North Carolina, especially in severe winters.

The spring migration seems to retrace the same routes, with only slight differences.

The Atlantic coast is also the guiding line for many birds flying south for the winter. These include gulls, especially the herring gull (Gross, 1940), the laughing gull (*Larus atricilla*) (see p.171), and the northern clapper rail (*Rallus longirostris crepitans*). By banding these birds in Virginia, R. E. Stewart (1954) showed that they were going south to winter on the coastal strip of the Southern Atlantic States.

Land-birds, including countless Passerines and birds of prey, take the Atlantic flyway, both the coastal route and farther inland.[1] The long ridges of the Appalachian system are guide lines for Raptores, and it is common to see large numbers of them during migration (see p. 257). Cape May, at the end of a long, narrow tongue of land between Delaware Bay and the open sea, and other points along the coast are also famous as observation posts.

But the Atlantic flyway does not end with the southernmost coasts of the U.S.A. It continues from Florida across Cuba and the West Indies, whose chains of islands permit migrants to 'hop' from one to the next. Few birds, however, take this route, doubtless for ecological reasons. Some winter in Cuba, Haiti and Puerto Rico, where some sixty species from the U.S.A., including ducks, have been found. Others continue by way of the Lesser Antilles, and still others fly straight to Jamaica, from which point they head south over the 500 miles of sea that separate the island from the northern coast of South America – Lincoln's 'Bobolink route.' Species which take this path include the black-billed cuckoo (*Coccyzus erythrophthalmus*), the yellow-billed cuckoo (*Coccyzus americanus*), the chuck-will's widow (*Caprimulgus carolinensis*), some flycatchers, vireos, thrushes and warblers.

MISSISSIPPI FLYWAY (or MACKENZIE-GREAT LAKES-MISSISSIPPI FLYWAY)

This great migratory route – the most important of all American flyways – originates in Alaska and on the Mackenzie. It follows this river valley south, passes west of the Great Lakes, and then descends

1. Landbirds on the coastal lanes of the Atlantic flyway risk being carried far out to sea by west winds. Scholander (1955) observed 44 species at distances up to 400 miles from shore; the list includes all of the 'accidentals' in Bermuda and the 'exceptional' birds in western Europe (see p. 202).

the Mississippi Valley to the Gulf Coast. A number of lateral branches from both East and West, such as the Ohio and Missouri valleys, feed the main trunk of migration.

This flyway is taken by many water-fowl, especially the mallards (*Anas platyrhynchos*), Canada geese and pintails (*Anas acuta*), all of which are abundant on the long trail leading south to the Gulf States, winter quarters for innumerable Anatidae. The flyway is excellent for water-birds because river basins lie all along the way.

Among the many Passerines which also take this route are the American robin (*Turdus migratorius*) and the myrtle warbler (*Dendroica coronata*), to cite only the most common. It is probable that nowhere else in the U.S.A. can one see such a concentration of migrants of so many species as along the Mississippi Valley.

Some birds do not winter on the Gulf Coast, which also constitutes a take-off point for tropical regions, and many of these migrants fly over the Gulf of Mexico at its greatest breadth. The first to assert that birds fly over the Gulf was W. W. Cooke (1905), who believed that four routes are possible for migrants heading for tropical America: Florida to Cuba; Florida to Yucatan; northern coast of the Gulf of Mexico to southern Mexico, across the Gulf of Mexico; by land along the Texan and Mexican coast. Cooke considered the second and third – those requiring the longer overseas flights – the most frequently followed, and he listed the species which take them. His statements were based on observations of land migrants over the Gulf and on surveys at various points on the Gulf Coast, which show that some species are unknown in eastern Mexico and in Florida but are observed in both North and South America. This can only be explained by a direct flight across the Gulf of Mexico. An analysis of the dates when birds appear at various places leads to the same conclusions, as some birds arrive in the spring at points north of the Gulf before they reach more southern areas. In one case they crossed the Gulf; in the other they followed the coast.

Lowery (1945, 1946) advanced a series of new arguments to support this theory. He checked the identity and number of birds found crossing the very centre of the Gulf of Mexico. On the basis of his own observations and those in the literature, he found that no less than seventy-three non-pelagic species have been identified above the Gulf (Lowery and Newman, 1954), including wood warblers, swallows (barn swallow, bank swallow), Turdidae (veery), Mimidae (catbird), and flycatchers. Many other proofs, such as the observation of concentrations of migrants at each end of the route – the U.S. Gulf Coast, and Yucatan and southern Mexico – have been assembled. The density of the flights across the Gulf was also revealed by telescopic counts, and later Lowery compared his results with the number of birds recorded at the two ends of the migration route.

Other observers have confirmed Lowery's findings. Siebenaler (1954) counted the migrants over the Gulf in the autumn of 1952; Bullis and Lincoln (1952) and Bullis (1954) undertook the same task in the spring of 1951 and 1952, and found large groups of migrants flying north as isolated individuals and in mass congregations. Their studies reveal that numerous birds of many species make the direct flight.

Stevenson (1957) undertook a tremendous task in the states bordering the Gulf. Thanks to a number of assistants, he had at his disposal many direct observations pertaining to the identity and density of the migrants and the dates of their appearance in different places. He found that, while a number of birds follow the coast, routes over the Gulf are frequently used. Some forty species are more often seen on the north side than at either the west or east ends of the Gulf, which indicates that the birds fly directly over the Gulf.

The existence of this route was, however, questioned by Williams (1945, 1947), who thinks there is no definite proof that migrants really cross the Gulf. He believes they follow the shore around the eastern and western edges of the Gulf (Texas, Mexico; Florida, Cuba, Yucatan), a route which involves only short flights across bodies of water. According to Williams, the birds occasionally take short cuts across the irregularities in the shore line but never cross the whole waist of the Gulf, unless they are carried out to sea by storms.

It is undeniable that many migrants do follow the natural lines formed by the coasts, and it is well known that by no means *all* migrants cross the central part of the Gulf. But evidence of the crossing, as outlined by Cooke and confirmed by Lowery and other observers, is so conclusive that denial is impossible. It is true, of course, that migratory behaviour varies with the species, and some of them cross the Gulf only by accident. This is the case with the cliff swallow (*Petrochelidon pyrrhonota*), certain birds of prey, perhaps some herons and other diurnal migrants. Others make it their normal migration route. There are similar phenomena in the Mediterranean region.

Meteorological conditions exert a strong influence on migratory behaviour and the selection of routes. Lowery insisted on the importance of this factor to explain the flocks of spring migrants that gather in the region of Yucatan and the Gulf of Campeche to await favourable weather before starting north.

Lowery called attention to another phenomenon of the Gulf States, the *coastal hiatus*, which runs the whole length of the shore. When spring weather is good for migration, birds belonging to species that breed north of the Gulf do not stop flying when they reach the north coast, but continue north for a considerable distance, perhaps as far as Tennessee. According to Lowery, the most southern locality in the Mississippi Valley with a 'normal' migration is Memphis, Tennessee, where migrants are not subjected to the irregularities found farther south. North-bound migrants land in the coastal strip only in bad weather, in which case they are literally thrown on the shore, occasionally in large numbers. They leave as soon as weather permits, and do not stop before reaching the northern edge of the hiatus. Thus there is an intermediate zone where migrants are theoretically never observed. This explains why some authors have denied that birds migrate across the Gulf because they were not found in the region they studied. Williams (1950b) does this when he calls attention to the gap on the coast between flocks of migrants from Florida and Texas.

CENTRAL FLYWAY (or GREAT PLAINS-ROCKY MOUNTAINS FLYWAY)

The northern part of this route merges with the Mississippi flyway. It also starts in Alaska and the Mackenzie, but southward it bends farther west, following the Great Plains just east of the Rocky Mountains from Montana to New Mexico. Farther east, the boundaries of this flyway are not distinct and can easily be confused with those of the Mississippi. The eastern edge of the Central flyway drains western Missouri and Arkansas. This route leads autumn migrants towards the Mexican plateaux, as well as the western part of the Gulf of Mexico. A large number of species of ducks use this flyway, including many pintails (*Anas acuta*) that winter in the southern states, Mexico, and Central America, baldpates or American wigeons (*Mareca americana*), which also winter in part of Mexico, and redheads (*Aythya americana*).

PACIFIC FLYWAY

The most western flyway in North America consists of several more or less parallel routes, linked to one another by branches correlated with the mountain ranges in the West. This flyway begins in Alaska, in the region of the Yukon River delta, and runs south, following the coast or the valleys of the mountain chains. It is less important than the others, since the favourable winter climate of the Far West induces many birds to make only short seasonal migrations.

Among the birds that nest in the most northern zones and are obliged to migrate are many Passerines, as well as most of the water-birds. The former include a number of sparrows which migrate south in the autumn, many of them going to California, which, because of its mild climate, is the wintering ground for a number of species. The western tanager (*Piranga ludoviciana*) also takes this route, which enables it to return rapidly to the breeding grounds (see p. 111).

Among the Anatidae the most interesting migrations are those of geese. The cackling Canada goose (*Branta canadensis minima*), the smallest in the group, breeds along the coasts of western Alaska and spends the winter in inland valleys from British Columbia to California. Its migratory route is at first along the coast, even a long flight over water, for there is every reason to believe that the bird crosses the Gulf of Alaska. At the level of the Columbia River mouth, these geese turn inland, then go up the Willamette River valley to winter farther south, in a region dotted with lakes on the borders of Oregon and California, and in the Sacramento and San Joaquin valleys. They share these winter quarters with other geese from arctic America, chiefly snow geese (*Chen hyperborea*). The latter also winter on the Gulf Coast.

This is also the winter habitat of the rarest and smallest American goose, Ross's goose (*Chen rossii*), which breeds in a very restricted part of the Perry River region in the far north of Canada, where its nesting grounds were only recently discovered, by A. Gavin and E. Donovan, in 1940. In the autumn this goose flies south-west, towards Great Slave and Athabaska Lakes, and accompanies numerous other water-fowl as far as Montana. Here the majority of them continue south and south-east, along the multiple lanes of the Central flyway, but Ross's goose veers diagonally west, crosses the Rocky Mountains, and winters in California, chiefly in the Sacramento and San Joaquin valleys. This goose migrates on very narrow lanes, which is logical in view of its small numbers.

Some migratory routes belonging to the Pacific flyway follow the western coasts of North America. These coasts are winter quarters of various species which go south for a greater or lesser distance, depending on their ecological requirements. Emperor geese (*Philacte canagica*) winter along the south-western coasts of Alaska, and only a few birds go farther south, but both white-winged scoters (*Melanitta deglandi*) and surf scoters (*Melanitta perspicillata*) winter all the way south to California.

PACIFIC OCEANIC ROUTE

Certain shore-birds make very extensive flights over the Pacific, as others do over the Atlantic. The Pacific golden plover (*Pluvialis dominica fulva*) winters in a large area throughout the south-western Pacific, including Oceania, New Zealand and Australia. Shore-birds with the same behaviour pattern will be discussed later (see p. 204).

These then are the great migratory routes across the North American continent. Of the four continental flyways marked by Lincoln, the most important, as we have seen, is the Mississippi flyway, which, for reasons of geography and climate, is the one used by the largest number and variety of Nearctic migrants. Aside from the very specialized western migrants, most birds return to their winter quarters by way of the eastern states. Their flights are made easier by the fact that the East is more humid and richer in food resources than the West, which is largely desert country. Furthermore, the South-east, especially the Gulf States, is the wintering area for many northern birds. Many species breeding in the North-east originated in the East and South-east and then extended their summer habitat north and north-east after the Ice Age; they thus retrace their old invasion routes during their annual migrations.

There is, of course, nothing rigorously exact about the flyways. Some lanes become entangled at various points, particularly in the northern central region, where certain branches of the Mississippi flyway overlap those of the Central flyway. Furthermore, a species which breeds over a vast area usually migrates along several flyways, perhaps merely indicating a preference for one. This appears from recent study of the migrations of the canvasback (*Aythya valisineria*) by Stewart, Geis and Evans (1958). This duck breeds in the northern interior plains of North America, from the mouth of the Mackenzie River to northern Iowa, and winters throughout an enormous area extending over the U.S.A., excluding the central states and Mexico.

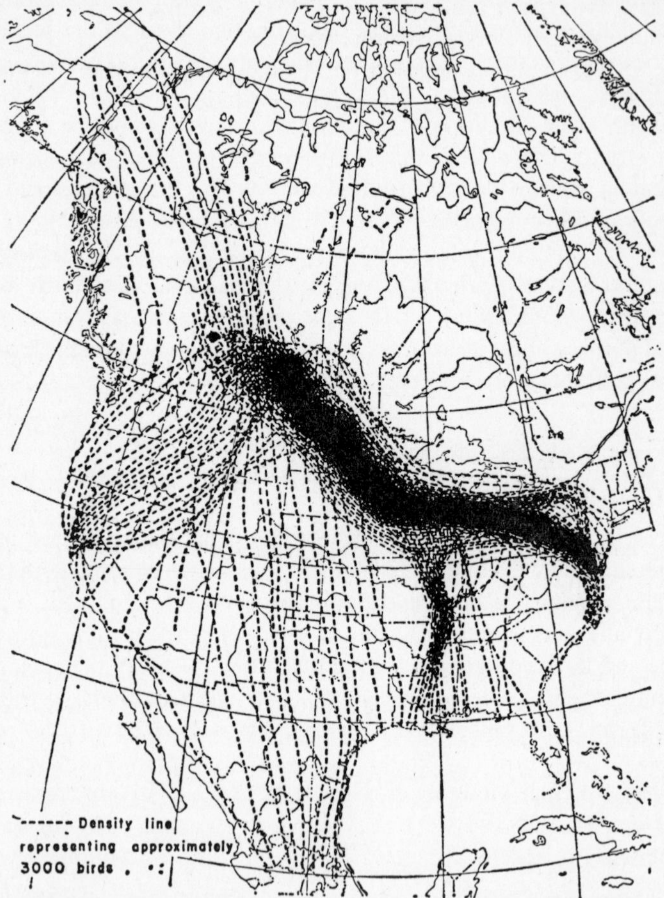

Fig. 50. Principal migratory routes of the canvasback (*Aythya valisineria*). From Stewart, Geis and Evans, 1958.

Many observations and banding records have shown that these birds use all four flyways (Fig. 50). The main wave of migrants crosses the continent on a diagonal from south-central Canada to Chesapeake Bay and beyond, one of the chief wintering areas for this duck. Another large group takes the Mississippi flyway to the Gulf Coast, and small numbers follow the Central and Pacific flyways. This illustrates how the populations of a species may be divided among the different flyways, while preferring one of them.

Aldrich *et al.* (1949) proved by banding that in a single group of Anatidae, particularly mallards, baldpates and lesser scaups breeding in the same geographic region, the migrants use several flyways, even all four!

Under these conditions, the notion of a flyway cannot be accepted too strictly. Flyways simply indicate the principal tendencies of migrants, whose routes are plotted according to the geographical and topographical conditions in North America. These considerations are, however, extremely important in regulating the 'kill' of wildfowl by hunters. Only a continuing study of the distribution of birds along migratory routes and in winter quarters can adjust bag-limits to the total number of the species, which cannot be estimated on the basis of local concentrations in wintering grounds.

Wintering Zones of North American Migrants

North American migrants obviously spend the winter in many different areas. Excluding the hardiest species, which remain, in more or less sedentary fashion, in the northern part of the continent, a great many migrants winter in the Gulf States, where the climate is favourable and the feeding areas sufficiently varied to satisfy the ecological requirements of diverse species of birds.[1] The South-west, especially California, also enjoys a mild winter climate, which attracts many birds.

The principal wintering area of most Nearctic bird species extends through Mexico and Central America to Panama. Griscom (1932) counted 161 species wintering in Guatemala, in addition to thirty

1. In addition to all those we have discussed, there is the whooping crane (*Grus americana*), whose long migratory flights from Saskatchewan to Texas pose a serious challenge to everyone interested in preserving one of the rarest birds in existence. The present flock migrates through Texas, Oklahoma, Kansas, South and North Dakota. But formerly (prior to 1858), some of the cranes spent the winter on the Atlantic coast, as far north as New Jersey.

transients and five accidentals. As the avifauna of that country comprises 736 species, it has the largest number of birds from North America of any southern country. Some birds which winter mainly in Mexico also reach their southern boundary in Guatemala, while individuals of many other species that go on to more tropical parts of Central America are also found there. In El Salvador, Dickey and Van Rossem (1938) counted 138 transients or winter visitors, as against 308 breeding species. More recently, Loetscher (1955) listed at least 211 species and thirty-two additional subspecies of North American non-breeders in the state of Vera Cruz, Mexico, out of the 700 species known there.

The numerical importance of the winter residents is even more striking than the number of species. Nowhere in America or in any other part of the world is there such an extraordinary congestion of winter residents. Every biological zone in Central America literally swarms with North American migrants. It is evident that during the northern winter they represent a very high proportion of the total bird population in these regions.

This density is, of course, correlated with an abundance of food, which is explained by geographical circumstances. A glance at the map shows that North America forms a gigantic triangle, with its base in the far north, and its tip in Panama. Following essentially convergent lanes, migrants mass in winter toward, or in, the southern tip of the triangle. There is a striking disproportion between the vast area of the breeding range and the small size of the winter territory. Skutch (1950) called attention to the fact that the latter is *one tenth* of the former in the case of the chestnut-sided warbler (*Dendroica pennsylvanica*). It is not surprising that this bird swarms in the forests of Costa Rica and Panama. The same proportion is true of many other species.

Such a concentration has exerted an influence on the sedentary avifauna of this part of the New World, both by limiting its numbers and by restricting its breeding period. Skutch states that native Central American birds seem to await the northward departure of migrants in April and May before nesting. The resulting 'vacuum' makes a much greater quantity of food available for feeding their young.

This situation is totally different from that in the Old World, especially in the African winter grounds. European migrants obliged to cross the Mediterranean and the Sahara can disperse throughout the enormous continental mass of Africa, and their density is nowhere high, except in local concentrations due to ecological factors.

In contrast to Central America, few North American migrants

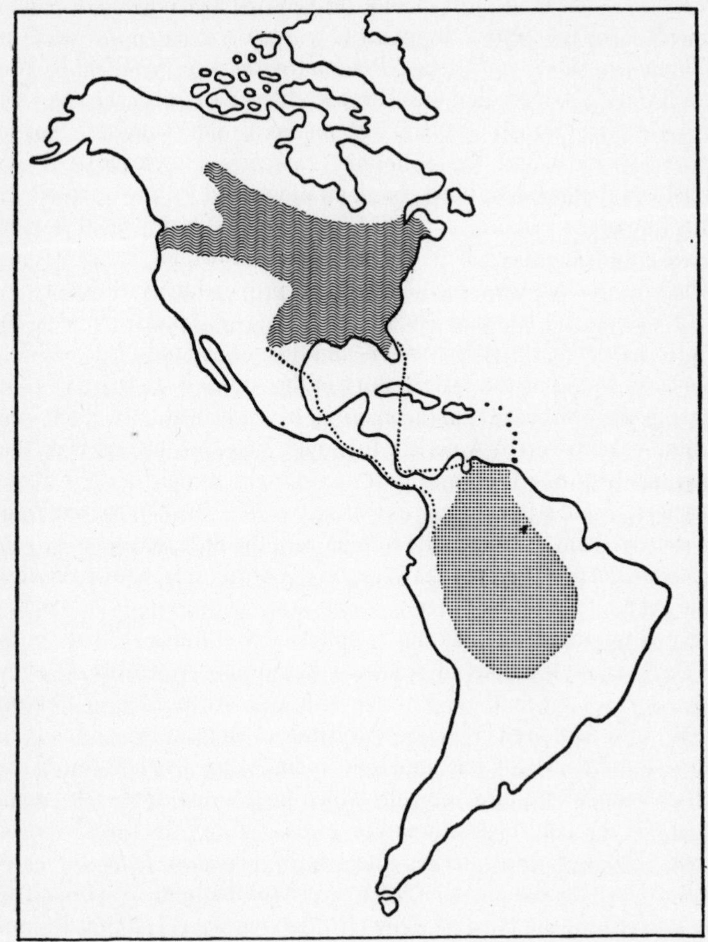

Fig. 51. Migrations of the red-eyed vireo (*Vireo olivaceus*). After Lincoln, 1935 b.

occupy the Caribbean region in winter, except close to Florida, in Cuba. This is partly due to the fact that only a small area in any of the other islands can supply sufficient food.

Nor does South America have a large number or variety of North American migrants T. A. M. Davis (1954) counted only some forty wintering species in British Guiana, including four gulls and terns, eighteen shore-birds, three other non-Passerines, and fifteen Passerines. The land-birds include the yellow-billed cuckoo (*Coccyzus americanus*), the eastern kingbird (*Tyrannus tyrannus*), the swallows (*Hirundo rustica erythrogaster*, *Riparia riparia* and *Progne subis*), four wood warblers (including the yellow warbler, *Dendroica petechia*), the grey-cheeked thrush (*Hylocichla minima*), the summer tanager (*Piranga rubra*) and the bobolink (*Dolichonyx oryzivorus*). Davis considers the barn swallows, bank swallows and yellow warblers the only abundant Passerines. G. F. Wallace (1958) estimates that there are eighty-four species of North American winter residents and transients in Colombia, including a large proportion of warblers.

In Ecuador, Chapman (1926) listed sixty-six species of Nearctic winter residents, thirty-five water- and thirty-one land-birds, most of which are found on the eastern slope of the Andes. Like Baird in 1866, Chapman emphasized that the majority of these birds have come from distant eastern North America. It should, however, be observed that migrants from the West and East occasionally mingle in their winter quarters. Traill's flycatcher (*Empidonax traillii traillii*), for example, an eastern form, is found side by side with the little flycatcher (*Empidonax traillii brewsteri*) of the West, in the winter quarters of Ecuador and Peru.

Some migrants, such as the bobolink, travel much farther south, to the swampy pampas of southern Brazil and Argentina, but few other species reach these extreme latitudes. According to Philippi (1940) and Bullock (1949), only thirty-four migratory species from North America visit Chile, and these include only five land-birds, the others being shore-birds or gulls which have come down the Pacific coast. Of the land-birds, three are birds of prey: the broad-winged hawk (*Buteo p. platypterus*), the osprey (*Pandion haliaetus carolinensis*) and the duck hawk (*Falco peregrinus anatum*). The other two are Passerines: the barn swallow (*Hirundo rustica erythrogaster*) and the blackpoll warbler (*Dendroica striata*); none of these land-birds visits Chile regularly.

Thus, only a few families of Nearctic migrants reach South America – swallows, wood warblers, cuckoos and the 'water-birds' – terns, gulls and shore-birds.

In our study of various species, we have noted the migratory routes across South America. Dennler de la Tour (1957) distinguished several

South American flyways, comparable to those described by Lincoln in North America. Geographical conditions are, however, altogether different, notably in the orientation of the great river systems. Moreover, the study of birds has not advanced to a point where it is possible to reach definitive conclusions about South American flyways. Our knowledge of migrations in correlation to the geographical structure of South America has, however, permitted Dennler de la Tour to make an excellent approach to the problem.

This writer distinguishes one coastal flyway along the Pacific, the other along the Atlantic, both prolongations of corresponding flyways in North America. But the most important route is a trans-Amazonian flyway which begins with a very broad front extending from Panama to the Amazon Delta. Its lanes converge near the great pampas in the centre of the continent, the Chaco and Matto Grosso among others. This flyway is used by large numbers of migrants of a small variety of North American species, particularly the bobolink. Another important South American flyway follows the cordillera of the Andes; its various lanes use the interandine high plateau (*altiplano*) or skirt the base of the eastern ridges, and still another traverses the plateau of eastern Brazil. These drain waves of Nearctic migrants, especially from eastern North America.

Some endemic South American birds also use these lanes for their migrations, which may be of considerable length. The movements are simultaneous and in the same direction, because of the alternation of the seasons, but the causes and patterns differ, since some birds are going to breed whereas others are leaving their nesting grounds.

As in similar regions of the Old World, a certain proportion of North American migrants, especially shore-birds, remains in winter quarters instead of returning in the northern spring to the breeding territories. Eisenmann (1951) observed several species summering on the beaches of Panama in June (black-bellied plover [*Squatarola squatarola*], willet [*Catoptrophorus semi-palmatus*], semi-palmated sandpiper [*Ereneutes pusillus*]). This is likewise true of the great blue heron (*Ardea herodias*), the osprey (*Pandion haliaetus carolinensis*) and various Laridae, notably the laughing gull (*Larus atricilla*). Haverschmidt (1955) found the same phenomenon in ten species on the coasts of Surinam. These observations prove that boreal migrants spend the summer in their winter grounds more frequently than was formerly supposed.

CHAPTER 5

Migrations in the Southern Hemisphere

Although birds migrate in the cold, temperate regions of the southern hemisphere, the patterns are totally unlike those of the northern hemisphere because of the great contrasts both in climate and avifauna. The amount of temperate land in the austral zone is very small in comparison. Climate varies with the continents, but only South America has, in Patagonia, an area with a warm summer and a cold winter; of all the austral countries it is the closest to the South Pole.

South Africa enjoys a warm temperate climate, and the cool ocean currents encircling it provide favourable living conditions for antarctic sea-birds in the coastal waters. Southern Australia is almost entirely subtropical, with an oceanic predominance in Victoria and Tasmania. The same influence predominates in New Zealand, where abundant rains throughout the year are responsible for cool summers and mild winters.

Only the southern tip of South America has an avifauna distinct from the neighbouring tropical faunas. Birds peculiar to Patagonia, although related to neo-tropical types, have evolved there. In Africa, on the other hand, all the birds belong to tropical types.

On account of the small area of really temperate or cold austral regions and the character of their fauna and climatic conditions, bird migrations are not so extensive as in the northern hemisphere. Although far southern temperate regions serve as a winter residence for a vast number of boreal migrants, not a single austral land-bird crosses the intertropical zone during its 'autumn' migrations. Most of them do not even fly as far north as the equator.

South America

A priori it seems that, as a result of these factors, the migratory phenomenon should be more marked in South America than in any other austral temperate or cold countries. Of course, all birds which breed in the most southern part of this continent do not undertake long migrations, for some are sedentary and others evacuate only the most southerly portion of their habitat, so the whole population seems to move north; still others – the most migratory – may even winter as far north as the Caribbean region.

The migrations of a number of South American birds were described by Hudson (1862); more recently Wetmore (1926b) and Zimmer (1938) have contributed further details, and much valuable information is contained in literature dealing with the neotropical fauna.

The water-fowl which breed in the most southerly parts of South America include several migratory types, especially the South American sheld geese. Although some of their migrations are only partial, in most species a considerable fraction of the populations goes north during the austral winter. Beginning in April, for example, the ashy-headed geese (*Chloephaga poliocephala*), which nest in southern Argentina and Chile, go to the Río Negro, in the Province of Buenos Aires, and to central Chile, where they stay, often in large flocks, during the winter. The same is true of the ruddy-headed goose (*Chloephaga rubidiceps*) and of the most southerly populations of the upland goose (*Chloephaga picta*).

A curious bird, the Chilean lesser seed snipe (*Thinocorus r. rumicivorus*), nests in the most southerly land reaches of South America and goes north to 'winter' in the central Argentine (Mendoza, Cordoba, Santa Fé), Uruguay, and Chile. The black-faced ibis (*Theristicus caudatus melanopis*) follows the same pattern, but it travels even farther north, reaching southern Argentina and Peru, where a sedentary race of this ibis (*Th. c. branickii*) breeds on the high Andean plateaux.

At least part of the population of the magellanic snipe (*Capella paraguaiae magellanica*) winters in Uruguay, well north of its breeding area.

The migration patterns of several Passerines are already quite familiar, and the number will increase as further information is acquired. The Chilean elaenia (*Elaenia albiceps chilensis*), a very common bird in Chile, is found from October to March across an enormous breeding area, from Tierra del Fuego north to Atacama in Chile and to Santa Fé in Argentina. During the southern winter, however, it spreads over a broad belt from eastern Peru to Brazil, where it reaches as far north as the Amazon.

The smoke-fronted ground-tyrant (*Muscisaxicola macloviana mentalis*) breeds in the Chilean and Argentine Andes from southern Valdivia to Tierra del Fuego but winters west as far as Lima (about 12° lat. S.) and east to Buenos Aires (about 35° lat. S.).

Other South American Passerines perform much longer migrations. The southern brown-chested martin (*Phaeoprogne tapera fusca*) nests as far south as Tierra del Fuego but winters in the Amazon Basin, Guiana and Venezuela. It is also a common migrant in Panama (Eisenmann, *Auk*, 72: 426–428, 1955). The Patagonian swallow (*Pygochelidon cyanoleuca patagonica*) travels from southernmost South America to Central America, where it was recently observed in Nicaragua and Mexico (Eisenmann, *personal communication*). Several flycatchers make similar flights, such as the fork-tailed fly-catchers, whose typical race, *Muscivora t. tyrannus*, nests in northern Patagonia but winters as far north as Colombia and Venezuela.

South America is also the scene of altitudinal migrations in which, of course, the towering peaks of the Andean chains are an important factor. Typical of these birds is Oustalet's cinclodes (*Cinclodes oustaleti*), one of the Furnariidae, which lives in Chile along the banks of streams; in winter it is found at sea level, but it nests up to 11,000 feet and even higher. Similar vertical movements have been observed among Andean flycatchers and Fringillidae.

The migration paths of birds moving up from the most southerly part of South America follow a number of routes. These may be grouped in flyways, as Dennler de la Tour showed (1957). But as in the case of North American migrants, in connection with which we have mentioned this author's studies, these routes are not so sharply defined as in the Old World.

SOUTHERN AFRICA

Since the climate of the temperate regions in South Africa is remarkably mild throughout the year, many species spread to its most southerly borders, and all the land-birds belong to tropical types. Mildness of climate also explains why the majority are sedentary; some, however, are nomadic, especially the plovers and water-birds which, during the non-breeding season, gather in little flocks and wander across South Africa in short flights.

The alternation of dry and rainy seasons produces a rhythm in the hatching of insects that doubtless determines the movements of a certain number of insectivorous birds, some of which are real migrants, notably the more common swallows. They generally arrive in South Africa in August and September and leave for tropical regions in April and May, sometimes earlier. The white-throated swallows (*Hirundo albigularis*), pearl-breasted swallows (*Hirundo dimidiata*), red-breasted swallows (*Cecropis semirufa*), larger striped swallows (*Cecropis cucullata*), and cliff swallows (*Petrochelidon spilodera*) are all true migrants; most of these, however, are not long distance migrants and go only to Tanganyika and the southern Congo.

Swifts also have several migratory species in South Africa, such as the horus swift (*Apus horus*), whose habitat was recently extended southward, where it does not appear from April to October, and the white-rumped swift (*Apus caffer*), although less is known about the migration ranges of the latter.

Among other regular south-north migrants we should mention the rufous-cheeked nightjar (*Caprimulgus rufigena*), which winters even in West Africa (Nigeria, Western Sudan), and the paradise flycatcher (*Terpsiphone viridis*), a migrant in the most southerly area of South Africa.

The majority of the cuckoos are migrants in South Africa, but more research is necessary to determine the details of the travels made by many species; the fact that they are silent during the non-breeding period suggests that they have evacuated their breeding area. Migration is definitely established in the case of the red-chested cuckoo (*Cuculus solitarius*), for which there are, however, a few winter records, the black cuckoo (*Cuculus cafer*), the great spotted cuckoo

(*Clamator glandarius*), the striped crested cuckoo (*Clamator levaillantii*), the jacobin cuckoo (*Clamator jacobinus*) and the didric cuckoo (*Chrysococcyx caprius*).

Glossy starlings often make short flights, occasionally in large flocks, but none of them are really migratory except perhaps the plum-coloured starling (*Cinnyricinclus leucogaster*), which migrates to South Africa but is not to be found there from April to October.

Further reference to migrations in Africa is made in the section on intertropical migrations.

AUSTRALIA

Australia is the wintering ground for a large number of migrants from the northern hemisphere. The majority are Charadriiformes nesting in northern Asia, with thirty-one visitors. These species make enormous flights along the coasts of Asia and the Malay Peninsula and usually spend the winter in large flocks.

Among land-birds, only the fork-tailed swift (*Apus pacificus*) and the spine-tailed swift (*Hirundapus caudacutus*) make regular long flights in great flocks from China and Japan to Australia. Few other north-south Palearctic migrant land-birds reach Australia, as the majority have their winter quarters in South-east Asia and Malaysia.[1]

This is noticeably different from Africa, where a much larger number of Palearctic migrants reach the most southerly part of the continent.

Australia, however, receives a large group of wintering sea-birds, some coming from Antarctica and flying from south to north to avoid the dark austral winter. The best example is Wilson's storm petrel (*Oceanites oceanicus*), some populations of which nest in the Australian sector of Antarctica and winter in the coastal waters of Australia, going as far as New Guinea and the Solomons (Roberts, 1940; Serventy, 1952). The southern skua (*Catharacta skua lönnbergi*) is also in this category. Other sea-birds, especially Procellariiformes

1. Some oriental and Palearctic migrants occasionally overshoot their mark and reach Australia. Ornithologists have observed there, among others, the yellow wagtail (*Motacilla flava*), the corncrake (*Crex crex*), and the Malay banded crake (*Rallina fasciata*).

(albatrosses, giant petrels), frequent the Australian coasts, particularly on the western side, during the course of their circumpolar flights. Incidentally, the pole is generally circled in a west-east direction, a point to which we shall return in a later chapter (p. 193).

Nesting birds in Australia include a certain number of migrants. The change in climatic zones from the humid forests of Queensland to the deserts of the interior and the temperate regions of Southern Australia produces great variety in the migratory behaviour of birds on this continent.

Most land-birds in the Australian avifauna, especially the Passerines, are, however, sedentary. Some are nomadic or make partial migrations. Only a few are really migratory, but it should be noted that birds nesting in Eastern Australia have a much stronger tendency to migrate than those in the west because the climatic cycle is more clearly marked in the eastern part. This difference in behaviour is occasionally apparent within a single species. The welcome swallow (*Hirundo neoxena*), a common bird in Australia, is sedentary in Western Australia but migratory in Tasmania and Victoria (which is deserted in winter), and partially migratory in New South Wales. Other birds with similar behaviour are the tree-martin (*Hylochelidon nigricans*), which is migratory in Tasmania, and the rufous whistler (*Pachycephala rufiventris*), which arrives in New South Wales in September and leaves in March or April. This is also true of some Tasmanian birds, including the swamp harrier (*Circus approximans*), one of the few Australian birds of prey to perform real migrations (in part of its area at least; see Sharland, 1958; Hobbs, 1959). Furthermore, many birds native to Eastern Australia are migratory, leaving the coldest parts of this continent in winter.

The most highly migratory bird in Southern Australia is the rainbow-bird (*Merops ornatus*). This bee-eater heads north from the southern part of its breeding area in February; although some populations winter in the northern part of Australia (the Gascoyne River is the southern limit in Western Australia), many spend the southern winter in Indonesia (Bali, Celebes) and in New Guinea. In October this bee-eater returns to its breeding area in noisy, compact flocks, whereas many other migrants settle down quietly in their nesting grounds.

Most Cuculidae are true migrants, especially the pallid cuckoo (*Cuculus pallidus*), which winters in northern Australia, the brush cuckoo (*Cacomantis variolosus*), the koel (*Eudynamys orientalis*) and the channel-bill cuckoo (*Scythrops novae-hollandiae*). The narrow-billed bronze cuckoo (*Chalcites basalis*) nests in Southern Australia and Tasmania but 'winters' regularly in the Sunda Islands from Java to Sumbawa; occasionally it has even been found in the Malay Peninsula, in Sumatra and Borneo. Its close relative, the golden bronze cuckoo (*Chalcites lucidus plagosus*), is also a migrant, going to the Little Sunda Islands (see p. 151). The sacred kingfisher (*Halcyon sancta*) practically deserts the southern part of Australia in March (a few individuals remain throughout the winter); some of these kingfishers go to Malaya (as far as Sumatra and southern Borneo), and others to New Guinea and the Solomon Islands.

Other definitely migratory species include the white-winged triller (*Lalage sueuri*), the brown song-lark (*Cinclorhamphus cruralis*), the rufous song-lark (*Cinclorhamphus mathewsi*), the Australian reed-warbler (*Acrocephalus australis*) and several wood swallows (*Artamus superciliosus*, *A. personatus*) (Keast, 1958).

In addition to these species, which are quite widespread throughout Southern Australia, others that breed in the eastern part of this continent leave the most southerly districts in winter; among them are the Eastern broad-billed roller (*Eurystomus orientalis*), some fly-catchers (rufous fantail [*Rhipidura rufifrons*], leaden flycatcher [*Myiagra rubicula*], satin flycatcher [*Myiagra cyanoleuca*]), cuckoo shrikes, especially the barred cuckoo-shrike (*Coracina lineata*), jardine triller (*Edoliisoma tenuirostre*) and warblers (white-throated warbler [*Gerygone olivacea*]).

In addition to these real migrants, the Australian avifauna has a rather large number of birds that perform local or occasionally altitudinal migrations. These seasonal flights, which are on a rather small scale, are chiefly in South-eastern Australia and concern, for example, the Muscicapidae (*Petroica multicolor*, *P. phoenicea*) and the Cracticidae (*Strepera graculina*, *St. fuliginosa*). Honeyeaters (Meliphagidae) also make local flights, which may be of notable length, in search of the blossoms from which they draw their nourishment. MacGill (1947), Hindwood (1948, 1956) and Robertson (1958) observed flights of this type (which may be 800 miles in length), by the yellow-faced honey-eater (*Meliphaga chrysops*), and the white-naped honey-eater (*Melithreptus lunatus*). The scarlet honey-eater (*Myzomela sanguinolenta*) is also quite nomadic, for it remains in New South

Wales if the bottle-brush trees (*Banksia*) and some other Proteaceae blossom abundantly but leaves the region if they do not. The movements of the painted honey-eater (*Grantiella picta*) between the Northern Territory and Victoria are controlled by the fruiting of the mistletoes, as it feeds on these berries.

There are analogous movements in South-west Australia. Serventy (1937) and Sedgwick (1949) report instances of birds which move to moist, hilly regions during the lowland dry summer season. Although these seasonal journeys do not cover great distances, they are clearly migrations.

Among these species are the white-tailed black cockatoo (*Calyptorhynchus baudini*), and a number of insect-eaters like the tree martin (*Hylochelidon nigricans*), grey fantail (*Rhipidura fuliginosa*), golden whistler (*Pachycephala pectoralis*), western yellow robin (*Eopsaltria griseogularis*), brown thornbill (*Acanthiza pusilla*), red wattle-bird (*Anthochaera caruncula*), and the Australian raven (*Corvus coronoides*). These short migrations are not always regular, for they are contingent upon the vagaries of the unpredictable Australian climate. The birds have had to develop a nomadic character without a set rhythm, especially in regions of great drought.

The budgerigar (*Melopsittacus undulatus*) belongs to this group, along with another of the Psittacidae, the cockatiel (*Leptolophus hollandicus*). Among water-birds, the grey teal (*Anas gibberifrons*) is certainly the best adapted to its surroundings, as was demonstrated by Frith (1957), on the basis of banding records, and by Serventy and Marshall (1957), who studied its breeding cycle. According to Frith, the grey teal, and also to a certain extent the Australian black duck (*Anas superciliosa*), constitute two distinct populations. The size of the sedentary one is determined by permanent environmental conditions. The other, a fluctuating population, is strongly influenced by occasional rains. Its movements vary in direction and extent in accordance with these rains, and it begins to nest as soon as it has found favourable sites. Serventy and Marshall have shown that these ducks have a breeding determinism corresponding immediately to favourable ecological conditions, a rare type of cycle. Perfectly adapted to the semi-arid region where they live, they move in correlation with the rains; upon finding a temporarily favourable biotope they nest, and they raise their brood before the area dries out. Such a cycle, closely adapted to the surroundings, is characteristic of many birds inhabiting arid zones with an irregular climate.[1]

The irregularities of the Australian climate are at times responsible for real invasions. Several favourable, wet years in Northern and Central Australia can cause an increase in bird populations, which, in a dry year, would have been driven to moister regions. An irruption of this type was observed in 1952 (Serventy 1953b, Glover 1952, 1956a, 1956b), especially among populations of the white-necked heron (*Notophoyx pacifica*) and the pied goose (*Anseranas semipalmata*).

On the whole, therefore, the Australian avifauna includes every form between the sedentary and the migratory. The latter are not very numerous proportionately because climatic conditions are generally favourable throughout the whole year. Most migrants do not leave the Australian continent but simply fly north, although some travel in an east-west direction.

Several Australian migrants go beyond the continent to New Guinea and Malaya, but for the most part the Little Sunda Islands constitute the northern limit of the winter quarters of most species leaving Australia. By way of confirmation, Stresemann (1941) listed only four Australian migrants in Celebes: *Merops ornatus*, *Halcyon sancta*, *Chalcites basalis* and *Stiltia isabella*.

Australian migrants are thus markedly less numerous in Malaya than are Asiatic migrants, but some birds from the south replace others from the north as the seasons alternate in the two hemispheres.

New Zealand

As New Zealand has a very mild climate, the only birds which make long flights are those inhabiting the far South and some especially delicate forms. On the whole, New Zealand is outside the great migration routes, and its avifauna, 'insular' in character, is usually sedentary, like that of many other islands. But the few migrants that breed or winter in this part of the world are so interesting that they deserve special attention, as Sibson (1951) has shown.

Like Australia, New Zealand receives some breeding sea-birds that

1. This recalls the rosy starling (*Pastor roseus*), which, in the arid regions of south-west Asia, gathers in places where grasshoppers swarm; it nests during a very brief period, then vanishes and wanders in a nomadic fashion great distances, which, however, can be fitted into a cycle of more or less regular flights.

nest in the subantarctic but move north during the austral winter. The erect-crested penguin (*Eudyptes sclateri*) breeds in large colonies, chiefly on Bounty and the Antipodes Islands, then travels north to winter off the New Zealand coasts. It never comes on shore (except accidentally), and its winter quarters are pelagic, in contrast to those of several other penguins. The breeding species in New Zealand, *Megadyptes antipodes*, *Eudyptula minor* and *E. albosignata*, are sedentary.

New Zealand territories also constitute the terminus of certain migrants from the northern hemisphere, especially waders. Falla (1936) found the following: turnstone (*Arenaria interpres*), Pacific golden plover (*Pluvialis dominica fulva*), sharp-tailed sandpiper (*Erolia acuminata*), pectoral sandpiper (*Erolia maculata*), rufous-necked sandpiper (*Erolia ruficollis*), curlew sandpiper (*Erolia testacea*), sanderling (*Crocethia alba*), knot (*Calidris canutus*) and bar-tailed godwit (*Limosa lapponica baueri*). These are merely the most common winter residents on a list which grows in length as observations multiply. Noteworthy is the fact that some migrants nesting in the American Arctic come to New Zealand but have never been found in the Malay Archipelago or in Australia.

Like Australia, New Zealand is visited by numbers of migrating sea-birds, among which is the parasitic jaeger (*Stercorarius parasiticus*). Some of these birds come from Antarctica, especially the Procellariiformes.

The spine-tailed swift (*Hirundapus caudacutus*) also appears at irregular intervals, occasionally in large numbers, as in 1942–1943.

Most nesting New Zealand birds are sedentary, and none of the resident Passerines are migratory, though some perform local movements while seeking food. The tui, for example (*Prosthemadera novaezelandiae*), a very unusual type of honey-eater, moves about in search of the nectar and berries that constitutes its diet. The New Zealand pipit (*Anthus novaeselandiae*) performs similar flights, but it should be observed that they are usually short and without specific character.

The curious wrybill plover (*Anarhynchus frontalis*), with its bill tip twisted towards the right, is one of several Limicoles known to nest only on South Island; it appears as a winter resident on North Island from December to May, and some immature birds, which are not yet nesters, stay there all year. Other species with a similar migration pattern are the pied stilt (*H. himantopus leucocephalus*) and the South Island oyster-catcher (*Haematopus ostralegus finschi*).

Four non-Passerine species that breed in New Zealand are highly migratory. The most interesting of these is the double-banded dotterel (*Charadrius bicinctus*), which crosses the Tasman Sea to Australia, migrating in very great numbers towards Southern and Eastern Australia, where it is found from March to August; a few have found their way as far as Western Australia. Their migration is, however, only partial, especially from North Island, which is not deserted by the whole population. For a long time it was believed that this dotterel also nested in Australia, since some individuals stay there all year; the fact is that all birds which remain on their Australian wintering grounds are immature. This is characteristic of many non-breeding young waders. Most of these dotterels wear winter plumage in Australia, but some assume nuptial plumage towards the close of their long residence there (Oliver, 1955).

The Australasian gannet (*Morus serrator*) makes somewhat similar flights, as Stein and Wodzicki (1955) and Wodzicki and Stein (1958) determined from numerous recoveries of birds banded in two colonies on North Island. These birds spread along the coasts of South-west Australia, even into the western part of that continent, in a zone extending from the Tropic of Capricorn to Tasmania, and west to the Indian Ocean. But again only part of the population is migratory, for these north-westward movements involve mainly immature birds which do not return to New Zealand for two or three years. The behaviour of this gannet is very similar to that of the European species (*Morus bassanus*), but the latter flies towards the equator, while the Australasian species migrates from east to west for geographical reasons.

The white-fronted tern (*Sterna striata*) is the most abundant member of the family in New Zealand. In studying the migrations of this bird, Hindwood (1946) found that some of its populations, consisting of juvenile and immature birds, cross the Tasman Sea and winter on the coasts of South-western Australia and Tasmania, chiefly from May to November; this movement is parallel to that of the Australian gannet (Fig. 52).

The fourth New Zealand bird to migrate to the neighbouring continent is the fluttering shearwater (*Puffinus gavia*). Although it appears in large numbers during the austral summer and even reaches the southern coasts of Western Australia, no nesting colony has been found, so its status is still somewhat uncertain.

The most interesting migrations are, however, those of two Cuculidae which nest in New Zealand.

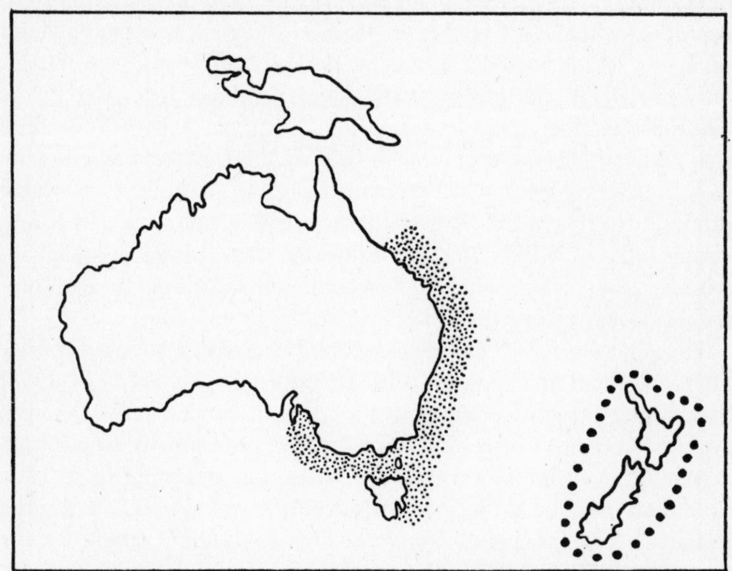

Fig. 52. Distribution of the white-fronted tern (*Sterna striata*), showing the breeding range in New Zealand and the non-breeding Australian distribution. After Hindwood, 1946.

Only recently has precise information been available about the seasonal flights of the bronze cuckoo (*Chalcites lucidus lucidus*), although even the aboriginal Maoris suspected this bird of being migratory in character. This cuckoo is replaced in Australia and Tasmania by a different but also migratory race (*Ch. l. plagosus*). Two of the sedentary races (*Ch. l. layardi* on the islands of Santa Cruz, Banks, New Hebrides, New Caledonia, and *Ch. l. harterti* on Renell) of this species of Cuculidae are also known in tropical regions. Studying the migrations of this cuckoo. H. Barraclough Fell (1947) revealed that it invades New Zealand from the north in the austral spring, starting 15 August, and arrives in the south in October, when it nests.

It leaves New Zealand towards the end of March and is found on its 'wintering grounds' between April and September in the Solomon Islands, from which it is absent from October to February. No specimen has been found in Australia, New Caledonia or in the New Hebrides. There are, however, records from Norfolk and Lord Howe Island, which the species apparently crosses while on migration (Fig. 53).

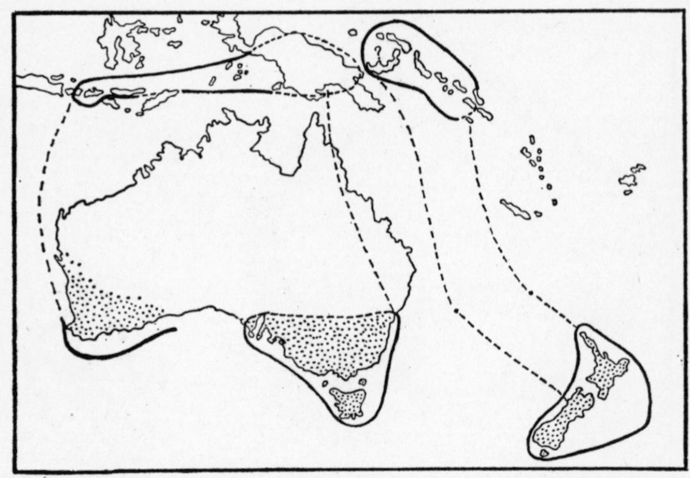

Fig. 53. Migrations of the bronze cuckoo of New Zealand (*Chalcites l. lucidus*) and Australia (*Ch. l. plagosus*). After H. B. Fell, 1947, completed with new data.

Migrants which leave New Zealand to fly north-north-west travel in the same direction as the prevailing winds blowing at this season from the south-east. It seems that cuckoos take advantage of these winds on postnuptial migration, which explains why their wintering grounds are well west of the nesting territories. This hypothesis seems to confirm the migrations of the race breeding in South-eastern Australia and Tasmania, whose winter territory includes the Little Sunda Islands from Lombok to New Guinea and the Bismarck Archipelago.

An even longer trans-oceanic migration is performed by the long-tailed cuckoo, *Urodynamis taitensis*, a rather large species, with black and brownish tan-striped plumage. This cuckoo has long been known to frequent a vast zone in the Pacific from the Carolines to the Tuamotus and New Zealand, where it appears in October (Bogert, 1937), (Fig. 54). It breeds in November and December, laying its eggs in the nests of various other birds. It seems to leave New Zealand in February, although a few individuals remain there all year. The migration routes of this bird apparently cross the Norfolk and

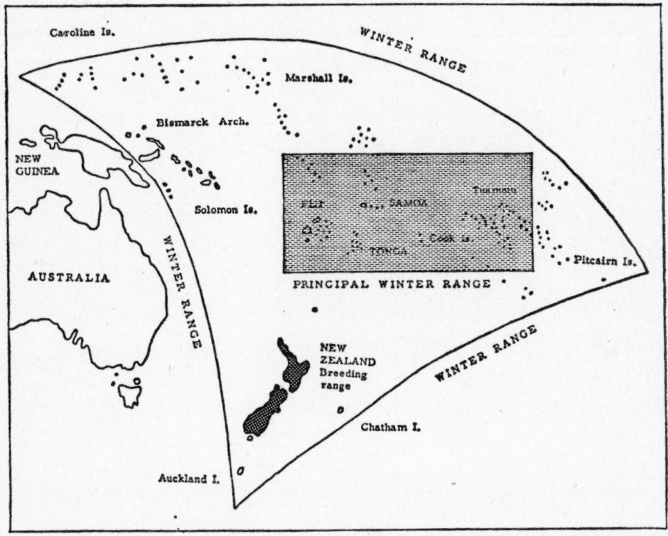

Fig. 54. Migrations of the long-tailed cuckoo (*Urodynamis taitensis*). After breeding in New Zealand, this cuckoo spreads throughout the whole of Oceania (zone surrounded by a solid line). The chief wintering area is marked by a hatched rectangle. Note that this bird avoids the continental masses of Australia and New Guinea. After Bogert, 1937.

Kermadec Islands to the Fiji, Tonga, Ellice, and the Samoa and Society Islands, where most of the cuckoos winter; some, however, go to the Carolines, Bismarcks, the western Solomons and the eastern Marquesas. They then return to New Zealand, but a few immature birds spend the reproductive season in the wintering zone, so the species was long believed to be an all-year-round resident of Polynesia.

It is worthy of note that migrants of this species, like the New Zealand bronze cuckoo, avoid the large continental masses of Australia and New Zealand to fan out to the myriad islands of Oceania. Perhaps these birds thus avoid some undetermined vital competition, which is stronger in the interior of large continental masses than in smaller areas.[1]

1. In our study of the migrations of Australian and New Zealand birds we have not examined the movements of the petrels, which cross the equator to go to their wintering grounds in the North Pacific. These migrations will be discussed in Chapter 7.

CHAPTER 6

Migrations in Intertropical Regions

It is widely supposed that bird migrations are restricted to cold or temperate countries because many species native to these regions perform such spectacular seasonal flights between their nesting zones and distant areas which provide more favourable wintering conditions. Furthermore, in the lands where these migrations occur ornithological information is much more widely publicized than it is in tropical countries.

Birds of intertropical lands also perform migrations, about which, on the whole, very little is yet known. But we may state, *a priori*, that many nesting species migrate in those tropical regions where the climate is characterized by marked seasonal variations.

Annual variations in length of day (photoperiod) and temperature in the tropics doubtless exert a minimal, yet somewhat obvious influence in comparison to periodic differences in rainfall that are so marked in most tropical areas. The rhythmic succession of wet and dry seasons exerts a profound influence on the annual cycle of animals and plants.

Equatorial regions, especially the great, steaming rain forest, with its constant climate, offer little migratory stimulus and, as a result, most bird species are sedentary. Yet, even in the forest, the seasons are revealed to a certain extent, usually by more abundant rain at one period of the year. This rhythm causes birds to make more or less wandering flights, which, although certainly not migratory, are a reaction to changing environment, just as aquatic birds wait for optimal feeding conditions at high and low river waters.

In most tropical countries some nesting species perform seasonal migrations, notably in Africa, although such flights also occur in eastern Asia, Australia and Latin America.

Africa

The most complete information yet available is that compiled by Chapin (1932), who distinguished several types of migrants among the nesting birds of the Dark Continent; Bannerman, Elgood (1959) and others have reported on this subject, but there are very few papers devoted to bird migration in this part of the world.

As Africa is a large continental mass bisected by the equator, its climatic division is clear. A series of zones, differing considerably from one another, are arranged symmetrically by latitudes away from the equator. This is, of course, an oversimplification of a complex system influenced by many local factors, but the succession, on each side of the equator, of zones affected by a cycle of rainy and dry seasons, reversed from one hemisphere to the other, has had a profound influence on migratory behaviour. These geographical circumstances explain why more regular seasonal movements occur in Africa than in any other hot country. There is a different situation in America and in Asia, where climatic zones are much less clearly defined and more complex.

Some tropical migrants never cross the equator. The standard-wing nightjar (*Macrodipteryx longipennis*) nests in a vast belt extending from Senegal to Kenya along the edge of the equatorial forest; its breeding period is from February to April, or *during the dry season.*[1] In April it migrates northward to avoid the wet season (Fig. 55). It thus nests during the dry season in a rather moist habitat and migrates to more arid regions for the rainy season. The migratory behaviour of the plain nightjar (*Caprimulgus inornatus*) is entirely different (Fig. 56). This bird inhabits the area from the French Sudan to the Red Sea, Kenya, the northern Congo and the Cameroons. It nests, however, only in the northern or most arid part of its habitat and only *during the*

1. Here, as with all African migrants, our fragmentary information is inadequate to supply details about movements, breeding, or wintering dates. The latter vary considerably according to the season and do not follow the exact pattern of birds in temperate or cold regions. Accordingly, the dates should be regarded as simple indications, which may vary to a rather large degree according to the area.

wet season, from July to September. In the dry season, from November to April, it moves to the Cameroons and the northern Congo, which are moister regions, closer to the forest girdle.

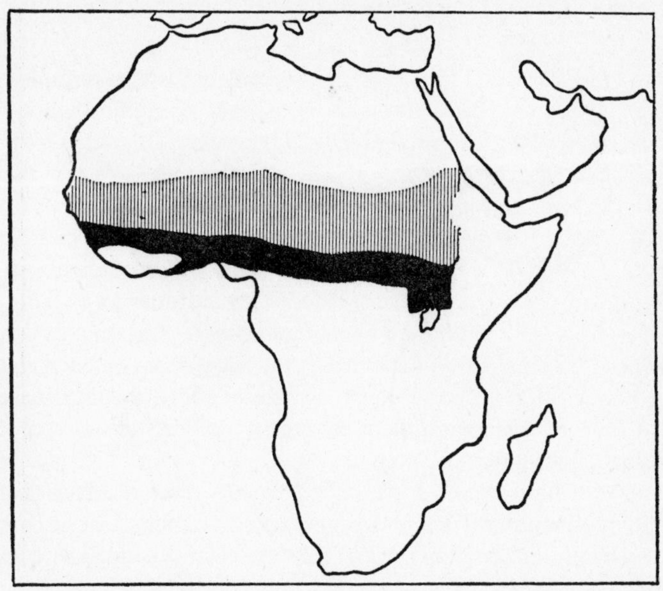

Fig. 55. Migrations of the standard-wing nightjar (*Macrodipteryx longipennis*). As in the following figures, the black area represents the breeding range, the hatched area the 'winter' range. After Chapin, 1932, modified.

The migratory movements of this nightjar are therefore simultaneous with, and oriented like, those of the standard-wing nightjar. They go together to the same regions, but one begins to nest just as the other leaves its breeding territory to fly to 'winter quarters,' Douaud (1957) pointed out movements of this kind in Togo, a narrow strip including some very different biotopes, which runs from north to south in West Africa. Although the moist southern part is in the zone of the Guinea savannahs, the arid north belongs definitely to the Sudan zone. In consequence, birds nesting in northern Togo are there in the rainy season (pied cuckoo [*Clamator jacobinus*], Abyssinian roller [*Coracias abyssinica*], grasshopper hawk [*Butastur rufipennis*]), while those in southern Togo nest in the local dry season (African cuckoo

[*Cuculus canorus gularis*], standard-wing nightjar [*Macrodipteryx longipennis*], red-necked buzzard [*Buteo auguralis*]); their *movements* are parallel, but the breeding seasons are reversed.

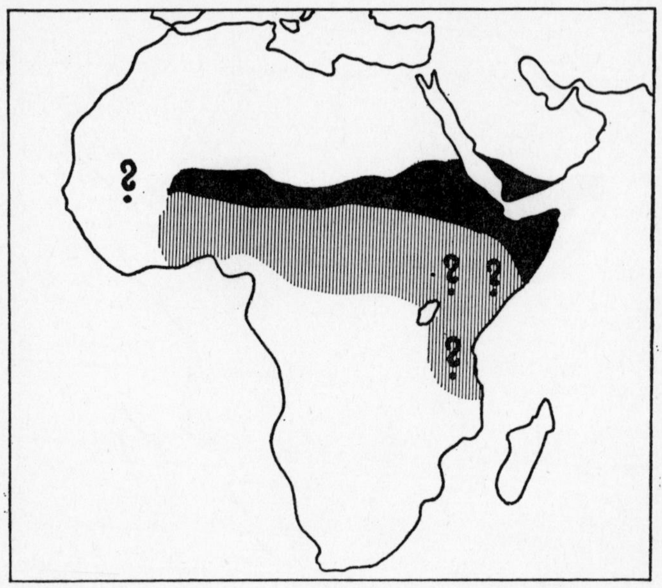

Fig. 56. Migrations of the plain nightjar (*Caprimulgus inornatus*). Question marks indicate the probable extent of the breeding area. After Chapin, 1932, modified.

The flights of these birds are confined to the same hemisphere, but other species winter across the equator. Abdim's stork (*Sphenorynchus abdimi*) is found in most parts of Africa south of the Sahara, but it nests only along the band extending east from Senegal to the Red Sea, thus avoiding the forests of Central Africa and Guinea. This stork arrives in its breeding territory with the first rains and nests from May to September. At the close of the wet season it begins the long flight to southern Africa, crossing the savannahs of East Africa as well as the great equatorial forest (Fig. 57). It 'winters' from Tanganyika through most of southern Africa. In February the stork starts north again, moving through the Congo in March and April, on its way back to the breeding area.

Other birds nest in the southern but winter in the northern hemisphere. This is probably true of the open-bill (*Anastomus lamelligerus*), which may be encountered in most parts of Africa south of the Sahara, although its nesting grounds seem to be in the southern part of

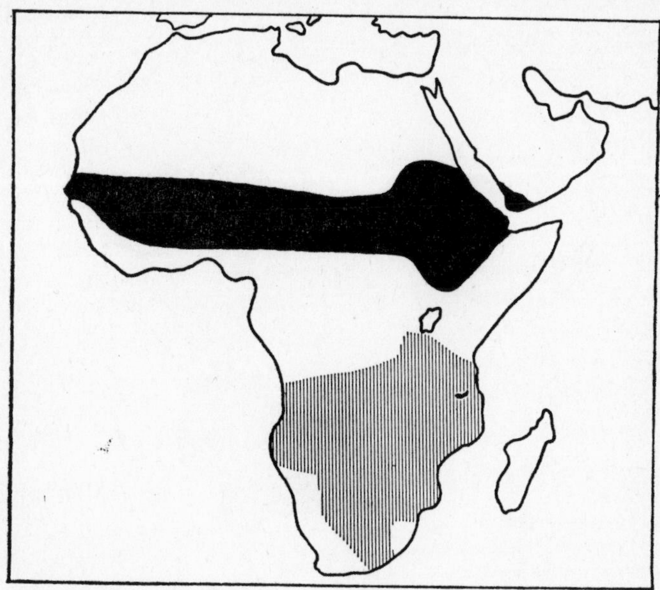

Fig. 57. Transequatorial migrations of Abdim's stork (*Sphenorhynchus abdimi*). After Chapin, 1932, modified.

the continent (June–August). As soon as the young have grown, it spreads northward as far as North-west Africa (Sierra Leone); the seasonal flights of this bird are not, however, clearly understood and will require further study.

A nightjar with long quill feathers, the pennant-wing nightjar (*Cosmetornis vexillarius*), performs similar migrations (Fig. 58). This is of particular interest, as it shows the influence exerted on migratory behaviour by diet and the quantity of food available at various seasons. Although this nightjar inhabits most sections of Africa (it is very rare in the extreme west), nesting is confined to the region south of the great equatorial forest, from Angola to Damaraland, and from Tanganyika to the Transvaal. It breeds at the beginning of the rainy season, from September to December. This is the period of greatest abundance of insects, especially of winged termites, which are a favourite food for the young. Once the brood is reared, the nightjars start north, apparently following the onset of the rainy season from place to place and, of course, feeding on the insect swarms caused by these rains. The birds reach the Congo in February and March and

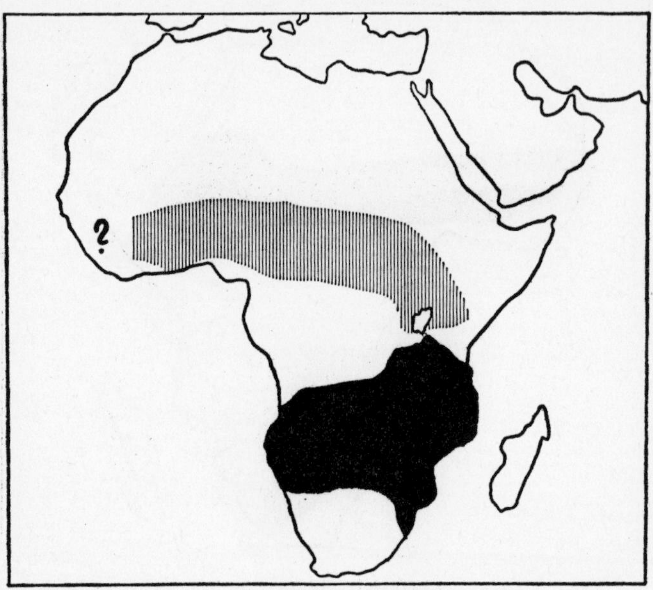

Fig. 58. Transequatorial migrations of the pennant-winged nightjar (*Cosmetornis vexillarius*). After Chapin, 1932, modified.

stay until August in the savannah countries, from Nigeria to Uganda, where they moult. In September they hurry towards their southern breeding territories (some seem to start as early as July).

Migrations are thus performed by nesting birds in both hemispheres, but the dates of the flights are reversed. This is especially true of two closely related species of carmine bee-eaters (some authors put them in the same species), one of which (*Merops nubicus*) nests in the northern, the other (*M. nubicoides*) in the southern hemisphere. *Merops nubicus* nests in a broad strip of land stretching from Senegal to the Red Sea. Its breeding period generally extends from March to August, when the bird goes south, but it does not travel far beyond the equator, except in East Africa (Fig. 59).

The southern form (*Merops nubicoides*) nests throughout a large part of southern Africa to Portuguese East Africa and north to Angola. It reaches the breeding areas between September and November, nests, then starts north in March. From April to July it is found in Tanganyika and the southern Congo.

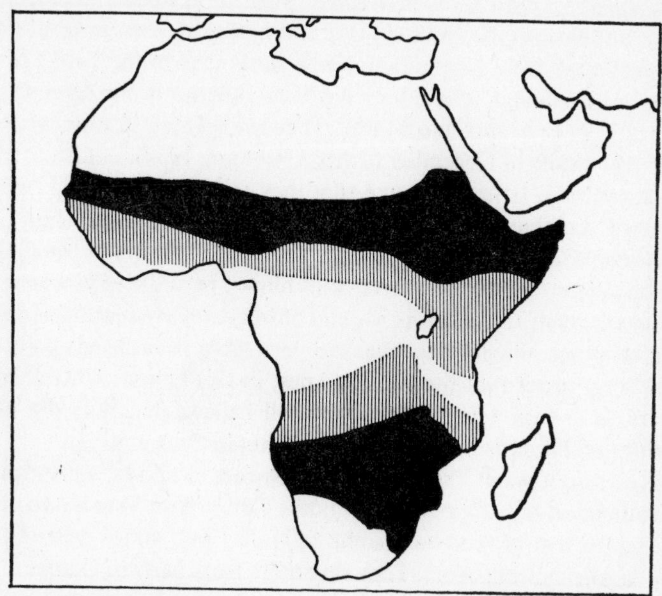

Fig. 59. Migrations of the carmine bee-eater (*Merops nubicus*), a species of the northern, and of the southern carmine bee-eater (*Merops nubicoïdes*), a species of the austral hemisphere. After Chapin, 1932, modified.

The birds so far discussed represent only the principal types of migrants. Doubtless many other African species perform migratory flights that are similar to one or another of them. Various water-birds, for example, make seasonal journeys which are so regular that they can be called migrations. To this category belong the reed cormorants (*Phalacrocorax africanus*), the darters (*Anhinga anhinga*) and certain ducks. Web-footed birds, storks and ibises are abundant on the upper Congo in July (the dry season) but disappear almost completely in December. These flights are doubtless explained by seasonal variations in the level of rivers and ponds. Low water makes it easier for fish-eating birds to find their favourite prey, while shore-birds like dry sand-banks. All these species disappear as soon as the waters rise in the rainy season.

The same pattern is followed by certain species which nest in river banks. The best example is the African river martin (*Pseudochelidon eurystomina*), a bird whose systematic position is somewhat puzzling, as it is attached to the swallows (Hirundinidae) but has some affinities to wood-swallows (Artamidae). These birds nest in the banks of the Congo and Ubangi, where they dig long galleries in the sand during low water in February and March. They are on their nesting territory from the middle of December to April (Chapin, 1954), but leave when the water rises. It was assumed that they migrated, but their 'winter quarters' remained a secret until 1951, when Rougeot (*personal communication*) found a colony of these aberrant swallows in the Gabon coastal region, where the natives told him of periodic appearances of the birds, which arrive before the end of May and live in tunnels dug in sand or other alluvial deposits. No eggs have been discovered, and there is no proof that the swallows nest in this region. Until there is reason to change our opinion, we shall believe that they dig holes similar to their nests but only to take shelter in them at night.

At present it seems likely that these aberrant swallows 'winter' in the coastal region of Gabon and the middle Congo from the mouth of the Nyanga to that of the Niari, some 600 miles west-south-west of their only known nesting areas. They stay there from May to October. It is curious that these birds should live in what appear to be nests, and one may wonder whether they are nesting for a second time. Obviously there is much still to be learned about the migrations of these swallows.

In addition to these fairly well-defined types of migrations, there are short but regular, rhythmic flights. This is true even within the great rain forest, although marked sedentarism is one of the characteristics of birds native to this region. Among the Congo birds, the splendid starling, *Lamprocolius splendidus*, flies back and forth periodically. Chapin recorded that from the beginning of October to the end of February it is absent from the wooded areas of Ituri but appears farther north, near the end of the forest. Such behaviour is doubtless due to changing local conditions.

Madagascar

We shall not discuss Palearctic migrants that simply winter in Madagascar. They include some small shore-birds: *Charadrius hiaticula*, *Ch. leschenaulti*, *Ch. mongolus*, *Squatarola squatarola*, *Erolia testacea*, *E. minuta*, *Crocethia alba*, *Totanus nebularia*, *T. ochropus*, *T. hypoleucos*, *Xenus cinereus*, *Arenaria interpres*, *Numenius arquata*, *N. phaeopus*, *Limosa lapponica*, Eleanora's falcon and some European barn and bank swallows.

The avifauna of Madagascar, like that of Africa, includes a number of migrants, some of which are endemic breeding species that winter elsewhere. Lavauden (1929) thought that he detected local movements on the island, and he refers to a 'shift' between the low eastern forest and the high western plateaus. It is true that the large eastern forest is very moist, and he states that, when the rainy season arrives, some birds, such as the kirombo courol (*Leptosomus discolor*) and the cuckoo shrike (*Graucalus cinereus*), leave it to seek the much drier high plateaus or western forests. Later observers, especially the Franco-Anglo-American Expedition, directed by Delacour, have not confirmed these observations (Rand, 1936). Flocks of insectivorous birds like kites and pied crows will follow swarms of locusts, and the rise and fall of the rivers cause local movements among aquatic birds, but these have neither the length nor the regularity ascribed to them by Lavauden.

There are, however, five species of birds which leave Madagascar to spend the austral winter in Africa. One is the Madagascar broad-billed roller (*Eurystomus glaucurus*), a species related to, but easily distinguished from, its African counterpart. This bird nests during October, at the beginning of the rainy season. It remains in Madagascar until March, when it migrates past the Comoro Islands and the Mozambique Channel (the Sakalava fishermen, hunting turtles at night, know these birds and identify them by their characteristic croaking calls) towards East Africa (Tanganyika) and the Congo (Kasai and Uele), where Chapin observed it from June to November (Fig. 60). As the advance guard returns to Madagascar at the end of September, at the time of the first rains, the natives called this species the 'thunder bird' (*fitilimbaratra*).

The Madagascar cuckoo (*Cuculus poliocephalus rochii*) migrates in much the same fashion. It nests in Madagascar, usually between August and December, and then goes to East Africa, even to the eastern Congo, according to Chapin, who often observed it there

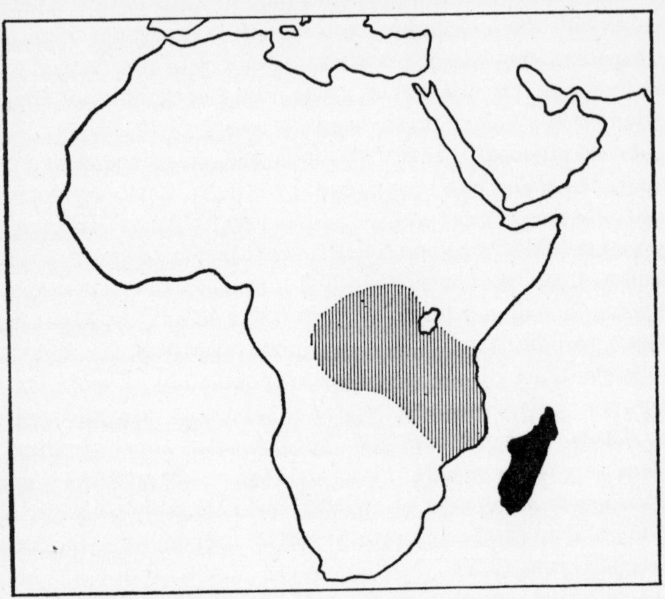

Fig. 60. Migrations of the broad-billed roller of Madagascar (*Eurystomus gl. glaucurus*). After Chapin, 1932, modified.

between June and September. In August or September it returns to the island, and the natives say that the bird heralds the season when they must clear the swamps to plant rice.

It should be observed that the migration dates of this cuckoo are not very precise. Some birds remain in East Africa after the majority have returned to Madagascar. Furthermore, that the migration is only partial may be assumed from the capture in late May of an individual on the east coast of the island by the Franco-Anglo-American Expedition. It is possible that some birds spend the whole year in the rain forests of the East, while those living in the West show a more migratory tendency, since seasonal differences there are more clearly marked.

Study of the migrations of this cuckoo can perhaps shed light on the origins of some Madagascar birds. We know that this cuckoo does not belong to the nesting fauna of Africa but that it is very closely related to *Cuculus p. poliocephalus* of India and China, from which it is distinguished by minor differences. The Madagascar cuckoo evidently originated in Asia but now migrates only towards Africa. This is at variance with the hypothesis that birds, in their annual migrations, follow paths along which the species advanced in post-glacial times, when they were extending their range. The theory does not apply to the Madagascar cuckoo, in any case.

It should be noted that the Asiatic race leaves its breeding area to winter in more southern regions (southern India, Ceylon, Indochina), but that it is seen occasionally in East and South Africa. The numbers vary considerably from year to year, so the exact importance of Asiatic migrants can not be determined without recognition of subspecies.

A somewhat similar problem arises in the case of the Madagascar bee-eater (*Merops s. superciliosus*), whose migrations are difficult to understand. Part of the Madagascar population is more or less sedentary or only wanders about the island. Other segments winter in East Africa, from Eritrea to the Zambesi, after breeding on Madagascar in September and October. Still another segment comprises a small number of bee-eaters which nest in Kenya in May and June and on Pemba Island in August and September (Mackworth-Praed and Grant, 1952).

This bee-eater arrives in Africa just as another race, *M. s. persicus*, which nests from the Caspian Sea to north-western India, is leaving its winter quarters in East Africa to nest in the northern hemisphere! The two forms, one of the northern, and one of the southern hemisphere, thus alternately occupy the same 'winter' quarters.

The sooty falcon (*Falco concolor*) of Madagascar also migrates to Africa during the dry season (hence the Sakalava name *tsiasara*, 'he who is not seen during the dry season'). Rand (1936) declares that the bird is abundant during the rainy season, between 13 November and 5 April.

Finally the Madagascar squacco heron (*Ardeola idae*), which nests on that island between October and December, 'winters' between June and October from the Congo to Uganda, Kenya and Tanganyika. Its migration seems much more regular than that of the birds we have just discussed.

East Asia

Regular migrations also occur in East Asia. Special mention should be made of the vertical migrations performed by many Himalayan birds which inhabit high or middle altitudes. The record seems to be held by the white-capped water redstart (*Chaimarrornis leucocephalus*), which lives along mountain torrents and nests as high as 16,000 feet. It descends before winter to the foothills of the Himalayas and even to the Indian plains. Some nesting birds of the Himalayas make much longer overland flights, such as the lesser cuckoo, *Cuculus p. poliocephalus*, which winters in East Africa, Ceylon and Indochina.

Much less is known about the migrations of birds nesting in the tropical regions of South-east Asia. They are far more difficult to study because of the climatic diversity and the differences in the timing of dry and wet seasons that often occur in adjacent areas. The influence of the monsoon is complex, and it varies to a certain degree from year to year. Real migrations are therefore doubtless less frequent than in other tropical parts of the world; many species merely wander, and the importance of this should not be exaggerated. Some birds have been called 'local migrants' merely because they had not been observed at the time when they were believed to disappear. The common hawk-cuckoo, *Cuculus varius*, for example, a sedentary bird that nests almost everywhere on the Indian Peninsula, ceases to utter its characteristic call after the breeding period, so it was thought that the bird had left the nesting territory.

Some birds, however, are true migrants, if only on a small scale, and every regional fauna contributes valuable information which, when assembled, will eventually provide data for a synthesis of the migratory cycles of the avifauna inhabiting the area. Several examples will suffice to show how widespread migration is. According to David-Beaulieu (*personal communication*), the Indian whistling duck (*Dendrocygna javanica*), which nests from India and China to Malaya, reaches Tranninh, Laos, in May and leaves in November, after the breeding period. The blue-winged pitta (*Pitta moluccensis*), which nests in Burma, Siam and Indochina, goes to the Greater Sunda Islands in autumn (October).

According to Delacour (1929), some green pigeons belonging to the genera *Treron* and *Sphenocercus*, parakeets, dollar-birds, drongos, nightjars and bee-eaters wander in a more or less regular fashion through southern China and Indochina. Certain Malayan birds also have a migratory pattern, although this situation is more complex.

South and Central America

The seasonal movements of birds that nest in warm regions of the New World are even less clearly understood than those of the Old (Zimmer, 1938). We have much to learn about the biology of neotropical birds, as well as about the climatology of these regions, which influences the migrations of their fauna.

Dry and wet seasons alternate in part of the Amazon basin, as in tropical zones of the Old World. This climatic cycle causes some of the avifauna to make regular flights of varying length, which are comparable to migrations. At certain times of the year, particularly in Paraguay and south-eastern Brazil, a temporary regional abundance of food induces insectivorous birds to nest, after which they must go elsewhere to find food. When differences occur within a single species, it is possible to distinguish both migratory and sedentary races. Among the Tyrannidae, the varied flycatcher (*Empidonomus varius varius*) nests between September and February, chiefly in northern Argentina, Paraguay, and southern Brazil, but 'winters' in Guiana, northern Brazil, Venezuela, Colombia and eastern Peru, where it arrives in March. Its tropical representative, *E.v. rufinus*, however, which lives from the Amazon to Guiana and Venezuela, is sedentary in those regions that have a more constant climate. Similar cases occur among several other forms.

Certain birds that are essentially vegetarian also travel in search of favourable climatic and feeding conditions. The humming-birds (*Trochilidae*) found in the tropical regions of South America, especially south-eastern Brazil, appear when certain plants flower, as they feed on the nectar. As yet, unfortunately, we do not know exactly where they go after the blossoming season. In northern Chile the evening humming-bird (*Rhodopis vesper atacamensis*), which lives in desert country bordering the Pacific, also makes seasonal flights that are timed according to the flowering of specific plants.

The moist Amazon basin shows much less seasonal change, and, as in the rain forests of the Old World, native birds are generally sedentary. Periodic climatic differences do, however, influence the avifauna, and a careful study of bird distribution in this part of the world would probably produce some surprises, as climatic uniformity is not nearly so stable as it seems, and even slight differences of weather or water-levels probably cause short movements. This is doubtless true of water-birds, which seem to perform local migrations like those of African species.

According to Spruce (1908), wood storks (*Mycteria americana*) make regular flights between the Amazon and the Orinoco, so these birds are always on river-banks when the water is at its lowest level. On the upper course of the Napo River, wood ibises fly north in November and return south in May. Since ducks apparently accompany them, the phenomenon must be fairly common. We are justified, however, in wondering whether this is not merely a dispersion, as the birds gather to breed in certain spots and scatter during the period of sexual inactivity. The matter deserves more careful study.

While Central America is the chief winter territory for migrants from North America, the vast majority of nesting birds are sedentary. Only a few delicate forms 'winter' in more southern regions; these include several Tyrannidae (*Legatus*, *Myodynastes*) and the yellow-green vireo (*Vireo flavoviridis*), which nests from Mexico to Costa Rica and winters in the Upper Amazon. It appears in the northern part of the breeding range about the beginning of April and leaves in early September. This bird crosses the Colombian Andes in both spring and autumn, and its long flights show that seasonal migrations extend throughout all the tropical American countries.

At times, migrants of the same species from north and south replace one another in a specific winter zone, somewhat like the bee-eaters in East Africa. According to Zimmer (1938), the red-eyed vireo (*Vireo olivaceus — V. virescens*) and related forms have such a vast territory that migratory races from North America spend the northern winter in tropical areas, where they are replaced by migratory races from southern South America, coming north to avoid the cold southern 'winter.' Furthermore, the common winter quarters is also inhabited by sedentary populations of the same species.

Little is yet known about migrations in the West Indies, but there seem to be regular flights from one island to another. The violet-eared dove (*Zenaida auriculata stenura*) which usually inhabits the southern

Antilles, especially Grenada and the Grenadines, goes north at certain periods, probably to hunt for seeds, and occasionally strays to Martinique (Pinchon and Bon Saint Come, 1952).

Some birds of the West Indies, particularly vireos and kingbirds, seem to touch the American continent. The black-whiskered vireo (*Vireo altiloquus*) nests in many of the West Indian islands but winters in Colombia, Venezuela, and even in the Amazon Basin. Only a fraction of the population remains in some of the Lesser Antilles. The grey kingbird (*Tyrannus dominicensis*), which breeds in the Greater Antilles and the Bahamas, as well as in Florida and Venezuela, winters in South America. The common nighthawk (*Chordeiles minor gundlachi*) nests in Cuba and winters in South America. But many detailed observations are needed to amplify these fragmentary data.

Although migrations of tropical birds are certainly not so extensive as those of birds in temperate regions, some are well-marked, whereas others can scarcely be distinguished from local nomadism.

Tropical migrants are chiefly birds of the savannahs and waterbirds. Forest birds, particularly those of the equatorial rain forest, are much more sedentary. The more striking climatic changes which induce seasonal migrations evidently occur in the savannahs. It is almost certain that alimentary factors trigger these migrations, since insects and vegetation are subject to cyclical seasonal variations that are bound to influence the birds dependent upon them. Some species of birds make transequatorial migrations, which, for geographical and climatic reasons, are particularly striking in Africa. Other birds, on the contrary, seem to move across only a few degrees of latitude.

It is possible that climate, especially heat and cold, exerts a direct influence on inter-tropical migration. As Scholander *et al.* (1950) showed, tropical birds are extremely sensitive to changes in temperature. This physiologist demonstrated that the critical gradient of manakins and widow-birds is extremely low (often only 18° F.) in relation to that of animals of temperate and cold countries. As they have a very narrow zone of thermo-neutrality, together with an extreme sensitivity to slight temperature changes, it is possible that they react to small variations in tropical temperature as keenly as do most species in cold and temperate countries to the great seasonal changes on their breeding grounds. That might help to explain the migratory impulse in tropical birds. In any case, it cannot be due, as in the temperate and arctic zones, to changes in photo-periodicity, because seasonal fluctuations in the length of daylight are so slight in equatorial regions (see p. 311).

CHAPTER 7

Sea-bird Migrations

Sea-birds, like their terrestrial counterparts, migrate to avoid winter, and some of them make the longest avian journeys known. A distinction must, however, be made between birds of the high seas – the only ones we shall examine here – and coastal birds. Many species well-known along the shore remain in the zone of the continental shelf, where they find an abundant supply of food. A number of guillemots, auks, cormorants, gannets and gulls generally stay in the continental marine zone.

Pelagic birds, most of which belong to the order Procellariiformes, the petrels and albatrosses, behave quite differently. These birds glide majestically on long, narrow wings over the high seas and come to land only to nest, usually on islands or atolls lost amid the oceans. The basic principle of their flight involves wind velocities at different altitudes, those at wave level being relatively static. The birds can thus cover great distances with no real exertion and no apparent fatigue. It also explains how, from a few small nesting areas, they are able to roam over a large part of the world's oceans.

Pelagic species often perform enormous seasonal flights up and down the latitudes of our planet, whereas coastal sea-birds usually skirt the continents, and few of them travel far out over the ocean. The migration pattern of the British gannet is a good illustration. The laughing gull (*Larus atricilla*), which breeds along the Atlantic coasts of the U.S.A. and California, winters within sight of the coast from the southern United States to Brazil in the Atlantic and from Mexico to Peru in the Pacific. And in Australia the silver gull (*Larus novaehollandiae*) moves north along the coasts in winter. Carrick, Wheeler and Murray (1957) recorded that individuals banded in the colonies of the east coast were recovered a maximum of 800 miles north of the banding site; the young go farther than the adults, which have not been found more than 200 miles from the area where they were banded.

The South American coast is the scene of similar flights, especially along the Pacific, where the Humboldt or Peruvian current brings cold water with a great abundance of food into the equatorial zone, thus permitting migrant sea-birds to make regular northward flights. Off West Africa, the Benguella current goes north as far as Cape Lopez in Gabon and, in the dry season in early June, it carries birds like the Cape gannet (*Morus capensis*) and the Damara tern (*Sterna balaenarum*), which return in October and November, often after moulting, to their breeding territory in South Africa (Rougeot, 1959).

Several species belonging to groups with a 'littoral' distribution, like kittiwakes and skuas among the Laridae, can, nevertheless, migrate over the high seas. Terns also prefer the ocean, and the Arctic tern makes very long migrations between the two 'lands of the midnight sun.'

It is exceedingly difficult to study the migrations of oceanic birds, for, with a few exceptions, like Lockley's systematic banding of Manx shearwaters on Skokholm Island, very few birds of the high seas are banded. In most cases recoveries are even rarer and harder to interpret than among land-birds.

Most of our knowledge about the seasonal flights of sea-birds is therefore based on observations and censuses undertaken in different parts of the oceans at various times of the year. For the Atlantic, the logs of a number of ornithologists, including Jespersen (1930), are especially important. No single observer can supply information that will give an accurate idea of the movements of birds over the high seas, but the methodical collation and comparison of many records furnish a very interesting picture. The monograph of Brian Roberts (1940) on the Wilson's petrel is a model of this kind.

Sea-birds have a highly developed sense of direction. Banding records show that breeding birds of various species return year after year, not only to the same island but even to the same nesting burrow.

Kittiwake

The migrations of coastal birds are discussed elsewhere. Here we shall begin with some sea-birds which do not belong to the order Procellariiformes. The kittiwake (*Rissa tridactyla*), unlike other Laridae, comes to the coast only at the breeding season and then leaves for the open ocean, where it spends most of the year. The bird is very seldom found over fresh water.

Its breeding territory extends across northern Canada, northern Siberia, Greenland, the British Isles, France and Scandinavia (another race, *R.t. pollicaris*, which we shall not consider here, nests on the shores of eastern Siberia and the Aleutian Islands and winters in California and Japan).

Atlantic kittiwakes leave the high seas about the middle of June and are then observed only around the nesting areas. Even immature birds about a year old, which are easy to recognize in flight because of their different colour pattern, sometimes stay with adults near the breeding colonies, although they themselves do not nest. Russian banding records, however, have shown that juvenile birds from colonies on the Murman coast of Russia spend their second summer on the western coast of Greenland, and do not return to their native land until later. Their return to the high seas begins in mid-August but may continue until October. Kittiwakes are then spread all over the North Atlantic. Generally speaking, they are found from November to April in a vast area extending from 60° lat. N. – at least in the eastern, and probably also in the western Atlantic – to the Tropic of Cancer and the Sargasso Sea. They occur most abundantly between 40° and 55° lat. N., and the most southerly records are from Jamaica and the Cape Verde Islands.

Several migrating groups of kittiwakes may be distinguished. Some go south; others, particularly those from western Siberia and Russian Lapland, migrate in autumn from east to west. Dementiev (1946, 1955) showed that they move slowly westward over the North Atlantic, and, although a small number do not go beyond the seas bordering Europe, the majority cross the ocean to Iceland, Greenland, and even North America, especially Newfoundland, where some birds, particularly young ones, have been banded in their nesting colonies near the Murman coasts (Kharlov Island), and recovered several months later. Likewise, birds banded on their nests in the British Isles have been recovered in North American coastal waters.

Jaegers and Skuas

The most notable oceanic migrations among other Lariformes are those of the jaegers. Although very little information is available, it seems certain, as Wynne-Edwards stated (1935), that these birds winter on the high seas after nesting along the northern coasts, and, as a result, their migrations were long a mystery. The long-tailed jaeger (*Stercorarius longicaudus*), which nests along the arctic coasts of America and Eurasia, moves south on migration as far as the coast of West Africa and the west coast of South America, from Peru to Chile. A very few birds follow the coasts, even flying overland. The autumn migration begins at the end of July and continues through August and September (by October a number of birds have reached the latitude of Argentina and Chile). Spring migration continues until May.

The migrations of the pomarine jaeger (*Stercorarius pomarinus*) follow the same pattern, but, after nesting along the arctic coasts of America and Eurasia, this bird winters even farther south, off West Africa, and throughout a good part of the South Atlantic and the South Pacific, especially along both South American coasts.

A favourite wintering zone is south of the Cape Verde Islands. Oceanographic conditions there are particularly favourable because the cold current (Canaries Current) and the upwellings of cold water bring up marine organisms on which the birds feed. Some pomarine jaegers also seem to winter in the Gulf of Mexico.

Migration begins in the Atlantic on the American side, where, according to Wynne Edwards, it occurs later than in the case of the long-tailed jaeger. Another two or three weeks pass before it starts in the eastern Atlantic, and it reaches peak proportions at the latitude of Portugal in mid-September.

Some Atlantic pomarine jaegers cross the Isthmus of Panama to winter over the Pacific Ocean, as in the case of the phalaropes (red and northern phalaropes), small Charadriidae that nest in the circumboreal region and winter south as far as Patagonia and New Zealand. They must travel very rapidly, for their migration begins in July, and the first arrivals reach the latitude of Buenos Aires by mid-August.

Their flights are also almost entirely pelagic (Wynne Edwards reports having seen them 500 miles from shore). They spend the winter in well-defined zones on the high seas.

The migratory pattern of the parasitic jaeger is much the same. After nesting in arctic and subarctic zones, it flies far south to winter at the Cape of Good Hope, and off the coast of Australia and Chile.

The winter flights of the great skua (*Catharacta s. skua*) are more nomadic than migratory. Less arctic than the preceding species, the bird nests in Iceland, the Faroes, Shetlands and Orkney Islands, where it is found both summer and winter along the coasts and on the open sea. In winter it spreads south to the Sargasso Sea, where Jespersen observed it, and around Madeira. At the same season it is observed in all European waters, but, in general, the great skua is more common in the western Atlantic. Unlike other skuas, which usually stay in groups, it leads a solitary existence, and more than two or three of these birds are seldom seen together.

Arctic Tern

The migrations of the Arctic tern (*Sterna paradisea*=*S. macrura*) are, no doubt, among the most striking in the entire avian world (Austin, 1928, Küllenberg, 1947; Storr, 1958). This bird, which nests along the northern coasts of Europe, Asia, and North America (it probably nests farther north than any other bird), spends the winter in the extreme southern Atlantic and Pacific, occasionally even beyond the antarctic circle. These enormous flights, covering up to 10,000 miles, made Forbush say (*in* Murphy, 1936) that this tern, which spends the northern summer in the land of the Eskimos and the northern winter along the shores of Antarctica, sees the sun for a longer time each year than any other creature on earth. 'For about eight months of the year it has twenty-four hours of daylight, and during the other four months, more daylight than darkness' (Fig. 61).

The most remarkable fact, as O. L. Austin, Jr. has shown, is that the Arctic tern seems to migrate in a very definite direction. The autumn flight of American and European populations moves down the eastern half of the Atlantic. Even terns nesting in North America first cross the Atlantic from west to east, thus avoiding the warm waters of the western Atlantic, and follow the coast of western Europe, as shown by one individual banded in Labrador and later recovered at La Rochelle, France.[1] Birds nesting in both America and Europe migrate south from the north European coast (individuals banded in America were

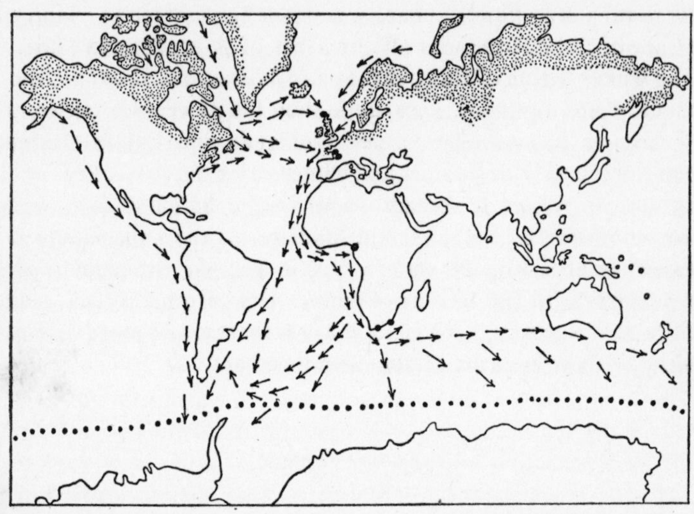

Fig. 61. Migrations of the Arctic tern (*Sterna paradisaea*). The dotted northern zones are the breeding grounds; arrows indicate the general directions of post-nuptial migration. Dots show the recovery points of individuals banded in North America. The line of large dots reveals the northern limits of Antarctic pack-ice. After Lincoln, 1935 b; Küllenberg 1947 and Storr 1958.

recovered along the western and southern coasts of Africa, in Nigeria and even in Natal)[2] and spend the northern winter in the South

1. This downy young Arctic tern, which O. L. Austin banded 22 July, 1927, at Turnevik Bay, Labrador, was recovered 1 October, 1927, at La Rochelle. There have been similar cases, such as a young bird banded 20 July, 1935 at Machias Seal Island, New Brunswick, and recovered 8 October, 1935, near St. Nazaire, France.

2. Some of these recoveries are as follows:

A downy young banded 23 July, 1928 (by O. L. Austin) at Turnevik Bay, Labrador, was recaptured 14 November, 1928, at Margate, near Port Shepstone, Natal, South Africa.

A non-flying juvenal banded 5 July, 1947, at Machias Seal Island, New Brunswick (by Hawksley), was recaptured 10 November, 1948, near Wilderness, Eastern Cape Province, South Africa. A downy young, banded 3 July, 1913, at Eastern Egg Rock, Maine, was found dead in August, 1917, in the Niger River delta, West Africa.

Atlantic. Autumn migration seems to begin at the end of July and continues into October, with September the peak month in European latitudes.

The return flight in the spring generally follows the eastern coasts of South and North America, but a number of birds also travel along the shores of Africa; they begin to arrive in Europe in April and disperse through the eastern part of their habitat, whereas some others probably recross the Atlantic to nest in arctic America. Very little information is available on the exact routes of this prenuptial migration.

Although Arctic terns cross the ocean, their style of flight does not seem adapted to such a long, difficult journey. Travelling singly or in groups numbering up to twenty or twenty-five birds, they never move resolutely in a straight line, like the plover, which also makes very long flights, and many other migrants. With their large wings and light weight, terns flutter somewhat erratically in the wind.

Arctic terns nesting on the Pacific coasts of North America journey south along the shore and spend the winter off the coast of South America, especially Chile and Argentina, where they may meet terns which have rested on the Atlantic coast. They seem to winter just off shore, as well as far out at sea.

There has been much discussion about the winter quarters of the Arctic tern. More than sixty years ago some birds were captured in the Weddell Sea, 64° and 66° lat. S., which led people to think that terns winter regularly in this region. At first that theory was refuted in lively fashion by various authors, who claimed that any such birds found over the Weddell Sea were vagrants. But later observations revealed that the zone of antarctic pack-ice is actually a very important 'winter quarters' for the arctic tern, probably the principal one.

Since more information on the avifauna of antarctic seas has become available, it is apparent that many arctic terns are found through this whole area, particularly in the sector south of the Indian Ocean. The discovery of arctic terns at Amsterdam Island (Paulian, 1953) and at Heard Island (Peter Young, *in litt.*), has been corro-

---

But the most spectacular recovery is that of a young bird, banded at Ikamint, in the Christianshab district of western Greenland, 8 July, 1951, and recovered 30 October, 1951, in Durban Harbour, Natal, South Africa. This flight of over 11,000 miles in less than three months is the longest so far recorded by a banded bird (Fisher and Lockley, 1954).

borated by a number of other observations in the same localities, as well as in Australia (where seven birds were recorded before 1958) and New Zealand. Since so many birds are involved, they must be part of a regular movement. In view of the fact that the arctic tern is unknown

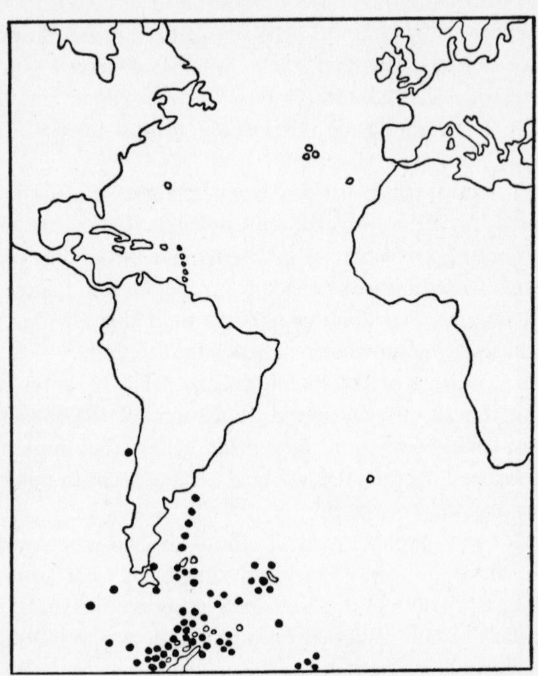

Fig. 62. Migrations of Wilson's petrel (*Oceanites oceanicus*) in the Atlantic. From Brian Roberts, 1940. Each dot indicates a record for the period.

A. January. All records are concentrated in the breeding areas. The northward movement begins.

throughout the western Pacific, between Japan and New Zealand, birds found in antarctic sectors south of the Indian Ocean and in Australia must come from the Atlantic; they are borne far east, in the zone of the 'Roaring Forties,' before they enter antarctic seas, where they spend the winter. Dunnet (1956a) confirmed this hypothesis by reporting the recovery in Australia of an arctic tern banded in the north-western part of the U.S.S.R. A young male banded 5 July, 1955, in the Kandalaksha sanctuary on the White Sea, about 125 miles from

Murmansk, was recovered eight miles south of Freemantle, Western Australia, on 16 May, 1956. This was 9,000 miles from its banding area, if the bird circled western Europe and Africa before crossing the Indian Ocean.

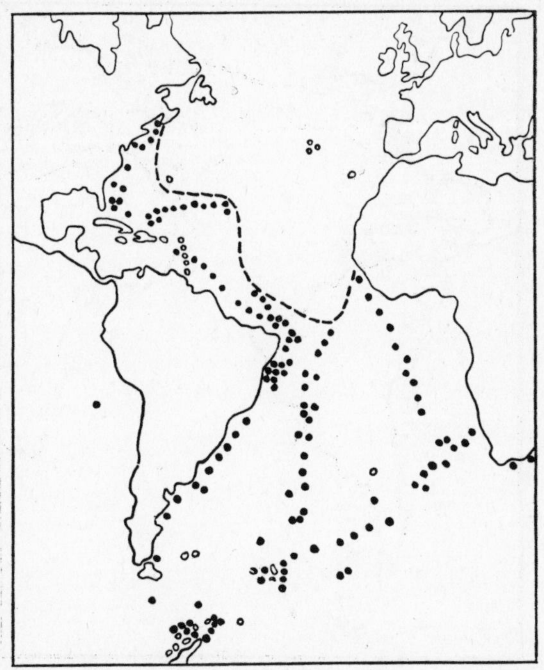

B. April. Large northward migration, which is much more rapid in the western than in the eastern Atlantic.

While arctic terns are perhaps the greatest of all bird travellers, other species also make long seasonal flights. But they follow the coasts and rarely make great pelagic voyages. The position of the arctic tern among the Sterninae is thus comparable to that of the kittiwake among the Larinae.

The common tern (*Sterna hirundo*), a familiar species closely related to the arctic tern and easily confused with it, also makes long flights but seldom goes far from the coast. European common terns winter on the shores of West and South-west Africa, from Senegambia to the Cape, while others go to Madagascar or even to the shores of

India. Yet some individuals, like arctic terns, must be driven east, at least as far as Australia, by west winds prevailing off South Africa. This may explain the recovery of a common tern banded as a nestling in Uppland, Sweden, 9 July, 1955, and recovered in Freemantle,

C. July. 'Wintering' (mid-austral winter) in the North Atlantic. A southward movement begins in the eastern Atlantic.

Western Australia, six months later (Dunnet, 1956b).

In America this tern winters along the Atlantic coast from Florida and Mexico to the Falkland Islands and the Strait of Magellan and north on the Pacific side to Ecuador. Asiatic common terns (*Sterna hirundo longipennis*) spread south to visit the eastern shores of that continent during the northern winter (Hitchcock and Favaloro, 1951).

The Sandwich tern (*Thalasseus sandvicencis*), another familiar bird along European coasts, has much the same migratory behaviour pattern, and it, too, winters on the African coasts. In this species the reproductive period is followed by an 'explosive' dispersal in every direction. Young birds, especially, scatter, and juvenile Sandwich terns from Norfolk were recaptured both south-south-west (Calvados, France) and north-north-west (Scotland). Although it is difficult to

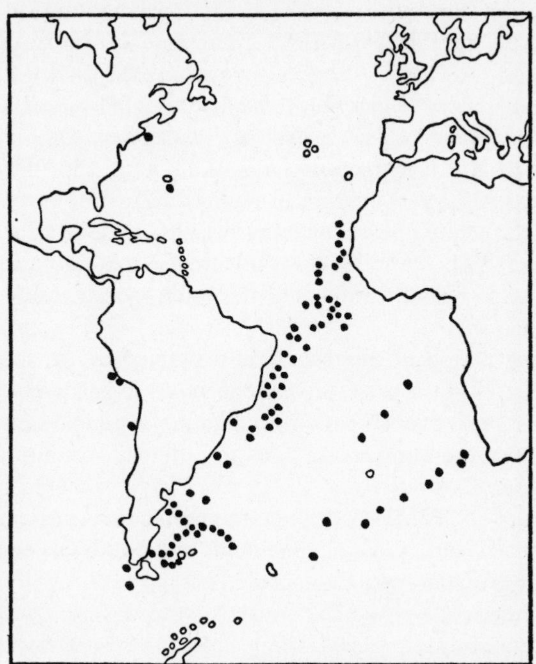

D. October. The return migration is in full swing diagonally across the Atlantic.

The migration routes indicated by these diagrams are artificial. There are numerous records along navigation lines because of the greater frequency of observations.

obtain a comprehensive picture, it is probable that among the Sandwich, and possibly some other species of terns, there is a juvenile dispersal like that of herons or other land-birds.

Wilson's Petrel

Wilson's petrel (*Oceanites oceanicus*) is a small species belonging to the group of storm petrels. Its extraordinary migrations, which show the importance of environmental factors in the migrations of sea-birds, have been admirably studied by Brian Roberts (1940). He collected scattered bits of information about this petrel, especially the typical race (*O.o. oceanicus*), which nests in the American Antarctic.

For a long time ornithologists debated the systematics and biology of this species. Bonaparte stated that individuals captured in the North Atlantic were specifically distinct from those of the Antarctic, and named them *O. wilsoni*. Other authors confused them with Leach's petrel (*Oceanodroma leucorrhoa*), which it resembles superficially, and thought that it bred only in the northern hemisphere. One of the first to surmise that the bird migrated was Audubon, who believed that Wilson's petrels breed in tropical regions and come to the Atlantic coasts of the United States at other periods. In 1918 Murphy (*Bull. Amer. Mus. Nat. Hist.*, 38:117–146) proved that the northern and southern birds belong to one and the same species, which migrates with the seasons.

This long period of uncertainty is explained by the fact that the seasonal flights of the petrel are too enormous to be imagined *a priori*. Outside the reproductive period no data are available save scattered reports about the numbers of birds in different latitudes at various seasons (Fig. 62 A–D).

In January and February these petrels nest in the American sector of the Antarctic (South Georgia, Shetlands and South Orkneys). At the end of March and in April they spread northward so rapidly that some birds are observed along the coasts of the U.S.A. The majority, travelling in groups up to 200 strong, cross the western South Atlantic (between the Brazilian coast and the Saint Paul Rocks), but a few take a more eastern route, off the African coasts. Travelling much more slowly, they are at lat. 10° N., in the vicinity of Gambia, when Wilson's petrels appear above lat. 40° N. along the American coasts.

The routes which seem traced on map B are based on frequent observations along regular navigation paths; little study has been possible in intermediate zones.

By June Wilson's petrels have left the southern hemisphere, and they are so abundant off the coasts of the U.S.A. that occasionally more than a thousand can be seen together.[1]

During July and August these petrels stay in the North Atlantic from the tropic of Cancer to lat. 49° N.; they are especially common

1. Brian Roberts (1940) states that these birds, like other Procellariiformes, were used as bait by fishermen, who sometimes captured 400 to 500 at one time.

in the whole area traversed by the Gulf Stream and off the Portuguese coast. When prenuptial migration begins in September, the birds leave the western Atlantic to travel east, then south-east. Observations in September and October reveal a great movement from west to east. In any case, the North American areas are evacuated before the birds leave European waters, but petrels have no set migration dates, and, while some tarry in the North Atlantic, others reach African waters in August. The birds then fly towards South America and to their nesting territories on antarctic islands off the southern part of that continent. Most of them arrive in November and begin to breed.

This petrel thus migrates over the whole Atlantic, making a loop in the northern part of the ocean. A comparison of its flights with prevailing winds reveals that, in most cases, the two are closely parallel (Fig. 63). Petrels are borne northward by S.E. trade winds, blowing towards America. The migration wave seems to hurry north through the warm waters of the Atlantic, probably because little food is available in the intertropical marine zone. The birds are next carried by westerly winds across the North Atlantic, where they turn around the anticyclone of the Azores; then again they are borne south-east by winds blowing off the African coast. This correlation with prevailing winds is observed among other sea-birds, particularly the arctic tern and greater shearwater.

Migratory sea-birds do not attempt to struggle against gale winds. Murphy and Vogt (1933) recorded observations of the dovekie or little auk (*Plautus alle*) which nests in the arctic circumboreal regions. During the winter this bird migrates southward, but violent tempests, like those which lashed the Atlantic coasts of North America in November and December, 1932, drove the birds to the coast and even inland. Dead and captured migrants showed every indication of a severe loss of weight, of a real 'melting away' of reserves of fat, even of muscular tissue, which in most cases soon caused death since the animals could no longer regulate their body temperature. When the storm drove the dovekies to shore, they struggled to keep from being carried inland, and this exertion exhausted them so completely that they lived only a short time.

In some years large numbers of Leach's petrel (*Oceanodroma leucorrhoa*) are driven by strong winds to the west coasts of Europe, even inland, where they appear completely exhausted on their arrival (see p. 186).

In February, 1957, a tempest struck western Europe, especially France and Great Britain (Jouanin, 1957, McCartan, 1958), and

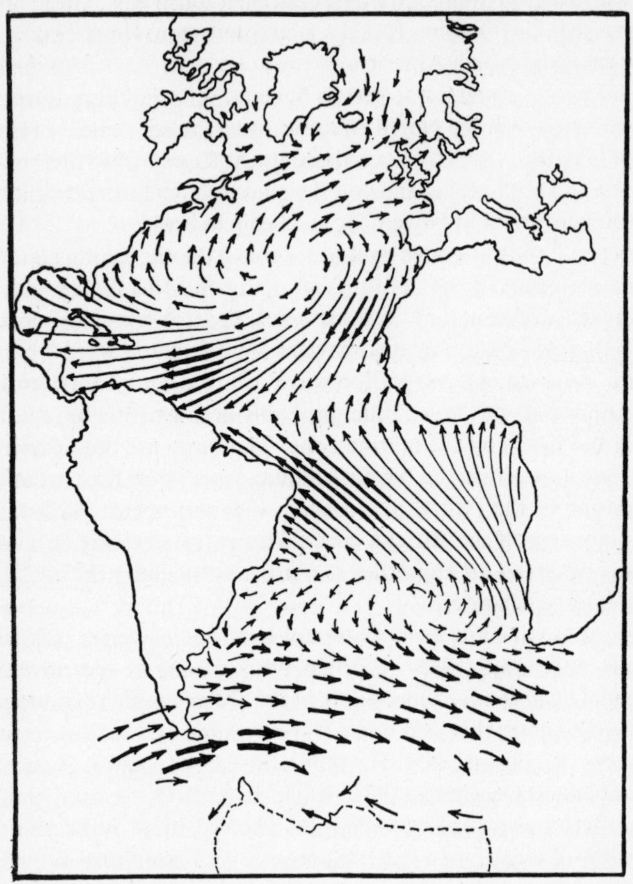

Fig. 63. Prevailing winds in the Atlantic in August. After Schott, *Geographie des Atlantischen Ozeans*. Hamburg (Boysen), 1926, simplified.

violent west winds drove many kittiwakes inland. All authors agree that these gulls were in a sorry plight and, when picked up, they were found to weigh thirty to forty per cent less than normal. Examinations made in England revealed a complete absence of fat deposits, atrophy of pectoral muscles (fatty degeneration) and of the liver (shrinkage of the cells, complete absence of glycogen, large quantities of fat). This is not because the birds were driven inland, where food was lacking, but because they were driven on to the continent when worn out from the struggle with contrary winds that weakened them and kept them from feeding in the raging sea.

Kittiwakes are liable to be driven by the wind at any time during the winter, so their density at any one point may change rapidly. This was observed on board French weather ships (Dorst, 1958) during the winter of 1956–57 at point 'Kilo,' located 45° N. and 16° W. off the Spanish coast. While normal censuses had recorded a few kittiwakes every day, in November, 1956, the birds were counted in the hundreds; then they vanished as suddenly as they had come. This was probably a kind of 'invasion,' caused by strong south and south-east winds, but it occurred on the sea so the birds were not harmed.

These observations show that sea-birds normally let themselves be carried by the winds, instead of fighting them. Furthermore, use of the wind is the basic principle of flight, especially among Procellariiformes.

Yet winds do not always govern migration. A glance at the wind map of the Atlantic shows that the movement of winds off the South American coast does not tally with the migration of Wilson's petrels (one might object that the map applies to the situation in August, which is not a period of autumn or spring migration, but prevailing winds are relatively stable there throughout the year). One must conclude that birds take advantage of a general meteorological situation whenever possible, but do not depend on it. This in no way detracts from the value of observations about the concordance of migratory movements with prevailing winds in certain regions of the Atlantic and other parts of the world.

Finally let us examine the migrations of a group of Wilson's petrels that breed in other sectors of the antarctic continent. (These birds are sometimes divided into subspecies which are difficult to distinguish.) These petrels breed in December, January and February. Migration begins in March, with the peak in April and May.[1] During the austral winter, from June to September, the bird has been observed in warm seas bordering the Old World. Most of the records are from the Red Sea and the Arabian Sea, but various observers have noted large

1. Paulian (*personal communication*) records that the birds fly north at Amsterdam Island in April and reach the breeding territories at Kerguelen Island in early December.

numbers, occasionally thousands, of these migrants throughout the whole region. It is possible that an abnormal abundance of food, occasioned by special oceanographic conditions, attracts the birds (these favourable conditions are attested by the presence of many other species of sea-birds). At times this concentration of Wilson's petrels seems as dense as it is off the American coasts.

Another group of Wilson's petrels spends the austral winter over the seas bordering New Guinea and Australia (see p. 144). Still others, taking advantage of favourable feeding conditions produced by the Humboldt or Peruvian Current, follow the Pacific coast of South America northward, but seldom go beyond lat. 8° S. Prenuptial migration begins in October, as with birds nesting in the Atlantic.

Much less is known about Leach's petrel (*Oceanodroma leucorrhoa*), a storm petrel which breeds in the northern hemisphere on both sides of the Atlantic Ocean from Massachusetts to Newfoundland, Greenland, Iceland, the British Isles and the North Pacific. During the northern winter it migrates as far as the South Atlantic and the eastern Pacific. In the Atlantic it winters in numbers along the coast of north-eastern Brazil, West Africa, and even the west coast of South Africa (these Atlantic zones, where plankton is very abundant, seem to be favourite wintering grounds for many sea-birds, among which, according to Stanford (1953), there are many red phalaropes [*Phalaropus fulicarius*]).

In autumn Leach's petrel migrates in very large numbers along the French coast. Gales often drive the birds on shore, even inland, bringing death to so many that the welfare of the nesting colonies may be affected. In October, 1952, a real invasion occurred in France and throughout western Europe. According to information checked by Jouanin (1952, 53), many individuals were captured in south-western France, as well as in Normandy and even in Paris, where one live bird was taken on the Austerlitz Bridge, near the National Museum of Natural History! Boyd (1954) estimated that at least 6,700 injured birds were found in the British Isles, all showing signs of exhaustion like the kittiwakes (particularly losses in weight up to thirty per cent). There had been no such disaster since 1891 in the British Isles. Jouanin and Boyd point to the singular coincidence between this invasion of sea-birds and a strong depression (that specialists in meteorology call D 12), which produced violent winds sweeping across western Europe from Great Britain and France. The 1952 wreck was spectacular, but 'invasions' of this kind occur quite regularly at the same season. They may even endanger the survival of the species, because nesting populations in Europe are not large (there are only 2,000 breeding pairs in the British Isles).

Shearwaters

Shearwaters, much larger Procellariiformes than Wilson's petrels, are also great travellers, which fly long distances to feed, even during their breeding period. Lockley (1942) studied the Manx shearwaters (*Puffinus puffinus*) nesting at Skokholm, in the Irish Sea, and found that these birds go daily in large flocks to find fishes and squids off the coast of Finistère and in the Bay of Biscay. Many recoveries on the French coast show that the birds often make a round trip fishing flight of 1,200 miles.

Among the most interesting migrations are those of the greater shearwater (*Puffinus gravis*), a species which roams over the whole Atlantic, from the Falkland Islands to Greenland, and whose migratory flights are circular, like those of Wilson's petrel (Fig. 64). These shearwaters nest from January to March at Tristan da Cunha. After the breeding season they fly north into the western half of the North Atlantic and, like Wilson's petrel, cross tropical seas very quickly (doubtless because little food is available). At the beginning of June they are abundant in the vicinity of the Grand Banks, off Newfoundland. They then travel to Greenland and start eastward, to reach the 'European' part of the Atlantic (Iceland, Faroes, Ireland, Scotland) in the second half of June, but it is August before they pass east of a line linking Ireland to the Azores. During this period greater shearwaters are found chiefly in the North Atlantic, north of the route taken by steamship lines between Europe and North America. In mid-August birds begin to fly south from the western part of their summer habitat, and they are often seen at that time along ship lanes of the North Atlantic. The south-bound movement is slower in the East Atlantic, where greater shearwaters tarry during October and even into November, by which time they have entirely vanished from the western ocean. At this season they are seen off the French coasts (very seldom in the English Channel). They converge over the South Atlantic on their return flight to Tristan da Cunha. That some birds do not follow this pattern is evident from recoveries made throughout the whole year in the South Atlantic, and by observations in the North Atlantic at the normal breeding period (in both instances these were non-breeding birds).

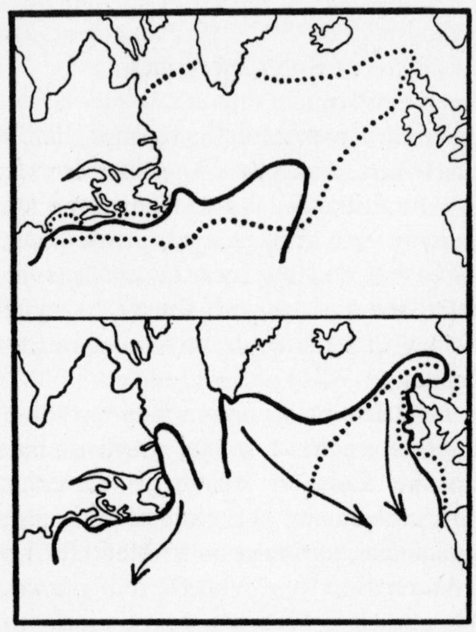

Fig. 64. Distribution of the greater shearwater (*Puffinus gravis*) in the North Atlantic at different times of the year. Northern limit of its distribution.
Above: Unbroken line: 25 May
Dotted line: 25 June
Below: Unbroken line: 20 September
Dotted line: 1 November.
Arrows indicate the principal directions of migration. From Wynne Edwards, 1935.

With the exception of this small group, and a contingent that flies directly from the western North Atlantic to Tristan da Cunha (by the same route taken on the postnuptial migration), greater shearwaters also make loop migrations. In the spring they cross the West Atlantic and then follow the European coasts, which they never visit in the autumn. In this respect the migrations of this species resemble those of Wilson's petrel.

Some authors, impressed by the correlation between the circulation of surface waters in the North Atlantic and the migrations of this shearwater, have suggested that the birds follow their food – plankton, especially fish and little cephalopods – whose movements are determined by the flow of surface waters. It seems more likely that winds are responsible for these movements, and a comparison of the birds' flights with the wind map of the North Atlantic reveals that the two are much alike, as in the case of Wilson's petrel.

Although greater shearwaters migrate in very large flocks in both spring and autumn, they disperse in the summer, though a number of birds may be present in a certain area. They formerly served as bait for fishermen on the Grand Banks, and Murphy states that from 200 to 500 were seen hanging from the rigging of a fishing-boat.

The Pacific Ocean is also the scene of cyclical flights, the most famous of which are those of the short-tailed (or slender-billed) shearwater (*Puffinus tenuirostris*), which were studied by Serventy (1953a), Marshall and Serventy (1956b) and Kuroda (1957), who also made a general study of the migration routes of sea-birds (Fig. 65). This shearwater nests in enormous colonies on the islands of Bass Strait and in neighbouring districts along the coasts of southern Australia and Tasmania. Since the beginning of the nineteenth century it has been exploited for food and as a source of oil, fat and feathers (Tasmanian 'mutton-bird'). About 1910 some 500,000 young birds were captured annually, but the population did not seem to suffer from this heavy toll.

The best description of these flocks of shearwaters was written by Flinders in 1798. He tells of a stream of birds 100 yards wide, fifty to eighty yards in depth, which flew past for an hour and a half at a speed almost equal to the flight of pigeons. Flinders believed that over 150 million birds took part in this flight (*in* Murphy, 1936). Even today this shearwater is the most common bird in Australia.

The birds appear on their nesting grounds in late September, lay their eggs at the end of November, raise their young (a single egg to a brood), and leave in April and May. They migrate across the eastern part of the Tasman Sea, go north, then north-north-west along the Japanese coasts. Recoveries of banded birds show that this journey requires about a month. These petrels cross the North Pacific from Kamchatka to the Aleutians, through Bering Strait and the Arctic Ocean to Wrangel Island (lat. 71° N.). According to Kuroda (1955), they remain there from June to August and are the most abundant

Procellariiformes in the area. On the return migration they go east and south-east along the Pacific coast of North America to California, then fly diagonally across the Pacific to north-eastern Australia, where they follow the coasts to their breeding grounds.

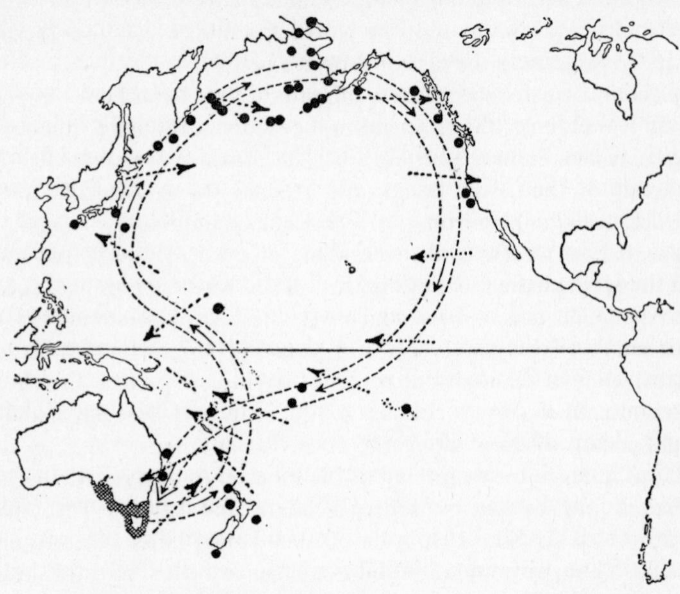

Fig. 65. Migrations of the short-tailed shearwater (*Puffinus tenuirostris*). The breeding area is hatched. Dots indicate the localities where specimens were collected. Solid arrows indicate the movements of birds, dotted arrows the direction of prevailing winds at the time when the shearwaters are migrating. After Marshall and Serventy, 1956 b, and Serventy, 1958.

These migrations are remarkable in every way. The enormous loop over the North Pacific is quite as astonishing as the regularity with which the shearwaters return to lay their eggs. At the end of September birds come back to their breeding area to prepare their burrows; they return to sea to find food early in November, but are back again about the 20th. Millions of eggs are laid during the next twelve days, most of them between 24–26 November. Commercial exploiters were aware of this exact schedule long before Marshall and Serventy made their scientific observations. The annual cycle of these birds is uniform in both the reproductive and moulting phases (see p. 283), but it is hard to explain the reasons for this calendar, especially as these shearwaters do not nest until they are six years old. A large number of young birds perform the same seasonal flights as the adults, although some remain in the North Pacific throughout the whole year.

Little was known about these almost incredible migrations of the short-tailed shearwater until recently. The noted ornithologist Dr H. H. Montgomery, former Bishop of Tasmania and father of the celebrated British field-marshal, believed this shearwater was an antarctic wanderer. But as the bird was recorded in both the North and South Pacific, many people thought there were two distinct populations, even two species. The bird of the North Pacific was called *Procellaria tenuirostris* by Temminck, and Gould described the southern form as *Puffinus brevicaudus*. Serventy established the fact that the same birds performed these gigantic seasonal migrations, and this was confirmed by banding experiments. Remarkable recoveries were made off the coast of Japan, Kamchatka, and in the North Pacific. A nestling banded at Babel Island, off Flinders Island, Tasmania, on 13 March, 1955, was recovered off Tanoura, Shikoku Island, Japan, 27 May, 1955 (Serventy, 1957).

These migrations are well adapted to the prevailing winds in these sectors of the Pacific. Serventy (1958) has published a map which reveals a striking parallel, especially in the Tasman Sea; the prevailing winds explain why these birds describe a loop on their postnuptial migration. North-east Australia is the only place where the winds are not favourable, and there shearwaters have to contend with strong south-east trades that blow all year. Occasionally there is a high mortality rate, particularly among birds only a year old that are trying to reach their ancestral breeding territory. The map of the winds and the map of these migratory flights are so similar, as in the case of the migrations of Wilson's petrel across the Atlantic, that flights and winds must be correlated.

No other migrant breeds in an area where the temperature is higher than in its 'winter quarters.' The surface temperature of the sea in Bass Strait runs about 57° – 63° F. in summer, whereas the water in the North Pacific is much colder. Kuroda found large flocks of these birds in an area where the water varied from 38° to 45° F.

This shearwater is by no means the only bird which migrates across the Pacific. The flesh-footed or pale-footed shearwater (*Puffinus carneipes*) flies north during the southern winter, the populations of

East Australia to the North Pacific, those of West Australia to the northern part of the Indian Ocean. Falla (1934) suggested that the white-faced storm petrel (*Pelagodroma marina*) may perform similar migrations, and he cites Buller's shearwater (*Puffinus bulleri*) and the sooty shearwater (*Puffinus griseus*) in a list of birds that nest in New Zealand but cross the equator.

Transatlantic as well as transpacific migrations of the sooty shearwater are well established. This bird nests in the most southerly part of South America (islands near Cape Horn), part of Chile, and subantarctic New Zealand, and 'winters' as far north as Labrador, Greenland and Europe. It appears in the North Atlantic in May, later than the greater shearwater, probably because its breeding territory is considerably farther south than Tristan da Cunha. Like the greater shearwater, this bird may depend on wind currents, which would necessitate a cyclical migration in the North Atlantic. This hypothesis seems corroborated by the fact that it visits European waters much later than North America; between August and November it appears in the eastern North Atlantic on prenuptial migration.

Among northern species, the Manx shearwater (*Puffinus puffinus*), which nests in the North Atlantic (Ireland, Faroes, British Isles, Brittany, Azores, Madeira, Bermuda), also makes long migrations. According to Lockley (1942, 1953), shearwaters nesting at Skokholm (Pembrokeshire, Great Britain) begin to fly south in August to fish for sardines, which occur in large schools at certain places along the French coasts and in the Bay of Biscay. When these schools move south in September and October, the shearwaters leave too. The majority seem to cross the equator and to spend the winter off the coasts of South America. Two recoveries corroborate this statement: one bird banded at Skokholm was recaptured in October, 1952, at Cape San Antonio, 200 miles south of Buenos Aires (a flight of 6,100 nautical miles), the other at Rio de Janeiro in November, 1951 (a distance of 5,050 nautical miles). It is probable, however, that part of the breeding population at Skokholm stays in Atlantic waters near Europe.

Colonies nesting in Ireland, northern England (the Orkneys, Shetlands), and the Faroes do not migrate to such extreme southern latitudes, but spend the winter mainly in the Bay of Biscay. This indicates that within the subspecies *Puffinus p. puffinus* there are local populations which cannot be recognized morphologically, but differ widely in migratory pattern and doubtless in other biological characteristics. Similar phenomena have been observed among other birds, like the Alcidae.

Other Species

Many other species of sea-birds make migratory flights of considerable length. The patterns are, however, not so clearly defined and, in the majority of cases, almost unknown. Some birds make important changes in latitude, but in most instances the movements resemble a dispersal rather than true migration. Flocks of Procellariiformes of the southern hemisphere, for example, nest only on some of the austral islands but migrate throughout antarctic seas.[1] One, the Cape petrel or Cape 'pigeon' (*Daption capensis*), breeds at several different places on the antarctic continent, as well as on islands south of the 40° parallel, particularly the South Shetlands, South Georgia and Kerguelen. After the breeding season it returns to sea and flies to about lat. 20° S. and even farther north when conditions permit. Cold currents, like the Humboldt Current, make it possible for the bird to go as far as Peru or even to Ecuador. In the Atlantic it seldom comes north of Cape Frio, Brazil, because a cold current assures plenty of food. No favourite routes appear in this winter dispersal, which seems based on the availability of food.

Most antarctic Procellariiformes are distributed in the same fashion. The blue petrel (*Haloboena coerulea*), which nests at Kerguelen, ranges at other seasons from the edge of the pack ice to about lat. 45° S. This huge dispersion sometimes resembles a circumpolar migration from Antarctica. Recent studies of the giant petrel (*Macronectes giganteus*), based on birds banded in various nesting colonies in the Antarctic (Downes, Gwynn and Howard, 1954; Hitchcock and Carrick, 1958; Stonehouse, 1958) show that, when young giant petrels leave the nest, they scatter widely east and north, driven by strong west winds which sweep 'the roaring forties,' and, in general, a zone 20° lat. wide (from lat. 40° to 60° S.), where most of the breeding colonies

1. This may be true of the South Polar skua (*Catharacta maccormicki*), although little is known about its migrations. Sir Edmund Hillary found this skua 80 miles from the South Pole (*in* Eklund, 1959), so it must be the most southerly of all birds.

occur. The birds are often carried to temperate, or even subtropical zones in the southern hemisphere (Fig. 66).

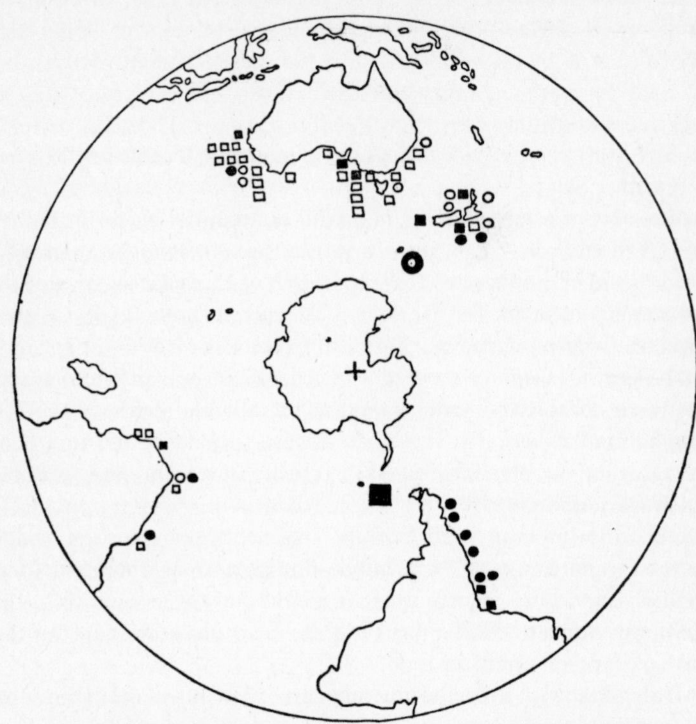

Fig. 66. Circumpolar flights of the giant petrel (*Macronectes giganteus*) as shown by banding in the Antarctic. Birds banded at Macquarie Island (a large circle) and recovered at different places in the austral hemisphere are marked by circles if they were recovered during the first winter (before July), by black dots if they were taken later. Birds banded at Signy Island, South Orkney Islands (large square) are marked by hollow squares if they were recovered during the first winter (before July) and by black squares if they were recovered later. After Hitchcock and Carrick, 1958, simplified.

Some recoveries of the giant petrel are highly spectacular. One young bird banded at Signy Island in the South Orkneys, south-east of the Falklands, was found, only five weeks after it left its nest, on the west coast of Australia, thirty miles south of Freemantle. Another young bird, banded on Heard Island, south-east from Kerguelen, was recovered eight weeks later at Buenos Aires, Argentina.

The speed and direction of these flights reveal that young giant petrels travel several times 'around the world' in the Antarctic, evidently borne by the winds that blow in these latitudes, Adults, on the other hand, are sedentary, and the majority of the birds nesting in the extreme south stay near their breeding grounds. The giant petrel is thus highly migratory in its youth but, in maturity, it settles down near the breeding colony.

Some northern birds have an equally vast winter territory. Fisher (1952) showed in striking fashion how the Fulmar (*Fulmarus glacialis*) has increased in numbers and extended its breeding area in correlation with human industry in the North Atlantic. Large flocks of this Procellariiforme breed along the coasts of the British Isles, in Iceland, Spitzbergen, Greenland and in the Canadian Arctic Archipelago (Ellesmere, Devon and Baffin Islands), to mention only this portion of its habitat. During the breeding season, from May to August in Great Britain, it is found up to 600 nautical miles from the rookeries. It then scatters widely over the whole North Atlantic, but apparently without following any special route. The bird frequents some spots, like the Grand Banks of Newfoundland, because of abundant food supplies. Its winter distribution resembles a dispersion, but the situation is difficult to describe, since the birds are found all over the North Atlantic.

Albatrosses, with the largest wing-span of any bird, usually nest on islands of the southern seas, but make tremendous flights between breeding periods. It is quite likely that these giants of the sea take advantage of prevailing west winds to circle the globe during their migrations.

Information derived from banded albatrosses is insufficient to reach any general conclusion. One can scarcely include the messages sailors attached to captive birds before releasing them. Among the very small number of recoveries of banded birds is a record of a wandering albatross (*Diomedea exulans*), which was banded near its nest on Kerguelen Island and found three years later near Cape Horn, or about 6,250 miles distant (thirty-eight per cent of the earth's circumference in that latitude).

Another wandering albatross, banded by Angot as a chick at Kerguelen 20 July, 1952, was found dead at Patache, Chile, 1 October,

1953. Angot (1954) thinks that this albatross probably left its nest about 10 December, or within three weeks of that date, and in less than ten months the bird travelled at least 8,100 miles. It is probable that it drifted with the west winds characteristic of the southern seas and then was borne north up the Pacific coast of South America. If so, the bird must have flown some 11,200 miles between the banding and recovery points.

A royal albatross (*Diomedea epomophora*), whose record was published by Sorensen (1954), was banded on Campbell Island, south of New Zealand, 4 October, 1943, and recovered about 1 April, 1944, at El Tabo in the Province of Santiago, Chile. This was not made public at the time because the band was thought to be a message from a submarine on a Pacific raid!

Little is known about the cycle of albatrosses whose larger species (wandering, royal) breed only every other year, so a number of non-breeding adult birds may be observed anywhere in the antarctic seas, without counting all the young birds. We have seen that the fulmar covered an area (radius) of 600 nautical miles around its nest during the breeding season, and a bird as large and powerful as the albatross must range even more widely. It is difficult to distinguish between flights for food, the wandering of non-breeding individuals, and true migrations.

Dixon (1933) collected some interesting records about the wandering albatross during 2,000 days of navigation south of lat. 20° S. This bird usually lives between lat. 60° S. and the Tropic of Capricorn, but, according to season, it varies very considerably in numbers in different parts of the Antarctic. Dixon reports that in the southern spring ninety-two per cent of the birds are observed between 30° and 50°, and only three per cent south of 50°; in summer seventy-three per cent are found between 30° and 50°, and 26.5 per cent south of 50°; in the austral autumn there is a definite northward movement, with 96.9 per cent between 30° and 50° and only 0.1 per cent south of 50° S.

This latitudinal shift is accompanied by a movement from west to east, parallel with the direction of the prevailing winds. In winter and spring the seas between long. 120° W. and Cape Horn are practically deserted, although in summer most of the wanderers occur in that region. In winter eighty-two per cent of the birds stay between 90° E. and 180°, but in spring one finds the largest number (73.5 per cent) farther east, between 90° E. and 90° W.; in summer sixty-seven per cent are in the seas between 180° – 90° W. and in the autumn sixty-three per cent between 90° W. and 90° E.

These percentages, which reveal the movements of the whole

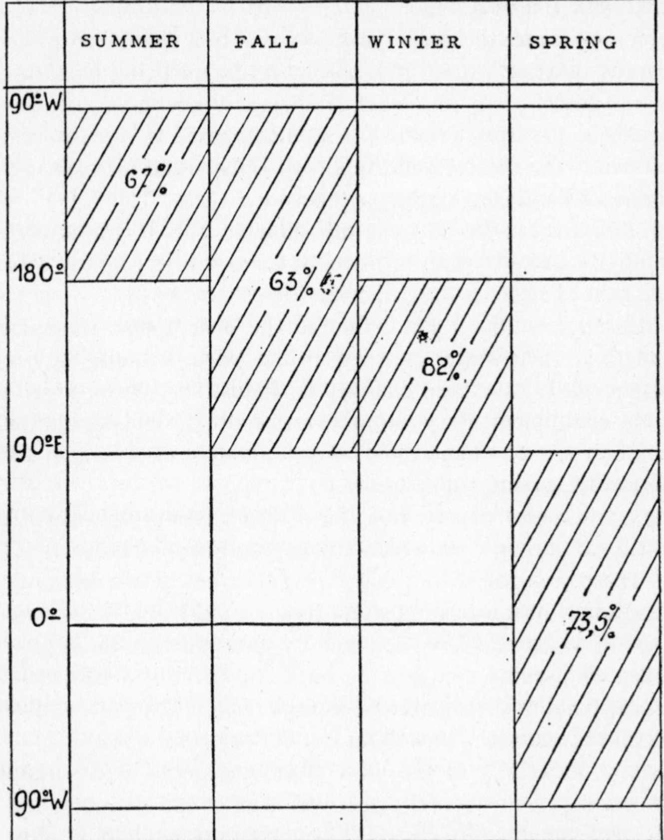

Fig. 67. Albatross distribution in the Antarctic sectors at different times of the year, after data published by Dixon, 1933. The hatched zone indicates the sector where most of the birds are found.

population, show that its centre of abundance moves from west to east according to season (Fig. 67). This seems to confirm the hypothesis, suggested by other observations and by several recoveries, that albatrosses drift around the Pan-Antarctic (Antarctica) on the west winds that circle the globe in the southern seas ('roaring forties') It is important, however, to bear in mind that Dixon's records deal with populations, not *individuals*; his results do not *prove* that the birds make a circular migration around the South Pole, although it is probable that they do so.

The importance of bonds tying a species to a definite marine zone must not be exaggerated, for sea-birds, like all living creatures, go where they will easily find food. As Fisher wisely remarked, the distribution of the arctic fulmar has been compared to the isotherms of deep water, the surface and the air, to isobars and isohyets, but no correlation has been established between them. The fulmar seeks food, and this is affected by so many factors that it is impossible to determine its relationship to physical surroundings; in any case, no single factor can control the distribution of most birds.

Artificial conditions can influence the distribution of sea-birds, especially in their winter quarters. In the North Atlantic the normal habits of birds have been changed by industrial fishing, which provides large supplementary resources and enables some populations to increase in size, to extend their habitat, and to concentrate in certain areas at various times of the year.

Navigation also plays a rôle, for a ship leaves in its wake a large quantity of garbage, on which scavenging Procellariiformes like to feed. These birds follow vessels for long distances to take advantage of such manna. Many records show how an individual shearwater or albatross, which could be identified by certain details in its plumage (broken wing-quills, spots) or by some conspicuous mark (such as a coloured band or ribbon around its neck) followed a ship for nearly a week and occasionally moved far out of its normal range.

Sailors, especially in the days of sailing ships, used to capture albatrosses and shearwaters with very simple contrivances, and the birds were sometimes released far from their normal habitat. Possibly this explains the capture of a wandering albatross at Dieppe in 1830 and another at Antwerp in 1833. Although albatrosses are capable of travelling great distances, it is nevertheless significant that few of these birds have been taken on European coasts[1] since sailors abandoned the pastime of making them prisoner. Furthermore, some albatrosses, which were captured long ago in European waters and preserved in museums, bear on their beaks scars left by the metal device used to

1. An albatross, probably an immature black-browed albatross (*Diomedea melanophrys*), was captured in August, 1952 in Derbyshire, Great Britain.

trap them. While there are authentic records of antarctic Procellariiformes in European seas, it is quite possible that human factors may make 'migrations' appear much longer than they are.

Sea-Birds Which Migrate by Swimming

The vast migrations of most sea-birds are linked to their flying ability, yet flightless birds, such as penguins, also migrate. Most of them swim north for the southern winter, but they are so difficult to observe that their migrations and winter quarters are practically unknown. Some observers, however, have seen them on the high seas; Murphy (1936) reports finding them in the South Atlantic, more than 625 miles north of South Georgia and even farther from the South American coasts. Gentoo penguins (*Pygoscelis papua*) 'passed' around the ship – like migrating birds in flight – swimming north, remaining for a long time underwater and uttering characteristic cries when they surfaced. These penguins spend the southern winter on the high seas and return to their rookeries in the austral spring, but their migration resembles a northward dispersion.

Penguins nesting on subantarctic islands with a milder climate – such as Kerguelen, Macquarie, the Falklands – disperse through nearby waters after the breeding season.

Unlike any species which flees the southern winter and comes ashore only during the summer, the emperor penguin (*Aptenodytes forsteri*), the giant and most antarctic member of the whole tribe, has a cycle which is reversed in a somewhat paradoxical fashion (see Sapin-Jaloustre, 1952, with a bibliography which was complete up to that date). When other birds desert the antarctic continent, this curious penguin settles down to breed. In May and June it lays its eggs on the sea ice (some of these birds never go on land) near spots where currents and tides keep the sea open even in deep sub-zero weather. The young hatch in August, in the midst of the terrible polar winter. In October, or spring, the breeding season is over, and then a *northward* migration begins. Unmated individuals go first, followed by parents which have finished rearing their single chick. They are borne along by the currents on rafts of ice. After spending part of the year on the sea, the adults return south, moult on the border ice, and prepare to begin their cycle anew in the austral autumn. Their migration thus differs from that of other antarctic birds, just as their annual cycle is an anomaly in every way.[1]

Since penguins have no normal wings, but flippers, they must migrate by swimming (in which they excel), but other sea-birds, which are good fliers, also migrate in that fashion. Murres (*Uria*), for example, often swim considerable distances during their winter dispersion. So do brant geese (*Branta*) and eider ducks (*Somateria*) among the Anseriformes, and Anderson (1954) observed similar behaviour among grebes. In the autumn great crested grebes (*Podiceps cristatus*) and red-necked grebes (*Podiceps griseigena*) follow the Swedish coast between fifty and 220 yards from shore at a swimming speed of about one and one-fourth miles an hour, in the direction of their nocturnal flight. Likewise many Passerines travel at night but flit from bush to bush during the daytime; they are hunting food but moving in the general direction of their migration.[2]

Pelagic birds thus perform seasonal migrations, although the majority seem to disperse rather than travel to definite winter quarters.

The two forces governing seasonal migrations by sea-birds are food and prevailing winds. The former explains the dispersion of many species that are distributed in correlation with the quantity of food available. Regions favoured from this point of view serve as winter quarters, just as tropical areas provide a winter residence for many land-birds.

That winds govern to a large degree the movements of some marine migrants is evident from a comparison of the migrations of Wilson's petrel and the greater shearwater with maps showing the dominant winds in the Atlantic. In other instances the relationship is less direct but, in any case, flight is largely based on utilization of air currents.

1. Penguins' stomachs often contain small pebbles from the bottom of the sea or the surface of floating ice. D. Stewart (1934) reports that a mineralogical analysis of such pebbles taken from emperor penguins captured in the Bay of Whales, in Antarctica, reveals that some of them were formed of kenyte, an igneous rock found only in the Ross Archipelago. This shows that the penguins had migrated from a sector of the Pan-Antarctic 350–400 miles from their point of capture.

2. Swimming birds resemble landbirds that migrate on foot. Prill (1931) found American coots (*Fulica americana*) moving northward overland in the driest zones of an immense swampy area in Oregon during May, 1929. At least 8,000 birds marched past one spot in a morning, and Prill estimates that 10,000 or more crossed the area in four days.

Before North America was settled, the wild turkey used to migrate great distances, on foot as well as by flight, through the eastern part of the continent.

A supplementary proof of the wind's influence is found in the occasional slaughter of sea-birds caught by gales. Typical instances are the migratory Leach's petrels and dovekies that are driven on the French coasts at relatively fixed dates.

Murphy has shown the effect of the great August and September Atlantic hurricanes on birds in the path of these depressions, which are accompanied by winds that may exceed 100 miles an hour. These hurricanes are born off the African coasts, sweep west over the Atlantic, enter the Caribbean area and then head north from the Gulf Coast, often far inland, from Florida west to Texas and north to Newfoundland. They carry autumn migrants so far off course that birds of the East Atlantic are found on the shores of the U.S.A., and many Wilson's petrels are driven hundreds of miles north-east to perish deep inside the U.S.A.

Sea-birds are not the only victims of these gales. Countless land-birds die on over-water flights when they are overtaken by great storms. Ships at sea during these cataclysms are sometimes actually covered by birds, more fortunate than others of the same species that have been hurled into the waves or up on the beaches.

Land Migrants Over the Seas

Sea-birds perform such long flights over the oceans that the greater part of their lives may be spent in vast peregrinations. But land-birds, too, are often forced to cross wide stretches of water to reach their winter or breeding territories. The Mediterranean is traversed at its greatest breadth. Many migrants travel between the Asiatic mainland and Japan, Formosa and Malaya, and other species, even tiny humming-birds, cross the Gulf of Mexico (Lack, 1959).

Land-birds are often even more audacious, for certain species go from India to Madagascar; the shining cuckoo of New Zealand winters in the Bismarck Archipelago and the Solomon Islands, and the long-tailed cuckoo of New Zealand scatters in winter through the islands of Oceania. Individuals that reach the Palaus must travel nearly 3,750 miles over water, and those that winter in the Tuamotus fly almost as far. The spine-tailed swift (*Hirundapus caudacutus*) goes from eastern Siberia, where it breeds, to Tasmania.

Many observers have reported finding land-birds all over the high seas. Four centuries ago Belon told how his ship in the Mediterranean was literally covered with migrating quail. Recently birds of many kinds, particularly small Passerines, have been seen far offshore.

Land migrants are also carried by storms far off their normal course. Several authors, notably Alexander and Fitter (1955) and Williamson (1954c), have studied this phenomenon, which explains why many North American migrants are found in western Europe, particularly Great Britain. The most common non-Passerine is the pectoral sandpiper (*Erolia melanotos*), but the buff-breasted sandpiper (*Tryngites subruficollis*) is a fairly frequent vagrant, and there are also the lesser Yellow-legs (*Totanus flavipes*), greater yellow-legs (*Tringa melanoleucus*), solitary sandpiper (*Tringa solitaria*), killdeer (*Charadrius vociferus*), Baird's sandpiper (*Calidris bairdi*), upland plover (*Bartramia longicauda*), white-rumped sandpiper (*Erolia fuscicollis*), short-billed dowitcher (*Limnodromus griseus*) and various ducks (including the blue-winged teal [*Anas discors*] and the American wigeon [*Mareca americana*]). (Fig. 68). It is surprising that a number of American Passerines appear in Europe, as many of them seem incapable of such prodigious flights because of their small size and dependence on terrestrial food. The most common land-birds are the black-billed cuckoo (*Coccyzus erythrophthalmus*), yellow-billed cuckoo (*Coccyzus americanus*), American robin (*Turdus migratorius*), Swainson's thrush (*Hylocichla ustulata*), black-and-white warbler (*Mniotilta varia*), water-thrush (*Seiurus noveboracensis*), meadowlark (*Sturnella magna*), and the red-winged blackbird (*Agelaius phoeniceus*).

The regular appearance in Europe of these typical North American birds, particularly from September to December, has occasioned much discussion. For a long time it was thought that the Passerines were 'hitch-hikers' on one of the hundreds of ships plying between America and Europe. That is possible in some instances, for many passengers have seen birds seeking shelter even on the bridge of a great liner. But this solution cannot account for all the birds, nor does it explain why so many American birds reach Europe, while European species very rarely visit the New World. If birds travelled on shipboard, they would go in both directions! Moreover, observations and experiments on the physiology of migrants show that Passerines need food at very short intervals, and there is little opportunity to find insects on board ships. Speed is thus the *sine qua non* for Passerine migrants, and experience has shown that the majority of birds which

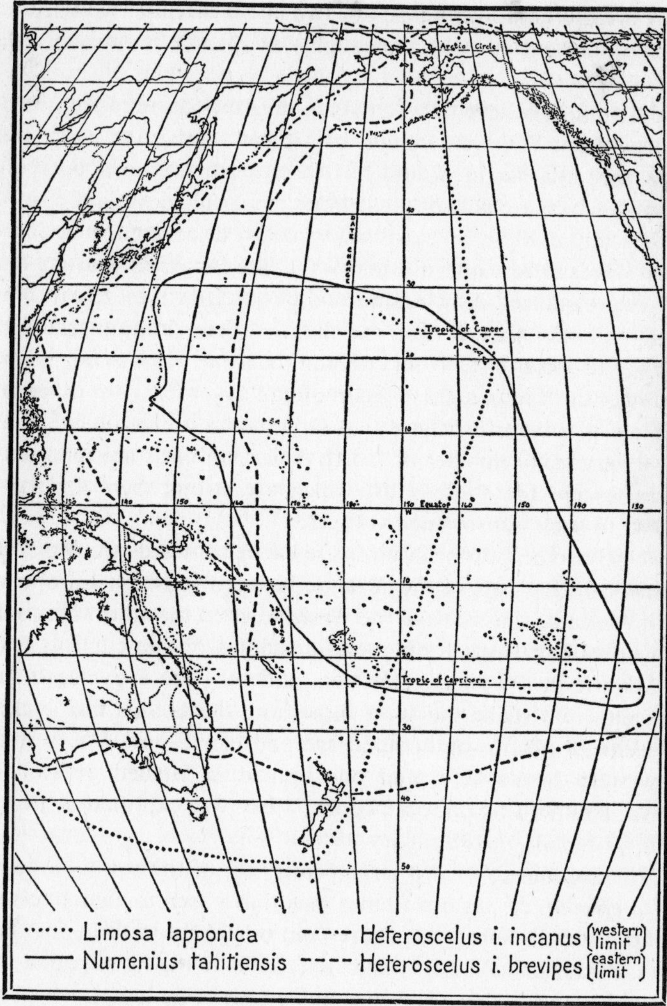

Fig. 68. Winter range of the bristle-thighed curlew (*Numenius tahitiensis*), the eastern limit of the ranges of the bar-tailed godwit (*Limosa lapponica*) and the Asiatic wandering tattler (*Heteroscelus brevipes*), and the western limit of the range of the American wandering tattler (*Heteroscelus incanus*). From Stickney, 1943.

settle on vessels die within a day or two either because they are weak (which would explain why they alight) or because they cannot find food.

We therefore believe that American migrants come to Europe unaided by man. Some are caught by violent winds that sweep them across the Atlantic in hours, but these birds are seen only after tempests, which are part of the definite meteorological pattern of the North Atlantic. Meteorologists have recently discovered jet-streams – violent winds at very high altitudes – that are capable of wafting birds over great distances. As winds normally blow from west to east in the North Atlantic, they favour the flight of American migrants but prevent European birds from crossing the same ocean. Only a small fraction of the birds caught in the jet-streams ever reach the other side, but there is reason to believe that large flocks are involved; in any case, a very small number of North American birds are reported in Europe except for shore-birds, which are strong fliers and better adapted to such transoceanic voyages.

Inversely some European birds are carried towards the American continent in that part of the Atlantic between southern Europe and North Africa on one side and the West Indies on the other. This is due to the prevailing winds, for in these latitudes strong air currents sweep the Atlantic in a westerly direction, and they are a nucleus of the hurricanes that strike the West Indies and the U.S.A. Cattle egrets (*Bubulcus ibis*) from southern Europe and North-west Africa invade the western hemisphere, and one individual banded at Doñana, Huelva, southern Spain, on 24 June, 1956, was captured at Port of Spain, Trinidad, on 13 January, 1957.

In the autumn of 1959 a large percentage of the common herons (*Ardea cinerea*) of western France must have been carried across the Atlantic; some reached the Azores and others got as far as the West Indies. Birds banded in May and June, 1959, in the Loire region were captured in the Azores (Terceira) in October. One heron, which was banded 20 May, 1958, on the Loire, was captured at Trinidad in August, 1959, and another was taken at Montserrat, Lesser Antilles. Thus there was a large flight of birds in conjunction with the violent winds that swept the Atlantic at this time.

Other birds, especially shore-birds, regularly perform very long migrations overseas. The golden plover winters in Argentina after a journey across the Atlantic, and a related race winters throughout a good part of the Pacific.[1] Many other instances could be mentioned, for shore-birds are excellent fliers, capable of making long journeys. Furthermore, these birds can rest on the water if it is fairly calm, and feed on marine organisms, although there is no indication that this is a common practice.

Stickney (1943) made an excellent study of some of the most remarkable flights of birds wintering in the innumerable oceanic islands. Most of these Charadriidae were known from their winter quarters long before the breeding grounds were discovered. The first bristle-thighed curlew (*Numenius tahitiensis*) was brought from Tahiti, as the Latin name implies, by Captain Cook in 1769, but its Alaskan breeding grounds were not known until A. A. Allen found them in 1948. This curlew annually makes the enormous flight to Polynesia. It also winters on the shores of many atolls and islands from Henderson (east of Tuamotu) to the Fijis and Tonga, and to the Santa Cruz and Carolines. Occasionally it has been found on the Bonin Islands, which constitutes a western record. Postnuptial migration begins in August, some of these birds remain in their 'winter' grounds until May, and a few individuals spend the whole year there.

The bar-tailed godwit (*Limosa lapponica baueri*) which nests in Siberia from the Lena to Bering Strait and Alaska, winters in Australia and New Zealand (its principal winter quarters), but also in the Hawaiian Islands and throughout most of Polynesia.

Another shore-bird, the American wandering tattler (*Heteroscelus incanus*), makes the same type of winter flight. While the Asiatic form (*brevipes*) winters chiefly between Micronesia to the west and the Solomons to the east, the American form (*incanus*) winters in eastern Oceania, although its area overlaps that of *brevipes*. The map (Fig. 68) shows this more clearly than a list of place names.

Although the Pacific is crossed in all directions by migratory Charadriidae, it does not have a monopoly on these flights. H. F. I. Elliott (1953) found on Tristan da Cunha, in the middle of the South Atlantic, a sharp-tailed sandpiper (*Erolia acuminata*), which breeds only in eastern Siberia – an equally long route.

Jouanin and Paulian (1954) indicate that winds may play an im-

1. Like other shore-birds, including the bristle-thighed curlew, plovers of this subspecies apparently fly non-stop over the 2,050 miles of ocean separating the Aleutians from Hawaii. Stresemann (1934) calculated that the golden plover flies at an average speed of 285 yards, or two wing beats, per second. The 2,050-mile flight thus requires 35 hours and 252,000 wing beats!

portant part in the selection of migration routes. Some birds go beyond the southern shores of the great continents to islets lost in the immensity of antarctic seas. Greenshanks (*Totanus nebularia*) have been captured at Kerguelen and New Amsterdam, and there are other records from these remote parts of the globe. At Amsterdam Island Paulian (1956) found common sandpipers (*Tringa hypoleucos*), which may have come from Madagascar and South Africa, from India (through the Chagos Islands) or Australia. A study of meteorological conditions indicates that they probably came from Africa. Kerguelen is in the centre of a zone where west winds blow throughout the year, between lat. 40° and 60° S. They are so strong that they could easily carry migrants to these southern islands, but it would be difficult for the birds to struggle against them from the Australian region (many sea-birds, in fact, are driven by winds to the west coast of Australia) or even from India and the Chagos Islands. Therefore it seems likely that accidental migrants found in Kerguelen start from some point in Africa or Madagascar.

Moreover, the vast majority of birds coming to Tristan da Cunha are New World species. Since the geographic position of Tristan da Cunha is to America what Kerguelen and New Amsterdam are to Africa, winds seem to play quite as important a part in oceanic flights of land-birds as in sea-bird migrations.

CHAPTER 8

Modes of Migration

Migration Routes

Migration maps based on banded birds can prove misleading, because the banding station is usually connected by a straight line to the point of subsequent recovery, and, when the station is in the nesting zone of a species, and the bird is recovered in its winter quarters, it seems natural to consider the straight line as the actual route followed by the bird in its travels from one to the other. Nothing, however, could be more deceptive, because the real routes deviate widely from a straight line.

Migration flights go in a primary direction,[1] which is, of course, determined by the geographical positions of the breeding and winter areas. For many European birds this primary direction is roughly south and south-west in the autumn, whereas in North America it is often north-south.

But migrants change their course in accordance with local (weather, topographic or feeding) conditions and at times describe a curve, all parts of which are not oriented in the 'primary direction.' Occasionally birds even fly for a time in a course diametrically away from their ultimate destination. The term *migration routes* applies to all sections of their flight.

These vary considerably, particularly in width. Some are very narrow routes used by a single species; others are wide and irregular. Although many intermediate forms exist, the differences between these two distinct types of migration routes have given rise to much

1. Geyr von Schweppenburg's 'Normalrichtung,' 'Primärrichtung'; Deelder's 'Standard direction.'

difference of opinion, as some early ornithologists argued that migration follows definite paths, while others denied the existence of any specific routes. It is most probable that these men were basing their ideas on theoretical plans founded on a few examples and that, to some extent, both groups were right, but they happened to be discussing different birds!

The term *narrow route* is applied when a species inhabiting a vast region migrates a long distance along a narrow strip of territory without leaving it (Geyr von Schweppenburg). German writers term this the *Schmalfront*. Very few birds make migrations of this kind, the classic example being that of the storks (see p. 59), which follow a narrow, well-defined route through eastern Europe and the Near East. The pattern is obligatory because this bird does not like to cross wide expanses of water, and the number of migrants is so great that there is a heavy concentration along a very narrow route. Cranes are in the same group, although the nature of their flight permits them to cross the Mediterranean. Nonetheless, they travel along relatively narrow paths, and birds migrating through western Europe (see p. 69) cross France in a line extending from Lorraine to the western Pyrenees.

Birds of prey migrating through the eastern Mediterranean region are in the same category (Raptores are especially noteworthy in eastern Europe because of their abundance). Migrating buzzards and short-toed eagles fly regularly over the Bosphorus. These birds are very seldom observed at sea and never over the open Mediterranean. Like storks, they employ rising warm air currents above land. Thus they cannot make a sustained flight over the sea, where atmospheric conditions require steady flapping rather than soaring.[1]

Narrow migration routes also occur, of course, in America. Ross's geese, which go from arctic Canada to California, follow this type of course (see p. 132), and the great migration route of many species across the Gulf of Mexico is in this category. The migratory front is very narrow in the case of various species on the coasts of the Gulf

1. We do not wish to imply that a gliding or soaring flight is restricted to land-birds. Innumerable sea-birds, including gulls and Procellariiformes (shearwaters, albatrosses) 'glide' above the sea. But the wings of these birds are constructed in a wholly different way; whereas gliders on land have broad wings designed to take advantage of rising thermal currents, sea-birds have very long, narrow wings, so they can make use of air currents over the waves (especially gusts and changes in wind velocity at different altitudes). The air over the sea calls for a wing structure of specialized shape to permit gliding flight.

States, and often in Central America as well. Certain migrants take narrow paths all the way across North America. Lincoln (1935b) showed that this is true of Harris's sparrow (*Zonotrichia querula*), whose behaviour differs greatly from that of other migrant Passerines, such as the American redstart (*Setophaga ruticilla*). The Ipswich sparrow (*Passerculus princeps*), probably an offspring of the Savannah sparrow (*P. sandwichensis*), also has a very narrow migration route along the seashore. Breeding only on Sable Island, a small sandy island 100 miles off the southern coast of Nova Scotia, it migrates in winter along the Atlantic beaches of the United States south to Georgia.

The majority of migrants, however, travel along multiple airways, often widely separated from one another and scattered over a vast territory (this is the German *Breitfront*, Geyr von Schweppenburg, 1929). The width of these migration zones varies according to species and region and is determined by geographical factors. The strip of territory may narrow until the dense concentration of migrants resembles that of migration on a 'narrow route,' but this concentration is never maintained over the long distances characteristic of the latter.

Within such a strip of land, migrants are distributed along a number of roughly parallel secondary routes, some of which are favoured more than others. These secondary routes, which we call lines of diversion, depend on local conditions.[1] The travellers follow low-contour routes and river systems, and many take migration corridors, such as valleys, which afford easier flying conditions than high plateaux or hilly areas. This is particularly apparent in spring, when migrants move 'north' through valleys before radiating to settle neighbouring districts. Numerous observations confirm the attraction of valleys; in some instances migrants even change direction to fly through one. In Sweden, according to some ornithologists, common chaffinches and meadow pipits occasionally leave their south-westerly course to follow valleys oriented north-west – south-east, or at a 90° angle from their migration route (Svärdson, 1953). Such movements along a line of diversion in a direction nearly opposite to that normal for the time of year are called *retromigrations* (see Lack and Williamson: *Ibis*, 101:255–256, 1959). Lakes and ponds also attract migratory water- and land-birds.

While the *attraction* of certain biotopes is sufficiently strong to alter

1. These correspond approximately to Geyr von Schweppenburg's *Leitlinie*.

the course of migrants, others constitute zones of *repulsion*. Land-birds, especially small Passerines, hesitate to cross wide waterways. Dutch ornithologists have shown how common chaffinches and other Passerine migrants in the Netherlands delay crossing stretches of sea as long as possible (Tinbergen, 1941; Dobben, 1953; Dobben and

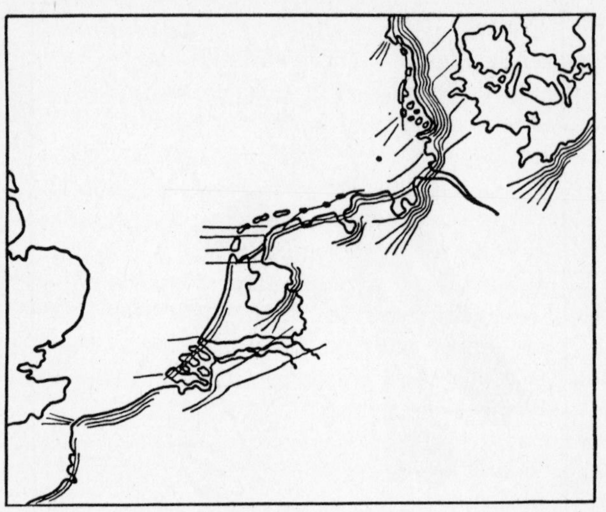

Fig. 69. Migration routes along the littoral of north-western Europe, where there is a large concentration of migrants in the autumn. After Van Dobben, 1953.

Makking, 1933; Deelder, 1949).

Common chaffinches from Scandinavia, eastern and central Europe are headed in a west-south-west direction when they reach Holland in the autumn (Fig. 70). At the coast they turn abruptly to fly south-south-west along the shore. Starlings veer from five-eighths of a mile to about two miles before they reach the coast, common chaffinches three miles, as they fly higher, and perceive the sea from a greater distance. Repeated observations show that the migrants seem to hesitate briefly; some birds venture a little way out to sea, then return over the shore and follow the coast. For a considerable distance there is such a concentration that migration in the region appears to follow a narrow front. That this 'traffic congestion' has been known for a long time is evident from ancient bird snares (*Vinkenbanen*) set up in this part of Holland to catch migrants, especially common chaffinches.

A multitude of assorted migrants gathers in the Kurische Nehrung on the Baltic Sea, site of the Rossitten ornithological station (now Rybatschi). This long tongue of land separating the sea from a large lagoon is an ideal location for a banding station and for the study of

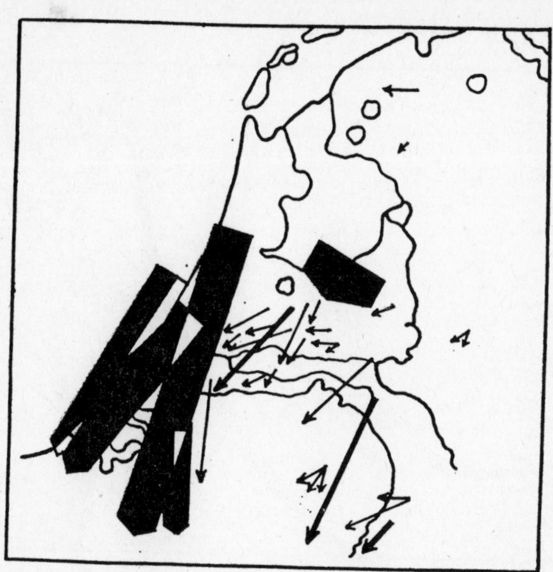

Fig. 70. Concentration of chaffinches (*Fringilla coelebs*) along the coast of the Netherlands. The size of the arrows is proportionate to the number of migrants. After Van Dobben, 1935, *in* Deelder, 1949, simplified.

migration (Fig. 71). In some parts of the U.S.A. there are concentrations, especially on the Great Lakes (Keweenaw Point, Lake Superior; Sand Point and Fish Point in Lake Huron) and along the Atlantic coast (Cape Cod, Cape May, Cape Charles).

Islands attract migrants too. Dutch observers report that land migrants which have crossed the sea separating the Netherlands from the Frisian Islands fly east-west, but shift course to fly the full length of these islands; the birds seem reluctant to leave when again they turn west over the water (Fig. 72).

These observations do not always apply, for species vary in behaviour, and other factors, such as physical surroundings and meteorological conditions, are important. Psychological factors can also influence migrants. One flock of birds hesitating at the shore may be encouraged to cross by the example of a second, more resolute group which continues its flight over the water.

Whereas the sea repels land migrants, land seems to repel sea-birds. Migrating gannets follow the Dutch coasts, clinging to the ocean, and

Fig. 71. Migration routes in the region of the *Kurisches Haff* along the shores of the Baltic. Migrants follow the coast and the tongue of land (*Kurische Nehrung*) in preference to crossing expanses of water. The arrow indicates the village of Rossitten, now Rybatschi, site of the ornithological station which was formerly German and is now Russian. After Schüz, *Vogelzug*, 1930.

changing their course to fly around small tidal flats instead of going over them. Swedish eiders (Svärdson, 1953) fly in a south-west–north-east direction from Denmark to the west coast of Sweden in the spring. They then follow the Swedish coast southward, altering direction countless times, as land looms or retreats, before they arrive in the Baltic region. Thus land is a barrier they do not cross, although they are quite capable of flying over it (Fig. 73).

Because they require food at the edge of water, shore-birds are guided by the nature of the terrain, especially by expanses of water and marsh. Their migration routes may thus follow very exact lines (Pynnönen, 1957).

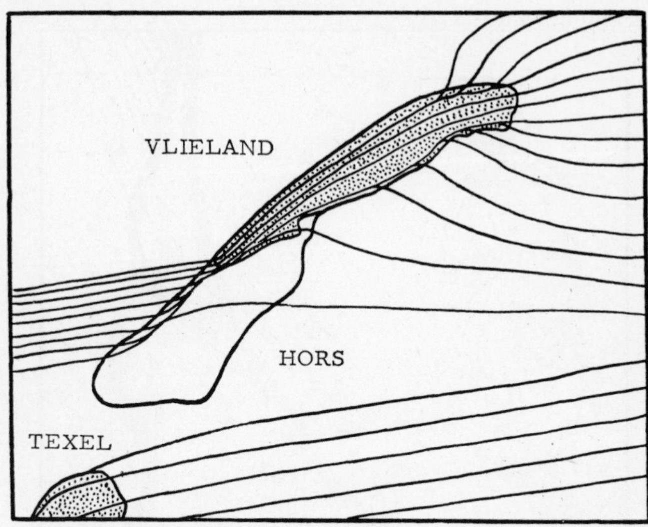

Fig. 72. Concentration of migratory routes of the starling (*Sturnus vulgaris*) in the autumn on the island of Vlieland, Netherlands. The birds arrive in a broad front from the East and gather over the island (dots); then they follow in a narrow line the waterline over the sandy flat (the Hors); from there groups continue west over the surf. After Van Dobben, 1953.

We should not conclude that all migrants take such precise routes. Although birds travelling along a migration front have a tendency to take certain paths, individuals are scattered everywhere. Distribution is influenced to a considerable degree by meteorological conditions, for in bad weather migrants tend to select the most favourable routes and in fine weather they disperse.

Many birds which usually inhabit a definite biotope do not hesitate to fly over strange territory. Lesser black-backed gulls (*Larus fuscus*) from the Baltic cross the whole continent of Europe to winter in the Mediterranean, and some go on to East Africa. At first sight, the Nile Valley would seem to present a favourable route, but lesser black-backed gulls are commonly found over the heart of the desert, far from any water and in a very poor area for sea-birds. Moreau's observations (1938) show that under certain conditions the 'natural' route does not seem to attract migrants, and that some prefer different biotopes. Cranes and a large number of water-birds cross the Libyan Desert instead of following the Nile.

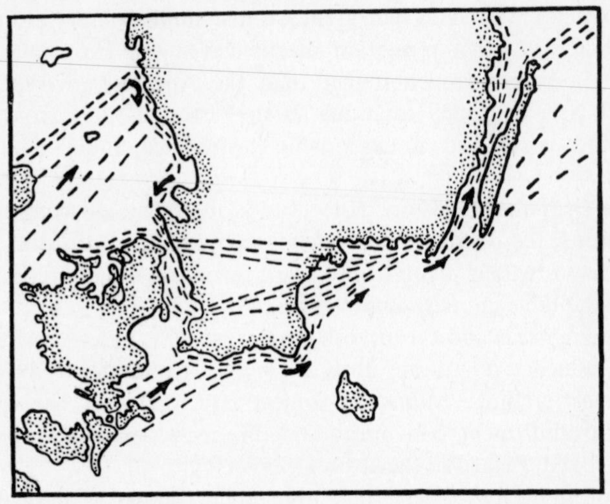

Fig. 73. Spring migration of the eider (*Somateria mollissima*) in southern Sweden. Note how the birds try to avoid the mainland and how they make detours to avoid flying over it. From Svärdson, 1953.

The same author revealed (1953) that the majority of migrants cross the Mediterranean on many different lanes. A number of birds, excluding storks and birds of prey, traverse this great sea at its widest point in the eastern basin. There is little migration over the western basin, between France and North Africa, where migration routes seem more influenced by land masses. In any case, it is apparent that large numbers of birds are not dependent on geography alone, since they can adapt themselves to diverse or even adverse conditions.

In the New World shore-birds gather on North Atlantic beaches before crossing the ocean in a straight line to winter quarters in eastern South America, yet the North American coast and the many islands in Central America and the Caribbean seem to offer much safer flying routes.

Birds do not even take the 'easiest' routes over mountains. Many migrants use the passes, especially in bad weather, but travellers do not hesitate to cross the highest peaks. Lack and Lack (1953) found various birds of prey, pigeons, swallows and small Passerines at the highest crests of the Pyrenees, especially in the Cirque de Gavarnie, when a short deviation west or east would have brought them to gaps which required no such great ascents. Similar observations have been made in other mountain massifs, even the Himalayas. This mountain barrier, much higher than the Alps, is traversed from central Asia by many migrants, both Passerines and large birds, including geese and ducks,[1] which winter in India or further south.

It is clear that birds are not entirely dependent on geographical conditions; the degree of dependence varies widely according to the species and regions involved, for some forms are exacting, others far more adaptable in their requirements.

Although seas and certain other areas, such as deserts and mountains, influence migration, birds are by no means strictly bound to their surroundings. Migration routes show that they can make a splendid adjustment to favourable conditions, yet many birds perform flights that disregard all the laws of human logic.

Loop migration, where the spring flight follows a very different course from the autumn trail, probably occurs when birds must be guided by practical considerations. Russian arctic loons (*Gavia arctica*) migrate south along interior routes, dotted with open Russian lakes, but go north in the spring along more westerly lanes, when the cold still holds Russia in its grip. Red-backed shrikes make a loop migration because of changing seasonal air currents (p. 85).

One final question comes to mind in connection with migration routes: does an *individual* bird always take the same migration route? We know that most migrants winter in a fairly definite region, and that they return the following spring to the territory they occupied during the previous breeding season. Swallows, orioles, ospreys, storks and many other birds have often proved they are faithful to a certain

1. Severe flying conditions, such as clouds and dense fog, alone keep migrants from crossing great mountain massifs. When swallows are caught by bad weather in the Alps, vast numbers die from starvation. At such times of disaster, societies for the protection of animals often carry rescued birds over the mountains by airplane!

(building, tree or other) nest location. We are thus tempted to believe that a bird follows a familiar route on each of its flights.

Such a question does not concern migrants like storks, where an entire population moves along the same routes from year to year. In other cases our information is fragmentary, and only numerous recoveries of a single individual could furnish definitive proof. Most banded birds, however, are recovered only once – at their death. In a few instances the bird has been recaptured in the same place a year later during its next migration trip, but most recoveries are made far from where the bird was first seen. Birds banded on their way through Heligoland have been recovered during succeeding years in England, Scotland, Saxony and Brandenburg – up to 440 miles away. There is no set migration route for an individual, and the bird seems to change course according to whim and prevailing conditions (Drost, 1941). Once again birds show that they can adapt their behaviour to the circumstances.

Speeds of Migratory Flights

Gätke, who founded the ornithological station in Heligoland, made surprising errors about the speed of migrants. Since birds often pass unseen, he concluded that they make their whole journey non-stop – and in a single night! He speaks, for example, of bluethroats (*Luscinia svecica*), which leave their winter quarters in Africa at dusk and arrive in Heligoland at dawn!

Gätke also mentions hooded crows that appeared in Heligoland between eight a.m. and two p.m. As he had been informed that such crows were seen crossing the east coast of England between eleven in the morning and five in the afternoon, he concluded that they require only three hours to cross the North Sea between Heligoland and England; he did not bother to wonder whether the *same* birds were involved.

According to Gätke, the speed of migrants is far in excess of normal flight. He credits birds with travelling in a region where altitude would make these unusual performances possible, and he claims that they undergo a real physiological metamorphosis.

Later observations have revealed the absurdity of Gätke's opinions. Various methods are used, but the most satisfactory is to place theodolites at each end of a definite course. This, however, requires so complex an apparatus that it is seldom done. Most records have been made by observers using automobile speedometers, an ideal method if the instrument is accurate, but this is not always the case. Other records have been made from aeroplanes.

There is often wide disparity in the results obtained. Although this may be the fault of the observer, one must remember that birds have two speeds: normal and accelerated when they are in pursuit of prey, or fleeing from an 'enemy' (which may be the car or the plane!). When the bird is frightened, it is the latter speed which is measured.

Under normal conditions birds modify their speed according to the terrain. Some birds fly more rapidly when crossing open areas where they might be attacked by a bird of prey, and slow down in a wooded tract, where there is less danger from predators. Birds flying in flocks travel faster than when they are alone. This is doubtless explained by psychological reasons, which are important for birds travelling in more or less co-ordinated groups. All birds have a considerable speed reserve, and some are capable of nearly doubling their 'normal' speed.

Meinertzhagen (1921), Harrisson (1931a), Storer (1948) and Mildenberger (1950) compiled statistics on the speeds of birds, especially migrants. A great many facts are scattered through the literature, much of which has been summarized in these studies and in one by Meinertzhagen (1955) which lists practically all that was known up to that time.

At first it was believed that migrating birds travel at 'normal' speed. But in 1931, by comparing the speeds of a number of non-migrating birds in England with those that Meinertzhagen had obtained for these same species on their seasonal flights, Harrisson found that migrants go faster.

Several examples taken from his study, are as follows:

	Meinertzhagen (all migrating)	Harrisson (none migrating)
Rook (*Corvus frugilegus*)	38–45 m.p.h.	29–35 m.p.h.
Swallow (*Hirundo rustica*)	34–37 3-4 m.p.h.	29–32 m.p.h.
Lapwing (*Vanellus vanellus*)	40–45 m.p.h.	30–40 m.p.h.

Further observations have shown that Harrisson was right. Even

Meinertzhagen (1955) admitted that the speed of migratory flight is above normal.

Some of the speeds listed by Meinertzhagen (1955) for the classic migratory species follow, and it is obvious that they vary widely. Although the bird flies in wind, which either slows or speeds its progress, figures are given in ground-speed. Speeds are never absolute, but these were obtained under average conditions, with only a slight wind, if any, because high wind would distort the results.

Species	*Place*	*Ground speed (m.p.h.)*	*Remarks*
Rook (*Corvus frugilegus*)	Germany	32.6	migrating
,, ,, ,,	France	38–39.25	,,
,, ,, ,,	,,	45	,,
Jackdaw (*Corvus monedula*)	United Kingdom	30–36.5	normal flight
,, ,, ,,	France	40	migrating
,, ,, ,,	Palestine	55–57	,,
Starling (*Sturnus vulgaris*)	United Kingdom	23–32	cruising
,, ,, ,,	Baluchistan	43–49	migrating
,, ,, ,,	Germany	46	,,
Chaffinch (*Fringilla coelebs*)	Germany	21–29	normal flight
Song sparrow (*Melospiza melodia*)	U.S.A.	17	,, ,,
Chipping sparrow (*Spizella passerina*)	U.S.A.	15–20	
Skylark (*Alauda arvensis*)	Arabia	22–28	migrating
Red-throated pipit (*Anthus cervinus*)	Kenya	26.5	,,
Yellow wagtail (*Motacilla flava*)	Kenya	29–30.1	,,
,, ,, ,, ,,	United Kingdom	22.5	normal flight
American robin (*Turdus migratorius*)	U.S.A.	17–32	
Wheatear (*Oenanthe oenanthe*)	United Kingdom	18–32	
,, ,, ,,	Ireland	17–32	migrating
Swallow (*Hirundo rustica*)	Germany	22–24	feeding
,, ,, ,,	Kenya	37.75	migrating
,, ,, ,,	,,	34	,,
,, ,, ,,	Ireland	21–23	,,
,, ,, ,,	South Africa	30–36	normal flight
,, ,, ,,	U.S.A.	20, 44–46	,, ,,
House martin (*Delichon urbica*)	United Kingdom	25, 29, 30, 46	,, ,,
,, ,, ,, ,,	,, ,,	27	migrating
Purple martin (*Progne subis*)	U.S.A.	20	
Swift (*Apus apus*)	United Kingdom	38, 42	normal flight
,, ,, ,,	Paris	54, 57	,, ,,
Ruby-throated humming-bird (*Archilochus colubris*)	U.S.A.	45–60	,, ,,

Species	*Place*	*Ground speed (m.p.h.)*	*Remarks*
Peregrine (*Falco peregrinus*)	Germany	37	migrating
„ „ „	U.S.A.	165–180	hunting (stooping)
Sparrow-hawk (*Accipiter nisus*)	Germany	25.8	migrating
Hawks (all species considered collectively)	Hawk Mountain	30 (average) 40–60	„ according to Broun, 1949)
Turtle dove (*Streptopelia turtur*)	Palestine	38–45	migrating
Bewick's swan (*Cygnus bewickii*)	United Kingdom	39–42	normal flight
Whooper swan (*Cygnus cygnus*)	„ „	41–44	
Geese (*Anser sp.*)	Iraq, United Kingdom, France	25, 44–56	
„ „	North Sea	25, 33–35	migrating
„ „	U.S.A.	44.3	„
Mallard (*Anas platyrhynchus*)	„	46–60	„
Pintail (*Anas acuta*)	Sudan	37–51	migrating
Oldsquaw or long-tailed duck (*Clangula hyemalis*)	Canada	54–72	
Ringed plover (*Charadrius hiaticula*)	United Kingdom	36	
Killdeer (*Charadrius vociferus*)	U.S.A.	28–55	
Dotterel (*Eudromias morinellus*)	United Kingdom	45–50	migrating
Lapwing (*Vanellus vanellus*)	„ „	28, 37	cruising
„ „ „	Germany	30	migrating
„ „ „	Palestine	37	„
Greenshank (*Totanus nebularia*)	Tanganyika	46, 49	normal
Willet (*Catoptrophorus semipalmatus*)	U.S.A.	27	
Whimbrel (*Numenius phaeopus*)	Ireland	40–45	migrating
Razorbill (*Alca torda*)	France	49–54	„
Crane (*Grus grus*)	Germany	22–36	„
Quail (*Coturnix coturnix*)	Mediterranean	57	„
Manx shearwater (*Puffinus puffinus*)	France	25–34	

These speeds would permit migrants to reach their winter quarters in a relatively short time if they flew steadily. The journeys are, however, broken by long stops, during which the birds rest and hunt for food. Swallows, martins and some birds of prey hunt during flight, but the majority cannot, and an analysis of the stomach contents of many migrants has revealed that their digestive system was usually empty.

In some instances migrants must cover long distances without a break. Land-birds flying from Scandinavia to Great Britain fly 220 to 400 miles non-stop; North American migrants fly 500 to 600 miles when they cross the Gulf of Mexico on their long trip south, yet this flight is made by small Passerines, even humming-birds, none of which can pause for rest on the sea! Migrants on their way to or from New Zealand travel 625 to 940 miles non-stop, but the record seems to be held by the American golden plover, which apparently flies 2,065 miles from Alaska to the Hawaiian Islands without stopping (see p. 194).

Migrants travelling overland seem to tarry along the way and to progress in stages, with rest stops in between which may last a day or more. An average 'day's' flight (often by night) is from ninety to 155 miles, which represents only six to eight hours in the air. Some migrants average only sixty-five miles a day. The European roller, for example, leaves its breeding territory in August, or September at the latest; most of the birds arrive in Kenya by the end of October or early in November, but do not reach Griqualand, South Africa, until early December. The bird seems to leave the latter region about the first of February, and large flocks appear in Kenya in March, but it is late April, or early May, before they arrive in central Europe. On the basis of arrival dates, Stresemann (1944c) figured that the 2,120 miles separating Cairo from Kenya were covered in fifty-five days, at an average of thirty-nine miles a day; the 2,240 miles from Kenya to Griqualand required fifty days, an average of forty-five miles a day. During spring migration the first stage trip takes thirty-five days, or an average of sixty-four miles a day, and the final stage only thirty days, or seventy-one miles a day. It is evident that these are approximate figures, based on the arrival dates of a whole flock rather than on observation of specific birds. Furthermore, they assume that birds fly in a straight line, whereas they actually do nothing of the kind. Detours lengthen the route, so the distance flown daily is probably greater than these figures indicate.

White storks from Europe arrive first in Cairo at the end of August. Early in September they are in Sudan, at the beginning of October in the Transvaal, and in November in Natal – by no means a rapid migration.

Swallows reach Egypt in late August (this is just the advance guard, for the autumn departures of this species embrace a long period). Large flocks arrive in Kenya in September, and in the Transvaal from mid- to late November.

In the autumn the golden oriole tarries along the way, especially in the Mediterranean region, to enjoy the ripe figs.

The red-backed shrike seems to migrate much faster. Stresemann (1944a) calculated the speed of the advance guard in the spring as follows:

Eastern Abyssinia	24 March	
		1,550 miles in 11 days = 141 miles a day
Sinai	4 April	
		1,678 miles (across Asia Minor) in 13 days = 129 miles a day
Salonica	16 April	
		1,120 miles in 9 days = 125 miles a day
Tarragona	25 April	

As the normal speed of this Passerine is about thirty-one miles an hour, the bird flies an 'average' of four hours a day, but this is not the case, for the flights are otherwise divided. The red-backed shrike flies from dusk to dawn, or about ten hours, so it covers 310 miles in a single night.[1] Stresemann states that the bird covers *620* miles in *five* days as follows:

2 nights for migration
3 nights for rest
5 days for feeding.

According to the same author (1944b), the black-headed bunting (*Emberiza melanocephala*), which nests in southern Europe (Dalmatia, Istria) and winters in India (Deccan), has a somewhat slower rhythm:

1. This speed is confirmed by birds captured shortly after banding. A. L. Thomson (1956) reports that a wheatear (*Oenanthe oenanthe*) was banded 16 August, 1949, at 1 p.m. at Skokholm, Pembrokeshire, and recaptured the 18th at 8 a.m. at Cap Breton, Landes, France. The bird had covered 585 miles in 43 hours, or about 300 miles a night.

2 nights for migration
5 nights for rest
7 days for feeding.

It thus requires seven days to cover 620 miles.[1]

In general, spring migration is faster than in autumn. This is evident in the case of the roller and other birds. Stresemann (1955) showed that the annual cycle of the wood warbler (*Phylloscopus sibilatrix*) is as follows in northern Germany:

1 May	8 August	in breeding territory	100 days
9 August	9 October	postnuptial migration	62 days
10 October	31 March	in winter quarters	172 days
1 April	30 April	prenuptial migration	30 days

(dates based on average figures).

The return trip in the spring requires only half the time taken by the autumn journey. Stresemann gives an *average* speed of 112 miles a day in spring, as against fifty-six days in autumn (the flight is not made by daily stages, but much resembles that of the red-backed shrike). In the spring, when birds are under the nesting urge, they hurry towards their breeding territory. Meteorological conditions play a less important rôle than in autumn, and migrants occasionally arrive on their breeding grounds in weather that is much more wintry than spring-like. In autumn, on the other hand, birds seem loath to leave the nesting area while temperatures and food supplies remain at all favourable.

Migration speed varies widely among bird species. Lincoln (1935b) studied this in great detail in North America and showed that each species has its own rhythm. Canada geese move slowly northward in the spring; blue geese start late, but travel at high speed towards their distant breeding grounds.[2] Many Passerines, notably thrushes (such

1. Some birds may travel more rapidly. A ruddy turnstone (*Arenaria interpres*), banded at 11 a.m. at Heligoland, Germany, was recovered 25 hours later on the coast of the English Channel in France, 510 miles from its banding site. Much longer daily flights have been recorded during homing experiments, but, on the whole, flights are longer during such artificial experiments than on migration.

2. The autumn migration of this species seems fully as rapid. Cooch (1955) noted that in 1952 the main flight of blue geese took less than 60 hours to cover the distance of over 1,700 miles separating James Bay, Canada, from Louisiana. This speed and the altitude (flights between 6,000 and 8,000 feet are common) explain why these geese are not observed more frequently, as they make few stops.

as the grey-cheeked thrush) and warblers resemble the blue geese, while others, like the American robin, move very slowly. Migration progresses at a steady rate among some species (Canada geese); in others it speeds up as the waves of migrants approach their breeding grounds or the northern limits of their range. It is evident that ecological factors of many kinds play a part in determining the speed of northward flight.

Finally some species spend so much time in travel over the enormous distance which separates their nesting from the wintering grounds that they have little time to 'rest' in the latter; they actually devote most of the year to migrations.

Altitude

Many early authors greatly over-estimated the altitude at which migrants travel. Gätke, who erred in determining the speed of migration, held that birds migrate at a height of about 20,000 feet or more, and thus explained why the majority are usually invisible! He stated that migrants rocket from the upper atmosphere, where they have been flying, and that they go up in the same meteoric fashion. Low pressure at great altitudes helps the bird in its flight and enables it to see much farther. Gätke thought that migrating birds come within our range of vision only under abnormal, particularly meteorological, conditions.

This German ornithologist was, of course, completely mistaken. In two of the best studies on altitudinal migration, Meinertzhagen (1920 and 1955) published his personal observations and some from different sources. Measuring altitude is quite as difficult as estimating speed, and, although modern instruments have largely supplanted former methods and inaccurate 'eye' calculations, it is very easy to make mistakes.

Most migrations occur at relatively low altitudes. Small Passerines often fly under 200 feet, and some birds literally skim over the ground or the waves. On the other hand, certain birds fly higher, even when there are no geographical reasons (such as mountain barriers) for doing so. Lack (1960b) recently computed the altitude of various migrants in the British Isles with radar. He found that Passerines often each 5,000 and occasionally 14,000 feet. Waders, especially lapwings, usually fly between 3,000 and 6,000 but may reach 11,000 feet. All but one of the following altitudes were given by Meinertzhagen.

Species	*Place*	*Altitude* (feet above ground)[1]	*Remarks*
Rook (*Corvus frugilegus*)	France	1,740, 2,008, 2,120	
" " "	United Kingdom	11,000	
Rooks and jackdaws (*Corvus monedula*)	France	690	
Starling (*Sturnus vulgaris*)	France	3,500	
Golden-crowned sparrow (*Zonotrĭchia atricapilla*)	California	10,000	Miller, 1957
Linnet (*Carduelis cannabina*)?	France	[10,000]	
Meadow pipit (*Anthus pratensis*)	Tuskar Rock, Ireland	70	average height
Red-throated pipit (*Anthus cervinus*)	Kenya	210	
Yellow wagtail (*Motacilla flava*)	Kenya	160–240	
Thrushes (*Turdus* sp.)	Syria	about 500	migrating over desert
Swallows (*Hirundo rustica*)	Kenya	235	
Swift (*Apus apus*)	Germany	2,200	
"	Holland	6,700	
"	Iraq	6,000	
Sparrow hawk (*Accipiter* sp.)	Israel	3,000	
Stork (*Ciconia ciconia*)	Jordan valley	400–2,000	
Geese (*Anser* sp.)	France	8,000–9,000	
Wood pigeon (*Columba palumbus*)	Germany	2,400–5,100	
" " "	North Sea	500	
Lapwing (*Vanellus vanellus*)	France	1,410	
" " "	Germany	1,300–1,800	
" " "	Egypt	8,400	
" " "	France	[2,000–8,500]	
"Sandpipers" (*Vanellus vanellus*)	France	[12,000]	
Crane (*Grus grus*)	Germany	[2,000–6,300]	
" " "	Finland	9,000	
" " "	France	[15,000]	

Various species are occasionally seen over the summits of the Andes and the Himalayas. Vultures, godwits, curlews and jackdaws have been observed at 19,700 feet, but the highest altitude recorded is at Dehra Dun, India, where geese fly at an elevation of nearly 29,500 feet.

1. Figures are bracketed in all cases where the altitude is not specifically above ground level.

Many birds nesting in Siberia and wintering in India are forced to cross the Himalayas, where even the passes are at great heights. That migrants use them regularly was proved by the discovery of the skeletons of a black-tailed godwit (*Limosa limosa*) and a pintail (*Anas acuta*) on Khumbu Glacier, over 16,000 feet, at the foot of Mount Everest (Géroudet, 1954). Flight at these altitudes presents a physiological problem because of the rarefied air in the upper strata of the atmosphere. Above 12,000 feet man is seriously affected by mountain sickness and severe cold, but birds apparently do not suffer any discomfort.

It is clear that birds migrate at various altitudes; by adapting themselves to local conditions, they can seek an elevation where they will find the most favourable wind direction.

Altitude is also determined by the nature of the terrain. As a rule, land-birds fly higher above the sea than over land, whereas the opposite is true of sea-birds. Eiders (*Somateria mollissima*) fly very low over the sea, but rise as soon as they reach land. Passerines, however, have often been seen migrating just above the waves. No strict rule can be applied, since Meinertzhagen states that some individuals in a group of migrating kites (*Milvus*) were flying at ground level, others at 5,000 feet.

While working with common chaffinches and starlings in the Netherlands, Deelder and Tinbergen (1947) found that the altitude of flight seems to be largely determined by meteorological factors, particularly the force and direction of the wind (Fig. 74). Birds fly at a lower altitude in a violent wind than when it is blowing moderately. Moreover, the altitude increases with the angle between the direction of the wind and the direction of flight. Visibility in rainy weather and the nature of the biotope may also play a part. Although common chaffinches fly higher over a treeless area than above a forest, starlings do not seem affected by these factors.

Lorenz (*in* Deelder and Tinbergen, 1947) noted that large birds, such as cranes, crows and gulls, fly higher on a tail wind than against a head wind for 'security reasons'; a tail wind does not support an airfoil so well, and it forms 'eddies' dangerous to large birds flying low.

Altitude of flight thus varies according to atmospheric conditions, and the variations explain why authors have given such conflicting figures, none of which can be said to be the *only* right ones.

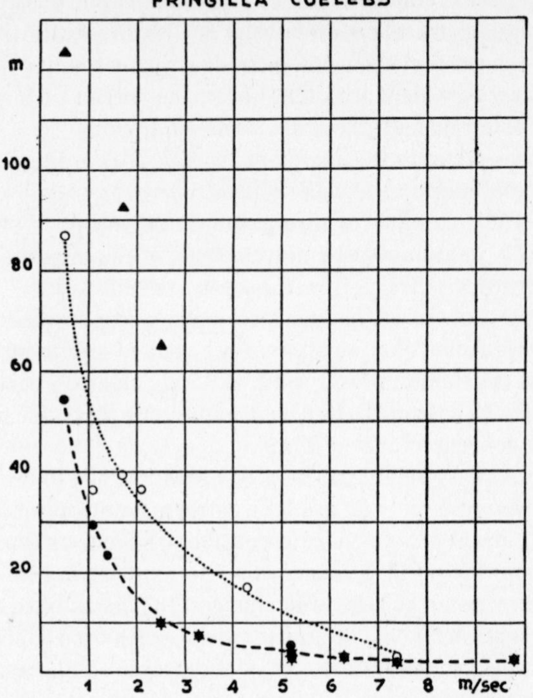

Fig. 74. Variations in altitude of the migratory flight of chaffinches (*Fringilla coelebs*) as determined by wind velocity (this is measured 2 m. from the ground)'

Curve in broken lines: series of observations with SSW-WSW winds.

Curve in dotted lines: series of observations with SSW-ESE and NNW-WNW winds.

Triangles: series of observations with ENE-NNE winds (asterisks indicate observations with the naked eye). From Deelder and Tinbergen, 1947.

Migrations and Wind

As the bird flies in a moving liquid which varies both in direction and speed, wind plays a major part in migratory flight. Although it has no influence on the general direction of migration, wind can serve to a certain degree in orientation, and it also has a bearing on the selection of local migration routes. Here we run into the old question about whether migrants travel on a following or fly into a head wind. There is no real reason for argument, since it is increasingly evident that behaviour varies widely according to: 1) the species of birds, 2) the nature of the terrain and, above all, 3) the wind velocity.

Some birds prefer to fly in a following wind. According to German observers the common skylark (*Alauda arvensis*) migrates in this fashion to Heligoland in the spring. But we may wonder whether the wind actually determines this movement or if the migrant is simply following warm air coming from the south and south-west.

Drost (1931) observed that many spring migrants fly mainly *against* the wind. He found that eighty-two per cent of migrating common chaffinches travel into a head wind, and only eighteen per cent on a tail wind. In the case of the linnet (*Acanthis cannabina*) the figures are ninety-five per cent and five per cent.

Most small Passerines seem to need adverse winds to migrate, and there are even cases of what has been called anemotropism (a tropism in which a current of air is the orienting factor). Some observers report that migrants flying in a certain direction will turn and go in the opposite direction when the wind changes. In *autumn* birds migrating south or south-west will fly north when north-east winds are encountered. Koch (1934) has described these reversed migrations in the case of the common skylark (*Alauda arvensis*), the wood lark (*Lullula arborea*), the meadow pipit (*Anthus pratensis*), the yellow wagtail (*Motacilla flava*), the starling (*Sturnus vulgaris*), the fieldfare (*Turdus pilaris*), the redwing (*T. musicus*), the common chaffinch (*Fringilla coelebs*), the brambling (*F. montifringilla*), and the tree sparrow (*Passer montanus*). Various species are affected differently by changing winds.

But several other factors influence the direction of migration. During a series of methodical observations in the North Sea and Germany, which were summarized by Drost (1931), many deviations, even reversed migrations, were recorded. At first, they were attributed to a sudden veering of the wind, but more thorough analysis indicates that migration against the wind is usually caused by thermal considerations, and that migrants seek the warmth carried by the wind rather than the movement of the air.

The wind's influence also varies according to the character of the terrain. When geographical features are clearly marked, the wind's influence is scarcely evident, and migration routes converge towards an island, for example, without regard for it. At the Kurische Nehrung the natural migration route traced by this tongue of land exerts such a strong attraction that birds pay no attention to the wind.

The wind's effect on migration also depends largely on its velocity. Observers who studied migratory common chaffinches in Holland (Deelder, 1949; Vleugel, 1950; Tinbergen, 1950) found that in autumn they migrated as freely into a slight head wind as in a following slight wind. As the wind becomes stronger, a head wind is preferred, and in a very strong wind, particularly a following wind, migration stops almost completely, as it does in a dead calm.

More detailed observations have shown that the wind's direction and force are capable of changing the migratory behaviour and routes of common chaffinches in Holland. It has long been known that there are large concentrations of these birds along the coasts when the wind is from the south-east, south, south-west and west, whereas very few appear when it is blowing from the east and north-east. Dutch net-hunters say that when the 'high' winds (that is the term used in Holland for north and north-east winds) blow, very few birds are captured. Deelder (1952) compared the number of common chaffinches taken in Dutch snares from 1768 to 1881 with the prevailing winds as they were registered by the near-by meteorological institute. It was evident that there was a close connection between the wind's direction and the size of the flight, as revealed by the number of birds caught.

It has also been noted that during years when large numbers of birds are captured in the snares there is an equal number of males and females. In 'scarce' years there is a great surplus of males. Year after year virtually the same number of migratory common chaffinches migrates to England and Ireland, so it is apparent that during bad years the larger contingent, which must be composed of a majority of females, takes another route than the one along the Dutch coast. Females travel farther on migration than males. They are more numerous in Ireland, whereas males predominate in England. Females, furthermore, are less reluctant to venture out to sea,[1] and they have a stronger migratory impulse (see p. 319). We may thus conclude that most of the common chaffinches go straight to England when the winds are from the north or north-east, instead of following the Dutch coast.

Since the birds fly too high to be observed, these were mere

1. There are more females than males at Heligoland.

hypotheses, but careful watching has shown that as soon as the wind veers towards the east, common chaffinches rise and cross the coast to vanish into the West. Only a few individuals leave the group to follow the coast at a much lower altitude (600–900 feet instead of 1,500–2,500). These two migration routes, used by such disproportionate contingents of migrants, tally with what we know about the flights of the common chaffinch on an east wind. The difference in altitude is explained by the fact that the birds fly higher when they are over the sea, which is a strange environment, fraught with danger.

This divergent behaviour appears in the graphs (Fig. 75 A and B); on a strong east wind common chaffinches keep to the same north-east – south-west direction and cross the Dutch coast without turning south to follow it. There is no concentration along the coast, as a large proportion of birds fly directly from Norway and Denmark to England. English observers have recorded these straight flights and noticed that they were more frequent on an east wind.

In a moderate south-west wind common chaffinches follow the Dutch coast for a much longer time but leave it when it turns sharply south. In a strong south-west wind there is a real concentration of the *Schmalfront* type on the coast, so it is evident that the wind plays a very important part in their migrations. These findings were later confirmed by similar observations along the coasts of northern Germany and Denmark (Westernhagen, 1954).

Yet H. G. Harrison (1954) recorded that spring migrants going north and north-east, especially small birds, cross the mouth of the Elbe, which is about nine miles wide, in greater numbers in a north and north-west wind than when it is from the south and south-west.

Wind must also be responsible for the seemingly capricious behaviour of migrants which stop their flight for no apparent reason. A thorough study of prevailing conditions will probably show how other species are affected.

In any case, no general rule applies to the relationship between migrations and wind, so it is not surprising that authors fail to agree on this complex problem. Once again it should be emphasized that the behaviour of birds is extremely plastic.

Many birds take advantage of rising air currents, which may be produced by wind deflected from a slope or by air that is heated by the ground (Forster, 1955). Mackintosh (1949) found from his observation

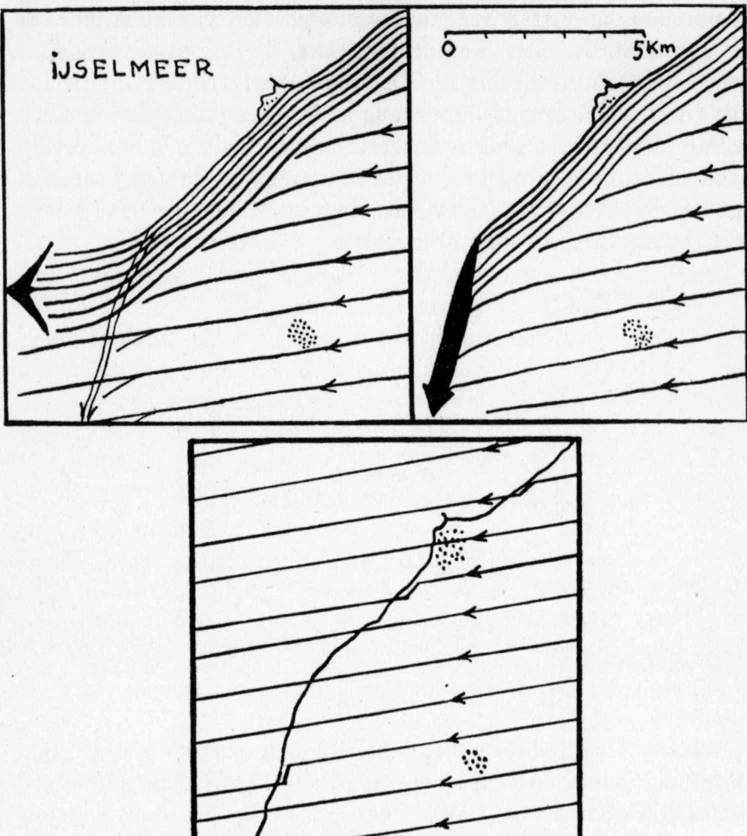

Fig. 75. Variations in the migratory behaviour of chaffinches (*Fringilla coelebs*) in the Netherlands in accordance with the direction and the force of the wind.

Upper left. Light wind in the south sector. Chaffinches coming from the East in a WSW direction reach the coast and then turn SW and follow the shore until it turns south. Most of the birds then veer west over the sea, and only a small number continue along the coast.

Upper right. A strong wind from the SW sector. The same phenomena occur, but no chaffinch risks flying over the sea. They all follow the coast, even when it turns definitely away from their original flight direction. This is a real narrow front migration.

Below. A light wind in the E and NE sectors. There is no concentration of migrants along the coast. They all cross it and continue in the same direction over the sea. Some show only a very slight hesitation. From Tinbergen, 1950.

of storks in the Gulf of Suez that these warm currents determine the birds' migration routes. Raptores also describe 'aerial carrousels' in which from ten to seventy birds generally participate, but in which there may be 250 or more. These migrants are not seen before ten a.m. because they have to wait for upward currents, which do not develop until the sun has warmed the ground. Then the birds soar in spirals, coming from east and north-east and drifting slowly south-west without beating their wings. (Fig. 76).

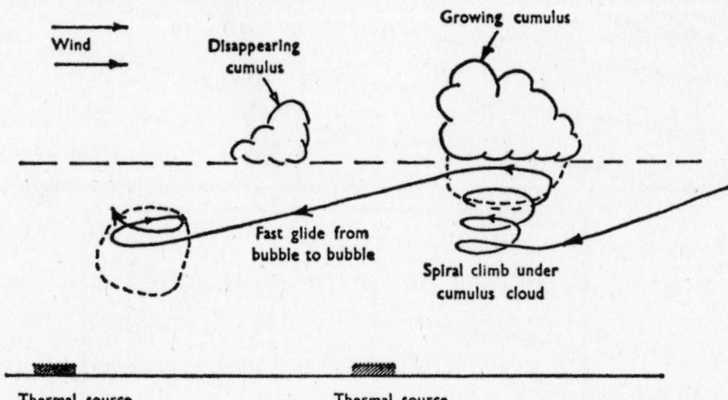

Fig. 76. Flight of a bird using thermals for cross country flying. We must remember that many bubbles do not reach the dew point before they disperse; a cumulus cloud merely indicates strong thermal activity. From Forster, 1955.

We have seen that the wind's influence on migrants varies and that birds reap as much benefit from it as possible. Strong gales, however, are terribly destructive to birds unable to reach shelter. Many migrants are carried far from their customary routes, and this explains why certain tropical and pelagic species are occasionally found in regions where normally they are never seen, especially sea-birds, which are sometimes blown far inland by hurricanes (see p. 183).

Migrations and Weather Conditions

Bird migrations and the climatic cycle seem to be remarkably well synchronized, for migrants everywhere leave in autumn and return in the spring. Even in tropical countries periodic flights coincide with alternating dry and rainy seasons, so it is natural that a cause-and effect relationship in these phenomena has long been sought.

In some cases, at least, there is a close link between bird migrations and the 'weather.' Meteorological conditions influence the migration pattern and may affect its route. There seems, moreover, to be a connection between the dates of arrival and departure on one hand, and regional climates on the other. But we shall see that seasonal changes are only one of the secondary causes that determine the timing and course of the migratory impulse.

Hasty generalizations about the relationship between migrants and weather have led many authors to diametrically opposite opinions. Some believe that weather is the exclusive factor determining migrations; others ascribe no influence to it whatsoever. The problem is all the more complex because bird migration is conditioned by many factors which cannot be isolated. In any case, meteorological influences alone cannot be responsible for it.

Some authors have attempted to classify migrants in two categories: 1) those closely dependent on surrounding conditions for both their spring and autumn migrations (German writers call these migrants *Wettervögel*). Their arrival in the spring is determined by the weather, and the pattern of their flight hinges on the thermometer and the barometer. This group includes the woodcock, which we shall discuss later, the snipe, lapwing, larks and the starling; 2) the other group, which is much more independent. As the dates of their arrival and departure are not regulated by the weather, they occur with remarkable regularity year after year (these are the *Instinktvögel* of German authors).[1] The best example is doubtless the swift, which reaches a certain summer or winter area every spring or autumn at about the same date, regardless of the weather. Some Passerines show similar behaviour, the willow warbler and the redstart in Europe, the northern cliff swallow,[2] the eastern ovenbird and Baltimore oriole in North America.

A sudden drop in temperature after their arrival causes high

1. The same regularity is sometimes observed in winter quarters. Harrisson (1960) noted that several migrants nesting in northern Asia and wintering in Malaysia come to Borneo so regularly in the autumn that the Kelabits, a tribe inhabiting the uplands of interior Borneo, set their calendar by their arrival. According to Harrisson, these birds are the yellow wagtail (*Motacilla flava*), the brown shrike (*Lanius cristatus*), the Japanese sparrow hawk (*Accipiter virgatus*) and the pallid thrush (*Turdus obscurus*). Several others behave in the same way.

2. As Bent reports in his classical *Life Histories*, it is claimed that cliff swallows arrive each year on 19 March at the Mission of San Juan Capistrano, in southern California. Even their hour of arrival is said to be constant!

mortality among these insectivorous birds, which cannot escape from the cold weather and scarcity of food by local or reversed migrations. Whole flocks may be wiped out by late spring freezes or snowfalls.

These categories cannot be too rigid, for it is often impossible to decide to which group a given bird belongs. The hooded crow, for example, has been put in the 'weather' group by some authors (Henning), whereas others declare it belongs in the 'instinctive' group (Koch).

That temperature is one of the most important elements of weather becomes clear when we consider the climatic aspect of migration. In the spring, as in autumn, migrants are guided to a great extent by thermal factors and their seasonal variations.

More than a century ago Middendorf (1855) showed how the migratory front advances northward in the spring. He had collected a great number of observations about the yearly dates of arrival of certain migrants in various parts of the Russian Empire.[1] He then calculated an average arrival date on the basis of observations over many years. He plotted these data on a map, linked the localities which migrants reach on the same date and thus obtained a line he called the isopiptes, by analogy with the lines of equal temperature, or isotherms, and those of equal pressure, or isobars (this line was later named the isochronal line). These successive lines show the northward progress of the spring migratory front. They have little to do with terrestrial parallels and are, indeed, highly inconsistent. Depending on the meridian of the observation post, the same latitude is often reached by a species at very different dates; birds arrive in western Russia long before they reach more eastern localities with a more severe climate. Middendorf drew no conclusion about climatic influence, as he was working on more general hypotheses pertaining to the mechanism of migration.

A similar method, used more recently by Sliwinsky (1938), established the isochronal line of several European birds: the swallow, house martin, swift, cuckoo, stork. Her maps show how Europe is

1. It is difficult to record the precise date of arrival of most migrants, for birds breeding or wintering in a restricted perimeter arrive in scattered groups, and the returns are spread over a rather long period. According to Schuster (1953), the 57 pairs and three unmated birds comprising the total summer swallow (*Hirundo rustica*) population in a German village did not appear until 53 days after the first contingent arrived. There is always a degree of error in computing the 'arrival' date, even when records are based on the advance guard.

invaded in the spring, and they also bring to light important variations between species, such as the swallow and the swift. (Figs. 77 and 78).

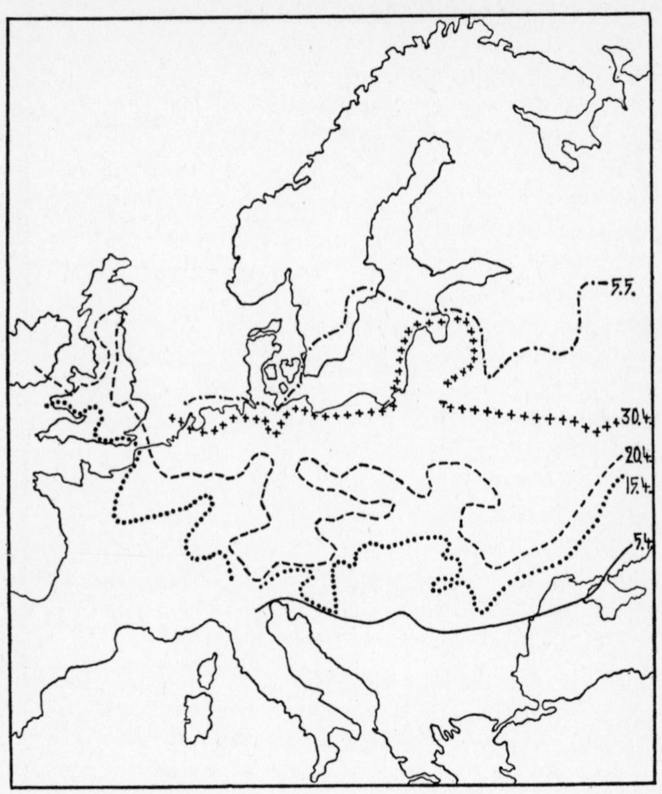

Fig. 77. Isochronal lines of the house martin (*Delichon urbica*) in Europe. After Sliwinsky, 1938, simplified.

But the most interesting feature of the maps pertains to the dates of arrival in different localities. In general, western Europe is populated before eastern Europe, and the swallow reaches the southern half of Great Britain before it appears in any part of Russia north of the Crimea. Climatic differences are clearly responsible for this contrast.

When Southern (1938a, 1938b, 1939, 1941) placed on a map the isochronal lines of a number of European birds and the isotherm of 48° F. at different periods in the spring, it was apparent that the two are amazingly similar. For the swallow the isochronal line of 15 March is south of the isotherm of the same date, but by 1 April the

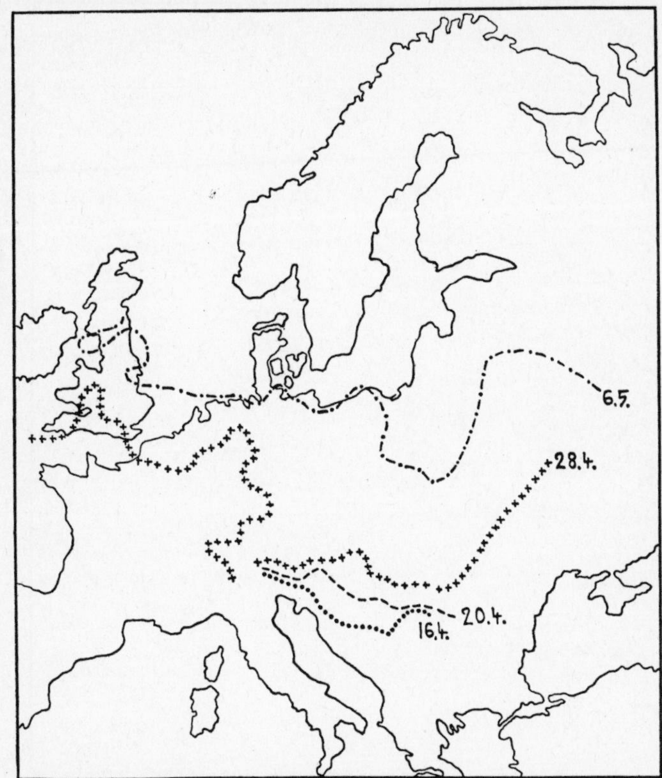

Fig. 78. Isochronal lines of the swift (*Apus apus*) in Europe. Comparison with the house martin (see Fig. 77) shows the extent to which the swift is behind it (note especially the lines at the end of April). After Sliwinsky, 1938, simplified.

two are closer together, and from then on the birds precede the isotherm northward, so they arrive at Varanger, Norway, a full month before the isotherm of 48 ° F. (Fig. 79).

The willow warbler (*Phylloscopus trochilus*) is similar, although with some interesting differences (Fig. 80). It, too, follows the isotherm of 48 ° F. northward, but its isochronal lines stay more nearly parallel to the isotherm. It flies north faster and earlier than the swallow, but this is doubtless explained by differences in the diets of the two birds. The swallow cannot live without aerial plankton, which does not appear so early in the spring as the insects living in shrubbery, which is the willow warbler's favourite habitat.

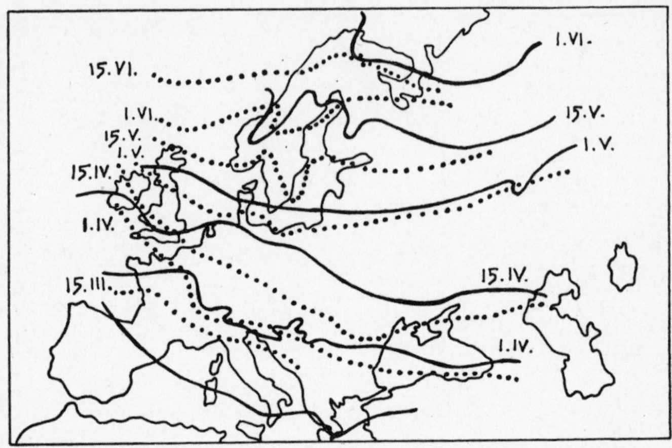

Fig. 79. Rate of spread of the swallow (*Hirundo r. rustica*) through Europe in the spring, compared to the movement of the isotherm of 48° F.

Unbroken black lines: isochronal lines of the swallow, dated at the right-hand end.

Dotted lines: movement of the 48° F. dated at the left-hand end.

The influence of temperature, revealed in this parallelism between isochronal lines and isotherms, may be less apparent because of other factors which also govern migration. First of all, there is the density of a species in various regions. When there is a large number of birds, individuals stimulate one another to migrate (at least when they migrate in flocks, as do many small Passerines); but if the population is less dense, this stimulus is weaker, migration begins later, and the birds do not move northward so fast as the isotherm.

These facts are apparent from the spring migration of the European redstart (*Phoenicurus phoenicurus*). Although this bird usually migrates more rapidly than the last two species, its migration front slows up along the Atlantic coast, and it is late in invading the British Isles, where the species is not very abundant.

Another important factor, which can also change the situation, is the former distribution of the species – a distribution which can often be inferred from the present migration routes. A study of the spring migration of the red-backed shrike (*Lanius collurio*) reveals a very

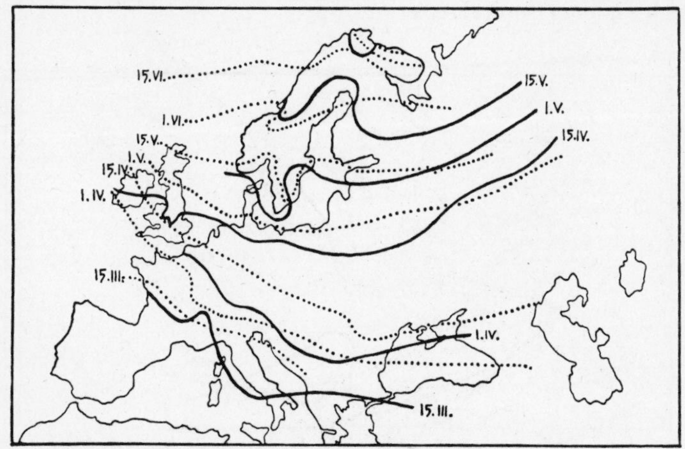

Fig. 80. Rate of spread of the willow warbler (*Phylloscopus trochilus*) through Europe in the spring, compared to the movement of the isotherm of 48° F. Same legend as in fig. 79. From Southern, 1938 b.

evident disparity between its isochronal lines and the isotherms (Fig. 81). These differences, however, are easily understood when it is recalled that the spring isotherm advances in a south-west–north-east direction, whereas the shrike invades Europe from south-east to north-west; hence it is impossible to correlate the thermal factor with the shrike's migration front.

Thus a parallel is not always found between the northward movement of spring and the advance of a migratory species, but the thermal factor is dominant in certain instances, usually because of its influence on the available food supply. In any case, there seems to be a connection between the *average* date when certain species arrive and rising temperatures.

W. W. Cooke (1915b) and Lincoln (1935b) have shown that there is a definite parallel in North America between the northward progression of a certain isotherm, marking the 'coming of spring,' and the northward flight of migrants. Canada geese and American robins both follow the isotherm of 35° F. Their progress is uniform, but some migrants, like many European birds, seem to follow an isotherm and then to pass it after reaching a northern latitude (Fig. 82). This is true of the yellow warbler (*Dendroica petechia*) and many small birds which winter in tropical America.

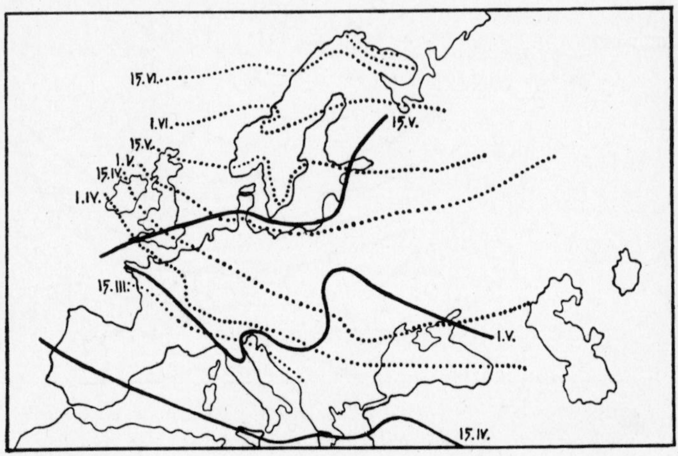

Fig. 81. Rate of spread of the red-backed shrike (*Lanius collurio*) through Europe in the spring, compared to the movement of the isotherm of 48° F. Same legend as in fig. 79. From Southern, 1941.

There are other links between the arrival of certain migrants and temperature, but now we are dealing with meteorological rather than climatic conditions. Temperature is often responsible for migration anomalies, such as those observed in the U.S.A. in the spring of 1947. An unusually early flight of migrants (Gunn and Crocker, 1951) brought various insectivorous species, especially Parulidae (wood warblers) and vireos, to the region just south of the Great Lakes in early April, a full month before the dates when they normally appear there. A number of southern birds, which usually do not visit these regions at all, were also observed.

This was a period of unusual meteorological conditions. A tempest from the Gulf of Mexico crossed the continent, carrying currents of warm air in a north-easterly direction, with the result that abnormally high temperatures were recorded in most of these areas. Violent winds doubtless carried a number of birds, but the warm atmosphere made it possible for many species to go north and survive there.

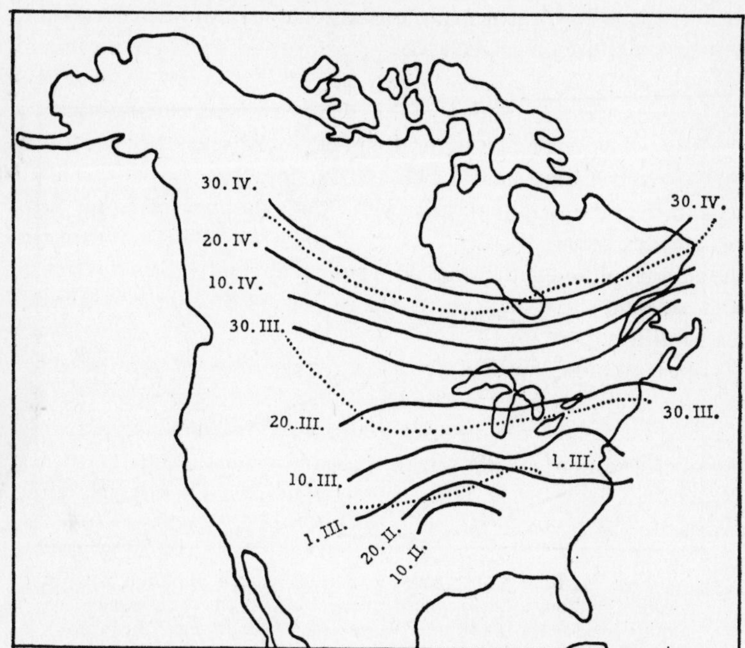

Fig. 82. Rate of spread of the Canada goose (*Branta canadensis*) through North America in the spring, compared to the movement of the isotherm of 35° F. Note the agreement of the northward movement of the isotherm and the isochronal line of the Canada goose. From Lincoln, 1935 b.

The influence of temperature on the migratory behaviour of birds is also shown by reversed migrations. These are local movements of migrants in the opposite direction from the normal one at a given season; they are not primarily related to a diversion line (*Leitlinie* of German authors). There have been many such observations, both in autumn and spring. Lack and Lack (1953) record common chaffinches in south-western France flying east-north-east in the autumn, when a north wind brought masses of fairly warm air. In Europe northward reversed migrations have been noted among starlings, common chaffinches, larks, pipits and some thrushes (in general, among all the birds the Germans call *Wettervögel*).

Natorp (1932) described movements of this kind at Myslowice in Silesia during the spring of 1931. A period of fine weather with a south-east wind, during which many migrants flew south-west–north-east, was followed by a cold spell with a strong wind from the north and north-west. This caused a large reversed migration, as countless common chaffinches and bramblings sought refuge farther south.

Migrants occasionally fly south in the spring when they encounter sudden cold fronts, and Lewis (1939) describes a great reversed migration in the vicinity of Lake Erie. Many authors think that birds change their course in order to enjoy the most favourable aerodynamic conditions; although the wind does not act directly, it brings warm or cold air, and these movements are caused by a reversal of normal temperatures.

Other authors, particularly Drost, have insisted that reversed migrations always occur in cloudy weather. Later we shall see that the sun plays a definite rôle in orientation; when it is hidden, and when thermal conditions are abnormal, these authors assume that birds are more or less disturbed and that, relying mainly on warm temperature, they fly in the opposite direction in search of it! This is a somewhat anthropomorphic explanation.

When temperature does not exert a dominant influence, it is often hard to trace migratory behaviour to any single climatic or meteorological factor. Migration seems governed by all the diverse components of 'weather' – temperature, winds, rain, fog. As these are all finally determined by high and low pressure areas, in other words, by the general meteorological situation, the 'weather map' and the migration map are surely related. Cooke (1915b) was aware of this, unlike many earlier writers who believed that birds were driven by an irresistible migratory urge.

Hungarian ornithologists, especially Schenk (1924), who has devoted much study to the problem, say that the dates of arrival of the woodcock (*Scolopax rusticola*) range from the beginning of March to early April. A comparison with yearly variations in meteorological conditions reveals that every arrival of a large flock of birds in Hungary is correlated to a barometric depression in the North-west, i.e. in western Europe, especially in the British Isles. (Fig. 83). Meteorological maps of Europe disclose similar conditions, year after year, on days when there is a large woodcock migration. Schenk found that the first north-westerly depression in western Europe, and usually in Great Britain at the end of February or early in March, generally brings woodcock to the coast of the Adriatic and up into

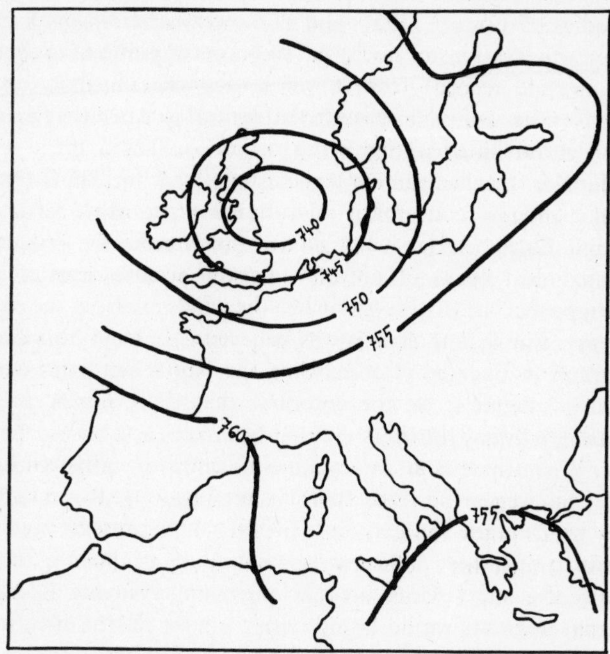

Fig. 83. Type of barometric situation favourable for spring migration of the woodcock (*Scolopax rusticola*) in Hungary. See explanations in the text. After Schenk, 1924.

the Drave plain. If it lasts several days and moves slowly east or north-east, there will be large migrations in this direction. If the depression does not last long enough, migration tends to stop and is not resumed until another low pressure area reaches western Europe. This cannot be considered a fixed law, for other factors may cause the birds to migrate or to linger; but meteorological conditions are so important that, according to Schenk, hunters can expect their quarry on the basis of advance information supplied by the meteorological map. These data have been confirmed elsewhere in Europe, especially in Germany, but it should be noted that the woodcock is influenced by meteorological conditions only during its migration periods.

Similar studies made in Germany, Finland and elsewhere indicate that migratory movements are usually closely connected with warm or cool air masses and the distribution of high and low pressure areas. The studies of Lowery (1951) and of Lowery and Newman (1955), based on observations of nocturnal migrants crossing the face of the moon, include records from a whole network of observers who worked together across the eastern and central part of the U.S.A., and even in Central America; they bring further confirmation.

Williamson reached similar conclusions, and he has theories of particular interest concerning migrational drift. More than thirty years ago Eagle Clarke, Miss Baxter and Rintoul (*in* Williamson) had noted that flocks of autumn migrants usually appear in the northern part of the British Isles when the winds are from the east and south-east. For a long time it was believed that most Scandinavian birds arrive in England after crossing the North Sea from Norway. Williamson suggests, on the contrary, that these nordic migrants travel along a flyway skirting the North Sea from Denmark to northern France. When there is an anticyclone in central or northern Europe (which encourages the birds to leave on their autumn migration), easterly winds at the southern border of this high pressure zone cause the birds to drift west and carry large numbers of them to England, especially if easterly winds are also prevailing over the North Sea. Nocturnal migrants would be still more subject to this drift, as they cannot correct their position by terrestrial landmarks.

The coastal route suggested by Williamson is much less hazardous than the direct crossing of the North Sea, and the latter necessitates a difficult detour for Scandinavian birds going south-west to winter quarters. In support of his theory Williamson cites various examples of migrants observed in the British Isles, especially at Fair Isle, in the South Shetlands, where there is an important ornithological station. This region, an important crossroads for migrations, is located at the meteorological frontier of the continental and oceanic zones, a frontier where frequent changes in wind direction or pressure cause rapid, marked changes in English weather. Furthermore, this island is on the route of autumn migrants from Greenland and Iceland, as well as from northern Europe, so it is possible to compare weather-patterns at the time of these flights.

European redwings (*Turdus musicus*), whose migratory behaviour was analysed by Williamson (1953, 1958b), are particularly enlightening. These Turdidae nest in northern Europe (the typical race), and in Iceland, where there is a different race (*T.m. coburni*) which can be

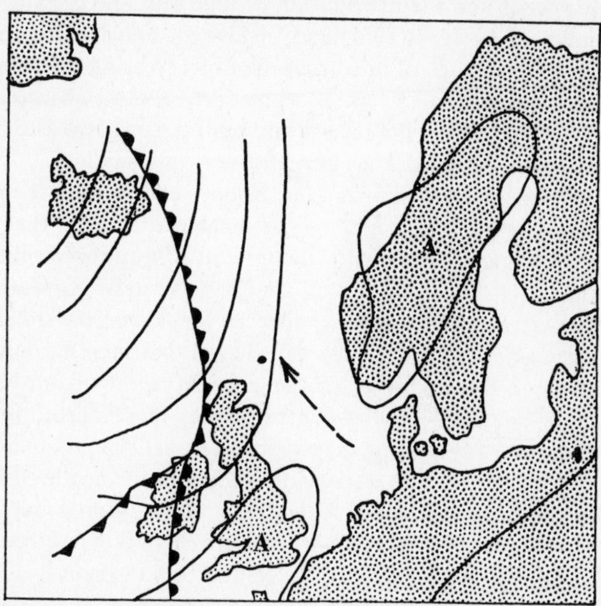

Fig. 84. Influence of the meteorological situation on autumn migrations of the redwing (*Turdus musicus*) in Great Britain. Favourable weather for the drift of Continental redwings (*T.m. musicus*) coming from Scandinavia. Situation during the night of 7–8 October 1954. This anticyclonic drift, which was confined to northern islands, brought at least 5,000 redwings to Fair Isle (the island is marked by a dot) on the morning of 8 October. A: Anticyclone. After Williamson, 1958 b, redrawn.

easily recognized in the wild if an adequate sample is trapped. Both races migrate to Fair Isle, but under totally different circumstances (Figs. 84 and 85).

After comparing meteorological maps showing the weather at the time of migration and the size and subspecific composition of the flocks of migrants on the island, Williamson discovered that the arrival of continental thrushes (*musicus*) usually coincides with an anticyclone centered on Scandinavia or northern Europe. If its influence does not extend to England, the migrants are carried by east winds to the level of Skagerak and the coasts of northern Europe, and then they drift across the North Sea.

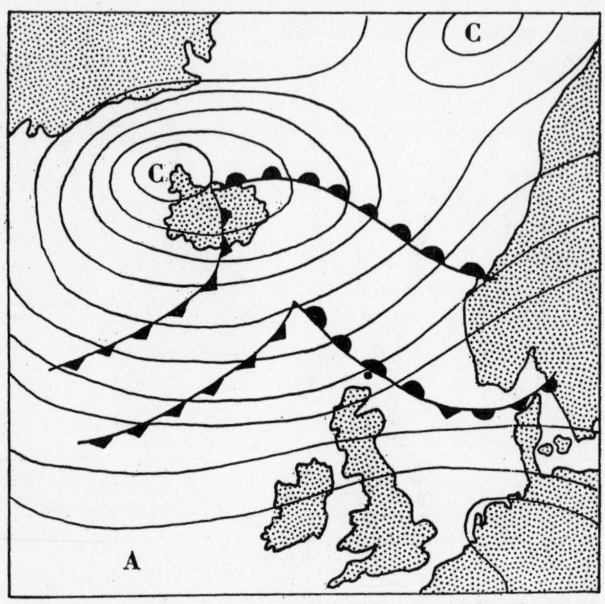

Fig. 85. Influence of the meteorological situation on autumn migrations of the redwing (*Turdus musicus*) in Great Britain. Favourable weather for the drift of Iceland redwings (*T.m. coburni*). Situation during the day on 11 October, 1956. This cyclonic drift brought 500 redwings from Iceland to Fair Isle on 12 October. A: Anticyclone; C: Cyclone. After Williamson, 1958 b, redrawn.

This occurred early in October, 1951, when an anticyclone developed in the eastern Mediterranean, moved across Russia, and turned towards Scandinavia. The east winds sweeping the North Sea carried countless Passerines, including European robins (*Erithacus rubecula*), several stragglers from the Orient, and a great number of redwings; 500 passed Fair Isle on the first and second of October and 200 on the third.

During the autumn of 1952 an anticyclone developed in Scandinavia after crossing England on 10 and 11 October. East winds brought 800 redwings to Fair Isle on 12 October, but these were only the forerunners of a 'rush' of more than 2,000 birds which arrived the 13th and 14th. After the weather changed in southern Scandinavia a few days later, the number of birds decreased, and then the anticyclone spread again, bringing another 'rush' on the 20th and 21st.

In October, 1954, more than 5,000 birds came to Fair Isle during similar meteorological conditions. But these situations are fairly rare, as the influence of the Scandinavian anticyclone is often counterbalanced by depressions based on Atlantic Europe. East winds, however, can be produced by the northward movement of such depressions.

The arrival of the Iceland redwings (*coburni*) is produced by entirely different meteorological conditions. It may be due to the development of an anticyclone to the west of Iceland, following the northward movement of an anticyclone from the Azores, or to the southward descent of a Greenland anticyclone. But Iceland redwings appear most frequently in cyclonic westerly or north-westerly weather, when violent winds drive the birds towards Great Britain. At such times large migrations have been recorded at Fair Isle, and in October, 1954, Williamson noted more than 1,000 birds a day.

Migrant land-birds which have been carried off course are always quite thin, as they have been flying long distances with inadequate food and water. They may lose twenty to thirty per cent of their weight while crossing the North Sea.[1] These losses are doubtless explained by the use of fat reserves, as well as by the loss and lack of water. Eliasson (1958) estimated that water represents an important constituent, of which only twenty-five to thirty per cent would be replaced by the combustion of fat, and the remainder from intestinal reserves.

Other instances have been cited, chiefly by Williamson, with particular reference to the spring migration of the willow warbler (*Phylloscopus trochilus*) as it occurred in Great Britain in 1952 (Williamson and Butterfield, 1954). Two waves of migrants, of slightly different races (varying wing length, among other characters), invaded the British Isles from the south-west and south-east in the spring; in the

1. Voous (1953) noted an even greater loss in the blackpoll warblers (*Dendroica striata*) he observed in the Dutch Lesser Antilles in the autumn. Hundreds of these warblers arrived in a state of complete exhaustion, and weighed only eight or nine grams, or 50% of the amount recorded by Beebe for individuals in winter quarters in Venezuela. Voous records similar observations of the yellow-billed cuckoo (*Coccyzus americanus*).

first case there was a vast anticyclone over western and central Europe, with a depression off the Hebrides and winds from south-east to south-south-east; in the other instance a depression centred east of Great Britain caused east winds which carried the birds from the German and Danish coasts of the North Sea.

Further studies by Williamson have been devoted to other migrants in Great Britain whose movements are also linked to meteorological conditions, for example, chiffchaffs (*Phylloscopus collybita*) (1954a,) the Iceland merlin (*Falco columbarius*) (1954b), the Greenland redpole (*Acanthis flammea rostrata* (1956), and the Lapland longspur (*Calcarius lapponicus*) (Williamson and Davis, 1956).

These show that he was right in drawing attention to the meteorological situation as an immediate stimulus for migratory flights. Several other British authors, notably Cornwallis (1957), have made similar interesting observations on the east coast of England.

As yet little information is available as to how meteorological conditions affect migratory behaviour, although certain studies throw light on the question. Miskimen (1955), who has worked with American ducks (black ducks [*Anas rubripes*], mallards [*Anas platyrhynchus*], and lesser scaups [*Aythya affinis*]), found by analysing the daily rhythm of activity in relation to the variations in intensity of light that ducks gather in flocks on cloudy days. This social organization, which is a response to pale light, violent winds and other meteorological factors, is therefore already established when the weather clears and the birds can depart at once. In any case, the factors inciting birds to migrate are very complex, and both meteorological and psychological influences are involved.

Studies in the U.S.A. (Bagg *et al.*, 1950; Raynor, 1956) show that the northward movement in the spring occurs when the atmospheric situation is quite settled. By grouping ornithological and meteorological observations during the period from 17 to 21 April, 1948, American ornithologists showed that the northward migratory movement usually begins when the barometric gradient falls from east to west. It increases with warm winds caused by a depression moving from south-west to north-east. The size of the migratory wave is almost proportionate to the lowering of the barometer and the extension of the depression.

Dennis (1954) found that migrants respond with surprising precision to variations in the weather. At Smith Point, Texas, the arrival of a cold front stops prenuptial migration immediately or within twenty-four hours. The birds' departure is usually prompted by south winds, rising temperature and a falling barometer. Devlin (1954) made similar observations in Philadelphia.

In autumn the phenomena are reversed. On 31 October–3 November, 1955, 6–8 November, 1956, and 23–25 October, 1957, there were spectacular migrations of water-fowl or 'grand passages' of hundreds of thousands of ducks across north central North America. According to comparative studies of Bellrose (1957) and Bellrose and Sieh (1960), this movement was produced by low pressure areas in 1955 and 1956 and by a high pressure area in 1957. There were storm conditions on the northern Great Plains with overcast skies, snow, strong winds and falling temperatures which drove the ducks south faster than the cold air (Figs. 86 and 87). Hochbaum's excellent book (1955) gives many examples showing that changing meteorological conditions can produce large movements of water-fowl.

Migrations of birds of prey are also influenced by the weather. Crowds of observers who gather at Hawk Mountain Sanctuary, Pennsylvania, to see autumn hawk migrations above ridges and valleys (see p. 257) know that great flights occur when a cold wave arrives with north-west or north-east winds accompanying a depression centred over the northern states and moving east (St Lawrence) from the Great Lakes region.

Lowery's studies on weather and migration reveal that the crossing of the Gulf of Mexico by large numbers of migrants on their way to or from winter quarters in tropical America is also greatly influenced by meteorological conditions.

Among the sea-birds which are caught during their seasonal flights in the great air currents caused by meteorological changes in the North Atlantic are Wilson's petrel, great shearwater and the arctic tern. Austral Procellariiformes doubtless circle the antarctic continent when they are driven by the great west winds of that region. These marine species depend on atmospheric conditions to a far greater extent than land-birds.

It thus seems that migrations occur in relatively precise meteorological conditions, which are found year after year at the same periods (with certain variations). This parallel between the annual migratory cycle and meteorological conditions is interesting, though never mathematically exact, and it is important in orientation.

Fig. 86. Weather conditions over the United States 6 November, 1956 (at 1.00 a.m. C.S.T.) according to the U.S. Weather Bureau. A low pressure area passed through North Dakota and then spread to form a trough from south-eastern Ontario to James Bay. Weather associated with this low consisted of falling temperatures, overcast skies, falling snow and winds from the north-west in the northern Great Plains region. These weather conditions initiated a massed waterfowl flight, bringing 1,000,000 ducks into Louisiana. From Bellrose and Sieh, 1960.

Electric conditions in the atmosphere also play a part in migration. 'Changes in the weather' are often accompanied by variations in the electric potential and in the degree of ionization in the atmosphere, which influences the behaviour of birds, especially migrants. Haart-

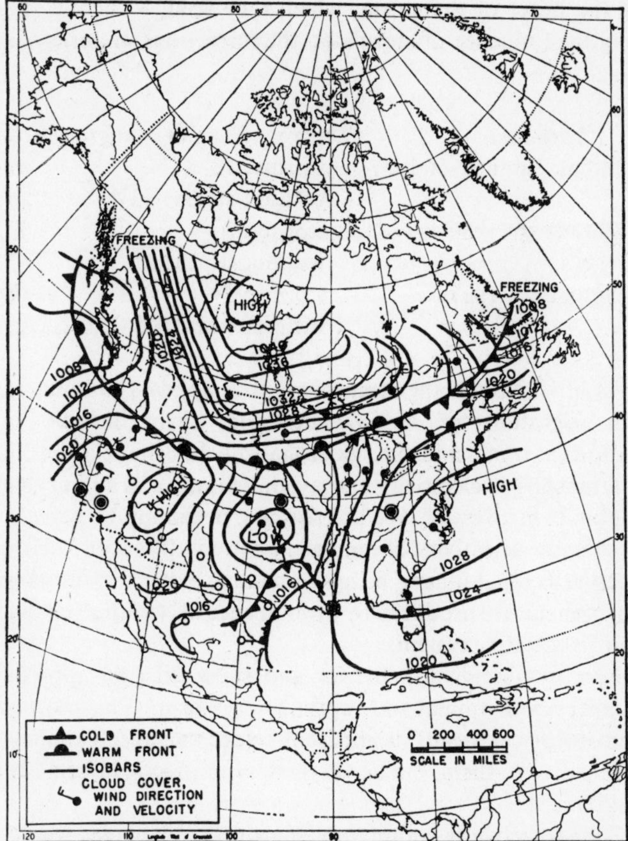

Fig. 87. Weather conditions over the United States 23 October, 1957 (1.00 a.m. C.S.T.) according to the U.S. Weather Bureau. A very large and strong high pressure area moved south-east from the Yukon Territory, Canada, to northern Alberta, and then southward, reaching the United States-Canadian border on 25 October. Mass migration of ducks began on 24 October in North Dakota. A half million ducks arrived in Louisiana on the night of 24 October and during the day and night of 25 October, 1957. From Bellrose and Sieh, 1960.

man's study (1939) on the curlew (*Numenius arquata*) is interesting in this connection. While observing a summer migration of these birds in Finland, he found the flocks were always larger on stormy days with severe electric disturbances. Curlews usually begin to fly several hours before the onset of the storm, which they seem to herald. Figures showing the influence of storms on the migrations of curlews are as follows:

Localities	*Days*	*Number of migrating curlews*
Lunsjäholm, summer of 1937	stormy: 13	60
	without storm: 53	21
Esbo, summer of 1936	stormy: 33	75
	without storm: 37	42
Esbo, summer of 1937	stormy: 29	68
	without storm: 25	29

The electric state of the atmosphere thus appears to influence the autumn migrations of curlews and other birds, including many Charadriidae (oystercatchers, greenshanks), but the relationship between atmospheric electricity and avian behaviour is still mysterious and highly controversial. We are scarcely beginning to perceive the meteorological sensitivity of animals, although this seems universal, and doctors say that human beings sometimes suffer seriously from it. The phenomena are produced by the influence of 'weather' changes on the neuro-vegetative system.

Changes in humidity in the air and snow, like an approaching storm, affect both animal and vegetable organisms. The approach of the meteorological 'fronts' is apparent before they reach animals and plants sensitive to them, but as yet there is no precise information on this matter.

Occasional recoveries of migrants far outside the areas where they are usually found may be explained by meteorological considerations. An abnormal situation may send birds as stragglers to regions they seldom visit. Edelstam and Snellman (1953) thus explain the capture in Sweden of two woodchat shrikes (*Lanius senator*), one in June, 1930, on the island of Aland, the other in May, 1953, at Öland (Ottenby). In both instances the authors believe that temperature was largely responsible for the northward flight of this southern bird. Williams (1950a) records that two waves of cold from the north-west, in late April and early May, 1946, crossed the U.S.A. diagonally and brought into Texas a series of migrants which normally live in the West. These included the ash-throated flycatcher (*Myarchus cinerascens*), the beardless flycatcher (*Camptostoma i. imberbe*), western flycatcher

(*Empidonax difficilis*) and several humming-birds like *Selasphorus rufus*, *Selasphorus platycercus* and *Calothorax lucifer*. The birds had flown far to the east of their normal migration route to avoid the cold.

Another question concerning migrants is whether, as numerous proverbs and legends say, birds are capable of 'predicting the weather.' Since many birds respond to the meteorological situation, it seems that the behaviour of migrants, in some instances at least, can foreshadow a change in weather. In autumn and winter certain northern birds, like geese and swans, herald the cold. When a cold wave strikes Europe, they move farther south, even before the thermometer drops. The arrival of swans and geese in France usually indicates low temperatures in England, Holland and Germany, and it is apt to get cold soon after their arrival. Snow often drives birds before it.

In the spring migrating birds may herald fine weather. Seilkopf (1952) reported that song thrushes arrived in Hamburg in March, 1952, in a temperature of 28° F. with a cold south-east wind. The thermometer rose immediately to 48°, so it seemed that the birds had announced spring warmth. Meteorological observations with sounding balloons showed, however, that the cold in Hamburg was due to a mass of frigid air above which it was warm; at about 3,000 feet the thermometer registered 45°, while at ground level the mercury was 28°. The birds had arrived with the warm air, but they came down to earth before it descended to ground level.

Hence there is a definite correlation between weather and the arrival of migrants, but it is one which has no absolute value. In any case, one swallow does not make a summer!

Migratory Behaviour

Every avian species has a behaviour pattern which may differ, even from that of its close relatives. The *period* of travel differs largely, and some birds seem much more sensitive to cold than others. Swifts leave their nesting area early in autumn and arrive very late in the spring, whereas swallows, which have much the same way of life, remain much longer. In some instances behaviour may be connected to feeding requirements that differ with the species, but other factors are still mysterious.

The *duration* of the migratory flight is just as variable. In some species it is relatively short, as the birds all seem to migrate together; in other cases flights extend over a long period, since the birds travel in successive waves. The first European swallows reach their African winter quarters while other swallows are still raising broods in Europe.

A study of the *composition of a flock of migrants* in a given species has revealed important variations in age and sex at different periods. Weigold found in Heligoland that most of the earliest autumn migrants among the common chaffinches, reed buntings, common skylarks and redstarts are young birds; then come the females and finally the males.[1] Deelder (1949) confirmed these observations when he was working with common chaffinches in Holland. There too females appear first and they seem to travel to more distant winter quarters than the males. Females are also more ready to cross the sea, probably because they have a stronger migratory impulse, while males are often sedentary. Thus the majority of the common chaffinches wintering in Scandinavia are males, for which reason Linnaeus called this Passerine *Fringilla* '*coelebs*' – bachelor.

In North America the same situation occurs in the song sparrow (*Melospiza melodia*), the mocking-bird (*Mimus polyglottos*), the hairy woodpecker (*Dendrocopus villosus*) and the greater prairie chicken (*Tympanuchus cupido*); here again females are more ready to migrate than males, and they travel to more remote winter quarters.

There are, however, important regional variations as to age and sex. In Egypt Moreau found that adult wintering cuckoos, red-backed shrikes, blackcaps and rock thrushes occasionally arrive before the young birds.

Male ruby-throated humming-birds start in July to leave their nesting territories in the northern part of their habitat. Males take no part in rearing the young, so they are free before the females have raised their broods.

In the spring, the two sexes may migrate together, but the males are usually the first to arrive in the north. They select the territory in the nesting area, defend it against invasion by other males, and act as hosts to the females when they arrive. As Heinroth quipped, their song seems to mean: 'Here is a bachelor with a house!'

Almost always the young seem to have the stronger migratory impulse. Young common herons, for example, scatter more widely,

1. These statements should not be taken too absolutely, as they concern the majority of, but not all, migrants.

whereas the adult birds are more apt to winter near the heronries. British gannets, which were studied by A. L. Thomson (1939), are distributed in winter along the Atlantic coasts of Europe and Africa; adults rarely pass the Straits of Gibraltar, but the young go on into West Africa.

Postjuvenile dispersion in some birds is doubtless linked to this behaviour. Starlings, herons, and possibly lapwings illustrate the pattern, which is only partially explained by the necessity of hunting for food.

One of the most debated questions with regard to the separate migration of young and adult birds concerns the white stork. Certain legends say that the young are taught by adults, who instruct them about the routes they should follow and winter territories. If this is true, there is a kind of tradition, transmitted from generation to generation, which obviates the necessity of real orientation.

In an effort to solve this problem, Rüppell (1931) kept young storks captive for three weeks after the departure of the adults. The young nevertheless started in the right direction, and some were recovered on the normal migration route. It is thus apparent that young storks can find their way without help from their parents, although they generally fly with their elders.

There are also important differences in the *hours of the day* at which migratory flights are observed. It is impossible to distinguish definite categories, since birds such as common herons, some shore-birds, ducks and cranes (which prefer day-time flying) travel both by day and at night, but on the whole there are two groups, *diurnal* and *nocturnal* migrants.

The former include pelicans, storks, birds of prey, turtledoves, bee-eaters, swifts, kingbirds, swallows, Corvidae, some Turdidae (American robin, eastern bluebird), shrikes and many Fringillidae. Among those showing a predilection for nocturnal flight are a number of water-birds (Limicoles and Anatidae), cuckoos, numerous New World flycatchers (Tyrannidae), Turdidae (with some exceptions), Old World warblers (Sylviidae), Old World flycatchers (Muscicapidae), vireos, New World warblers (Parulidae), American orioles (Icteridae), tanagers and some insectivorous Fringillidae (buntings). Among Passerines, most seed-eating birds prefer to migrate by day, most insect-eating species, except swallows, at night. It is interesting to see how the daily rhythm and simple habits of the Passerines are modified, for they are strictly diurnal in all other circumstances.[1]

This change of behaviour has been attributed to various causes, such as the desire to escape diurnal birds of prey and a fondness for spending the day hiding in bushes. But these reasons are obviously

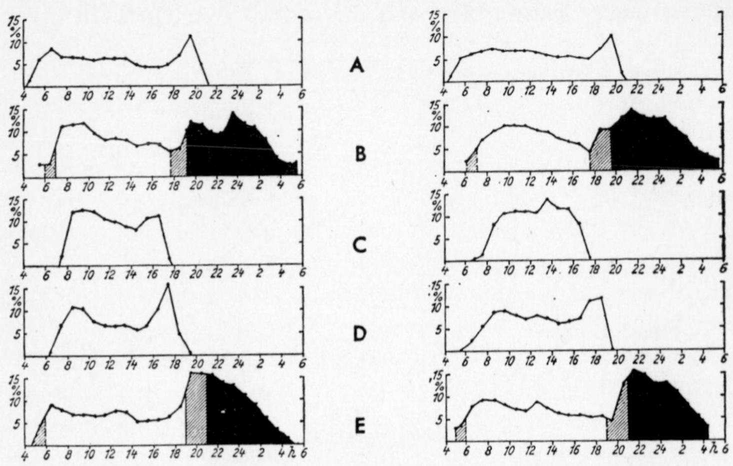

Fig. 88. European robin (*Erithacus rubecula*) — Whitethroat (*Sylvia communis*)

Rhythm of activity of the European robin and the whitethroat and its variations during the year. The birds were studied in captivity. Diurnal activity in white; nocturnal activity in black. A. July – August. B. August – November. C. November – December. D. January – March. E. March – May. Hours of the day on the X-axis; activity of the bird (percentage) on the Y-axis. Each curve represents an average of at least 100 nights of observation.

Note that the migratory activity does not replace normal activity but is added to it at night during migration periods. From Merkel, 1956.

insufficient. Palmgren (1936) called attention to the fact that diurnal migrants are usually capable of accumulating reserves of energy by feeding during flight (swallows, swifts). Nocturnal migratory Passerines, on the other hand, have a high metabolism and poor thermal regulation.

1. The nocturnal migrant shows an astonishing change of behaviour, and its resolute persistence is in striking contrast to its diurnal habits. A similar situation is found among Lepidoptera, for the pyralid snout or rush veneer moth (*Nomophila noctuella*) makes only short flights during the day but can easily cover long distances at night.

An analysis of the daily cycle of activities of migrants (see p. 289) shows that diurnal 'customary activity' and nocturnal migratory activity are quite different. At dusk the bird grows quiet. Some time after nightfall migratory restlessness begins (for example, the icterine warbler, many leaf-warblers and the spotted flycatcher). In other

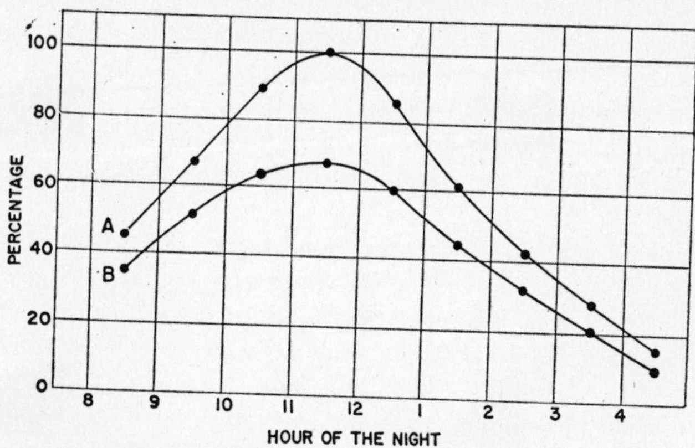

Fig. 89. Nightly pattern of spring migration as indicated by telescopic observations in the United States. The curves are based on hourly values plotted as a percentage of the peak value. The upper curve (A) is a plotting of the hourly means of the flight density for all stations and all nights, expressed as percentages of the peak value after computation of the means. The lower curve (B) shows the result obtained when the separate sets of data for single nights at single stations are expressed as hourly percentages of their respective peaks before computation of the means. From Lowery and Newman, 1955.

birds, like thrushes, there is no intermediate resting period. The difference between the bird's daily activity and its nocturnal activity appears in Merkel's studies (1956) on the European robin (*Erithacus rubecula*) and the whitethroat (*Sylvia communis*). The graphs taken from his work show how migratory activity is added to normal activity during migration periods, and actograms show the annual variations (Fig. 88).

By focusing telescopes on the moon, Lowery found that the largest flights occur between ten p.m. and one a.m., with the maximum between eleven p.m. and midnight (Fig. 89). Sutter (1957a and b) got the same results in Switzerland with radar. Although there was some variation from one night to another, Sutter discovered that the maximum frequency occurs before midnight; there follows a slowing down, and nearly all flights stop by four a.m. Similar results were thus obtained by different methods on two continents, and they were corroborated by Merkel, who was working under experimental conditions.

In addition to these purely physiological factors, which include the necessity for diurnal feeding, Palmgren believes that psychic factors are also involved. During the day birds are more or less absorbed by their surroundings and the search for food, but at night, when all activities cease, they are driven by their migratory impulse to start a flight which may last until dawn. This is a somewhat anthropomorphic explanation.

Nocturnal migrants often utter special cries that call them to the attention of observers. These cries, which may be quite different from their habitual calls, are reputed to keep the flock together, but this explanation is not very satisfactory, as some solitary migrants cry continuously.

Nocturnal migrants probably fly from dusk to dawn. Landing at night, except by moonlight, would doubtless be fatal, and during severe storms the large number of fatalities is due to the fact that birds strike trees, the ground or other obstacles when they alight.

A great many birds migrate in large flocks. Subscribers to anthropomorphism attribute this to a feeling of mutual comfort or assistance, and claim that the birds gather together so they can cope to better advantage with the perils of the flight.

Without our accepting such theories, it is true that most birds are gregarious during migration, though at all other times they may display a fierce individualism. Most non-colonial nesting birds show a highly developed instinct of territoriality during the breeding season, when every individual defends against others of the same species an area around his nest which he regards as his exclusive property. Even birds nesting in colonies defend a small 'territory' against individuals of their own species, or of species which offer keen competition.

As soon as the young are grown, this territorial isolation usually gives way to tolerance, even to a social attitude. We find a gregarious instinct even among sedentary species, like the flocks of tits which gather in Europe in autumn. It appears most clearly, however, among migrants.

Authors differ considerably as to the sociability of certain species.

Undoubtedly it varies geographically and individually, and psychic factors are even more difficult to formulate than other types of behaviour.[1]

A tendency to gather in large groups while resting does not, however, imply that the groups are homogeneous or that the birds travel together. Numerous little Passerines travel alone or in loose 'flocks,' but gather along the way into much larger groups, which split up once again in flight. *Sylvia* and *Phylloscopus* are examples among the Sylviidae. Resting flocks are always larger, and they usually represent several distinct migratory flights. There may be several thousand swallows in a resting place, while the ever-sociable starlings gather in colonies of thousands and even millions of individuals at roosts scattered along their routes.

It is easy to err when counting the number of migrants in a flock because the large number of individuals in a species passing a given point creates the illusion of a homogeneous group. Actually there are just as many independent fliers. Many birds of prey, for example, can appear simultaneously without forming part of a homogeneous group. This is true of eagles and other large Raptores crossing the Bosphorus. That birds of prey, however, lose their aggressiveness during their seasonal flights is evident from the enormous concentrations to be found in certain places; in Europe, the classic migration route of buzzards (*Buteo*) and Scandinavian honey buzzards (*Pernis apivorus*) leads from southern Sweden (Skåne) to Hamburg over the eastern islands of the Danish archipelago. Westernhagen (1955) counted 3,000 buzzards in a single day.

But the most spectacular autumn flights of birds of prey are along the crests of the hills crossing central Pennsylvania from east to west. Hawk Mountain Sanctuary is surely the finest observatory in the world, for in twelve years 75,207 broad-winged hawks (*Buteo platypterus*), the most common species which represents 41.86 per cent

1. There is no space here to study avian behaviour in winter quarters, where the sociability characteristic of migratory flights is often observed. It would be interesting to examine the notion of territory, since birds form little groups, composed of one or several species. Wagner (1958), who studied the behaviour of North American birds wintering in Mexico, noted that wood warblers collect in small flocks around sedentary Mexican birds (Mexican chickadee [*Parus sclateri*], red warbler [*Ergasticus ruber*], slate-throated redstart [*Myioborus miniatus*], golden-browed warbler [*Basileuterus belli*], in addition to several Tyrannidae, Dendrocolaptidae, etc). It seems as if migrants associate with sedentary birds in order to take advantage of their knowledge of the terrain!

of the birds counted, 44,851 red-tailed hawks (*Buteo jamaicensis*), and 42,419 sharp-shinned hawks (*Accipiter striatus*) have been observed, and this number certainly represents only a fraction of the birds which actually passed over the site. Maurice Broun states in his remarkable book (1949) that the record was probably set on 16 September, 1948, when 11,392 birds were counted! And this is all the more surprising, as more than 7,000 of them were seen between eleven a.m. and noon (Broun, 1951).

Repeated observations show that the manner of flight varies a great deal. Some birds, such as cuckoos, nightjars, orioles, numerous birds of prey and humming-birds, journey alone, so it is hard to watch their migrations. Shrikes usually fly alone, even when a large number are migrating; each bird keeps a certain distance from the others and seems to defend its aerial 'territory'. Simmons (1954) observed this in the case of the red-backed shrike in Egypt, and the same is true of the woodchat shrike in French North Africa. We find this phenomenon again among spotted flycatchers (*Muscicapa striata*) both in autumn and winter, and it doubtless applies to other insect-eaters (even to tanagers), to some shore-birds (like the pectoral sandpiper, see Hamilton 1959, and the common sandpiper [*Tringa hypoleucos*] see Curry-Lindahl, 1956), and to birds of prey, for there are instances where they also defend a winter territory (see Cade, 1955, for the American kestrel or sparrow hawk [*Falco sparverius*]).

Some extremely solitary birds become sociable during migration, such as little bitterns (*Ixobrychus minutus*) and bitterns (*Botaurus stellaris*). Ardeidae that nest as isolated pairs in an impenetrable biotope will gather in flocks of ten to a hundred to migrate. Fiercely solitary in their breeding territory, black storks migrate in flocks of sixty to seventy, but disperse as soon as they reach winter quarters. Short-eared owls (*Asio flammeus*) and scops owls (*Otus scops*) often form large flocks, which is surprising behaviour for these generally solitary birds. On the other hand, common herons nest in large colonies but migrate in groups of only a few birds. It is true that the extent of their migratory urge, which varies widely among individuals, does not permit the formation of a coördinated flock.

Some migrants, such as wild ducks and geese, travel in pairs or in families. Others form much larger flocks. There are often fifty to 100 Brant geese (*Branta bernicla*) and 500 to 1,000 common scoters (*Oidemia nigra*) in a flock. Flocks of 5,000 doves have been counted.

Rooks usually travel in groups of 1,000 to 1,500, but may number as many as 8,000 individuals. Numerous birds that nest in colonies, such as gulls and terns, some Anatidae, cranes, bee-eaters and swallows, migrate in large groups, but these birds are gregarious during the whole life cycle.

Flocks of migrants do not always consist of individuals of the same species. At nesting places along migration routes birds of different species but similar habits often gather in favourable spots. This is particularly true of small Passerines and shore-birds. Water-birds collect in flocks consisting of greenshanks, dunlins, oyster-catchers and other lovers of aquatic prey. The birds fly separately, and the flocks can be mixed for various reasons, such as feeding.

Two species that have similar habits can travel together, provided they fly at the same speed. A slight difference upsets the flock's cohesion instantly. That is why species which fly together are usually closely related, such as the dunlin (*Erolia alpina*) and the little stint (*Erolia minuta*), the dunlin and the knot (*Calidris canutus*), the greenshank (*Totanus nebularia*) and the spotted redshank (*Totanus erythropus*). These species form homogeneous flocks in which every bird flies with the same rhythm because they all have a similar anatomical conformation.

Among Passerines, jackdaws often migrate with rooks, although there is always a much larger proportion of the latter. Common chaffinches and bramblings are often together, the former in much greater numbers. Other little Passerines seem to migrate together, but their flocks are never homogeneous. There are, however, records of meadow pipits (*Anthus pratensis*) and common skylarks (*Alauda arvensis*). The tendency to form flocks consisting of several species is strongest among American warblers, which mingle on both the spring and autumn migrations. Among the Icteridae, grackles, red-winged blackbirds and cow-birds are often together. In all these Passerines, especially the warblers, similarity in conformation, size and speed of flight favours a mixture of species.

A very curious case is that of the migratory quail (*Coturnix coturnix*) and the corn crake (*Crex crex*). In some instances every fifteen quail are accompanied by one of these Rallidae, which prefers to travel with gallinaceous birds rather than with its own kind. In ancient times this gave birth to the legend that the rail was the leader, so it was called 'King of the Quail.'

Storks and large birds of prey are often observed together in the Near East and the Bosphorus. This partnership, doubtless of short duration, is explained by the similarity in the soaring tactics of these gliding birds which turn rising air currents to the best possible advantage.

Flocks often seem to fly in a disorderly fashion, and there is no set distance between individuals so long as they do not get in one another's way. Some species, however, have remarkable cohesion. The manœuvres of shore-birds like plovers or sandpipers are proof that the troop is completely homogeneous, for the flock presents its light bellies and dark backs in perfect synchronization. Even if the dicipline is not so rigorous, the group may preserve a fairly constant shape. Migrating rooks often form an elongated crescent whose depth is only a small fraction of its width, and geese move in Indian file, each bird following the leader.

The most characteristic migratory formation is a reversed 'V,' with the point turned in the direction of flight. This is typical of geese, ducks, pelicans, cranes, and even shore-birds like the golden plover and many sandpipers. That this figure was observed in ancient times is apparent from numerous drawings preserved from the Greco-Roman era and the Middle Ages. The 'V' formation is never used by soaring birds, and most of the so-called 'storks' which are said to fly in this way are cranes.

Numerous explanations have been offered for this formation. It was suggested that the movement of each bird forms a wave which spreads towards the rear; the leader flies in an unchanged 'fluid,' but all the birds which follow benefit from the wave. Storer (1948) says that a bird moving through the air leaves a wake like that produced by a vessel; birds flying in a triangle rest on this wave and thus save precious energy. Photographs of V formations give the impression that each bird is placed so as to rest one wing on the currents left by the opposite wing of its predecessor.

Aviators tell us that planes which follow the patrol leader in this manner use less fuel, as they take advantage of eddies. This would explain why the bird which 'points' the way occasionally comes to the end of the line to rest, and also why birds move from one side of the V to the other to change the wing that is resting on the air currents.

This hypothesis was criticized by Franzisket (1951, 1952). Although he believes that aerodynamic factors are involved, he states that the bird does not create any regular waves in flight; the currents are produced in a motionless surface, not by the animated wing of a vertical movement. This author thinks that the turbulence of the air mass behind a bird in beating flight is unfavourable to the individual in the rear. According to Franzisket, the reversed V formation is adopted to evaluate respective distances. It is advantageous to fly in groups (if only to escape enemies), and each bird needs to know the precise distance separating it from other members of the flock. Distances are hard to judge in the air, as perspective is lessened. Birds flying side by side can best judge the distance separating them in the line of flight; in Indian file they can observe any lateral deviation. Oblique flight combines the advantages of the two systems and prevents collisions that may prove fatal to birds the size of a duck. This would never be true of smaller birds, such as Passerines, which explains why they never fly in regular formation. But some sandpipers are smaller than many Passerines, and they fly in beautiful formation!

Authors obviously do not agree on the utility of the V formation; while it offers real advantages in determining the distances between birds in a flock, it does not fully explain the reasons for such behaviour. The basic reasons are doubtless aerodynamic, although perhaps not so mathematically exact as some writers have assumed.

On the whole, there are among most migrants increased gregariousness and sociability, which are due to the fact that, once the breeding season is over, even the most solitary birds have less cause for aggressive behaviour. Psychic factors, including imitation, are involved. In a summary of his own observations and those of others, Verheyen (1952b) showed that birds, like many animals, tend to follow moving objects, particularly individuals of their own and other species. That is how he explains the 'carousels' in which hundreds of kites, storks and vultures take part, until even small Passerines are stimulated to join the game.

Flights of migrants start various movements among birds found along the way, and occasionally there are simulated migratory manœuvres even among sedentary birds, such as partridges, pheasants, magpies and sparrows. This is a common phenomenon among swallows, crows (especially rooks and jackdaws) and, generally speaking, among all sociable birds[1]; but it is not universal, for black

1. According to Van Sanden (*in* Verheyen, 1952) even an aeroplane flying slowly over an area will cause diurnal birds of prey to start a carousel during the migration season.

kites (*Milvus migrans*), which are abundant at Istanbul and in all parts of the Bosphorus, will describe their regular circles but pay no attention to innumerable individuals of their own and other species flying over them.

This instinct for imitation certainly plays a part in uniting and co-ordinating flocks of migrants. The restlessness of some individuals spreads to others and finally causes the whole flock to depart. Certain external characters, such as the "mirrors" on the wings of ducks, areas often brilliantly coloured and edged with contrasting colours which adorn the posterior edge of the wing, may serve as releasers. These 'signals' play a rôle in co-ordinating the flock, synchronizing its movements, and giving the same rhythm to every individual.

Finally, we should observe that migrating birds show a persistence which is quite different from their normal behaviour. They are much less afraid of man or their natural enemies, and birds of prey can seize one individual without arousing the panic or hostility which the flock would normally show. Most migrants appear to be driven by such an imperious need that they disregard the very hazards and safeguards that exert the greatest influence on their behaviour in all other circumstances and at other seasons.

CHAPTER 9

Bird Invasions

Some avian mass movements lack the regularity of true, rhythmic migrations. Occasionally a bird appears in an area in great numbers, remains for a time and disappears. Several years may then elapse before large flocks return. Movements of this type, irregular both in time and location, are called *invasions* or irruptions. The birds show no attachment to their original breeding territory (the German *Ortstreue*) and seldom go back to it. Some of these movements, indeed, resemble real 'death marches.'

Invasions also occur among insects and mammals – notably locusts and lemmings. Other mammals, such as squirrels and rats (the Germans call the brown rat *Wanderratte*), make trips of this explosive kind.

These invasions have been regarded for centuries as omens, generally evil. The Bohemian wax-wing, for example, is known to the peoples of western Europe as a herald of war (*Kriegsvogel* of the Germans) or plague (*Pestvogel* of the Dutch).

Almost all animal invasions have their origin in northern, especially arctic and subarctic, lands, doubtless because yearly fluctuations in plant productivity in that part of the world exert great influence on the populations of birds which depend on plants directly (fruit- and grain-eating) or indirectly (carnivorous). Although we shall discuss only the better known of these movements, certain distinctions are necessary in view of the fact that invasions differ widely both in cause and pattern. The list of birds making them is a rather long one. In addition to the species we shall study in detail, we should mention among European birds the jay (*Garrulus glandarius*) (see Berndt and Dancker, 1960), the great spotted woodpecker (*Dendrocopus major*), and the pine grosbeak (*Pinicola enucleator*), without counting the coal tit (*Parus ater*), the brambling (*Fringilla montifringilla*) and the redpoll (*Acanthis flammea*). In America there are the pine grosbeak (*Pinicola enucleator*), the evening grosbeak (*Hesperiphona vespertina*), the three-toed woodpeckers (*Picoïdes arcticus*, *P. tridactylos*), the black-capped (*Parus atricapillus*) and boreal chickadees (*Parus hudsonicus*) and the purple finch (*Carpodacus purpureus*).[1]

Birds With A Vegetarian Diet

Most fruit- and grain-eating birds depend largely on the *quantity* of food available; this is particularly true of highly specialized forms whose diet is based on the product of a single plant (stenophagous or monophagous species). In these instances population density is determined by the amount of food to be obtained in a given region.

1. CROSSBILL

One of the most typical birds in this group is the red crossbill (*Loxia curvirostra*), a fringillid which owes its name to the curious twist of the tips of both mandibles. Its beak is a wonderful tool, adapted to prying seeds from between the tight scales of pine cones. This Passerine nests chiefly in coniferous forests of Scandinavia and central Europe, but also in the Alps and the French Massif Central, in part of the Iberian Peninsula and Greece. Occasionally it invades western Europe, especially France and England, where large flocks begin to arrive in June. Related races replace the Palearctic form in North America; other species such as the white-winged crossbill (*L. leucoptera*) and the parrot crossbill (*L. pityopsittacus*) usually mingle with flocks of red crossbills.

According to the studies of Reinikainen (1937) flocks of breeding crossbills vary from year to year in Finland in proportion to the crops of spruces (*Picea excelsa*), whose cones provide almost all their food. The Finnish author has established a remarkable correlation between the density of the crossbills and the cone crop.

1. Very little is known about invasions in arid regions, especially in Asia (rosy star [*Pastor roseus*]), in southern Africa (wattled starling [*Creatophora cinerea*]) and in Australia. These phenomena are related to the irregular rainfall and movements of locusts.

When food becomes scarce, the birds travel in search of more favourable conditions. Invasions in western Europe are not necessarily caused by lack of food in winter quarters, but it is noteworthy that the years 1927 and 1930, when large numbers invaded western Europe, were marked by a meagre crop of cones in Finland. When the breeding season is over, crossbills begin to wander as soon as their food supply runs low. Great invasions are clearly related to these cyclic phenomena (Fig. 90).

The movements of American crossbills are very similar. In winter they are erratic nomads which occasionally make real invasions far outside their usual quarters, probably because of a food shortage.

2. NUTCRACKERS

The Siberian nutcracker (*Nucifraga caryocatactes macrorhynchus*) has a similar behaviour pattern. Formosov (1933) showed that its diet consists largely of seeds of the Arolla pine (*Pinus cembra sibirica*) which it disseminates by hiding a winter supply of seeds between roots in the soil or in rocky crevices. Some of these seeds germinate, whereas those that drop on the soil seldom develop, so the distribution of the plant is almost identical to that of the bird. Within the nutcracker's bill an apparatus with a kind of cavity in the upper mandible and a projection in the lower is a 'nutcracker' admirably adapted for breaking the seed's hard covering.

Arolla seeds are the favourite food of many other animals in the Siberian taiga; nutritious, considerably larger than the seeds of other coniferous trees, they supply food for creatures as diverse as nutcrackers, rodents, including squirrels, ungulates, such as wild boar and deer, and even bears. Like the nutcracker, Siberian squirrels are very dependent on the Arolla.

The crop of this conifer is by no means constant (it may be 223 to 267,000 lbs. per acre). A bumper year is usually followed by several years when the yield is mediocre or even a total failure, although there seems to be no definite rhythm. (Fig. 91). Some authors think the cycle lasts two or three years, whereas others believe there may be four good crops, followed by eight to ten lean ones. This periodicity varies, of course, with the locality, the tree's rhythm and environmental conditions.

The importance of the Arolla crop is reflected by the fluctuating abundance of squirrels dependent on it; these variations are accurately revealed in the yearly quantity of pelts brought by trappers to the great Siberian fur markets.

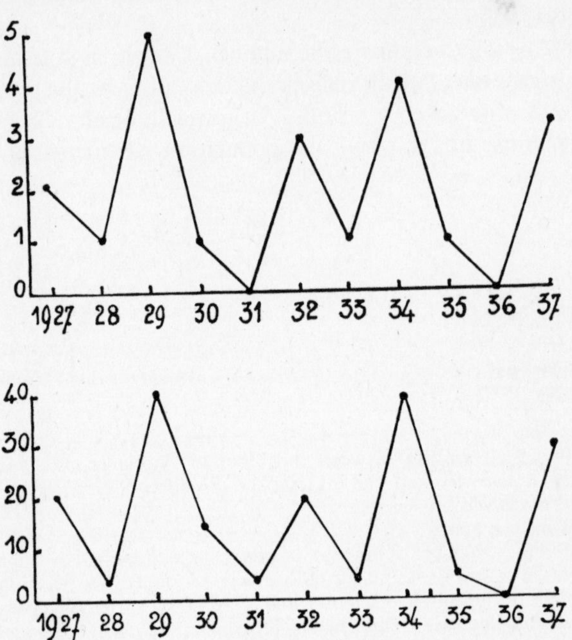

Fig. 90. Diagrams showing the parallelism between the crop of spruce trees (*Picea excelsa*) (above) and the density of crossbills (*Loxia curvirostra*) (below) in Finland. From Reinikainen, 1937.

Above: X-axis O – – – – – no crop
1 – – – – – – a poor crop
2 – – – – – – a very mediocre crop
3 – – – – – – mediocre
4 – – – – – – average
5 – – – – – – abundant

Below: Y-axis Number of pairs counted on a 75-mile trip.

It has long been known that the nutcracker population also varies from year to year, and that the abundance of this bird, like that of the squirrel, follows the cycles of the Arolla seed output. When these conifers have a poor crop, nutcrackers must either starve or leave the forests where they usually winter. They fly westward, sometimes in large flocks across Russia and on to France and England. Some breed in their new territories the next spring, but the majority never return to their original forests. Nutcrackers appear in eastern Europe in the autumn; they reach the most westerly part of the continent in January and February, although they have been recorded in England as early as October.

It is interesting to compare the number of squirrels sold each year at the Siberian fairs (which reflects the size of the Arolla crop), with the years of nutcracker invasions. An invasion occurs whenever an abundant crop (during which the population has increased, due in

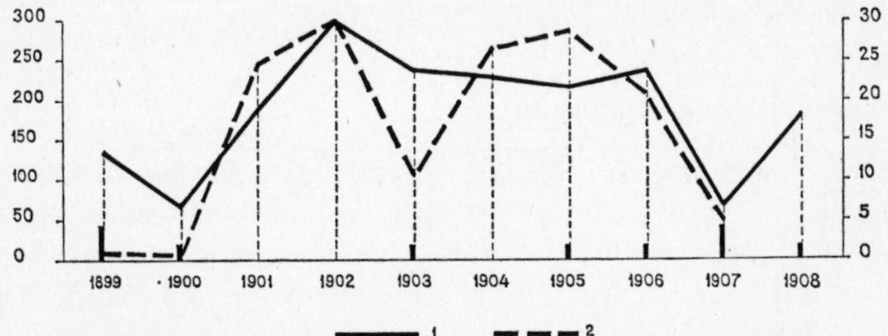

Fig. 91. Relation between the Siberian Arolla crops (*Pinus cembra sibirica*) and the nutcracker (*Nucifraga caryocatactes macrorhynchus*) invasions

X-axis: years

Y-axis: Weight of Siberian Arolla seeds transported by trans-Siberian railway (1) and by the railway at the Tomsk junction. Weight in thousands of *puds* (1 *pud* = 16.38 kg.). Heavy vertical lines indicate the years when Siberian nutcrackers invaded Europe. Their length is proportionate to the size of the invasion. Original document transmitted by Professor A. N. Formosov, Moscow.

part to lower mortality in the winter) is followed by a poor year, when the birds are driven to seek food elsewhere. These invasions have caused terror in the Ukraine, Poland and Germany, where for centuries people have considered the birds as portents of disaster.

Clark's nutcracker (*Nucifraga columbiana*) of the American West makes similar invasions. Davis and Williams (1957), who studied this bird in California, found that its normal winter habitat is the coniferous forests of the mountain ranges, but that it also comes to lower levels. Occasionally almost all the local populations take part in such occupations of the coastal and desert regions. Since 1898 there have been five spectacular invasions – in the autumn and winter of 1898–1899, 1919–1920, 1935, 1950–1951 and 1955.

These invasions, like those of the Old World, are caused by a shortage of the normal winter food supply, and they occur after a series of favourable years during which populations greatly increased. This was noteworthy in 1935 and 1955; for the preceding years, 1933, 1934 in one case, 1951–1954 in the other, were years of abundant yield of at least one of the conifers on which the birds feed (piñon pine, sugar pine, white fir, ponderosa pine, etc.). Such a big crop led to a rise in the bird population by reducing winter mortality. During ensuing famines the birds made huge invasions, which brought the size of the populations down to a healthier level.

3. PALLAS'S SANDGROUSE

Pallas's sandgrouse (*Syrrhaptes paradoxus*) is like the nutcracker, although the bird belongs to a different systematic group (Pteroclididae). This species nests on the steppes of central Asia, migrates a short distance every year, but occasionally makes the long flight to France and Great Britain. During the last century invasions occurred in 1859, 1863, 1872, 1876, 1888, 1891 and 1899. A famous one which occurred in 1908 was studied by Tschusi von Schmidthoffen (1909) and Sudilovskaya (1935). During the winter of 1907 a number of flocks appeared in Siberia. The next spring they were observed in Russia, chiefly in the South, but also in the more northern wooded provinces, where they had hitherto been scarce. Most of these flights took place in the spring; then the birds spread from Russia through central and western Europe to France and England.

Later some Pallas's sandgrouse returned to their breeding territories, but the majority perished. This did not, however, cause any marked reduction in the number of breeding birds during succeeding years. A few birds tried to nest in France and England, but the species did not succeed in establishing itself in the newly invaded territories.

The 1908 invasion was restricted to central and western Europe, but others reached as far north as Norway and south to the Mediterranean; some Pallas's sandgrouse also travelled east towards northern China.

These long 'escape flights' are prompted by a combination of meteorological and biological factors which cause a shortage of seeds, especially the Chenopodiaceae *Agriophyllum gobicum* that constitute the birds' diet. Chiefly responsible are heavy snow and a frozen crust, which the sandgrouse cannot break with its soft beak and rather weak feet. Spring floods caused by a sudden thaw may also lead to an invasion.

4. TETRAONIDAE

Much less is known about the movements of birds of the grouse family. Although most of them are thought to be sedentary in their forests, some perform seasonal migrations of considerable length (Grote, 1939, 1940). When heavy snowfalls prevent the birds from finding food, they travel to regions affording more favourable conditions, chiefly to the great coniferous forests. During years when there is a great deal of snow and food is scarce, such migrations become invasions.

Willow grouse (*Lagopus lagopus*) start south in September from their breeding territory in the tundra to the edge of the forest. At this season birches and dwarf willows are covered by snow so thick and hardened by ice that they cannot break it to feed. In addition to these regular migrations, there are erratic movements, real invasions during which the grouse disperse in every direction, even north. They have been seen flying in considerable numbers along the coast of the Arctic Ocean and out over the frozen sea, where large numbers perish.

In autumn capercaillie (*Tetrao urogallus*), the world's largest grouse, leave the leafless hardwood forests, where they can no longer find food, and go north towards the coniferous belt which provides the needles that constitute the base of their winter diet. Black grouse (*Lyrurus tetrix*) go south in winter.

These migrations become disorderly invasions when there is too much snow and the food supply fails. In 1927, a particularly bad year, black grouse appeared in such numbers around the city of Tomsk that more than 50,000 of them were shot.

5. BOHEMIAN WAX-WING

All these fruit- and grain-eating birds perform invasions at regular or irregular intervals when an abundance or scarcity of food leads them to make trips of varying length from which they do not return to their breeding territory. There are other invasions whose more complex pattern is determined by a rhythm quite independent of the food cycle. The Bohemian wax-wing (*Bombycilla garrulus*) is a bird belonging to a small family, the Bombycillidae, that inhabits circumboreal regions.[1] Birds of the typical race (*B.g. garrulus*) breed in the forests of northern Europe and Siberia and engage in more or less extensive migrations, some of which resemble invasions. The Bohemian wax-wing's migratory cycle has been studied by a number of authors, including Warga (1939); the best general work on the subject is a monograph by Siivonen (1941).

The Bohemian wax-wing breeds in Scandinavia, chiefly in coniferous and birch forests, and feeds on berries, especially those of the rowan tree (*Sorbus aucuparia*). Every year part of the population migrates to central Europe (Hungary) and then returns to its breeding territories.

In some years Bohemian wax-wings are much more abundant than usual throughout their winter quarters, and they scour the country in search of berries. In Hungary large flocks were observed in 1847–48, 1866–67, 1877–78, 1897–98, 1898–99, 1900–01, 1905–06, 1906–07, 1910–11, 1916–17, 1919–20, 1921–22, and 1937–38. There is nothing regular about these appearances, and the intervals between them vary widely.

Great invasions of wax-wings are quite different. Beginning much earlier in the autumn, they spread out over far greater areas. This Passerine does not remain in the plains of central Europe – notably Hungary, where it may be regarded as a regular migrant – but appears in large flocks in western Europe: the British Isles, France and occasionally Iceland. It also reaches the Mediterranean countries and North Africa. Individuals linger until late in the spring in these regions.

Invasions of this kind occurred in 1882–83, 1892–93, 1903–04, 1913–14, 1923–24, 1932–33, or at about ten-year intervals, and records show that this was true in earlier periods as well.

It is interesting to see how these observations compare with what happens in Finland where they breed. Every year part of the wax-wing population leaves in autumn and returns in the spring. In certain years flights are larger and more irregular because of local feeding conditions, and at such times they occur later than usual.

These sporadic movements are not real invasions, which are characterized by an early departure (September), rapid flight and an almost complete disappearance of the population from Finland, where such movements also occur at about ten-year intervals.

1. Except for some tropical American species, which are quite different.

Finland:	1883–84	1891–92	*1903–04*	*1913–14*		1931–32
Hungary:	1882–83	1892–93	*1903–04*	*1913–14*	1923–24	1932–33

Although there is an approximate ten-year interval in both instances, only two dates actually coincide: 1903–04 and 1913–14. This indicates that the birds which invade Hungary do not necessarily come from Scandinavia, but, in all probability, from more easterly breeding territories. It seems that the invasions originating in northern Europe and spreading chiefly across western Europe can be clearly distinguished from those coming from the North-east which also reach eastern Europe.

The Bohemian wax-wing thus performs invasions about every ten years; during the intervals partial migrations or nomadic wanderings affect variable fractions of the population. Some authors have tried to attribute these regular invasions to food factors, especially to fluctuations in the crops of the Scandinavian rowan tree, which play such a large part in the wax-wing's winter diet. There seems, however, to be no direct connection between invasions and an abundance or dearth of these mountain ash berries.

Food does play a rôle, however, in the erratic movements between invasions. When there was an abundant berry crop in Finland, as for example in 1908–09, 1910–11, 1912–13, 1915–16, 1917–18, 1920–21, 1923–24, 1928–29, 1930–31, 1933–34, 1936–37 and 1939–40, wax-wings spent the whole winter there instead of going in large numbers to Hungary.

Invasions are, in fact, determined by numerical fluctuations in the wax-wing population. On the basis of many years of observation, it appears that wax-wings breeding in Finland reach their minimal and maximal abundance at intervals of a decade. The breeding territory is expanded in every direction during maximal years (Fig. 92).

A peak in the wax-wing population usually precedes the great invasions:

Maximum	1881–83	1891–93	1900–03	1913	1930–31
Invasion	1883–84	1891–92	1903–04	1913–14	1931–32[1]

The population may thus increase for several years before a great invasion spreads into central and western Europe.

A study of Bohemian wax-wing invasions reveals that large move-

1. More recent invasions were observed in the winters of 1948–49 and 1953–54.

ments always follow the same pattern. They are preceded by a period during which the species increases in numbers and greatly expands its breeding range. The invasion begins in the early autumn, with most of the birds taking part. Even though some areas offer plenty of food,

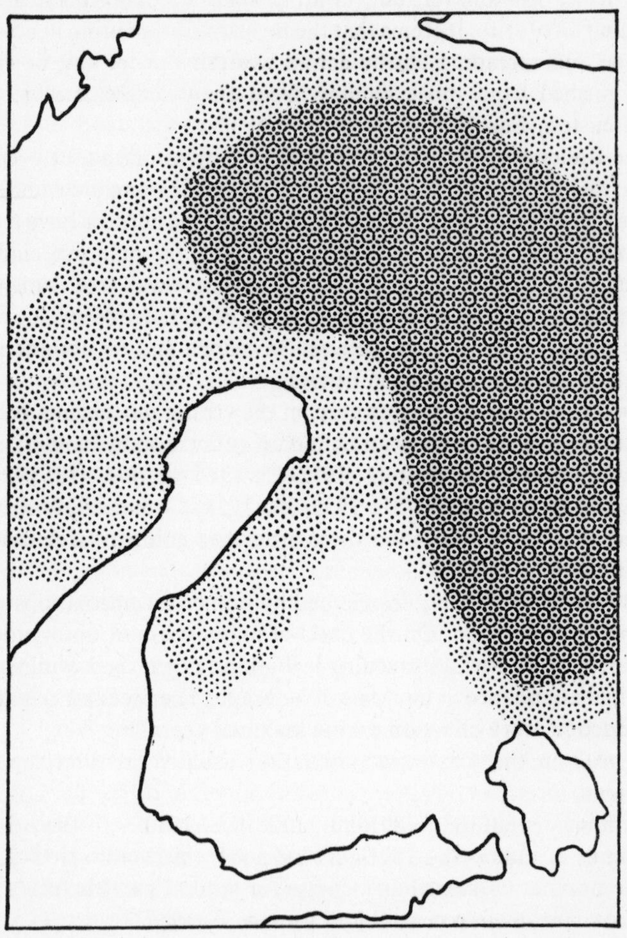

Fig. 92. Nesting area of the waxwing (*Bombycilla garrulus*) in Finland and Sweden. The darker portion represents the normal breeding zone, the dotted section the maximal extension. After Siivonen, 1941.

they do not stop until they reach their winter grounds, vast regions which they do not visit at other periods.

Only a fraction of the population returns to the breeding grounds, so the numbers of birds there are reduced. Others try to remain in the areas they have 'invaded' and some even nest there. But all the wax-wings which do not return to the normal breeding grounds soon disappear.

Increases in number and invasions are certainly more or less related. There is, however, no relation between 'cause' and effect, and both are probably triggered by factors we do not yet understand. Bohemian wax-wings resemble certain mammals, such as lemmings, whose population cycles run from three to five years. These rodents of the arctic regions have very regular maxima and minima. During peak years populations increase rapidly, the range is enlarged, and the animals overflow the normal area in a mass movement in all directions that terminates in the death of every lemming taking part in it.

Although intervals differ, there is an evident relationship between the wax-wing cycle and that of the lemmings. Various reasons have been suggested to explain these numerical variations and the massive emigrations accompanying them. Some authors thought they could find a parallel between the ten-year cycles and sun spots which appear every eleven years. They believed that these cosmic phenomena exerted an indirect influence on vegetation (and on the production of essential elements) and a direct influence on the fecundity of animals. Other factors, such as periodic diseases, were mentioned, but no correlation has been established between these cosmic and biological phenomena and the reproductive rhythm of the wax-wings. The cyclic fluctuations of this song-bird are determined by a natural internal rhythm which we do not yet understand.

A closely related American form (*B.g. pallidiceps*) breeds in the coniferous forests of Alaska, Canada and some of the far northern states. It winters in irregular abundance in Montana, Colorado, and sometimes in the north-eastern states, but from time to time it performs massive invasions of California and New Mexico. Such invasions were observed in 1908–09, 1916–17, 1917–18, 1919–20, and 1930–31, during which some flocks (also including robins and finches) numbered thousands of individuals. Lincoln (1939) described an invasion in Denver, Colorado, by a flock of more than 10,000 wax-wings in February, 1917.

Another species belonging to the same systematic group, the cedar wax-wing (*Bombycilla cedrorum*), winters in its breeding range, but part of the population goes south to Central America. It wanders around Panama instead of settling down like most winter residents, a behaviour probably explained by the birds' feeding habits.

Carnivorous Birds

Periodic invasions also occur among carnivorous birds, and they, too, are caused by variations in the food supply. The best example of such movements is afforded by the snowy owl (*Nyctea scandiaca*), a great owl often with almost completely white plumage, which nests in arctic regions of the Old and New World but makes periodic irruptions in winter into the temperate regions of America and Europe.

This owl, which appears at fairly regular intervals in temperate North America, has been studied by Gross (1931, 1947) and Shelford (1945). Its migrations are closely related to the cycle of lemmings, which form the basic diet of both adult and young birds. Food supply also plays a considerable rôle in determining the number of owlets that reach maturity. There are six to eight eggs, occasionally as many as thirteen. During summers when rodents are scarce few owlets survive because the parents have difficulty finding the large quantities of food required by these ravenous birds. During years of abundance, on the other hand, parents are able to satisfy the appetite of a much larger number of young birds, and there is an increase in the owl population. This is also true of fur-bearing predators, especially foxes and lynxes.

When the lemming population drops, snowy owls must find food elsewhere. A number die in the Arctic, but many others fly far south into the U.S.A. Some owls also perish at sea, occasionally 500 miles offshore. The invasion generally begins in September, but most of the birds do not arrive in the south until November. A large number of birds take part in these movements. During the 1945–46 invasion, the largest on which we have precise data, 14,409 owls, 4,475 of which were found dead, most of them in south-eastern Canada and New England (Snyder, 1947) were reported to the Snowy Owl Committee.

Although a fraction of the population may return to its breeding grounds, the majority of the birds are shot, trapped or die of starvation. During the 1945–46 invasion, the highest mortality rate was in New

York State, where 839 owls were killed out of 1,104 reported.

These invasions of the U.S.A. occur at regular intervals; Gross lists twenty-four between 1833 and 1946.

Years	*Intervals*	*Years*	*Intervals*
1886-87		1917-18	
	3		4
1889-90		1921-22	
	3		5
1892-93		1926-27	
	4		4
1896-97		1930-31	
	5		4
1901-02		1934-35	
	4		3
1905-06		1937-38	
	4		4
1909-10		1941-42	
	3		4
1912-13		1945-46	
	5		

These dates and intervals correspond exactly to the cycle of lemming scarcity, but the correlation is shown even more clearly in Shelford's diagram. As each 'crash' in the lemming population is quickly followed by a southward invasion of snowy owls, it is evident that food shortages trigger these massive emigrations (Fig. 93).

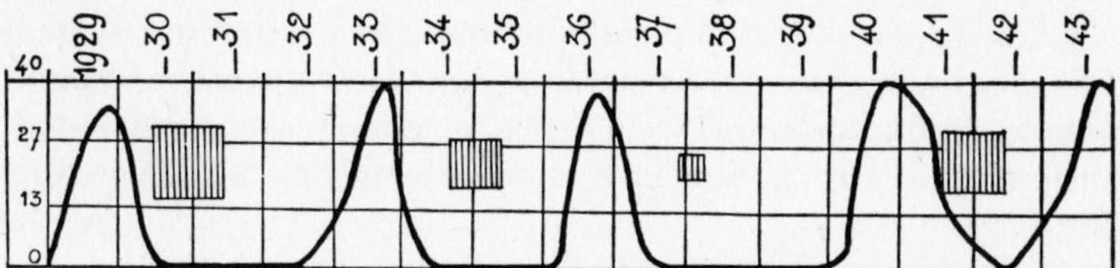

Fig. 93. Numerical fluctuations of lemming populations in Canada (Churchill area) and their relations with snowy owl (*Nyctea scandiaca*) invasions in New England. The density of the lemmings is estimated by their number to the hectare (2.5 acres); the surface of the shaded square is proportionate to the size of the invasion. Each decrease in the lemming population is followed by a large movement of snowy owls toward the South. After Shelford, 1945, simplified.

A similar correlation appears among other predators, such as some diurnal birds of prey, skuas, which also feed on lemmings, and certain North American shrikes. Davis (1937) showed that the northern shrike (*Lanius borealis*), which breeds in northern Canada, appears in the U.S.A. on an average of every 4.2 years, like the snowy owl. Its rhythm is identical, and it, too, is linked to numerical fluctuations in the lemming population, the principal source of food of this small, predatory Passerine. Gyrfalcons also fly south in large numbers in the autumn when there are few lemmings in arctic regions. Rough-legged hawks (*Buteo lagopus*) are frequently observed migrating through Germany when rodents have become scarce in Scandinavia. They do not, however, occur at such regular intervals as do the snowy owls. Other Strigiformes, like the hawk owl (*Surnia ulula*), also depend on the supply of rodents. But rodent scarcity does not always cause these invasions, for cyclic variations in other prey can exert the same expulsive influence. Numbers of ruffed grouse (*Bonasa umbellus*) vary considerably in Canada, and the American goshawk (*Accipiter gentilis atricapillus*), which feeds chiefly on this bird, suffers the consequence of these fluctuations. During famine years, which occur once every six to ten years, the goshawk appears in winter in considerable numbers in the U.S.A., although under normal conditions it is rare in the eastern states. Many of these birds remain to breed in the area they have invaded.

The rose-coloured starling (*Pastor roseus*) is one insectivorous species that performs invasions at highly irregular intervals. It nests over a vast area from south-eastern Europe to Turkestan and the Altai Range. As this bird feeds chiefly on locusts, it follows swarms of these insects. It arrives in great numbers, breeds in five or six weeks and then disappears in pursuit of its prey. It winters as far as England, Ireland, France and even North Africa. There is nothing regular about these movements, and the 'invasions' are simply large-scale wanderings.

On the whole, invasions are clearly distinguished from migrations, although some movements may be regarded as intermediate. The chief differences are the return to the breeding area (which is regular in migrations, very infrequent in invasions), the great irregularity of invasions in time and space, and the fact that they are often directly prompted by lack of food. Birds are driven more or less blindly by impulse, so at times they do not pause to satisfy their hunger in regions which offer abundant resources. Meteorological factors must also play a very large part in these erratic movements. Whereas migrations are annual, invasions may either follow a regular rhythm, covering a variable number of years, or may have no rhythm at all. Svärdson (1957) noted that migrations represent an adaptation to a *seasonal* food shortage, whereas invasions represent an adaptation to an occasional *annual* food shortage. He believes that the two phenomena are triggered by the same factors, but that invasions do not occur when food is abundant, whereas migrations take place regardless of it. It seems, however, that there are more basic differences between the two.

Moreover, some invasions are not directly influenced by these ecological factors. Bohemian wax-wings seem to have an internal rhythm controlling their increase or decline. Certain mammals pose similar problems, but at the present time there is no valid explanation. The only known facts relate to physiological irregularities; some studies of mammals have been made in this connection, but there are as yet none on birds. It is possible that the basic reasons behind these unexplained invasions are similar, and this would provide an interesting parallel between these two very distinct groups of vertebrates.

CHAPTER 10

The Hibernation of Birds

Early ornithologists explained the autumn disappearance of many birds by saying that, like batrachians, turtles, and certain mammals, they became torpid after taking shelter in a reed bed, a hollow tree, or in the mud of a stream. Only within the past century has migration been wholly accepted as the reason for the seasonal absence of large numbers of common birds from their breeding ranges.

Everyone knows that dormice, marmots and ground squirrels spend the winter in a state of complete dormancy. Apparently 'asleep,' they are perfectly motionless, and their bodies are cold. Tests made by physiologists reveal that the internal temperature of these hibernating animals is considerably lower than when they are awake, and that their rate of metabolism is also greatly reduced. Bats behave in similar fashion, but they have a daily cycle as well. Such higher vertebrates are called 'poecilothermes' (*with changing temperature*) in contrast to the 'homeothermes' (*with constant temperature*).

Recent observations have disclosed that such changes occur among certain species of birds. The temperature of nestlings often varies considerably during the first few days after hatching and before their thermal regulation is established (Baldwin and Kendeigh, 1932). Koskimies (1948, 1950) proved that this alternating temperature may be prolonged in the black swift (*Apus apus*). While studying black swifts four to five weeks old, he found that some of them lived nine days without food. It is probable that fledglings in the wild would have an even higher resistance to starvation, for frequent tests disturbed the young birds. Hugues (1907) cited an instance where young black swifts actually survived fasts of twenty-one days!

During the very first days of such hunger tests the internal temperature seems fairly stable (about 102° F.), but it falls to 70.2° when the temperature of the air drops to 66°. Other metabolic processes slow up very considerably, and breathing is reduced from forty to ten times a minute. As young black swifts are then in a state of complete but temporary lethargy, they have a much greater resistance to starvation than other insect-eating birds, which cannot survive more than two or three days without food. Less resistant to 'starvation' than their offspring, adult black swifts nevertheless can live for four days without food, which is longer than other species of the same size.

This curious physiological adaptation is doubtless related to the fact that the birds are entirely dependent on flying insects for food. When prolonged periods of bad weather make it almost impossible to hunt, black swifts and their young employ torpidity as a mechanism for avoiding starvation.

Other birds also become torpid, with important changes in both their energy exchanges and the internal temperature. In 1861 Gould found that his caged humming-birds were overcome with cold, but he revived them by placing them in a warm place.

'The vessel in which I made the passage took a northerly course, which carried us over the banks of Newfoundland; and although the cold was rather severe during part of the time, the only effect it appeared to have upon my little pets was to induce a kind of *torpidity* from which, however, they were readily aroused by placing them in the sunshine or in some warm situation, such as before a fire, in the bosom, etc. . . . I do assure my readers that I have seen these birds *cold and stiff, and to all appearances dead*, and that from this state they were readily restored by a little attention and removal into light and heat . . .' (*Monograph of the Trochilidae*, vol. I, p. xviii). Pearson (1950) made a detailed study showing that the metabolism of these birds has a daily cycle, and that at its lowest point the bird is in a state of torpor.

As this change of temperature is very closely akin to that observed among hibernating mammals, a prolongation of this physiological condition would enable a bird to pass the whole winter in a torpid state. This seems true of at least one bird, a North American poor-will (*Phalaenoptilus nuttallii*), which nests in the western and central parts of the U.S.A. from southern British Columbia to Mexico. During the winter of 1946–47, Culbertson (1946) and Jaeger (1948, 1949) were astonished to find poor-wills of this species in the foothills of the Sierra Nevada and the Colorado desert in California. They were huddled in rock crevices, their heads turned towards the wall, their grey and blackish mottled backs blending perfectly with the stone, and they were in a state of complete lethargy! No breathing or heart beat could be detected, and a bright light focused on the eye produced no reaction. Furthermore, the rectal temperature was very low, between 64° and 68° F. (the temperature of the air was between 63° and 75° F.), whereas, according to A. H. Miller's records (1850), the internal temperature of this bird when it is awake is usually 106° in summer. This poor-will evidently hibernates, just like some mammals, in response to falling temperatures. Howell and Bartholomew (1959) have shown that torpor can be experimentally induced by low temperatures (36°–40° F.). A period of slightly lower activity is followed by a rapid decline in internal temperature and oxygen consumption. During torpor environmental and body temperatures are more or less the same. Awakening is induced by increasing the ambient temperature.

This bird was found on several occasions during the winter in the same spot. Even more curious is the fact that some poor-wills were observed during three successive winters in an identical crevice, which denotes a singular 'memory' and an unusual attachment to one place.

The birds thus examined are not exceptions. It is now common knowledge that at least part of the California population of this species hibernates to avoid a shortage of food and harsh weather; the Hopi Indians have long referred to the poor-will as the *Hölchko*, which means 'the sleeper.'

This poor-will's ability to hibernate seems to be a phase of a temperature change which lasts throughout the year. Miller (1950) found that during the summer, or the active feeding period, the internal temperature may drop from a normal 106° to 93° F., which is an exceptional variation among birds.

Studies of Fog and Petersen (1957) indicate that the European nightjar (*Caprimulgus europaeus*) does not become torpid, but further observation is needed. J. T. Marshall's experiments (1955) showed that the trilling nighthawk (*Chordeiles acutipennis*), whose range extends from the south-western United States to South America, can also become torpid. It would be interesting to study this and other nightjars in the wild.

At present the poor-will is the only species on which precise data are available; it is tempting, however, to form similar conclusions about European swifts and swallows, whose behaviour recalls old beliefs about hibernation. Migrating swallows and black swifts are often victims of a sudden cold wave which deprives them of the flying insects they require. Paralysed by cold and hunger, these birds are unable to travel far enough to find more favourable conditions. Great flocks then take refuge in natural caves (trees and rocks, spaces under roofs, in attics and towers), where they huddle together in groups and fall fast asleep. Some of the most recent observations of swallows were made by Lorenz in the foothills of the Austrian Alps. Mennig (1939) found torpid black swifts in France in the tower of the château at Cannes; Burckhardt has studied the birds in Switzerland and Kühk (1948) in Germany. Torpor, by slowing down the birds' metabolic processes, makes it possible for them to withstand starvation resulting from cold. But no record of internal temperature or energy exchanges seems to have been made, and such information is needed to reveal their physiological state during this 'sleep,' which we cannot term a true hibernation, since prolonged low temperatures are always fatal. This torpor seems to be only an adaptation in the struggle for survival against brief cold waves that may be encountered during migration.

Early writers, especially Olaus Magnus, reported that ptarmigan in Greenland and Spitzbergen hibernated in holes under the snow. More recent observations have confirmed that they are, indeed, often found in holes which they seem to dig for themselves, but this does not constitute true hibernation, for the bird uses the hole simply as a shelter where it can stay for varying periods to preserve its body warmth. The ruffed grouse (*Bonasa umbellus*) does the same on winter nights.

Thus it is evident that some birds are capable of reacting to climatic conditions, particularly to a scarcity of food, by becoming torpid. This enables them to withstand both cold and hunger for a certain period of time; but in most cases such torpor cannot be likened to the real, annual 'hibernation' of bats and various other mammals.

The only instance of hibernation which has been scientifically proved among birds is that of the North American poor-will, whose physiological condition in winter seems to correspond in every respect to the definition of hibernation. It is possible, however, that other species may share this adaptability to seasonal change, and there is much still to be learned about the ways in which birds react to variations in their surroundings.

CHAPTER 11

The Physiological Stimulus of Migration

The simplest theory suggested to explain the migratory impulse is that Providence guides birds on their migrations, that it tells them when to depart and when to arrive. Reasoning of a more scientific character was based on climatic considerations. It was said that seasonal rhythm, especially variations in temperature, caused birds to migrate in one direction or another. Some of these theories proposed an unexpected cause; for example, Wallace believed that migrants leave when trees turn yellow in the autumn.

It is impossible to accept climatic conditions as the primary factor in determining the departure or arrival of migrants. While it is undoubtedly true that the meteorological situation plays a part in the migratory impulse, it can influence only those birds already physiologically disposed to migrate. Some of them, moreover, like cuckoos and swifts, leave temperate countries at a time when the change of seasons is not yet apparent and when their supply of insect food is still abundant.

Like moulting (or moultings) and reproduction, migration is a part of the life cycle of birds, and they all depend on a complex internal rhythm, which affects the whole organism, especially the endocrine glands and the gonads. The relationship of the bird to its environment is still rather mysterious, but migration must be considered within the framework of the annual physiological evolution.

Migration and Moulting

The connection between migration and moulting is especially interesting. Change in plumage occurs at definite periods in relation to migrations, and it too is controlled by an endocrine balance. That it is often difficult for the bird to moult is apparent from numerous observations of both caged and wild birds.

Sometimes moulting is annual, sometimes it occurs twice, but this second moult is usually only partial. The first occurs after the reproductive period, when there is a regression of the gonads. Moulting usually takes place before migration, and the bird leaves its breeding territory with new feathers. But some migrants, which make a very early postnuptial migration, moult in their winter quarters. The European swift replaces its flight feathers in its African territory. Sometimes moulting, especially of the body feathers, is continued during migration, and migratory Passerines are captured while growing new feathers. There is no definite rule, even within the framework of a species, but some differences are determined by age. Among European red-backed shrikes, for example, adults moult in winter quarters, whereas young birds moult their juvenile plumage before migration, a phenomenon which is probably connected with their later departure.

Migratory birds are more apt to moult twice than sedentary species, but the second moult occurs in winter quarters. This is noteworthy in families where most birds are sedentary. Among woodpeckers only the wryneck, and among gallinaceous birds only the quail, migrate; both these birds moult twice a year, while their sedentary relatives have a single moult.

Moulting body feathers has no immediate effect on flight, but moulting quill feathers is a different story, especially flight feathers which are moulted in a definite order, each feather being replaced in turn. Although this progressive renewal of worn feathers enables the bird to retain its ability to fly, it creates a definite handicap.

Some birds, such as various rails, cranes, geese, ducks, divers, grebes and auks, to mention only the most important, moult all the flight feathers at once, so for a certain period the birds are absolutely incapable of flight. Deprived of its wings, the bird has to seek shelter from enemies while waiting for the new flight feathers to grow. Likewise certain shearwaters make long migrations from one hemisphere to the other and need full possession of their flight feathers during migration. Observations of the greater shearwater (*Puffinus gravis*) by Meinertzhagen (1956) in Greenland and of the short-tailed shearwater (*Puffinus tenuirostris*) by Marshall and Serventy (1956a) indicate that, if moult begins in the breeding territory at the close of the reproductive season, it affects only the body feathers; these shearwaters then leave on postnuptial migration and do not begin to moult flight feathers until they reach 'winter quarters' in the North Atlantic and North Pacific. In June Meinertzhagen found great shearwaters off the coast of Greenland in large flocks; they were resting on the water, many of them unable to fly. The late moult of young birds appears to be an adaptation to migratory flights.

Yet migrants of various systematic groups have been observed moulting at the time when they normally leave their winter quarters. Broekhuysen (1956) saw swallows (*Hirundo rustica*) and house martins (*Delichon urbica*) moulting in South Africa in April, when they return to Europe. So moult seems geared to the timing of migrations in some groups, not in others.

A particular adaptation, in the form of a *moult migration*, appears among certain birds, especially ducks, which are subject to a total moult. This was first observed in Russia (Wuczeticz and Tugarinow, 1937–1939), where mallards (*Anas platyrhynchos*), gadwalls (*A. strepera*), shovellers (*Spatula clypeata*), pintails (*A. acuta*) and wigeons (*Mareca penelope*), which nest in northern Europe and Asia, gather in enormous flocks in the mouth of the Volga. Males arrive about mid-July and are followed by females. These birds rest and moult on the waters of the Volga delta, where they are safe from their enemies. In the first part of August they scatter in different directions.

E. Schäffer noted similar behaviour in Tibet (*in* Stresemann, 1940). On a lake at a 15,000 foot elevation on the border of Tibet and Sikkim he found flocks of ducks: mallards, pintails, wigeons, tufted ducks and gadwalls, some of which had lost only a few flight feathers, whereas others were already unable to fly. This moult migration, which carries ducks nesting in northern Asia to lakes at high altitude, is comparable to the situation at the mouth of the Volga. There too, as Schäffer's observations show, males seem to precede females, and, once the moult is completed, the ducks fly south towards their winter quarters.

Studies of Coombes (1950) on the population of Great Britain reveal that shelducks (*Tadorna tadorna*) of north-western Europe perform the same kind of moult migration. They gather in July along the coasts and migrate in great flocks overland to the south-east part of the North Sea, particularly the area around Heligoland, where they moult; as the flight feathers all drop off at once, the birds are unable to fly for a certain period. After moulting the shelducks return in slow stages to their breeding territory, but there are no great flights like those on the outbound trip. Although the return takes place during the autumn and winter, dates vary from one year to the next, and six months may elapse before all the birds come back. A similar phenomenon is observed among other groups, especially shore-birds, whose migrations are still not clearly understood. Studies of L. Hoffmann (1957) on the wood sandpiper (*Tringa glareola*) of the Camargue show that this bird, which nests in northern Europe, appears in large numbers between the end of July and early September in the Mediterranean region after flying swiftly across Europe (Hoffmann lists the average speed as 240 miles a day between Ottenby, in the southern part of Öland Island in the Baltic, and Morocco, but he states that the bird can fly 600 miles a day). Hoffmann found that woodsand pipers moult their flight feathers as soon as they reach the Camargue. Although this does not affect all the feathers, the birds are forced to interrupt their migrations, and, like ducks, they make two migratory flights with a pause between.

Migration and Sexual Cycle

ROWAN'S GONADAL HYPOTHESES

Migrations are part of a cycle in which reproduction plays the chief rôle. The two are very closely linked, for birds return to their breeding territory to nest and leave as soon as the young are able to care for themselves. Hence a relationship of cause and effect has long been sought between reproduction and the migratory impulse.

Seebohm first conceived the idea that migration was connected to the annual cycle of activity of the gonads. During the year important changes in these glands cause them to vary in size and appearance; they become greatly enlarged before the reproductive period and decrease in size when it is over. But it was Rowan who developed the first complete theory based on histological research and experimental study.

In his pioneer experiments Rowan stated that the migratory impulse is determined in autumn by regression and in spring by recrudescence of the gonads; this evolution is itself stimulated by a shortening or lengthening of the day, depending on the season or, in other words, on variations in photo-periodism. The stimulating factor is not the maximum or minimum development – these stages do not involve any activity – but rather the intermediate stages, where the texture and physiology of the gland are being modified.

Rowan tested his theory by a series of experiments on the slate-coloured junco (*Junco hyemalis*), a bird which breeds in Canada and winters in the central and southern United States. He carried out the experiments at Edmonton, Alberta, or far to the north of the winter quarters of this junco.

The birds were placed in aviaries where they were subjected to the intense cold that prevails in this part of Canada; one aviary contained birds serving as controls, the other could be lighted by powerful electric bulbs, which maintained an artificial daylight. The birds in this cage saw their days lengthened or shortened according to the wishes of the operator, whereas the juncos in the control aviary lived under natural conditions.

Rowan submitted one group of juncos to an illumination which increased five to ten minutes a day during autumn and winter; he found that the birds presented every sign of a resumption of glandular activity and that the testes increased until they attained the size they normally have during the reproductive period in May. A histological study of these 'forced' sex organs revealed that the gonads had attained a state comparable in every way to their natural state in the spring; the interstitial tissue of the testis was as fully developed in these experimental birds as in the normal period of testicular spring recrudescence or autumn regression.

Rowan tested the connection which seems to exist between gonadal development and photoperiodism. The birds stimulated by a daily increase in illumination were now subjected to a ten-minute daily decrease, which made the gonads regress completely. Better yet, after the gonads of some birds had reached their maximum through increasing exposure to light in December and after they regressed in February following a decrease in photoperiodism, they developed again in May under natural conditions. Thus in the course of a single year the juncos had attained the maximum development of the sex glands three times and the minimum twice.

These facts are extremely interesting, as they reveal that annual variations in the period of illumination can cause important changes in the structure and physiology of sex glands, which were long thought to be dependent on variations in temperature.

Temperature exerts no influence; the experimental birds were, like the control juncos, submitted to the rigours of the Canadian winter, during which the thermometer dropped to –53° F., but the gonads developed normally. There is thus no basis for the opinion that the autumn regression of the sex glands is due to a drop in temperature and their spring recrudescence to warm weather. Furthermore, observation of birds in the wild shows that this regression can occur in July, at a period when it is still very hot.

One of Rowan's experiments seemed to throw some light on activity during illumination. He equipped a cage in such a way that the floor and perches were jolted every twenty seconds. This cage was then placed in a room where all the light came from a low-watt bulb which kept the bird from hurting itself but was insufficient to exert any influence. A study of the gonads of birds submitted to this treatment reveals that they attained a stage of development comparable to that of birds exposed to light for long periods. The sex glands of control birds placed in cages where there was no mechanical stimulus failed to develop.

This experiment suggests that it is not the *light itself* which influences birds but rather the fact that it enables them to remain active for a longer period each day. This conception is somewhat too elementary and direct, but the observation is interesting nonetheless.

All these facts advanced by Rowan had no evident connection with migration, so it was still essential to discover the relation between variations in the physiological state and migratory behaviour. With this in mind, during the winter Rowan liberated juncos which were in different stages of sexual evolution. A series of traps made it possible to recapture those individuals which remained in the vicinity, and special bands permitted their identification. Rowan found that the control birds, whose gonads were at their minimum, showed no inclination to leave the area; they remained in a region far from their normal winter quarters despite the rigorous climate. This was also true of the experimental birds, whose sex glands had reached their *maximum* development. On the other hand, all individuals in an *intermediate* state of gonadal development, regardless of whether the gonads were regressing or developing, disappeared, and no one knew in which direction they had flown.

Rowan concluded that these results verified his hypotheses, which can be summarized as follows: the annual evolutionary cycle of the gonads, stimulated by an increase or decrease in daylight,[1] is characterized by a winter minimum and a spring or summer maximum, without influence on migratory behaviour. Certain stages of partial evolution or involution, on the other hand, stimulate the migratory impulse, which drives the birds to make seasonal flights.

The experiment with juncos did not reveal what became of the birds that disappeared, so Rowan began again with American crows (*Corvus brachyrhynchos*), which are easier to trace in the wild. Individuals that had been submitted to artificially lengthened days during October and November were banded and liberated, together with control crows. The results were rather disconcerting, for most of the control birds were recaptured south of the point where they were set free, while some experimental birds were found north and others south of the point of liberation. The theory was that all experimental birds would fly north, as the birds were physiologically in 'spring' condition. We must, however, recall that the area to the north of the point of liberation (Edmonton, Alberta) is uninhabited, so there are few opportunities for recovery. We may presume that many more birds flew north than was indicated by the number recaptured, and, in any case, it is significant that at least some of the experimental birds migrated in the direction they normally take in the spring.

Rowan also released a number of castrated crows. He found that longer exposure to daylight had no effect on these birds, which flew south, just like the control birds. This observation caused Rowan to decide that autumn migration is the result of sexual regression as a whole and not of a stage in this regression, since individuals at the minimum point or castrated birds migrate south. He stated that only the spring migration was dependent upon the evolution of the gonads, and he admitted that endocrine influences from other glands may be involved, especially at that season.

Gonadal theories, like those of Rowan, were accepted by a number

1. Light exerts a similar influence on other animals, notably mammals (deer, ferret, mink) and even on invertebrates (snails, Crustacea, insects) in which the alternation of periods of light and darkness stimulates or inhibits reproduction.

of ornithologists, including Schildmacher, whose methods, quite different from Rowan's, are based on observations of birds in captivity. It has long been known that during the migratory season caged birds belonging to migratory species seem very restless (*Zugunruhe*). This behaviour is especially apparent among song-birds that migrate at night (Sylviidae, for example), which manifest a great deal of activity during the day but are quiet at night except during the migratory period. A number of authors have proved that the daily and annual cycle of the caged bird can be superimposed on its cycle in the wild and that this is especially true of the 'flight fidgets' of migrants. Naumann, in 1822, noted that this was true of the nightingale, and Merkel (1956) demonstrated it for both the white-throat (*Sylvia communis*) and the European robin (*Erithacus rubecula*). Cages were devised with various mobile sections, especially the perches, which operated electric contacts attached to recording cylinders. The bird's cycle of activity was thus recorded as it was influenced by weather and various other conditions (for the equipment, see Palmgren, 1938, 1943, Farner and Mewalt, 1953a, Eyster, 1954, Wagner, 1957a).

Schildmacher (1933, 34, 37, 38b) used similar installations in his experiments with female European redstarts (*Phoenicurus phoenicurus*). He found that these birds are very restless in autumn, but that moderate injections of progynon[1] cause this agitation to subside. The dose of the hormone varied with the birds and the season, but a massive one failed to calm the birds.

He interpreted this to mean that a moderate injection re-establishes the equilibrium in the bird's physiology and counterbalances the glandular insufficiency which causes the bird to migrate. A stronger injection tends to produce a migratory impulse similar to the one that develops in the spring when the birds are stimulated by the development of their gonads. So Schildmacher's explanations agree with Rowan's, some of whose experiments were repeated by the German author. He demonstrated that an increase in photoperiodism calms caged birds in autumn, while it increases their excitement in the spring. As the threshold of sensitivity to the internal secretions of the ovary or testis varies according to species, there are differences in the dates of migration.

1. Progynon is 'the ovarian stimulating hormone from the anterior pituitary gland.' This hormone is the same in mammals, birds, fish, etc., and it causes ripening of the ovum-containing follicles.

Schildmacher's experiments, however, were not so well controlled as they might have been, and they have been sharply criticized by various authors (G. Steinbacher, 1933; Desselberger and Steinbacher, 1934).

Rowan's theories were again advocated by Bullough (1945), who also believes that migration is part of the bird's sexual cycle and that it is directly connected to the annual cycle of the gonads. This author states that spring migration is linked to gonadal development, that the sex organs are fully developed when migrants reach their breeding territories, and that this development begins before the birds leave winter quarters. Rowan and Batrawi (1939) found that various European migrants collected in the spring in East Africa, just before their departure for Europe[1] – garden warblers (*Sylvia borin*), red-backed shrikes (*Lanius collurio*). lesser grey shrikes (*L. minor*), yellow wagtails (*Motacilla flava*), willow warblers (*Phylloscopus trochilus*), and olivaceous warblers (*Hippolais pallidus*) – showed varying differentiation in their sex glands, which were usually in full development. Bullough (1942) himself studied European starlings that were wintering in England and concluded that their gonads were in full evolution before they departed for the breeding territory. Yearly variations in the date of departure of these starlings would correspond to the sexual development of the birds.

According to Bullough, there is supplementary proof in the fact that birds which do not become sexually mature until they are at least two years old often remain throughout the year in winter quarters. Similar observations have been recorded of some shore-birds, the gannet and the pomarine skua. Young storks also wander across tropical Africa, instead of returning to Europe, like their breeding parents. Lack of differentiation in the gonads is thus accompanied by a deficiency in the migratory impulse. The problem of partial migrations may be related to phenomena of this kind (see p. 317).

Possibly there are similar explanations for differences of migratory behaviour between the sexes. In general, males tend to return to their breeding territories before females, probably because there is less winter regression and the testis develops before the ovary. That would

1. Marshall (*Proc. Zoöl. Soc. Lond.*, 112, 287–294, 1952) studied the testes of migratory songbirds which had just arrived in Great Britain in the spring and discovered that, with a few exceptions, their gonads were mature. This recrudescence is confirmed by observation of males which sing during prenuptial migration.

explain why males of some migratory species make shorter flights than do the females. Again, young birds have a stronger tendency to make winter flights than adults because they are not affected by the activity of the sex glands.

CRITICISM OF GONADAL CAUSATION OF THE MIGRATORY IMPULSE

Although Rowan's ideas are interesting, they are subject to criticism. They seem accurate in the case of migrants that remain in the same hemisphere, like the juncos; but many migrants winter in intertropical regions, where annual variations in photoperiodism are much less important, and some go to the other hemisphere, where lighting conditions are reversed. A strict application of Rowan's theories, as he first presented them, would lead one to think that birds wintering near the equator could never leave this area, as they receive no stimulus from variations in photoperiodism. And birds going from the northern to the southern hemisphere would begin to breed at once because the days are longer!

Rowan explains behaviour in terms of a fixed internal rhythm, which makes birds react only to boreal influences (in the case of northern migrants), and excludes any influence from conditions in the other hemisphere. He recalls fixed rhythms in nature: some worms and fishes react to cyclic factors, even when the individual is withdrawn from their direct influence. This is because the rhythm, originally conditioned by environmental factors, has become automatic. Trees, when transported from one hemisphere to the other, continue for a time to follow the rhythm of their native land, and certain birds do the same when transported to zoölogical parks of the other hemisphere. But these phenomena are not equivalent and do not correspond to the conditions a migratory bird encounters every year. We would have to assume, as Rowan implies and Moreau (1931) states, that originally all migratory species made short flights, remaining within the boundary of the temperate zone. The birds were thus constantly subject to variations in photoperiodism, which impressed on them a rhythm they retained even when their flights became longer and they entered the tropics. Shorter days in autumn would maintain this rhythm.

A few individuals do not conform to this cycle, for we find boreal birds breeding in the austral hemisphere, like the storks in South Africa and certain North American migrants in South America, but these are exceptional cases.

This highly improbable hypothesis is not supported by proof. There is nothing to indicate that migrants of temperate countries have progressively extended their distribution towards the tropics, and in certain cases there is evidence to the contrary. Although trans-equatorial migrations constitute a serious objection to Rowan's theory, recent experiments have revealed the existence, following breeding, of a latent period during which the bird does not react to external influences. This refractory phase permits the supposition that the bird does not react to external influences of the other hemisphere.

Another objection to Rowan's theories is that birds of various species, hooded crows, European blackbirds, American sparrows, have migrated in a normal fashion after castration. According to Rowan, spring migration should be directly influenced by the gonads. We might say that, as among domesticated birds, the testes can grow again, and that psychological factors cause birds to imitate migrants. Nonetheless, the apparently normal migration of castrated birds throws some doubt on the direct influence of the sex glands.

Moreover, although Rowan and Batrawi found that many birds show a differentiation in their sex glands at the time they leave winter quarters, others reach the breeding area before the gonads develop.

Furthermore, as sedentary birds frequently have a rhythm that can be superimposed on that of closely related migratory birds, there must be physiological differences which are not revealed by gonad development.

On the whole, Rowan's experiments proved the concomitance between the development of the genital glands and the migratory impulse, but they did not demonstrate that one was the determinant of the other. We may assume that the two phenomena are independent and that they are stimulated simultaneously by the same factor, which conditions both gonadal development and the migratory impulse. Most recent authors have accepted an explanation of this kind.

THYROID CAUSATION OF THE MIGRATORY IMPULSE

Careful analysis of the behaviour of caged birds has been convenient as well as useful. The first problem was to check the bird's restlessness during the migration period to see if its rhythm was natural, and Siivonen's monograph (1936) showed that the curves tracing nocturnal restlessness in captivity correspond exactly to those of migratory flights. This makes it possible to study determinants and the influence of external factors.

Several authors, particularly Wagner (1936), took birds captured in Europe – including garden warblers, whitethroats, blackcaps – to different latitudes and climates, especially Mexico. Wagner found that the rhythm of these birds varied, as indicated by the record of the migratory restlessness (*Zugunruhe*), in accordance with the new environmental conditions. The quantity of food supplied to the bird can also influence its behaviour (Wagner, 1937). Here there is considerable variation from one species to another, for, although the European blackbird becomes quiet when well-fed, real migrants, like warblers or the European redwing, show just as much impatience when they are offered plenty of food. Other observations show that the blackbird, unlike the warbler, is content to spend the winter in a number of European countries, provided conditions are not too difficult and the food supply is adequate.

Temperature also has an important influence on migratory restlessness, for low temperatures tend to accelerate it, while warm weather calms the birds.

Many observations by Palmgren and Siivonen show that environmental conditions influence the characteristic activity of caged migrants, which may be increased, maintained, or inhibited. From these studies it is apparent that migratory restlessness is produced by a number of factors. When the bird is in a receptive 'phase' of its annual physiological cycle, external influences may affect it, but only when it is in this premigratory state. Otherwise they have no influence. Thus there seem to be factors inherent in the bird's physiology which cause it to be receptive. German authors call the former *Zugdisposition* and the latter, which actually initiates migratory behaviour (*Zug-unruhe*), they term *Zugstimmung*.

A physiological study of the metabolism of migrants during the migratory phase revealed that the premigratory metabolism of migrants usually undergoes many changes. Naumann noted in 1822 the deposition of fat,[1] and it has long been known, although little importance was attached to the fact, that migrants usually weigh more than sedentary birds or than they weigh at other times of the year.

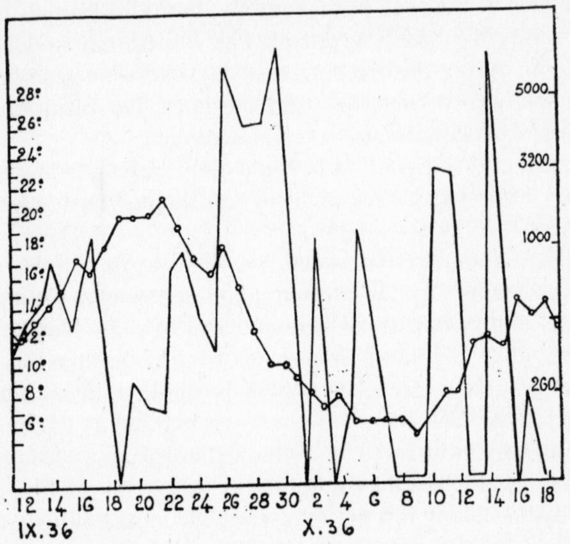

Fig. 94. Influence of temperature on the migratory restlessness of the caged whitethroat (*Sylvia communis*).
Curve with circles: temperature variations (in centigrade degrees)
Unbroken curve: migratory restlessness
From Merkel, 1940.

A number of authors have studied periodical variations in birds' weight. By weighing captive birds, studying their behaviour and migratory restlessness, and measuring their daily food requirements Merkel found (1938, 1940) that there is a fairly precise weight cycle (Fig. 94). During the breeding period weight reaches its minimum. It

1. Merkel (1958b) noted that in the whitethroat (*Sylvia communis*) and the robin (*Erithacus rubecula*) the respiratory quotient reaches its peak in the spring and that in the autumn it is also very high during premigratory periods (*Zugdisposition*). (The respiratory quotient is the ratio of CO_2 produced to O_2 used, which is studied by collecting exhaled air. High quotients, over one, mean that fat is being made from starchy foods, up to one that more sugar than fat is being burned. 0.7 means that pure fat fuels the animal. High quotients occur only when sugar is being converted to fat.)

tends to increase after the prenuptial moult and attains its maximum during the first manifestations of migratory restlessness. This maximum lasts until December. When there are two annual moults, the second comes at this time and is accompanied by a drop in weight, followed by a rise before the spring migration; this spring maximum is not so high as the peak in the autumn, but it far exceeds the bird's weight during the breeding period. The whitethroat weighs twelve–thirteen gm. during the breeding season, sixteen–nineteen gm. in the autumn and twenty–twenty-two gm. in winter. The European robin's weight varies between fourteen and nineteen gm.

There is a close correlation between daily variations in weight and migratory restlessness. One night of restlessness may cause a small Passerine to lose one to two gm.

Correlative food consumption forms an interesting study. The need for food increases with the autumn moult and reaches its peak at the beginning of the migration season. (Fig. 95). In November and December, after migration, food requirements lessen but rise again as spring migration approaches. There is another drop during the breeding season. The increased weight of migrants is, of course, connected to the quantity of food consumed, but a more basic phenomenon is involved in the deposition of fat. Although the bird's energy is taxed by migration, it replaces reserves far more easily than during other periods of the year. Sudden losses of weight are rapidly made up, although food intake does not change perceptibly. So it seems that a notable decrease in metabolic exchanges occurs at the beginning of the premigratory period. These fundamental changes in physiology correspond to the 'migratory disposition' (*Zugdisposition*).

Several authors, particularly Groebbels (1928), attempted to attribute these changes to the reduction of the gonads; their inactivity, he claimed, causes a physiological castration resulting in a heavy deposition of fat. It is, however, more likely that the bird's increase in weight is controlled not by variations in the activity of a single gland, but rather by the whole organism. Everything occurs as if the bird, which is 'preparing' to migrate, accumulated reserves like a traveller about to leave for a distant journey. This 'explanation' is, of course, purely anthropomorphic.

Some of Merkel's observations had already been made, although not so precisely, by Zedlitz in his studies of winter variations in weight of European birds. The most complete analyses of weight, including those of Baldwin, Kendeigh and Nice, do not show the increase shortly before migration, but this may be due to the manner in which the results are presented.

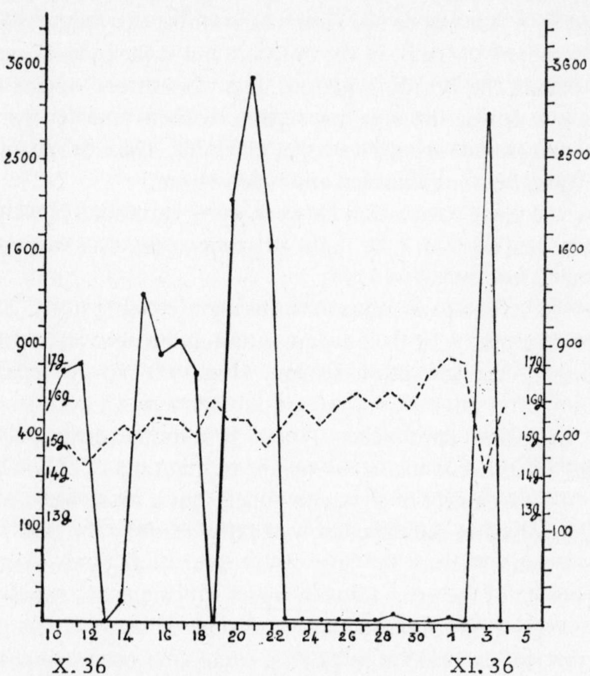

Fig. 95. Relationship between weight variations and migratory restlessness in the caged whitethroat (*Sylvia communis*)
Dotted curve: variations in the bird's weight
Unbroken curve: migratory restlessness
From Merkel, 1940.

The golden-crowned sparrow (*Zonotrichia atricapilla*) reaches a maximum weight in January, and another, much more marked peak, in May, before the spring migration (Linsdale and Sumner, 1934). This is true of other birds in this family, such as the fox sparrow (*Passerella iliaca*) and the tree sparrow (*Spizella arborea*).

While studying a related species, the white-crowned sparrow (*Zonotrichia leucophrys*), Blanchard (1941) found parallel phenomena among migratory races (*Z.l. pugetensis*), whereas among sedentary races (such as *Z.l. nuttalli*), no variations in weight are comparable. There is no metabolic cycle among sedentary birds.

Wolfson reached similar conclusions in his remarkable studies of the Oregon junco (*Junco oreganus*) (1945). Migratory populations always have a deposition of fat before they leave, while individuals belonging to sedentary races never accumulate large reserves. These experiments prove that the behaviour of American birds is the same as that of European species. Eyster (1952) worked with the slate-coloured junco (*Junco hyemalis*), the white-crowned sparrow (*Zonotrichia leucophrys*) and the white-throated sparrow (*Zonotrichia albicollis*); and Farner and Mewalt (1953b) got the same results with white-crowned sparrows. (For studies on premigratory restlessness [*Zugunruhe*] and the deposition of fat, see Linsdale and Sumner [1934], and for the golden-crowned sparrow [*Zonotrichia atricapilla*] see de Bont [1947].) Morris, Connell and Johnston (1957) found a similar increase in weight among ruby-throated humming-birds (*Archilochus colubris*), among which the proportion of fat changes from eleven–fifteen per cent in June to forty-one–forty-six per cent in individuals that are ready to migrate (about two gm. of fat, which is sufficient to supply energy for a flight of 800 miles).[1] Rautenberg (1957) compared the metabolism of the migratory brambling (*Fringilla montifringilla*) and the sedentary house sparrow (*Passer domesticus*) from the point of view of increased weight and showed the differences in their annual cycles and exchanges of energy.

Authors thus generally agree that birds tend to accumulate fat during their premigratory phase; this denotes a slowing down of metabolic exchanges and a manifest change in the physiology of assimilation.

Now we must see how this energy can be mobilized, in other words, how the bird can be brought to migrate. Since it had been suggested that various glands produce an internal secretion, Wagner injected extracts of the thyroid gland and thyroxin.[2] As some of his results were

1. Recently Odum (1960) has shown that among migrants killed in autumn by striking a TV tower in Florida the total lipids varied from less than 2% in individuals of *Zonotrichia albicollis* (not migrating beyond the Gulf Coast) to 50% in individuals of *Piranga olivacea* and *Dolichonyx oryzivorus*, which migrate to South America. This author states that the energy of these fat deposits is quite sufficient to make flights of hundreds of miles over the Gulf of Mexico (some of them have enough 'fuel' for 1,500 or more miles).

2. Thyroxin is the protein-free specific molecule which has all the actions of the thyroid gland and which replaces its function after the gland's removal.

positive, Merkel (1940) repeated the experiments and developed a complete theory of the thyroid as determinant of the migratory impulse.

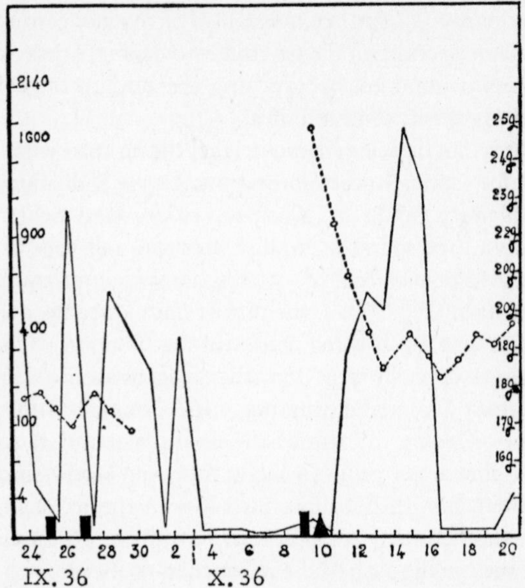

Fig. 96. Influence of the injection of small quantities of thyroxin on migrants with increased weight. Experiments on the whitethroat (*Sylvia communis*)
Black rectangles: injection of thyrotropic hormone
Black triangles: injection of thyroxin (0.1 cm3)
Each injection is followed by a decrease in weight (dots) and by renewed migratory restlessness. From Merkel, 1940.

He stated that after an injection of a large dose of thyroid extract or thyroxin (0.3 of the latter substance) the bird loses a considerable amount of weight. But the important fact is that this hormone, while destroying fatty reserves by activating oxidation and the energetic metabolism, inhibits premigratory physiological activity; restlessness either ceases or becomes markedly slower. The injection of a small dose of the same substances (0.1 cc. of thyroxin, for example) in a bird with a heavy deposit of fat seems to increase migratory restlessness while causing a loss in weight (Fig. 96). It has no effect on birds without fatty reserves. The same results are obtained when thyrotropin[1] or the

1. Thyrotropin (TSH) is the chain of amino acids specific for activating thyroid.

thyrotropic hormone from the anterior lobe of the pituitary[1] is injected. Merkel (1958a) repeated these experiments and confirmed his earlier results. He also showed that migratory activity could be inhibited by a dose of 0.2 $cm.^3$ of a solution of five per cent of methylthiouracil,[2] whose action on the thyroid is to decrease thyroxin levels. The same effect is obtained by exposing the bird to ultraviolet rays (for four periods of forty-five minutes).

Thus it seems that these hormones trigger the impulse when birds are in a premigratory state. Studies of the annual cycle of the thyroid gland of wild birds were made by Küchler (1935), who dealt with the European robin, tree sparrow, English sparrow and yellow-hammer, and Watzka (1934), who worked with sparrows, domestic geese and various mammals. (Fig. 97). Their results have since been confirmed by other work. There are three phases in the function of the thyroid gland: secretion, deposition of the reserve in the follicles, reabsorption and liberation of the hormone in the organism (this is rather diagrammatic). During the winter the gland accumulates colloid in the follicles which are large at the time; this deposit can be stained by histological reagents. In February and March the follicles diminish in size, while their content can no longer be stained. This phenomenon is more apparent in the case of the robin than of the tree sparrow and yellowhammer. The English sparrow continues to accumulate colloid in its follicles.

Between April and July colloid again accumulates, the follicles fill and the contents again take histological staining, at least in the case of the birds which have been studied (except the English sparrow, which at this time is reabsorbing the contents of the follicles). Another reabsorption occurs in August and September in the robin, tree sparrow and yellow-hammer, and this is followed by a period of accumulation from October or November to February.

1. The anterior pituitary is close to and under the constant control of the vegetative centres of the brain. It puts out short chains of amino acids which are specific stimulants – one for thyroid (TSH), one for adrenal cortex (ACTH), one for androgen ('maleness') producing cells of testis, one for ovarian follicles and for testicular tubules (egg and sperm-producing tissues). The latter is FSH, folliculin progynon: it works on germ producers of either sex. Pituitary cells are under nervous influences, and 'feed back' from the concentration of substances they evoke in fluid about the cell.

2. Methylthiouracil (related to the goiter-causing substance in cabbage, turnips, etc.) interferes with formation of thyroid and acts like the removal of the gland.

From the purely physiological point of view, the gland produces the hormone during the secretory period, but it accumulates in the follicles and is not spread through the birds's organism. During reabsorption

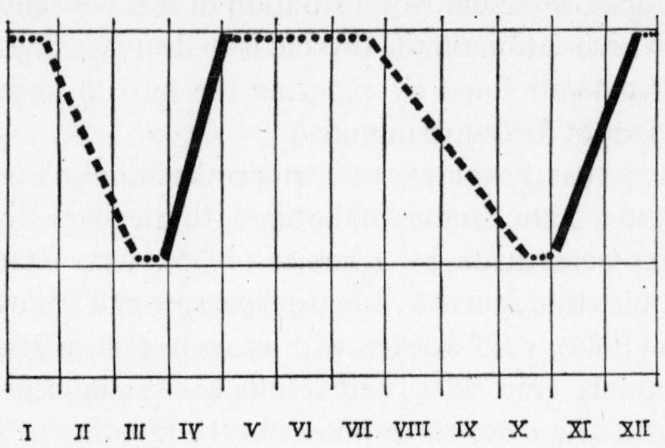

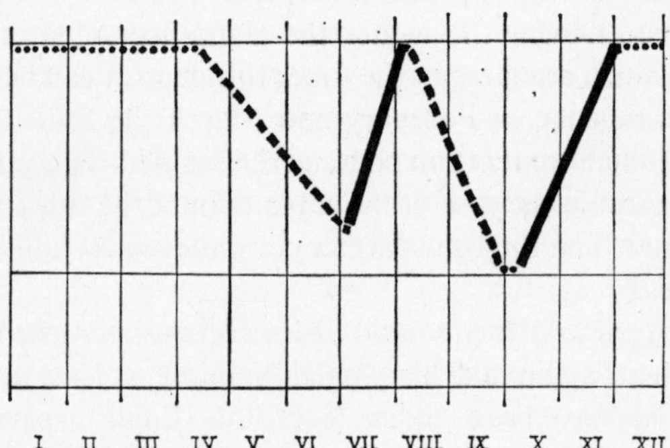

Fig. 97. Annual cycle of the thyroid glands of the European robin (*Erithacus rubecula*) above and the English sparrow (*Passer domesticus*) below.

Dotted line: period of retention (the highest part of the curve) or of inactivity (the lowest part)

Unbroken line: secretion period

Broken line: colloid resorption

From Küchler, 1935.

the hormone is liberated, and it then plays an important part in the bird's physiology.

The diagram shows the annual cycle of the gland. Aside from the secretory period, a certain quantity of hormones passes directly into the organism without going first into the follicles. This seems to be negligible, however, in comparison to the amount discharged during the reabsorption of the follicles.

The cycle of thyroid activity varies with the species, especially between the English sparrow and the other birds tested. Biological differences, which cause some forms to be migratory, others sedentary, are no doubt parallel.

The thyroid gland is important in the energy metabolism and rate of combustion. It has a dominant influence on moult, for thyroidectomy inhibits moult, while hyperthyroidization stimulates it. Furthermore, the follicular reabsorption of the gland corresponds to annual moults.[1]

But the interesting fact is that this reabsorption also coincides with migratory periods. Küchler found that in a real migrant like the European robin (he tested individuals in migratory German populations) the important spring reabsorption occurs in February and March; the autumn reabsorption (starting in July) continues during moult and postnuptial migration, or until the beginning of October. It lasts longer than in the less migratory tree sparrow and yellow-hammer, where spring reabsorption is less marked. In a sedentary bird, like the English sparrow, there is no spring reabsorption, and at that time the gland is even accumulating colloid in its follicles. Schildmacher (1951) also found that the spring migratory period in some birds was characterized by intense thyroid activity.

A similar theory to that of Küchler was adopted by Merkel, who believes that the determinant of the migratory impulse is in the thyroid cycle. He states that the functioning of the thyroid triggers the migratory impulse of birds in 'premigration' (*Zugdisposition*). As cold stimulates the thyroid, a drop in temperature triggers the bird's departure. Caged birds show much more migratory restlessness when it is cold.

Conditions in the spring are altogether different, for the temperature tends to rise, and many birds arrive with currents of warm air. The bird usually has less fat, but the thyroid gland is developing, while in the autumn it tends to diminish. It therefore spreads throughout the organism sufficient quantities of hormone to mobilize the reserves without the aid of an external stimulus such as autumn cold.

1. This was recently observed in the case of the emperor penguin, whose thyroid is more active during the moulting period than in winter when it controls the bird's defence against cold (Prévost and Bourlière, *Acta XI Congr. Int. Orn. Basel*, 1954: 252–257, 1955).

When spring migrants are overtaken by sudden cold, their energy requirements, stimulated by a greater thyroid secretion, increase rapidly. This causes the bird to lose weight quickly, while it emerges from the premigratory state and migration stops.

During spring, as in autumn migration, there seems to be a direct relation between the migratory impulse and a rise in the rate of metabolic exchanges; this entails mobilization of the fatty deposits under the influence of and through the thyroid.

After making a comparative physiological study of a migratory mourning dove (*Zenaida macroura*) and a sedentary pigeon, Riddle, Smith and Benedict (1932) advanced theories involving the thyroid, but their explanation does not agree with Merkel's. These authors claim that metabolism is higher in a migrant than in a sedentary bird of the same size; hence the migratory species has to do more work and liberate more warmth to maintain a constant body temperature. Contrary to Merkel, they state that the thyroid of migratory birds is not stimulated by the cold, so the birds have to seek the best environmental conditions, and this stimulates their migratory impulse. The thyroid of sedentary species, on the other hand, is stimulated by the cold; they have a higher metabolism and can withstand a drop in temperature.

Kendeigh (1934) found the same physiological difference between the sedentary bird and the migrant in his study of the English sparrow and the migratory house wren (*Troglodytes aedon*).

After studying the metabolism and physiology of various species, including some shore-birds, Groebbels (1928) concluded that their chief problem is to preserve a constant internal temperature. He divides birds into two categories: First, those which have a good thermal regulation and are characterized by moderate food requirements, a rather slow digestion and a high resistance to fast; these include the little owl, jackdaw and domestic pigeon. The other group, with a higher metabolism, has a poor thermal regulation and greater food requirements. Their internal temperature is relatively high, and they have little resistance to fasting. This category includes a number of song-birds, particularly the insectivorous Sylviidae and Turdidae. According to Groebbels, this distinction is very important, and migratory birds leave when unfavourable changes occur because they are incapable of adjusting to their surroundings. The thyroid gland is the link between the surroundings and the organism. This theory is, however, too over-simplified to be applied to the complex facts involved.

Putzig (1937–38a,b,c,d,e) also devoted a long study to the influence of the thyroid as the determinant of the migratory impulse. During the course of his work on shore-birds, he found that migration is related to the thyroid cycle, but he thinks that generalization about the interdependence of the two phenomena is dangerous, since so many specific, even individual, variations are involved. While Putzig was studying the thyroid glands of the lapwing on its spring migration, he found birds whose thyroid contained follicles with colloid which would not take staining, an indication of glandular activity. But some individuals on prenuptial migration had thyroid glands with the normal characteristics of the accumulation period.

This same author injected robins with thyrotropic hormones in October to activate their thyroid glands. Although captured under the same conditions, the birds differed considerably in behaviour; one group had no reaction, a second manifested a great amount of restlessness during the day (in one case eleven times more than before the injection), and a third group showed excitement both during the day and at night.

Small doses of thyrotropin produced no effect, probably because the experiment was conducted at the close of the migration period. Although this late date reduces the value of the results to a certain extent, the experiment proves how individuals vary in behaviour.

Putzig also studied the structure of thyroid glands of nomadic birds or of species which make invasions at intervals. In these instances the influence of cold is most apparent, so the thyroid could be dominant. Results, however, are variable. Some birds do not show any reabsorption, while certain European jays, which wander in nomadic flocks, had thyroid glands in a state of accumulation or theoretically inactive.

Putzig observed that some birds migrate at a time when external influences cannot operate: shore-birds which leave in July are not driven by either a drop in temperature or a scarcity of food, so they seem to have their own rhythm.

Putzig deserves credit for showing how migratory patterns vary. Hypotheses based on the annual cycle of thyroid glands can be applied to certain birds, but not to all.

Our information on the physiology of thyroid glands is still incomplete and highly contradictory, but these glands do seem to play a part in migration. Although their action is no more direct than that of the gonads, we may assume that they are part of a system which determines and conditions migration.

Pituitary Causation of the Migratory Impulse

Since the thyroid alone cannot explain migration, experiments were begun some time ago with another gland, the pituitary, which controls the thyroid. The hypophysis, a glandular apparatus in the lower part of the brain, acts like a command post and sends out 'orders' in the form of multiple hormonal secretions. The anterior lobe of this complex gland is of pharyngeal embryonic origin; the posterior lobe comes from the nerves (*pars nervosa*). As even less is known about the physiology of the latter,[1] we shall deal only with the former, known as the pituitary gland, although that term is frequently applied to the whole organ.

Before studying the influence of the pituitary on migration, let us recall that this gland affects the whole organism, particularly its metabolism and reproductive cycle. One of the chief hormones secreted by the anterior lobe of the pituitary, thyrotropin or thyrotropic hormone (TSH), stimulates the thyroid. Another group, the gonadotropic hormones, affect sexual maturation and the annual sexual cycle, which most authors, especially Benoît and Wolfson, believe is closely dependent upon the pituitary.

That the activity of this gland is partially independent of environmental factors is proved by recent observations (Curry-Lindahl, 1958, see below); in certain instances birds have been taken to the opposite hemisphere, where they breed during the winter, thus preserving their 'internal rhythm.' Furthermore, the young, which have never known natural conditions, may keep this rhythm for a time.

But the pituitary is not altogether independent, for a definite relation has been established with cyclic changes in the surroundings, especially light. Benoît and his collaborators proved that variations in light affect the sexual glands through the pituitary. Light stimulates

1. The posterior neural pituitary controls pigmentation and water excretion. Its hormones have been synthesized. Those of the anterior pituitary have been obtained in pure, single molecular, types, but have not yet been synthesized.

this gland, which then affects the gonads. It seems to act through the eye and its retina, as well as by more direct means (encephalic regions near the orbit, the hypothalamus and the rhinencephalon); blind birds react as well as normal ones, for flesh is receptive to light. So it is possible to have an opto-pituitary sexual reflex through the eye, or an encephalo-pituitary sexual reflex through the brain.

These observations are extremely interesting, because they reveal how the sexual cycle and migratory movements are related to variations in illumination and the influence of light on birds. They explain the results obtained by Rowan with the juncos.

In short, determinants of the pituitary cycle are an internal rhythm, whose patterns are still unknown, and external influences, among which seasonal variations in light are of chief importance. These factors help us to understand migrations, which are also periodic and a concomitant of cyclic variations in the environment. The sexual and migratory cycles, which Rowan thought were linked together, are really connected through the pituitary, which regulates both. This is the theory of Wolfson, who has written a series of excellent studies on the subject.

Wolfson began by repeating experiments similar to those of Rowan on the Oregon junco (*Junco oreganus*), some of the more northern races of which are migratory (*oreganus*, *montanus*, *thurberi*), whereas those that breed farther south are sedentary (*pinosus*) (Figs. 98 and 99). By keeping juncos and white-crowned sparrows under experimental conditions, he proved (1954a) that there is a close relationship between photoperiodism, the evolution of gonads and the deposition of fat. In the course of a year he alternated seven periods of long and short days, and each time obtained the corresponding change; regression of gonads, loss of fat, loss of weight, moult were always correlated to the short days and inversely. This was a spectacular demonstration of the way in which the physiological state is related to illumination.

In another experiment the birds were exposed to longer artificial days starting at the beginning of December, and daylight seemed to increase just as it does in the spring. When the birds were liberated at the end of January and the beginning of February, the migratory juncos started north two months before the normal date. This was proved by the recovery of one of the birds 180 miles north of the spot where it was set free (Berkeley, California).

Wolfson also kept some migratory juncos in captivity until late May and early June. These birds then flew north two months behind schedule on a 'delayed migration.' If Rowan's first hypothesis were correct, they should not have left the place where they were liberated

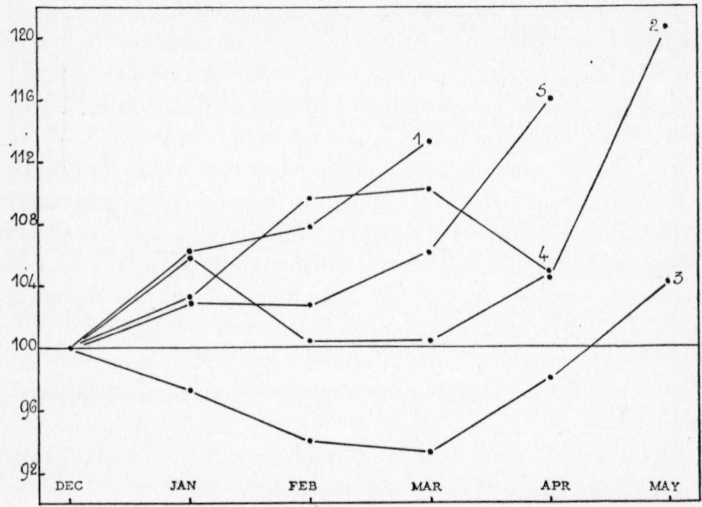

Fig. 98. Changes in body weight from December through May in five migratory sparrows, expressed in terms of percentage of December body weight. 1. Oregon junco (*Junco oreganus*); 2. Golden crowned sparrow (*Zonotrichia atricapilla*); 3. Fox sparrow (*Passerella iliaca*); 4. Tree sparrow (*Spizella arborea*); 5. Puget Sound white-crowned sparrow (*Zonotrichia leucophrys pugetensis*). They all tend to gain weight before the spring migration period. From Wolfson, 1945.

because no migratory impulse would manifest itself once the sexual evolution was completed; they would have attempted to breed there instead. Wolfson explains this behaviour by the fact that the birds were not in their regular breeding area, that their normal behaviour was upset by being kept in groups, and that they had not expended their energy in migratory flights. He decided that their physiological and psychological condition was sufficiently close to the premigratory state to trigger their departure.

Juncos belonging to sedentary races were submitted to the same artificial conditions but did not migrate.

Wolfson then studied the development and evolution of gonads during the winter among different types of birds. Migratory and sedentary populations mingle to a certain degree in winter quarters near Berkeley, but the testes of sedentary birds increase in size more

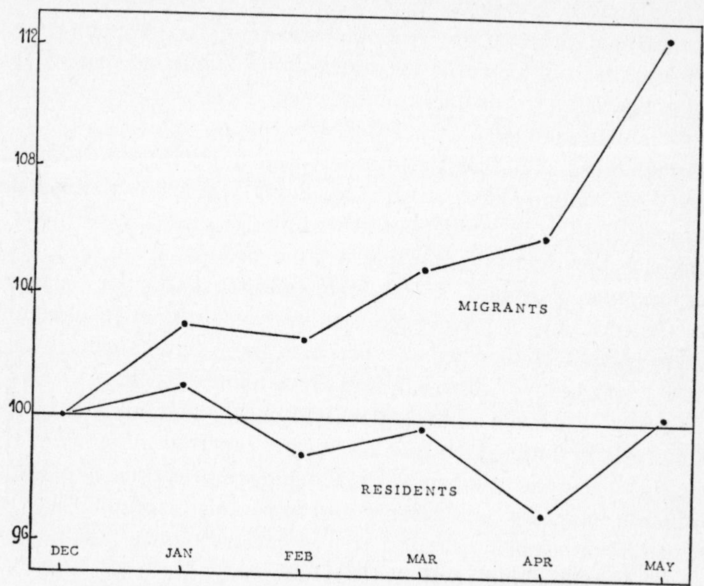

Fig. 99. Comparison of changes in body weight of residents and migrants from December through May, expressed in terms of percentage of December body weight. From Wolfson, 1945, simplified.

rapidly and at an earlier date than those of migrants; when migrant juncos leave at the end of March, their testes have a volume of about four $mm.^3$, while those of resident birds measure 220 $mm.^3$. Contrary to Rowan's opinion the testes of migratory birds are very slightly developed at the time of their departure from winter quarters.

Wolfson concluded that there is no cause and effect relation between gonadal development and the migratory impulse. He believes that the two may be concomitant and that they result from the action of the pituitary, which acts on them and on all the endocrine glands; it creates a physiological state in which the evolution of a certain organ is part of the whole.

One of the most important aspects of premigration seems to be the accumulation of a quantity of energy in the form of deposits of fat which are not found in sedentary birds. When Wolfson studied the relation between the sexual cycle and the deposition of fat on one hand, and the activity of the pituitary, he found that the injection of a gonadotropic preparation from the serum of the pregnant mare stimulates recrudescence of the testes and a slight increase of the ovaries but that it has no effect on the general metabolism, and there is no accumulation of fat.

On the other hand, an injection of Antuitrin G (anterior pituitary extract of mammalian origin containing mainly somatotropic hormone and small amounts of other anterior pituitary hormones) stimulates the organism, causing a large deposition of fat and a recrudescence of gonadal activity. This hormonal complex seems to put the bird into a premigratory state. An injection of adrenalin inhibits Antuitrin G when the two are given simultaneously and causes a regression of gonads in sexually developed birds.

Wolfson next made a histological study of the anterior lobe of the pituitary and examined its structure at various periods of the year. He used the development taken by the Golgi apparatus (this cytological formation increases considerably during periods of cellular activity because it takes part in secretion, so it reveals the gland's evolutionary state) to test this gland's activity (Fig. 100).

When the sex glands are at their minimum, the Golgi apparatus is compact, barely developed, and it reveals a very limited or non-existent activity on the part of the pituitary. During the breeding period, however, the Golgi apparatus in the cells of the anterior pituitary is enlarged and forms a network in correlation with the intense activity of the secreting gland. The same cytological test, under artificial lighting, revealed that the cycle of pituitary activity is influenced to some extent by surrounding conditions, especially light.

All these observations prove that the pituitary plays an important rôle in physiology and as a determinant of migration. It governs the cycle of the genital organs, especially the accumulation of fat, and influences the general metabolism.

The pituitary appears to be partly dependent on light, whether directly or through its reaction to activity. Wolfson believes that the bird's daily rhythm has a great influence on the activity of the pituitary. The hypothalamus (a basal part of the brain), which is connected to the pituitary gland, can also control the secretion of pituitary hormones. Thus the bird's daily rhythm is to a certain degree capable of influencing, through the nerve centres, the development of the sex glands and the whole metabolism. Psychic factors, such as the be-

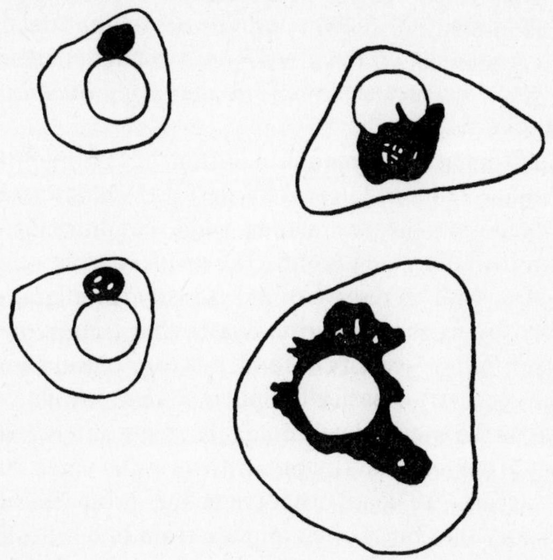

Fig. 100. Cells from the anterior lobe of the pituitary of migratory juncos illustrating the condition of the Golgi apparatus. The Golgi apparatus is indicated by black areas; the nucleus is circular.

Left: wild migrants with testes at winter minimum.

Right: captive residents subjected to increases in day length; their testes were approaching breeding condition.

From Wolfson, 1945, simplified.

haviour of other birds, optical and auditory stimuli, probably also play a part.

Benoît, on the contrary, thinks that light stimulates the pituitary directly. One of his experiments consisted of starting gonadal development by illuminating the hypothalamus and pituitary region directly with a quartz tube.

All these explanations are not contradictory because the direct action of light does not exclude indirect action through a recrudescence of physical activity and metabolic exchanges.

Along with these external influences, there are internal factors which are still almost unknown (see Marshall, 1960). That an intrinsic cycle of the pituitary gland and the entire organism exists is attested by the fact that migratory and sedentary birds respond to the same conditions in a totally different way, as we know. Wolfson found that when the testes of sedentary individuals are exposed to lengthening periods of daylight, they increase rapidly in size, but the birds do not gain weight: migrants, on the other hand, accumulate reserves of fat, and their testes increase slowly. Thus the bird's organism does not respond automatically.

In short, Wolfson and some other authors believe that the pituitary, under the influence of an internal rhythm and variations in daylight, sends its orders to the sex glands while conditioning the whole metabolism, including the thyroid. The result is a physiological state where the bird, with its reserve of fat, is ready for migration and can be influenced by minimal external causes that trigger the migratory impulse (*temperature*, scarcity of food, meteorological stimuli).

Such an hypothesis is basically similar to that postulated by earlier ornithologists; the trigger determining the migratory impulse through the pituitary is the seasonal rhythm, with its cyclic variations in length of daylight. Thus we again encounter the principal objection to Rowan's theory that birds often migrate from one hemisphere to the other.

Following Bissonnette, Wolfson suggested a very interesting explanation, which has been verified many times since. Migratory birds, which fly to the other hemisphere in autumn, do not react to increases in length of daylight because their pituitary, following reproduction and during autumn migration, is in a refractory period and not sensitive to variations in daylight. Wolfson submitted several Fringillidae, Oregon juncos (*Junco oreganus*) and white-crowned sparrows (*Zonotrichia leucophrys*) to increasing periods of artificial illumination and obtained quite different results; while many Zonotrichia and some other species like the fox sparrow (*Passerella iliaca*) and the song sparrow (*Melospiza melodia*) reacted at once by developing gonads and depositing fat, the juncos, which belong to the same systematic group, gave evidence of a refractory period and paid no attention to the increased light.

All migrants which cross the equator do not have such a period, but we must not forget the juncos. A physiological cycle involving such a non-receptive period would explain the independence of migrants in relation to their winter surroundings in the opposite hemisphere.

The observations of Bissonnette and Wolfson were confirmed by Riley (1946), who found that in the case of the English sparrow a progressive increase in daylight made no impression at the end of September. Normal results were obtained when the experiment was undertaken in mid-November. Miller (1948a, b, 51, 54) found the same to be true of the golden-crowned sparrow (*Zonotrichia atricapilla*), which is related to the white-crowned sparrow (*Z. leucophrys*), in which Wolfson did not find evidence of a refractory period. Miller demonstrated that in the golden-crowned sparrow this period always lasts until after 10 October, and that in some individuals it is prolonged until 5 or even 20 of November. Shank (1959) found that the slate-coloured junco (*Junco hyemalis*) has a refractory period lasting until the beginning of December, but marked by certain individual differences. At this time of year the refractoriness of the bird to external stimuli seems to reside at the pituitary level. An injection of gonadotropic hormones stimulates increase in the size and activity of the testes in any season, and the sex glands are therefore always ready to respond to the action of hormones. The refractory period is thus caused when the pituitary does not respond to increasing day length by hormonal secretion.

Causation of the Migratory Impulse in Tropical Birds

Thus we return to theories based on variations in day-length. As this depends on astronomical considerations, independent of other conditions in the surroundings, it constitutes a fixed landmark in the seasonal cycle. Although this may be the determinant of some migrations, it cannot be applied to all, and few migratory cycles correspond exactly to the rhythm of increasing and decreasing day-length. We must assume that there are a large number of qualifying factors and that the glandular system functions in many ways.

Such a theory cannot explain the migrations of tropical birds, because in regions near the equator variations in light are too slight to influence the animal. Yet many tropical birds perform regular migrations.

Moreau, Wilk and Rowan (1947) analysed the annual cycle of

several tropical birds at Amani, which lies at lat. 5° S. in Tanganyika. A histological study of the gonads of the speckled mousebird (*Colius striatus mombassicus*) and two song-birds in the bulbul group (the black-capped bulbul [*Pycnonotus barbatus micrus*] and the yellow-streaked bulbul [*Phyllastrephus flavostriatus tenuirostris*]) shows that the testes in all these species reach their greatest development between September and March and then regress rapidly until August. During the rainy, 'cold' period the condition of the gonads is comparable to what is observed among birds of temperate regions during the winter. The testes increase considerably when daylight lengthens so imperceptibly that the bird cannot perceive the change, almost nothing in June and sixteen seconds a day in August! In the New Hebrides Baker, Marshall and Harrisson (1940) found that the testes of the golden whistler (*Pachycephala pectoralis*), a song-bird characteristic of oceanic regions, increase, although day-length is decreasing only thirty seconds a day.

Thus we must assume that other factors are involved in migrations near the equator. The alternation of dry and rainy seasons probably influences migratory behaviour. In most instances birds seem to be hunting food; fruit-eaters follow ripe fruits; insectivorous birds the hatching of their favourite prey. But plant cycles, like those of arthropods, are seasonal, so that indirectly the seasons influence avian behaviour and the birds' annual cycle.

The last word has not yet been said on this subject. The sexual cycle of tropical birds – which is closely related to the migratory cycle – seems to be tuned to what is *going* to happen; among insect-eating birds the young often hatch at the time when insects are at their peak, and this implies that a sexual impulse preceded the action of some alimentary factor. There is a mysterious cause which may depend on the factor responsible for the hatching of insects.

However, birds which inhabit regions near the equator are capable of reacting to variations in photoperiodism. Brown and Rollo (1940) and Rollo and Domm (1943) found that the paradise whydah (*Steganura*) and the orange bishop (*Euplectes franciscana*) of tropical Africa react admirably to experimental conditions in day-length, particularly with regard to moult. Daily periods of illumination of ten to eighteen hours induce nuptial plumage in the male (in many species this plumage represents an addition produced under the influence of gonadotropic secretions). Changes in external appearance are accompanied by gonadal development. The objection may be raised that the experimental birds were reared, not wild, but this does not lessen the value of the work.

The relation of plumage to illumination proves that the organism of these birds, especially their endocrine system, can react to such conditions. We may therefore assume that light can play the same rôle in the migratory behaviour of birds that live at higher altitudes, although in the tropical zone.

Conclusions

The various theories which have been offered to explain the determinants of the migratory impulse have often carried us far from the subject. Migration is only one phase of the annual cycle, of which other essential phenomena are breeding and moult. They all depend on the endocrine system, and, since the same glands govern different activities, the physiology of migration must be studied within the framework of the yearly cycle.

However, if migratory patterns reveal an infinite number of special cases, their determinants may be even more variable. Many authors think they can apply the conclusions they reached when studying one species to all migrants, but nothing is more erroneous. The physiology of a little song-bird and its annual cycle are not the same as those of ducks or sea-birds. In addition to these specific differences, important variations in migration behaviour are caused by environment; populations of a species differ, and there are even individual distinctions.

From a purely general point of view, migration periods in the annual cycle constitute two physiological 'crises' which are dependent on the endocrine glands, especially the pituitary. Physiological mechanisms have to adapt themselves to the considerable expenditures of energy required in long flights. This requires a physiological metamorphosis when strictly diurnal birds become nocturnal during migration. The most obvious modification in energy exchanges consists in accumulating reserves of fat that are unknown at other times of the year. Physiological changes in this premigratory period also consist of a great ability to 'recuperate' and replace weight (primarily fat) rapidly. Large quantities of food are stockpiled for reserve energy as fat, rather than glycogen,[1] which has a great advantage in the caloric value per weight unit (nine calories per gram instead of four).

These changes are controlled by the pituitary, which doubtless undergoes its own cyclic variations, although it is not affected by any known external factor.[2] This is particularly true during spring migration when the pituitary, which has now ended its refractory phase, exerts both a direct and an indirect influence over the whole organism. It stimulates the bird's general metabolism, and acts on the thyroid (spring moult) and on the gonads. But this activity does not seem to be determined or controlled by external factors among birds wintering in intertropical regions. After studying the winter behaviour and physiology of the yellow wagtail (*Motacilla flava*)[3] in the Congo, Curry-Lindahl (1958) found that an analysis of the patterns of physiological rhythms in five races wintering in Central Africa proves that their 'internal timer' is independent of environmental factors, among which variations in photoperiodism have little importance in low latitudes. This internal cycle seems to be fixed genetically in relation to conditions in the breeding area. No wagtail shows any sign of sexual activity in December and January, when gonads are inactive. In February part of the winter population begins to moult and to gain weight while the gonads are developing. These birds belong to populations that breed in southern Europe, where spring migration is

1. There is a place to store fat, but very little space for glycogen in the active cells (muscle, gland).

2. This internal regulation, which seems to affect the bird's whole cycle, was demonstrated in some of Sauer's experiments (*Z.f. Tierpsych.* 11: 10–93, 1954). Whitethroats (*Sylvia communis*), which had been reared from the egg stage in sound-proof rooms – these experiments were conducted to study the vocal manifestations of birds that had never been in contact with their kind – were kept at an even temperature, artificially lighted and given abundant food all year. They nevertheless displayed migratory restlessness at the normal times and were able to get their bearings, although they had never had any contact with nature.

3. Marshall and Williams (1959) reached the same conclusion with regard to yellow wagtails wintering at Entebbe, Uganda, where environmental conditions, including photoperiodism, are constant almost throughout the whole year. They state that 'sexual recrudescence and fat deposition, like plumage change, are under rhythmical control and uninfluenced by any particular, overall, external stimulus.'

Marshall and Serventy (1959) also proved that in the short-tailed shearwater (*Puffinus tenuirostris*), a transequatorial migrant (see p. 189), there is an internal reproductive rhythm; the bird is not influenced by the decrease of photoperiodism in its winter quarters, although the phenomenon is very marked.

early. In March and April *M.f. flava* of central Europe pass through the same phases before leaving for their breeding grounds. In April and May *M.f. thunbergi* finally depart for the nesting areas in Scandinavia which are not 'habitable' until long after the others. While a certain overlap is possible, this phenomenon indicates an internal rhythm that is not influenced by environmental conditions, and which seems correlated with the latitude of the European breeding area. In any case, metabolic changes, among which deposition of fat is the most obvious, make the bird receptive to migratory influences (*Zugdisposition*), some of which may be internal, although the majority are external.

At the time of migration northern birds seem more influenced by variations in photoperiodism, and we now know that its cyclic variations have a great bearing on the postnuptial premigratory changes which put the bird in a state of *Zugdisposition*. But there again some internal rhythm affecting the pituitary may be involved.

Wolfson (1959a), who has contributed most of our knowledge on the physiology of migrants, recently summed up his theories, saying that, in his opinion, the action of light is the source of all the processes determining the migratory cycle.

Two distinct phases intervene in the timing of spring migration: a preparatory phase and a progressive phase.

The preparatory phase, in late summer and autumn, is conditioned by short days; in experiments it is produced by a daily rhythm of nine hours of illumination and fifteen hours of darkness. Since at this period longer days (sixteen hours of light and eight hours of darkness) arrest this phase, Wolfson concluded that the determinant is the duration of darkness. (This may be 'a period of synthesis of gonadotropin in the pituitary, the mechanism requiring long periods of darkness each day or probably more correctly, being inhibited or arrested by stimulatory doses of light.') Thus short autumn days condition migratory behaviour and breeding six months later.

The second, or progressive, phase begins for northern migrants in November and December. It is stimulated to a considerable degree by lengthening photoperiodism, but not inhibited by short days.

The preparatory phase is thus conditioned by the daily dark periods, whereas the progressive phase may be conditioned by the dark (inhibitory) or the light (stimulatory) period – it is not known which; both may play a rôle at the same time.

Wolfson's data are important with regard to equatorial or trans-equatorial migrants. The fact that a photoperiodism of constant duration, like that in equatorial regions, is effective in gonadal development shows that constant light can no longer be considered non-regulatory, which was one of the chief objections. Thus birds wintering in intertropical regions could respond to days about twelve hours in length. But birds going to the other hemisphere would be exposed to days of sufficient length – although decreasing in the period preceding their spring migration – to determine the progressive phase.

Once the bird is in a premigratory state, it is subject to external factors, which change in importance from species to species and in accordance with the spring or autumn migration. Some of the chief factors are meteorological, such as barometric pressure, winds, a drop in temperature, and scarcity of food in autumn.[1] Psychological factors are also involved, particularly flocking behaviour. An analysis of the behaviour of caged migrants reveals their sensitivity to these factors (*Zugstimmung*) and explains their departure. But this sensitivity varies considerably according to species (see p. 232), and the differences relate to that phase of behaviour which concerns us here. Mascher (1955) showed the importance of variations in temperature as a stimulus for migration in Sweden. A rise in temperature in the spring causes large flocks to start northward, especially song-birds. According to Mascher, other weather phenomena have no importance unless – like heavy rains, fog and high winds – they can restrain this impulse. Raynor (1956) on the basis of observations in the U.S.A. believes the stability of the atmospheric situation and the wind direction play a similar rôle. Nisbet (1957), after studying migration in Scandinavia, also insists on the importance of external factors. Ball (1952) found there was no single stimulus for migration of thrushes on the Gaspé Peninsula; it was triggered by shortage of food, weather, or other disturbances.

Some birds will not migrate without an immediate stimulus, whereas others seem to have a sufficiently strong migratory impulse to leave without it. Swifts, for example, leave at almost the same date every year. They have a very well-regulated internal cycle or else they are influenced by environmental factors of which we know nothing.

1. By preventing birds from feeding the formation of ice triggers the autumn migration of arctic water birds in the far north of Canada, as Ellis (1956) has shown.

Premigratory periods vary greatly in length. Birds which wander throughout the winter are apparently in this state during the whole season. Furthermore, birds reveal a 'vagabond' temperament at all times except during the breeding period; the stable, territorial instinct seems to be a direct result of the sexual impulse in the reproductive period.

Partial Migrations

Within species, even within a population, some individuals are sedentary, whereas others reveal a more or less marked migratory temperament. These differences in behaviour imply important physiological variations.

There are striking instances of partial migration, such as European common herons. Lack (1944) cited quite a number of examples among British birds: song thrush, starling, white wagtail, blackbird, robin, lapwing, curlew, woodcock, black-headed gull, gannet and cormorant (Fig. 101). There are also a number of cases among North American birds, including the black-capped chickadee (*Parus atricapillus*), song sparrow (*Melospiza melodia*) and cowbird (*Molothrus ater*).

Two groups of partially migratory species may be distinguished: one includes all forms between the sedentary, which winter in the place where they were hatched, and migrants, with nomadic birds (for example, common herons and European black-headed gulls in between). In other species a single population is clearly divided into sedentary birds and migrants, all of which travel a long distance. Lack mentions British song thrushes and lapwings in this second group. The birds have three alternatives: they winter where they are; go to France, Spain and Portugal (south-south-west); to Ireland (west), or to the far west of England. So there is a real dimorphism in behaviour, even a polymorphism, in the case of thrushes and lapwings.

The proportion of sedentary and migratory individuals varies.[1] Many birds are much more migratory in eastern and northern Europe than in the western part of the continent. Lack has shown that these

1. The migratory behaviour of an individual bird can vary considerably from year to year, as Nice (1937) demonstrated in the case of the song sparrow and Brackbill (1956) of the mocking-bird (*Mimus polyglottus*). A female mocking-bird spent two winters in its breeding territory in Baltimore, migrated the third winter, and returned the following spring.

differences appear even within such restricted zones as the British Isles.

It has also been known for a long time that young birds and females are much more migratory than adult males. This is apparent in Lack's diagrams of some birds in Great Britain, although proportions vary according to species.

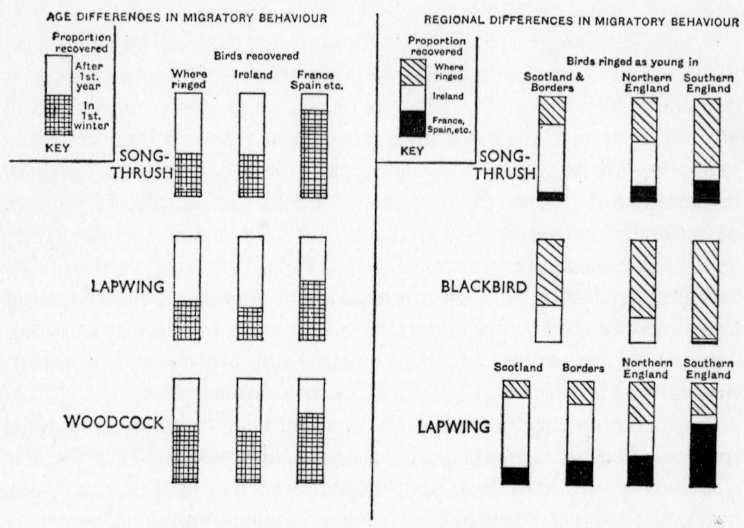

Fig. 101. Partial migrations in the British Isles
Left: variations in age. Most individuals banded in England and recaptured on the continent are not more than a year old.
Right: variations in local populations. Birds wintering in their breeding area are more numerous in the south than in the north of the British Isles. From Lack, 1944.

Nice (1937) made similar observations in North America on the song sparrow (*Melospiza melodia*), mocking-bird (*Mimus polyglottus*), hairy woodpecker (*Dendrocopos villosus*) and prairie chicken (*Tympanuchus cupido*). This is also true of some altitudinal migrations, like those of the grouse (*Lagopus scoticus*) and the Himalayan monal (*Lophophorus impeyanus*), where females descend in winter to lower altitudes than males (Morley, 1943).

It is thus possible to attempt a physiological explanation of partial migrations in relation to an inhibition of the migratory impulse, under the influence of male sexual hormones. These hormones would act on adult males in the autumn and counterbalance any influence stimulating them to migrate; they could not affect females and young birds.

This hypothesis is confirmed by a number of observations, especially with regard to sexual behaviour in autumn. As Lack demonstrated in the case of the robin, many song-birds have a sexual recrudescence that is displayed in song and a territorial instinct which even induces warfare.

There are similar explanations for the behaviour of species where the males do not go so far as the females, show a greater repugnance to overcome certain obstacles (like the migratory common chaffinches in Holland; see p. 228) and return at an earlier date to their breeding grounds. All this indicates an antagonism between the migratory impulse and the sexual instinct. As behaviour depends on the balance of these various elements, the result varies according to individuals and the populations of a species.

The physiological study of migration is incomplete. Although recent years have brought us closer to the goal, most problems are still unsolved. Our better understanding of endocrinology should, however, make it possible to reach more satisfactory explanations.

It is important to remember that no gland can be considered apart from its association with the bird's whole organism. The glandular system, like the highly developed nervous system, reacts on the whole, and the nervous centres have both a direct and an indirect influence on migratory behaviour. A group of external and internal conditions must determine reactions of behaviour already fixed by hereditary potentialities in the form of an evolutionary preadaptation. What we measure or cause to vary during our experiments represents only the immediate causes that trigger a much more complex mechanism which we are still unable to evaluate.

CHAPTER 12

Orientation of Migratory Birds

Orientation is one of the most complex puzzles in the whole realm of migration, even of the whole biology of birds. They return to breed in the regions where they were hatched, after wintering in a specific area, perhaps many thousands of miles distant, to which they travel every autumn. The apparent ease with which birds find their way is surprising. As Thomson said, the two main questions are: Why do birds choose a particular place for their winter quarters? And what guides the bird towards the region where the species or population has its winter quarters, and then back again, as the sun swings northward?

Unfortunately, we have as yet no answer to the first question, for most factors determining animal behaviour are still not understood. Although many attempts have been made to answer the second, there is at present no completely satisfactory solution. It appears, however, that the answer is to be found somewhere in a web of contradictory possibilities.

The Ancients explained orientation very simply, saying that Providence guides birds on their long flights, so there was really no problem at all! We may discard more modern explanations, more philosophical than scientific in character, involving *instinct*, a vague term that usually refers to innate, hereditary behaviour. Välikangas's experiments (1933) seem to prove that there are no hereditary factors in migration. In Finland he reared mallards (*Anas platyrhynchus*) hatched from eggs brought from England. Although their relatives in southern England are sedentary, these ducks left their adopted country in November, flew south-west like the Finnish mallards and returned the following spring to breed in Finland. Putzig (1938b) repeated this experiment in Germany, and Mac Cabe (1947) did the same thing with wood ducks (*Aix sponsa*) in the U.S.A., so it is apparent that heredity does not determine migratory behaviour in those species at least. Birds, however, adapt so quickly to an environment that we cannot be surprised at the results of these experiments where physiological factors – reaction to a different climate and other surroundings – are important.

Välikangas's experiments do not, however, take psychic factors into consideration, and imitation is so common among birds that we do not need to dwell on it (see p. 256). This is shown in a series of experiments conducted on young storks in Germany (Schüz, 1949, 1950b).

As we know, European storks are divided into two distinct groups, one of which migrates south-west in autumn, the other south-east (see p. 51). Schüz took 754 young 'eastern' birds, carried them into western Germany (the south-west migratory zone) and reared them there. After banding the birds, he released them at the normal migratory period and found that a very large percentage flew south-west. This might seem to confirm Välikangas's remarks about the absence of hereditary factors. But Schüz had also noted that these young storks migrated with 'western' adults, so imitation was involved. He then took 144 storks from eastern Prussia, released them in western Germany (Essen) *after the departure* of the native birds, and found that the vast majority (at least eighty-three per cent) flew south-east, like the population from which they had sprung. So it seems that, in a few cases at least, a genetic factor may influence avian behaviour. It is variable according to species, certainly does not justify the term 'instinct' of philosophical authors, and it is believed to be a hereditary response to the bird's surroundings which determines the orientation pattern.

Methods of Studying Orientation

The first method of studying the problem is to observe birds in the wild. Careful observation of migratory flights reveals a relationship with certain characteristics of the surroundings, but the results are hard to interpret, since so many factors are unknown and cannot be controlled.

The experimental method furnishes more precise information, and most of our knowledge of orientation has been derived from 'homing' experiments. Essentially this method involves taking adult birds from a specific point (usually their nests), transporting them for various distances, and analysing their speed and rate of success in returning. The method is based on the bird's attachment to its nest.

Since these experiments deal with the orientation of birds on trips which, *a priori*, have no connection with migrations, the data they supply must then be adapted to the latter. Orientation on migration is a greater problem, but it is probable that the bird guides itself by means of landmarks similar to those it uses in 'homing' experiments.[1]

These homing experiments reveal how birds differ in their orientation abilities. Sedentary birds have very little ability to 'find their way.' In Germany Creutz (1949) showed that adult great tits (*Parus major*) and blue tits (*Parus caeruleus*) do not return to the nest if they have been carried more than six miles away. The behaviour of these birds upon liberation, the long delays and small proportion of returns reveal that tits have no real sense of orientation; those which came back merely happened to see landmarks they recognized from previous flights.

Similar experiments were conducted (Rüppell, 1940, 1948) on European goshawks (*Accipiter gentilis*), sedentary Raptores, whose winter flights, as shown by banding records, are restricted to a circle barely thirty miles in circumference around the breeding area. Very few of them return to the nest from a point only 120 miles away.

Matthews's work with gulls (1952b) shows that related species may differ markedly in orientation ability. The lesser black-backed gull (*Larus fuscus*) and the herring gull (*Larus argentatus*) are common in Great Britain, but their winter dispersion differs (see p. 40), for British lesser black-backed gulls spread over France, the Iberian Peninsula and even West Africa (so they are real migrants), whereas sedentary herring gulls rarely go south beyond the territorial waters of Great Britain. The lesser black-back has much better homing ability than its relative, even when it is taken to regions which normally it never visits.

Homing experiments have revealed that some adult birds, parti-

1. The time interval between the bird's release and its date of return to the nest can give useful indications about its orientation during flight. But this period includes pauses for rest and feeding, and the important item is the amount of time actually consumed in flight. Wilkinson (*J. exp. Biol.*, 27: 192–197, 1950) devised an ingenious flight recorder, consisting of a plate sensitive to a ray as emitted by a strip of radio-active metal (polonium). A steel ball slips between the plate and the source of the ray whenever the bird alights. The duration of the flight can then be obtained by measuring the blackening of the plate.

cularly migrants, have an extraordinary ability to return to the nest from remote points. In the following table compiled from material from Griffin (1944) and Matthews (1955b) and completed by other data found in the literature, the principal experiments and most remarkable returns are listed. Some are spectacular because of the great distances involved.

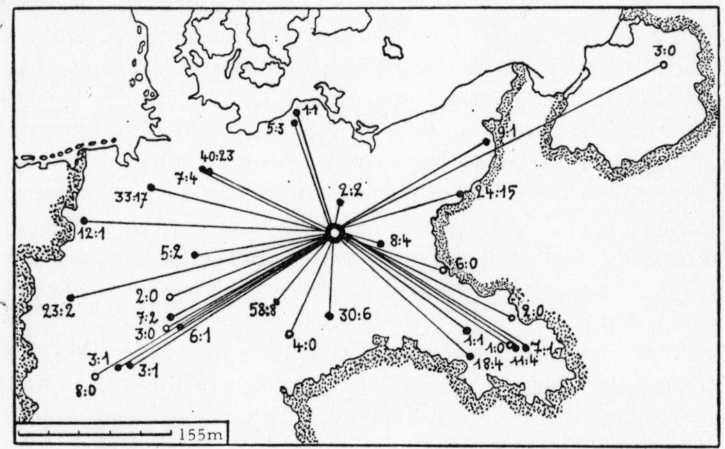

Fig. 102. Homing experiments on starlings (*Sturnus vulgaris*). The release point (Berlin) is marked with a circle. Homes are indicated by dots and linked to Berlin by a line. Figures indicate the number of birds carried away from their homes and the recoveries recorded. After Rüppell, 1935.

During the course of numerous experiments with starlings (*Sturnus vulgaris*), Rüppell (1934a, 1935, 1936, 1937, 1938a) transported 333 birds to Berlin from places from thirty to 410 miles away, and 120 of them returned to their nests. When birds were taken to Venice, about 500 miles from Berlin, one starling was recovered in Austria, some eighty miles east of a straight line connecting the two points (Fig. 102).

There was about a twenty per cent return in the case of swallows (*Hirundo rustica*) carried from Berlin to London (560 miles), to Madrid (1,150 miles), and to Athens (1,100 miles). The maximum speeds of these flights ranged between 120 and 180 miles a day (Rüppell, 1937).

When five wrynecks (*Jynx torquilla*) were taken from Berlin to London (560 miles), two returned to their nests in twelve days, and another came back from Berlin to Salonica (930 miles) in twelve days (Rüppell, 1937).

SOME EXPERIMENTS IN LONG DISTANCE HOMING

Species	*Author*	*Distance (miles)*	*Number of birds used*	*Returned*	*Speed (m.p.h.)*
Leach's petrel (*Oceanodroma leucorrhoa*)	Griffin, 1940	65	10		10.5
		135	13		18.5
		470	18		42.3
		500	5		71.4
		710	5		101.4
Storm petrel (*Hydrobates pelagicus*	Lack and Lockley, 1938	125	3	1	back 7 days later
Manx shearwater (*Puffinus puffinus*)	Lack and Lockley, 1938	125	1	1	back in 10 hours
		265	20	18	6 returned on 1st night
		340	2	2	one back 12 days later
		415	20	18	
		600	3	1	
		930	2	1	back 14 days later
		930 (3,700 by sea)			
	Matthews, 1953 c	3,050 (across the Atlantic)	2	1	back 12 1-2 days later
Laysan albatross (*Diomedea immutabilis*)	Kenyon and Rice, 1958	1,665	5	5	fastest bird returned within 8 days
		2,625	1	1	returned within 20 days
		3,200	4	2	fastest bird returned within 10 days
		4,120	1	1	fastest bird returned within 39 days
Gannet (*Morus bassanus*)	Griffin and Hock, 1949	206	1	1	256
		213	18	11	51–213
White stork (*Ciconia ciconia*)	Wodzicki, 1938, and Wodzicki, Puchalski and Liche, 1939	190	2	1	
		410	4	3	
		530	4	3	
		1,410	4	2	

Species	*Author*	*Distance (miles)*	*Number of birds used*	*Returned*	*Speed (m.p.h.)*
Peregrine falcon (*Falco peregrinus anatum*)	Wimsatt, 1940	60	1	1	
Great black-backed gull (*Larus marinus*)	Matthews, 1952 b	95–335	4	1	
Lesser black-backed gull (*Larus fuscus*)	Matthews, 1952 b	30–515	225	136	
Herring gull (*Larus argentatus*)	Griffin, 1943	62	1	1	74
		247	10	10	80
		302	8	6	84
		540	5	3	57
		872	6	4	58
Common tern (*Sterna hirundo*)	Griffin, 1943	94–456	80	43	28–350
Arctic tern (*Sterna paradisaea*)	Dircksen, 1932	22–255	16	10	28–278
Swift (*Apus apus*)	Spaepen and Dachy, 1952	155	6	4	one returned 4 hours later
Alpine Swift (*Apus melba*)	Spaepen and Fragnière, 1952	250	5	4	
	Schifferli, 1942	1,000	9	7	370
Wryneck (*Jynx torquilla*)	Rüppell, 1937	211–930	19	6	17–78
		560	2	2	returned 12 days later
		930	1	1	returned 12 days later
Swallow (*Hirundo rustica*)	Rüppell 1934 b–	240–310	21	11	returned within about one day
	1937	560	8	2	125–190
		1,150	10	2	
Purple martin (*Progne subis*)	W.E. Southern, 1959	175–234	16	16	27
Rough-winged swallow (*Stelgidopteryx ruficollis*)	Gillespie, 1934	33	1	1	
House martin (*Delichon urbica*)	Rüppell, 1934, 1936	320–340	6	1	
		450	6	4	250
Red-backed shrike (*Lanius collurio*)	Rüppell, 1937	750	3	1	returned within 13 days
Cowbird (*Molothrus ater*)	Lyon, 1935	620–1,200			21–71
	Fox, 1940	80–184	4	4	13–54
Starling (*Sturnus vulgaris*)	Rüppell 1934 a, 1935, 1936, 1937	44	8	4	
		93	58	9	
		130	24	16	
		200	33	20	
		285	23	2	
		420	2	2	
		440	10	7	

A red-backed shrike (*Lanius collurio*) from Berlin, released 760 miles away, in Marseilles, returned to its nest in less than thirteen days, even though this region was unknown to the bird, which ordinarily migrates through more easterly regions of Europe.

Griffin (1943) worked with herring gulls (*Larus argentatus*) in the U.S.A. and observed returns of captive birds that had been liberated about 870 miles away.

In England Lack and Lockley (1938) conducted homing experiments with Manx shearwaters (*Puffinus puffinus*), which revealed the orientation ability of these birds in unfamiliar regions. Some of them, trapped on the island of Skokholm, between Ireland and Wales, were transported to Berne, Lugano, even Venice, and came back in fourteen days. Regardless of whether this flight crossed the continent (which these shearwaters normally never traverse), or whether the bird followed the Mediterranean coast and the Atlantic shoreline bordering Europe (banding records have proved that Skokholm shearwaters never visit the Mediterranean), it had to cross vast stretches that were completely strange.

Matthews's experiments (1953c) confirmed the homing ability of the Manx shearwater. One bird returned from Boston, Massachusetts, to Skokholm in twelve and a half days, after being released in a place 3,050 miles away, across the Atlantic, where this species is never seen.

Recent homing experiments were conducted on Midway Island in the Pacific in an attempt to remove the Laysan albatrosses (*Diomedea immutabilis*), which constitute a hazard to planes using this important American military base. The birds returned after flying enormous distances across the Pacific, one of which constitutes the record for swift homing (Kenyon and Rice, 1958). Released in the Philippines, it covered the 4,120 miles in 32.1 days. The fastest flight was that of an albatross released at Widby Island, Washington, U.S.A., which returned to Midway in 10.1 days, an average speed of 317 miles a day, for the 3,200 mile flight.

Most of these homing experiments indicate an attachment to the nest (*Ortstreue*), which is linked to breeding. Others show a certain attachment to winter quarters (*Winterortstreue*) among birds which do not make long migratory flights (Rüppell and Schifferli, 1939). Black-headed gulls (*Larus ridibundus*) returned to their winter quarters in Berlin when they were taken to Lucerne (430 miles southwest), and coots (*Fulica atra*) also returned to Berlin from Lucerne.

The proportions of such returns, however, are low, for birds scatter widely in winter throughout regions for which they have no special attachment.

In addition to these experiments, all of which deal with wild birds, much work has been done with carrier pigeons. Since orientation ability has been developed in these sedentary, domestic birds by training and selection, care must be taken in interpreting information obtained from them.

As it is clear that many species possess a sense of 'aerial navigation,' efforts have been made to apply this to migratory flights. A great many theories have been advanced, some of which are based on development of the senses, particularly vision. But a number of observers were so impressed by the length of the flights and the precision with which the bird returns to its familiar territory that they believe unknown factors are involved. Some credit the bird with ability to measure the intensity and direction of the lines of force of the earth's magnetic field. Still others think the bird can sense forces derived from the rotation of the earth or from unknown radiations.

It is true that both natural and experimental observations are difficult to explain by a system involving only those landmarks which we ourselves can use. We have trouble understanding the enormous flights of some migrants, especially across the sea. Furthermore, during the course of homing experiments, adult birds returned to the nest so soon (like Lack and Lockley's shearwater, which crossed unknown territory on its flight from Venice to Skokholm) that they could not rely solely on simple visual landmarks. In other experiments birds were captured on the direct route between the point of release and their nests. Sensational returns have been recorded by Kramer and Matthews during their work with untrained carrier pigeons. Aeroplane observation showed that birds in homing experiments flew in the right direction immediately (Griffin and Hock, 1949; Hitchcock, 1952). The same is true of birds liberated outside the territory normally frequented by the species or population, where ordinary visual landmarks can be of limited use.

In addition to a 'sense of locality' (*Ortsinn*) which enables birds, particularly migrants, to return to the place where they were hatched, Rüppell (1944) proved that they have a true sense of direction (*Kompassinn*) of quite a different type. Working with hooded crows (*Corvus cornix*), Rüppell began by locating the breeding and winter areas of the birds which migrate through Rossitten (now Rybatschi), the famous ornithological station on the Baltic Sea. By banding a number, he was able to trace the perimeter of these areas on a map (Fig. 103).

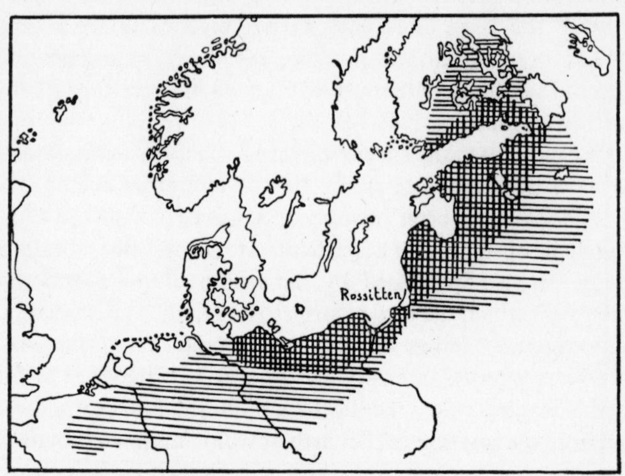

Fig. 103. Breeding and wintering areas of hooded crows (*Corvus cornix*) migrating through Rossitten. Cross-ruled areas indicate the breeding area (in the north) and the winter quarters (in the south), where most recoveries have been made; the hatched zone shows the area where fewer migrants occur. After Rüppell, 1944.

During succeeding springs he captured at Rossitten hooded crows which were migrating north-east to breed in the Baltic countries and Finland. These birds were taken to Flensburg (460 miles west of Rossitten), Essen (640 miles west-south-west), and Frankfurt-on-Main (630 miles south-west). The crows were released after being banded and marked with paint to facilitate their recognition in the wild (Fig. 104).

Of some 900 crows which took part in the experiments, 176 were recaptured, the majority *west of the area where they would normally have nested.* Birds liberated in Flensburg, for example, were recovered in southern Sweden and on the island of Öland. Only a very small number returned to the original breeding area, and most of those were at least two years old. Experience in previous migratory flights had enabled them to find their way home, doubtless with the help of visual landmarks. The vast majority nested in a region similar to their homeland but west of it. This appears on the map of recoveries. Even more curious is the fact that during succeeding winters the birds migrated

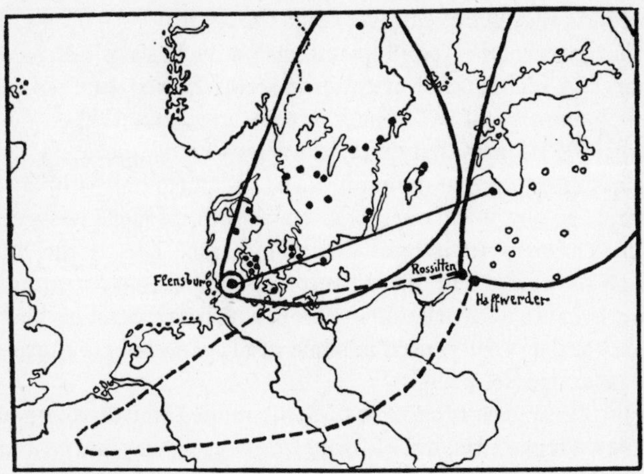

Fig. 104. Recovery sites of hooded crows (*Corvus cornix*) taken at Rossitten and transported to Flensburg (470 miles west). The crows migrated in the spring in their original direction but shifted their territory toward the west. Right: normal breeding area (surrounded by an unbroken line) and winter quarters (surrounded by a broken line). Left: new breeding area shifted toward the west but shaped almost like the original area. Dots indicate the recovery points during the spring and summer following the experiment. After Rüppell, 1944.

to a point west of their normal winter quarters. This reveals a real sense of direction, for having once been shunted towards the west the hooded crows maintained their general north-east – south-west direction and did not return to their original country (except in the case of a few older and more experienced birds).

Rowan (1946) obtained similar results from experiments on the American crow (*Corvus brachyrhynchus*).

Flights oriented in a certain direction were also observed during the course of homing experiments with common terns (*Sterna hirundo*); Griffin and Goldsmith (1955) and Goldsmith and Griffin (1956) found that birds released in the eastern U.S.A. (Connecticut, Maine) headed immediately south-east if the sun was visible, but not if it was hidden behind heavy clouds. This orientation can probably be attributed to the fact that terns on the east coast of the U.S.A. tend to fly south-east or east when they are lost or released over land. This may be an inherited tendency, for the birds are apparently aware that by flying in this direction they will eventually reach the coast.

It is hard to account for all these facts on the basis of simple, visual landmarks. A real sense of orientation seems to exist, one linked with natural phenomena of which man remains unaware.

Griffin (1955) states that there are various kinds of orientation and establishes three types of 'homing.' Type I requires only simple, visual landmarks, geographical ones, over which the bird flies in a somewhat random fashion until it finds a familiar area. This is the method employed by a man without a compass, who wanders around until he comes across a known landmark from which he can get his bearings. The gannets that Griffin used in some of his experiments suggest this kind of guidance (see p. 343).

In Type II the bird is capable of flying in the same direction across an unknown region, but not of flying from one given point to another. It flies in that direction, regardless of the position of the release point with relation to its home. This is what happens when a man has a compass but no map, which alone could tell him which way to go. He decides to walk in a direction which may or may not lead him to his destination. Rüppell's crows were capable of doing this.

Type III, the most complex, implies that the bird is capable of connecting the release point with its home. It must therefore be able to calculate which direction to take and to maintain it. This is like a man who, having both a compass and a map, decides which way to go, a decision depending on the respective positions of his place of departure and his destination.

The first type involves simple landmarks, but the other two require real navigation. Birds have shown themselves capable of taking their bearings during homing experiments, and the same happens on migration. The existence of a true sense of orientation is proved by observation no less than by experimentation. It is interesting that in a single species the various systems may be used simultaneously, or independently, as Perdeck (1958) demonstrated in a remarkable way with starlings (*Sturnus vulgaris*). This Dutch writer repeated Rüppell's experiments on hooded crows by capturing migratory starlings at the Hague and carrying them south-east to Switzerland, where they were released in Basel, Zürich and Geneva (Fig. 105). Preliminary banding had shown that the populations to which the birds belonged nest in countries on the Baltic Sea, in northern Poland, northern Germany, Denmark and the Netherlands. They winter in the Netherlands, Belgium, north-western France, southern England and Ireland.

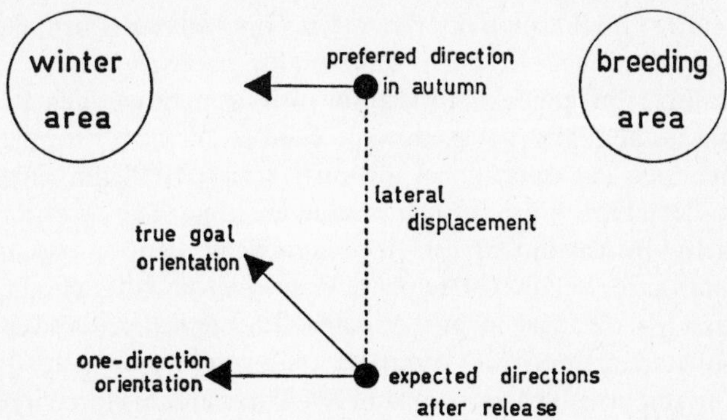

Fig. 105. Outline of A. C. Perdeck's experiment on starlings (*Sturnus vulgaris*). From Perdeck, 1958.

Of the 11,000 birds which were carried south-east, 354 were recovered, and Perdeck found that the behaviour of young birds differed from that of adults. The young, like Rüppell's crows, kept their main south-west direction, and flew to southern France and the Iberian Peninsula, or to a point well south of their normal winter quarters (Fig. 106). Adults, on the other hand, returned to their customary winter area by flying north-west, a very different direction from that of their normal migration. Even more curious, young starlings left the next spring to breed in their original territory, but returned the following autumn to winter where they had gone the preceding year after their displacement.

This remarkable experiment, which was repeated with common chaffinches (*Fringilla coelebs*), shows that orientation behaviour differs according to age. Young birds orient themselves according to Type II, adults according to Type III (true goal orientation). Furthermore, the young learn to recognize their winter quarters the first year and are able to find the way back the following year, although the route is at a marked angle to the migration path of the population to which they belong.

On the basis of similar experiments with blue-winged teal (*Anas discors*) in the U.S.A., Bellrose (1958b) showed that these birds were capable of Griffin's Types I and II, but he did not observe any Type III orientation.

Explanations Involving Unknown Senses

The first 'magnetic' explanation was apparently advanced by Viguier (1882), who believed birds capable of measuring both the intensity and the direction of the earth's magnetic field. The points where the intensity has the same value are aligned to form magnetic parallels, whereas those where the magnetic declination (the angle of the magnetic needle's lateral deviation from the geographical meridian) is identical form meridians. Theoretically, therefore, this constitutes a system of co-ordinates analagous to, although not the same as, our geographical co-ordinates. There are, however, a number of irregularities because of wide anomalies in the earth's magnetic field.

Theoretically it is conceivable that a bird can guide itself according to these two co-ordinates of the earth's magnetic field. When it is in a strange place, it flies so that the magnetic conditions tend to approach those to which it is accustomed. This system is, however, impractical because of the declinations in the magnetic field; as the lines of force and equal intensity occasionally run parallel to one another, it is impossible to have a system of useful co-ordinates. In any case, Viguier's ideas were purely theoretical.

Although many of the old studies were more argumentative than scientific, Thauzies (1898) and Casamajor (1926) presented some stimulating ideas about the orientation of carrier pigeons. These magnetic theories were revived by Yeagley (1947, 51), who formulated an interesting approach to the orientation problem as early as 1942.

Yeagley, whose ideas form a coherent doctrine, is convinced that the flight of migratory birds, and of birds during homing experiments, involves real navigation. The following factors must be considered:

1. Birds are sensitive to the earth's magnetic field which they are able to measure.

2. Birds are sensitive to forces produced by the rotation of the

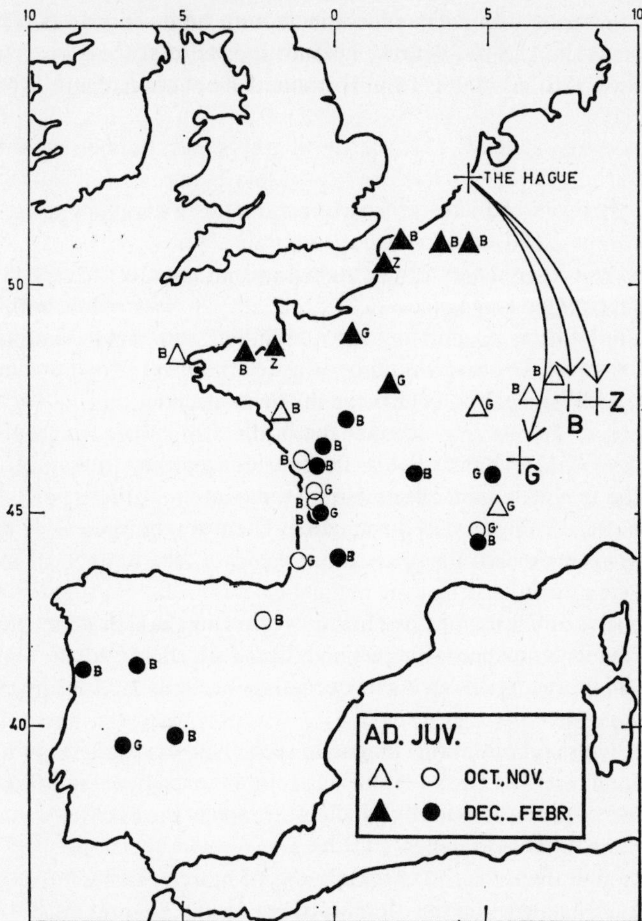

Fig. 106. Experiments on the orientation of starlings (*Sturnus vulgaris*) undertaken by A. C. Perdeck. Migratory starlings captured in the autumn at the Hague, Netherlands, were transported to Switzerland, where they were released at Zürich (Z), Basel (B) and Geneva (G). Recoveries during the winter show that young birds continued their flight toward the south-west. Most of the adults, on the other hand, found their normal winter quarters by flying in a direction other than the one they generally take at this time of year. This experiment shows that adult starlings have a true goal orientation (homing orientation) in the autumn, but that juveniles have a one-direction orientation. From Perdeck, 1958.

earth, which acts on every object in motion on its surface (Coriolis Force), and they are capable of measuring these forces.

3. Birds can compute their own speed in relation to the earth's surface.

Some birds at least, particularly migrants, can thus orient themselves 1) in relation to magnetic co-ordinates and 2) in relation to geographical co-ordinates (the two are quite distinct, as the magnetic pole is about 1,600 miles from the geographical pole).

Magnetic co-ordinates. Physicists tell us that any electric conductor which moves in a magnetic field produces an electromotive force, whose intensity is proportionate to the intensity of the field and the speed of travel. The bird would be aware of the effect of its movement in the earth's magnetic field through the intermediary of its vertical component. Taking into account the bird's own speed, which it can gauge by visual landmarks, this effect varies according to the distance from the magnetic poles. It reaches its maximum at these poles and decreases to a minimum at the magnetic equator, approximately half-way between the two magnetic poles. When a bird finds itself in an area where the intensity of the magnetic field is different from that of its 'home' it can fly towards the normal region, i.e. 'in a direction which will bring its land-speed, magnetic vertical-field effect back to that to which it is accustomed during its normal flight around home territory' (Yeagley).

The lines representing magnetic parallels describe somewhat irregular concentric circles centering around the magnetic poles. They form one of the basic grids by which birds can get their bearings.

Geographical co-ordinates. But this alone would not be sufficient for birds to find their way, so there is a second system, based on laws of motion. This hypothesis, developed by Ising (1946), constitutes Yeagley's second method of reference.

Since the earth rotates, objects resting on the ground have a certain *momentum* which is due to the rotation of the earth proportionate to their masses and to the linear speed at a given place (in an easterly direction, of course); from zero at the poles it reaches its maximum at the equator (the speed of travel is about 1,000 m.p.h.) and it varies, as a little trigonometry shows, like a cosine Φ, where Φ represents latitude. Any object moving horizontally at a uniform speed at a given spot is subject to a deflecting force (always directed towards the right, in the northern hemisphere). This force, the horizontal component of

Coriolis Force, is zero at the equator and rises as it approaches the poles. It is proportionate to the speed of the object in relation to the ground (v), to the sine of latitude (Φ), and to the angular speed of the earth (Ω). Its mathematical formula is

$$f_h = 2\,\Omega\,v\,\sin\Phi$$

Yeagley assumes that birds are capable of perceiving the effects of Coriolis Force. As this is dependent on the bird's own speed in relation to the earth, the bird must be able, as in the case where electromagnetic forces are involved, to gauge its own ground-speed.

Lines where Coriolis Force has the same value form concentric true circles around the geographical poles and are coincident with parallels of latitude. They form a second grid, independent of the magnetic set, with which they form co-ordinates that can theoretically serve to orient birds.

In order to test this theory Yeagley used carrier pigeons, with the help of the American Army. He began by repeating old experiments involving the effect on the bird of an artificial magnetic field. By placing magnets under the pigeon's wings, as Casamajor had done before, he created an artificial magnetic field around the bird's head, of approximately the same intensity as the vertical component of the earth's field. This made it difficult for the animal to perceive the natural field. At the same time he released control birds, carrying *non-magnetized* pieces of metal under their wings, to eliminate the risk of error arising from mechanical difficulty in the experimental birds.

The first experiment indicated that pigeons flying in an artificial magnetic field had more difficulty finding their way back to the nest. Later tests, however, somewhat weakened this hypothesis and furnished no significant results.

By tracing on a map of North America Coriolis lines of equal force (superimposed on the parallels) and lines of the same magnetic intensity (isodynamic lines of the vertical component of the earth's magnetic field) a network is obtained whose lines intersect at certain points at rather low angles (Fig. 107). Since these 'conjugate points' have the same magnetic and kinetic characteristics, it follows that, if Yeagley's theory is correct, birds accustomed to one of these points should confuse it with the other. The author, who was working at Pennsylvania State College, found a conjugate point at Kearney, Nebraska, some 1,100 miles west. He trained pigeons to return to a particular dovecote in Pennsylvania, then took this trailer, together with its inhabitants, to Nebraska, where he undertook his experiments. He thought that the birds should return to the closest spot where the magnetism and Coriolis Force corresponded to those to which they

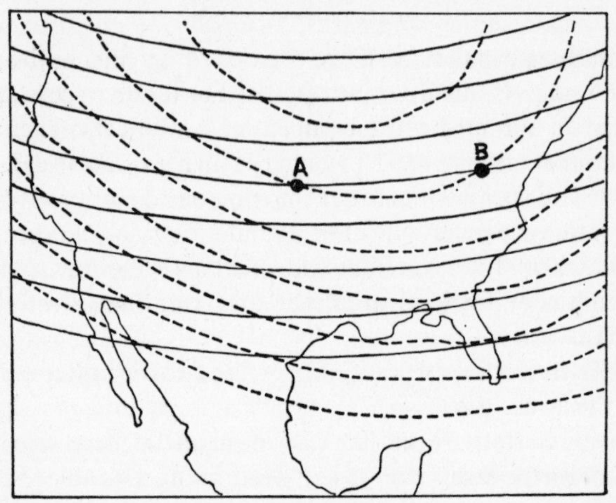

Fig. 107. Lines of equal Coriolis Force (unbroken lines which are identified with geographical parallels) and lines of the same intensity of the earth's magnetic field (broken lines) in the U.S.A. The points of intersection are called conjugate points, as they have the same characteristics with regard to the earth's magnetism and the Coriolis Force (A and B, for example). After Yeagley, 1947 simplified.

were accustomed. The proportion of returns to the Nebraska dovecote was, however, small (about thirty-one per cent), and the author's system of interpreting his results is open to criticism (Wynne Edwards, 1948).

Criticism of the 'Physical Theories'

Yeagley's theory is coherent and perfectly valid *from the physical point of view;* thanks to the system of geographical and magnetic co-ordinates, experimental birds are theoretically capable of finding their 'home', and true migrants could use the same techniques on seasonal flights.

Yeagley's tests are, however, not wholly satisfactory, and the scanty number of returns was never convincing; but the chief weakness in his work is his application of physical theories to living animals. Although this means of orientation may be *theoretically* valid, it is imperative to know whether the forces involved are able to influence the bird's behaviour and to supply landmarks. As Griffin (1955) asked, are these forces sufficiently powerful to be perceived by the bird's sensory receptors, and to be distinguished from other forces of the same kind which may act upon them at the same time? A bird flying about forty miles an hour at latitude 45 ° N. would be subject to an electric force of about 10–5 volts per centimetre. By moving one degree north or south – or about seventy miles – this force would vary only 1.3 per cent, or about 1-10,000,000 of a volt; (action-potentials in nerves are expressed in thousandths of a volt). Under the same conditions Coriolis Force would have varied 1.7 per cent. Even if birds were sensitive to the forces themselves, they are incapable of feeling such minute variations (Wynne Edwards, 1948).

Moreover, Coriolis Force, like electro-magnetic force, depends to a great extent on the bird's own speed, which it must be able to compute with extraordinary precision. This is certainly not true, even if it has visual landmarks, lacking in cloudy weather, at night, or during overseas flights. Wynne Edwards calculated that the slight change in speed from forty to thirty-nine miles an hour would cause a variation in the Coriolis and electro-magnetic forces of 2.5 per cent, the same as a flight of about 150 miles. Variations in altitude would produce similar disturbances.

Yeagley could be right only if no disturbing factor intervened in the bird's measure of the electro-magnetic force. But the terrain alone causes irregularities in the earth's magnetic field, which would more than offset any directional advantage the bird might enjoy from this source. Physicists once attempted to construct a speedometer for aeroplanes based on the principle of force induced by movement in the magnetic field, but they found the undertaking impractical because disturbances 'drown' the usefulness of this phenomenon.

Scientists have often tried without success to prove that birds, especially carrier pigeons, are sensitive to magnetic or electromagnetic fields. They showed no reaction, even when exposed to far more powerful magnetism than the earth's magnetic field. Griffin (1944) reported that pigeons failed to respond to this stimulus after 570 tests, while they responded perfectly to the action of light after only twenty to seventy tests. Even Yeagley (*in* Griffin, 1952a) is forced to admit this, after testing the effect of the magnetic field on birds. Orgel and Smith (1954) tried to condition carrier pigeons to magnetic fields but obtained no response, although they used fields twenty-five times more intense than the earth's magnetic field.

It is not known, of course, what organ or organs of the animal could be capable of registering and measuring the intensity of the magnetic field and the Coriolis Force. Yeagley had assumed that a bird feels Coriolis Force throughout its whole body, but other authors believed this perception is centred in the inner ear. Ising localizes the perception of these forces in the semi-circular canals of the inner ear, essential in maintaining balance. He believes that a bird circles when trying to orient itself in order to make Coriolis Force act on its inner ear in different directions. This hypothesis was adopted by Pumphrey (1948) and Beecher (1951, 1952); the latter, who made a complete study of the inner ear and its rôle in orientation, states that the semi-circular canals are the seat of movements of the internal liquid under the influence of Coriolis Force and, as such, could give indications about the declination of the magnetic field.

Ising also considers organs to measure pressure in the circulatory system, which would, of course, be influenced by changes brought by Coriolis Force. (Mammals have such sensory receptors in the carotid sinus and some arteries.) But these variations are too small to be perceptible, and they have no effect in comparison to those produced by other causes, including cardiac pulsations.

Although these studies pertaining to physical phenomena have aroused a great deal of interest, they are still only hypotheses. No proof has yet been supplied of the perceptibility of the birds' sensory organs. Nor is there any proof of the action of a magnetic field among birds or other animals.

Meise (1933) advanced 'kinesthetic' theories which deal particularly with homing experiments on domestic or wild birds. He suggests that during transportation birds are subjected to accelerations and pressures transmitted to the inner ear through sense organs. These effects are registered to form an 'image' of the road which has been covered. Either a wild or domesticated bird could follow the 'directives' of this unconscious memory, although it might not necessarily lead the animal back over the same route.

This theory, however, presupposes purely hypothetical abilities on the part of the bird. Furthermore, birds which have been anaesthetized or which are rotated constantly or intermittently during transportation (such as the gulls or petrels in some of Griffin's experiments) have returned almost as quickly as those not so treated. Finally, this sort of theory cannot explain how migrants orient themselves when they are travelling enormous distances over land and water to precise goals.

Explanations Involving Known Senses

1. Familiar Landmarks

Yeagley's theory, like others based on magnetic explanations, fails to explain the orientation of birds. Not a single idea advanced on this subject during the past eighty years has proved anything. For this reason a number of authors have recently returned to explanations involving simpler phenomena, perceptible to the ordinary senses.

Sight is the sense most frequently mentioned. It is certain that the visual acuity of many birds is two to three times superior to that of human sight (Pumphrey, 1948) and that a bird can perceive details not visible to man. Visual landmarks must be all the more conspicuous, too, when the bird is flying high enough to observe them from afar. Menner (1938) and Crozier and Wolf (1944a, b) observed that the bird's eye is particularly well adapted to perceive *movement*, because of the ocular pecten. This organ, characteristic of birds, is a more or less conical, foliated structure placed on a level with the blind spot and running towards the pupil. The pecten is fed by a large number of blood vessels, and it is especially well developed among insectivorous birds and diurnal birds of prey. The latter, however, do not have such a 'piercing' glance as many people like to think. Observation of experimental birds, still unfortunately incomplete, has shown that the pecten makes it possible for the bird to perceive even slight movements at great distances. This perception is important in hunting prey (insects, mammals, etc.) but also in regard to solar landmarks, which we shall discuss later.

Birds are gifted with a highly developed visual memory which enables them to recall a large number of landmarks within the more or less vast perimeter constituting their living area. This ability varies, of course, according to species. Skinner (1950) trained domestic pigeons to peck at a certain area of an aerial photograph representing a particular region. They then received food. Since they could still give an exact response four years after seeing the photograph, it is apparent that birds can orient themselves, thanks to keen vision and a well developed visual memory.

During recent years Griffin, author of a number of homing experiments, has defended the 'visual' hypothesis. The speed of return is definitely below normal flying ability, even allowing for the time birds devote to feeding and rest. Matthews (1952b) found in England that the lesser black-backed gull (*Larus fuscus*) averaged forty-three miles a day on its return, a distance it can easily cover in an hour.

The speed of return and the proportion of birds which find their way back to the nest at all are notably higher when experiments are carried out in regions familiar to the bird. These are often very large areas, because strong fliers, especially migrant species, are well acquainted with a vast circumference around their nests. Long flights are often necessary to find food for both young and adult birds, particularly in large colonies of sea-birds; Manx shearwaters, for example, nest on the island of Skokholm but fish in the Bay of Biscay, hundreds of miles away (Lockley). Migration routes also seem to be known visually, and Griffin found that terns find their way much more quickly when released in a zone they have explored during hunting flights. On a second 'homing' experiment the birds experience much less difficulty, and Griffin (1943) states that herring gulls profited from the knowledge they had thus acquired.

2. METHODS OF EXPLORATION

On certain 'homing' experiments birds are forced to cross areas where there are no familiar landmarks. They seem to make a methodical exploration until they find a familiar region, but, of course, they do not have to continue this search all the way back to the nest. As soon as they find a point inside the perimeter of known territory, they can head directly 'home.' The same is true of migrations, for it is the whole area constituting the winter quarters of the species which the birds seek, not a tiny, particular spot in it. In the spring a bird which nests every year in the same yard, marsh or orchard simply has to find the region around it.

Careful observation of the flight of birds released in alien regions has led to conflicting interpretations.

As such birds are often seen heading towards the horizon in all directions, Claparède (1903) deduced that they scatter arbitrarily all around the point where they are released. Only those return to the nest which find visual landmarks within some familiar region. (Fig. 108).

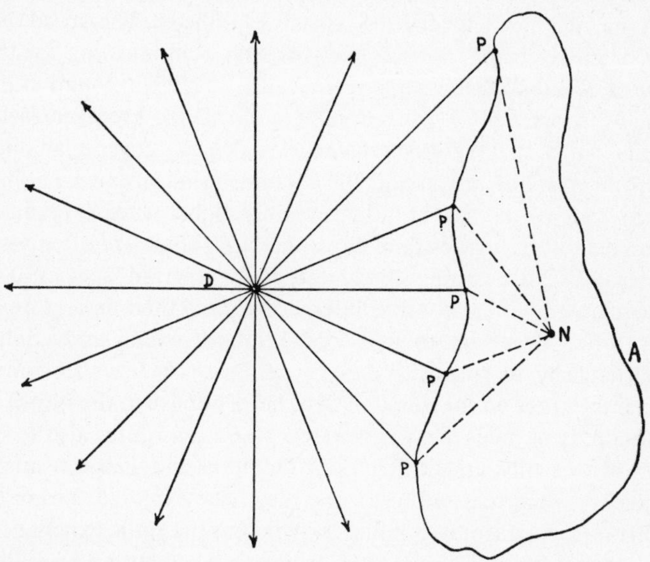

Fig. 108. If birds scattered at random and flew in all directions from the release point D, only those which reached P points on the perimeter of the known area A could return to their nest N. In this case the proportion of returns would depend on the extent of the known area and the distance from the point of release D to the nest N (goal area). After Griffin, 1944.

The distance involved and the surface representing the area already known to the bird make it possible to explain variations in the proportion of returns and the time required for the homing flight. When Rabaud (1928) released 1,500 carrier pigeons 300 miles off Croisic on the French coast, only 300 returned to their dovecote within forty-eight hours. Others were recovered in England, Spain, Portugal, the Cape Verde Islands, Egypt, even in the Caucasus. This would seem to indicate that the birds scattered to all points and that the only ones which returned were those guided by chance towards familiar landmarks. But a method based on chance does not explain the facts.

Most observers have credited birds with more rational methods of exploration. Some believe that each bird flies in a zigzag, which greatly

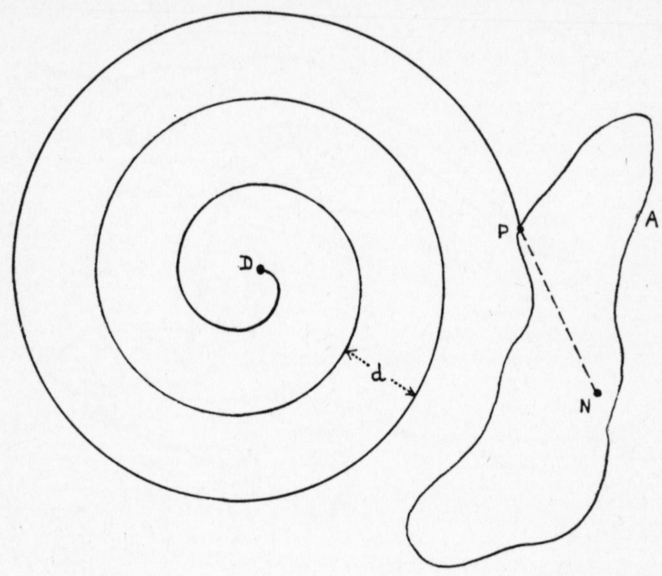

Fig. 109. Spiral exploration. The birds would fly in spirals from the point of release D, and the turns (d) would be so widely separated that no spot could escape their scrutiny. They would finally reach a point P on the limit of the known area A, from which they could easily return to their nest N (goal area). After Griffin, 1944.

increases the likelihood of finding a familiar landmark. Several patterns have been suggested (rectangular search, expanding zigzag), but they are all purely theoretical.

A more interesting hypothesis is that birds spiral upward around the point where they are released. Like many other authors, Hodge (1894) stated that birds fly in spirals of increasing radius in order to embrace the whole area around the point where they were set free. (Fig. 109). The spacing of two spiral turns is such that no point escapes the bird's vision. It can thus connect familiar points and get its bearings easily. Although this explanation is quite ingenious, it is not documented, and, while birds circle around the point of release, the big spirals described by Hodge have never been observed.

None of these hypotheses are substantiated. Homing experiments had furnished no data on the behaviour of birds during flight, so

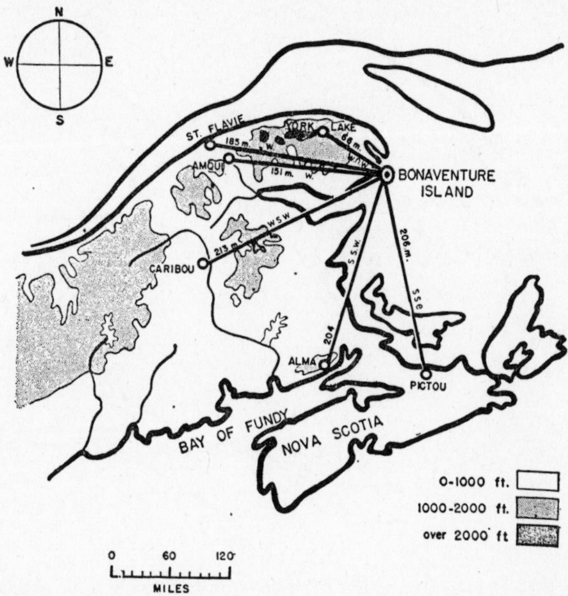

Fig. 110. Release points of gannets (*Morus bassanus*) captured at Bonaventure Island. These birds were followed by planes on their return flight. From Griffin and Hock, 1949.

Griffin and Hock (1949) began to study this very interesting problem. They removed gannets (*Morus bassanus*) from their nests in the large colony on Bonaventure Island off the Gaspé Peninsula, in eastern Canada. While these big birds were not really migrants at the time and, as sea-birds, their behaviour may change when they are transported inland, they offer a number of experimental advantages, if only because of the ease with which their return to the nest can be observed.

The gannets were watched from an aeroplane, which did not seem to disturb them, provided it did not come too near. They came back with the same delays, and in the same proportion, as the control birds, which were not followed.

Griffin then transported gannets from Bonaventure Island to various points, some of which were 200 miles from their nests. The birds released near the sea (St Flavié, Pictou) returned more rapidly than those taken inland (Caribou, Maine), although the distance was

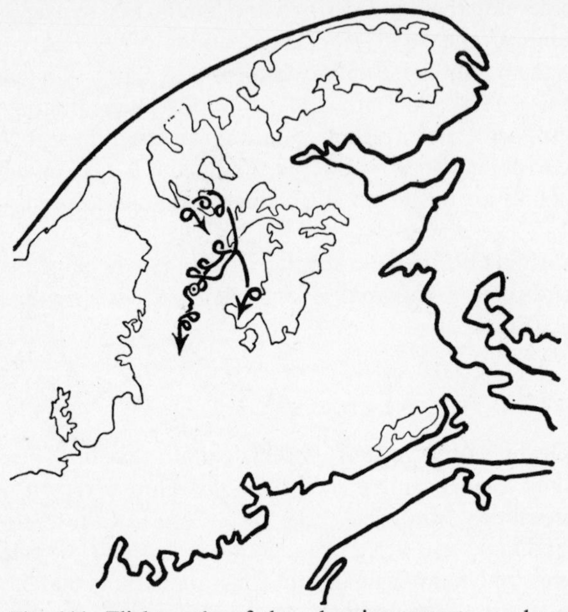

Fig. 111. Flight paths of three homing gannets as observed from an aeroplane. After Griffin and Hock, 1949.

the same. These more rapid flights were probably due to a better acquaintance with the region.

The most interesting information was supplied by the gannets released inland (Fig. 110). At any altitude the sea was invisible from Caribou, 213 miles from Bonaventure Island; yet of the sixteen birds released there, ten (or 62.5 per cent) were back on their nests after an interval ranging from twenty-four to 101 hours (which corresponds to a speed varying between 213 and fifty-one miles a day). By following the birds in a plane, Griffin found that the gannets explored the region carefully. The itineraries on his published maps show how the birds hesitated as they hunted for landmarks (Fig. 111). Their routes indicate that they were exploring, whereas a sense of orientation would have enabled them to fly immediately in the right direction. This experiment seems to prove the importance of visual factors in the orientation of birds seeking familiar landmarks in strange surroundings.

After a number of tests Heinroth and Heinroth (1941) decided that visual landmarks guide carrier pigeons to their nests. The birds are trained to develop their abilities – to find landmarks, to exercise their visual memory, and to fly for long periods (*Fliegemut*) – which stimulates them to traverse unknown regions in search of a point they can recognize. Platt and Dare (1945) confirmed these findings of the German authors. Carrier pigeons return much faster in clear weather, with good visibility, than when it is cloudy and foggy; in such conditions not only are the delays much longer but losses are considerably greater.

When Griffin (1952b) followed carrier pigeons by plane, he found that the birds used topographical landmarks such as elevations, lakeshores, etc. (Fig. 112).

3. NATURE OF THE LANDMARKS

From Griffin's observations it seems certain that birds use visual landmarks to a considerable extent. They explore a region, making use of its prominent features.

Some landmarks are strictly topographical, such as mountain and river systems, which give valuable information to birds that have been carried to strange surroundings, or to migrants. Tinbergen (1941) found that in Holland starlings fly west-south-west to the coast and then follow it.

Landmarks of a more ecological nature are forests, vegetation zones, bare plateaus and valleys, all of which constitute different environments that birds seek out or avoid. Tinbergen showed that the border line of the forest and open spaces influences the direction of flight, which, as everyone who has studied migration knows, is affected by the configuration of the terrain.

Climatic landmarks guide the bird, which can distinguish much that is not apparent to human beings. Meteorologists know that masses of air, differing both in temperature and humidity, are often separated from one another by clear-cut fronts. Since these conditions are often almost identical from year to year in certain regions, it is not impossible that they provide useful information. Winds are also remarkable landmarks, and wind influences both bird migration and its direction.

Vleugel (1952) recorded that common chaffinches in Holland orient their flight according to the direction of the wind. When it changes slowly, the direction of flight varies accordingly. We may assume that

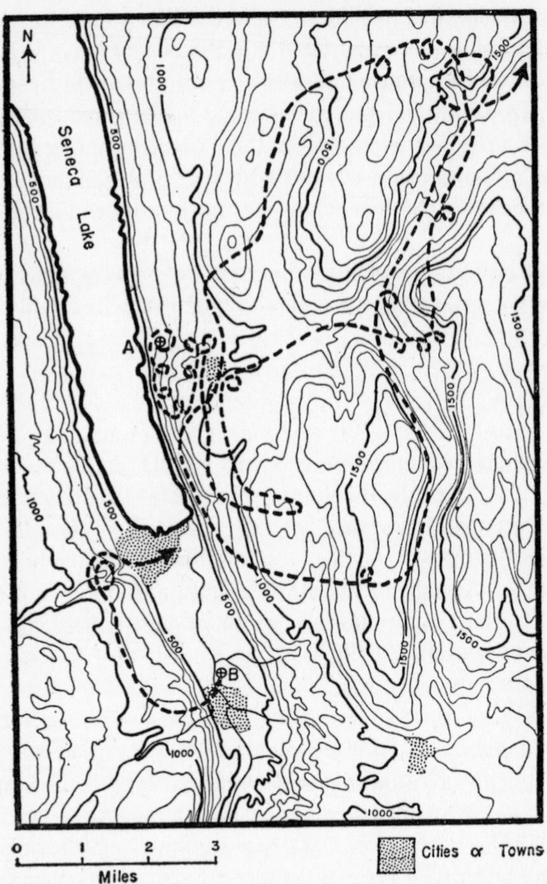

Fig. 112. Route flown over unfamiliar territory by four pigeons as observed from an aeroplane. From Griffin, 1952 b.

the wind makes it possible for the bird to maintain its flight in a given direction (by maintaining the angle of flight with the direction of the wind). This hypothesis seems confirmed by the fact that migration stops in a dead calm, when birds seem to lose their bearings.

4. ASTRONOMICAL LANDMARKS

All observations seem to demonstrate that there is no need to invoke the most subtle laws of physics to explain avian orientation. Birds rely on their sight to find landmarks in familiar or unknown regions.

Wilkinson (1952) showed that the percentage of returns in many 'homing' experiments, the birds' speed and timing in accordance with the distance involved, are often mathematically compatible with the hypothesis of exploration but not with that of real 'navigation.' The results substantiate the theory, at least in the case of Griffin's Type I homings.

But some especially rapid returns cannot be satisfactorily explained in this fashion, even if they are termed the 'fortunate cases' which the exploration theory anticipates. Rüppell's classic experiments on the hooded crow, which were confirmed by Rowan's work with the American crow, indicate a 'compass sense' which is hard to reconcile with the simple landmarks thus far encountered. It implies an orientation based on astronomical landmarks, such as the sun. This hypothesis has recently inspired a multitude of studies, the most significant of which are those of the late Gustav Kramer and his collaborators. They constitute a homogeneous doctrine, substantiated by all kinds of experiments on migrants and carrier pigeons. Matthews devised a similar theory in which other astronomical elements are involved.

Kramer had observed that, from early October, captive starlings remain in the south-west corner of their cages and show the characteristic behaviour of captive birds that wish to migrate (*Zugunruhe*, see p. 293). The surroundings seem unimportant because the same result is obtained by putting the cage in different places and even by placing it so the bird can see nothing save the sky. This orientation towards the south-west – the direction in which the starlings would fly if they were set free – is not stimulated by any action of the earth's magnetic field; when piles of iron were placed near the cage, the birds paid no attention to this local disturbance of the magnetism and continued to face south-west.

A complete local modification of the magnetic field by an electric current made the magnetized needle respond drastically but did not affect the birds in the slightest.

The following spring the starlings headed north-east for about ten days, then settled in a north-west direction, which they maintained during the whole period of the spring migration. This behaviour makes it unnecessary to follow individuals over long distances because birds orient themselves in the cage itself; it considerably simplifies the study of orientation.

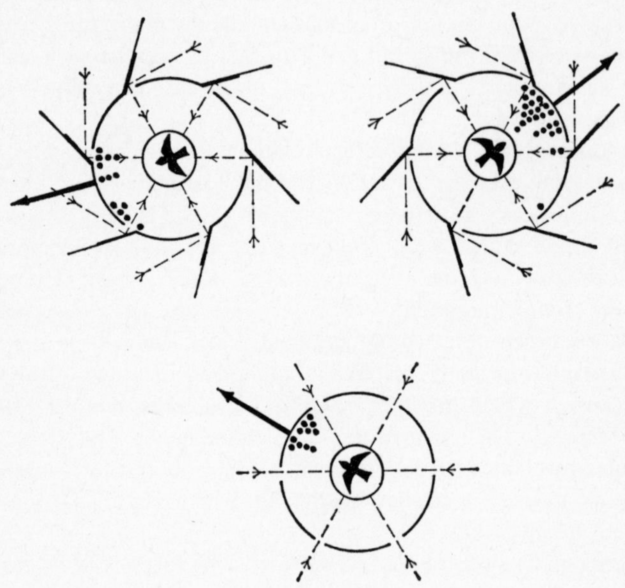

Fig. 113. Deviations from the general migratory direction in the caged starling (*Sturnus vulgaris*).
Below: When the windows are open the starling heads NW.
Above: Deviations of the sun's rays by mirrors. As conditions are modified, the starling changes its course.
Dots show the records. The heavy arrow marks the direction which the bird usually takes. After Kramer, 1951 a.

The starlings seemed to get their bearings from the sky. To check this, Kramer built a sort of pavilion with six windows and put the cage in the middle. Each window was closed by a movable shutter, above which a mirror could be placed to let light rays into the enclosure at a definite angle. The bottom of the cage, made of transparent plexiglass, had a number of sectors. An observer, placed under the cage, checked the bird's position every ten seconds by noting the sector where it appeared at the moment (at this season migratory birds have 'flight fidgets' which make them flutter about the cage while heading repeatedly in a specific direction). Observations were repeated until the results had statistical importance.

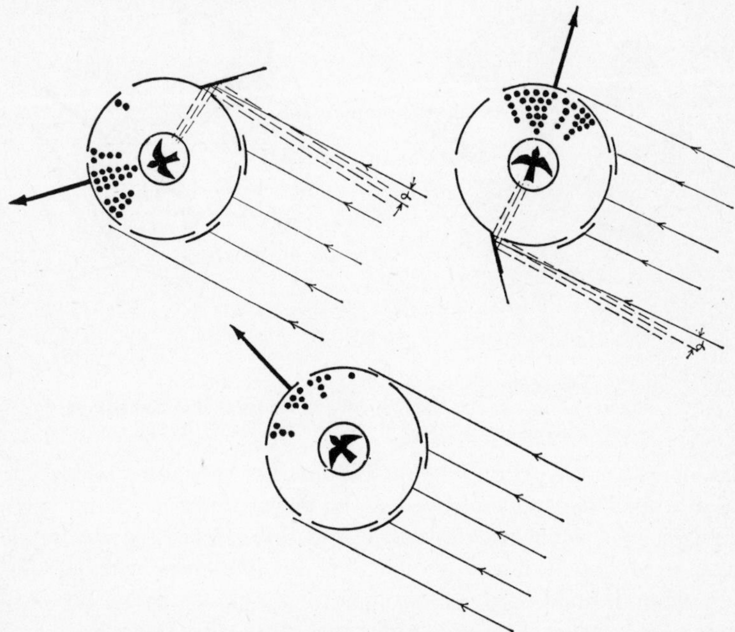

Fig. 114. Changes in direction obtained by the use of a single mirror; the windows through which the sun's rays could enter directly are covered. The starling changes its course according to circumstances. After Kramer, 1951 a.

Kramer began by making some tests to be sure that his method and equipment did not upset the birds and he found that when all the windows were open the starlings headed north-west. He then placed the mirrors in such a way that the light entering through the windows was deflected 90° right or left; the starlings changed their general direction accordingly (Fig. 113). This first series of experiments was repeated many times to demonstrate the rôle of celestial landmarks in orienting birds under experimental conditions.

Kramer next showed that the sun and the heavens near it are responsible for this orientation. After closing all the windows which gave direct access to the sunlight, he used a mirror to guide the rays coming from the sky near the sun and found that the bird changed its course in accordance with them (Fig. 114). Thus the sun determines

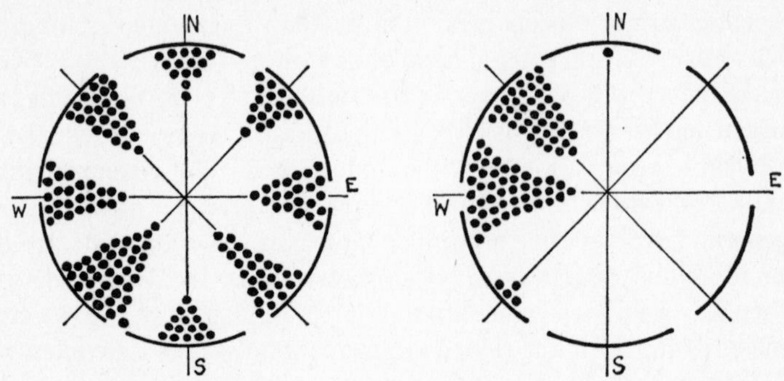

Fig. 115. Influence of clouds on the captive starling's orientation ability.
Left: Dense clouds; the starling wanders at random.
Right: Clearing: the starling gets its bearings immediately in the direction in which it is flying. After Kramer, 1951 a.

the starling's orientation, although it does not have to be visible; an area around the sun subtended by an angle of about 45° provides enough light to change the starling's course. Hence the governing light need not be direct sunlight. We do not know whether this behaviour is influenced by the light's intensity or by its physical qualities (a greater richness in radiations of long wave length). In any case, polarization of light rays does not seem involved as it is among insects (for example, bees, von Frisch, 1950); Montgomery and Heinemann (1952) tried unsuccessfully to train pigeons to respond to polarized light.

But all observers know that migrant birds very often travel in cloudy weather when it is impossible to determine the sun's exact position. A similar situation can be created artificially by covering the windows with more or less heavy translucent paper. Kramer found that when the 'clouds' so caused are so heavy that it is impossible to locate the sun, the birds fly around at random, but as soon as a ray of sunlight appears, or even a slight clearing, they get their bearings easily (Fig. 115). This must help in orientation, for clear intervals usually occur during the course of the day, especially when a long distance is covered. Geographical or topographical landmarks would keep the bird on its course between two astronomical fixes. The starling's skill in spotting topographical landmarks is apparent, for a change in the direction of the light entering through the pavilion windows is not always followed immediately by a change in the birds's direction. It is using certain objects inside the pavilion as landmarks, objects which replace natural geographical ones. For this reason Kramer tried to make the interior of the pavilion as uniform as possible in order to eliminate any possibility of error on this score.

Kramer's observations on the influence of the meteorological situation on orientation confirm a number of previous observations. In general, birds find their way much more easily in clear weather than when it is cloudy. Matthews, whose observations (1952b) on gulls are particularly significant, found that in good weather sixty-five per cent of the birds started in the right direction as soon as they were released, only forty per cent in cloudy weather; and when visibility is good, the birds do not hesitate just after take-off, as they do on a grey day (Fig. 116). Similar results were obtained with pigeons during homing experiments (see Kramer, Pratt and Saint Paul, 1956). It is true, of course, that starting in the right direction does not guarantee a safe return, but the observations are valuable in that they indicate orientation by the sun.

These experiments can only be made during migration, a relatively short period, but Kramer succeeded in training starlings and pigeons to respond to artificial light stimuli in order to complete his demonstration of birds' sensitivity to light and its rôle in their orientation.

Kramer's experiments settle a number of points. They prove the bird's receptivity to optical stimuli. Furthermore, the sun's rôle in the orientation of captive starlings makes it possible to explain, in part at least, the possibilities of similar orientation in the wild, for birds are certainly capable of using these landmarks. Griffin (1944) had envisaged the possibility of checks of this kind, and Kramer's experiments confirm his hypotheses.

One objection occurs immediately. Although Kramer's first experiments proved that starlings can determine the sun's exact position and get their bearings accordingly, the sun's position varies both with the season and with the time of day. The starling's migratory activity covers at least six hours, starting at daybreak, and during this interval the sun 'moves' approximately 90°. Meanwhile, the bird seems to fly in the original direction, which shows that it can compensate for the swing of the sun. The starling must have a 'clock' and some means of gauging the sun's height above the horizon in its nerve centres!

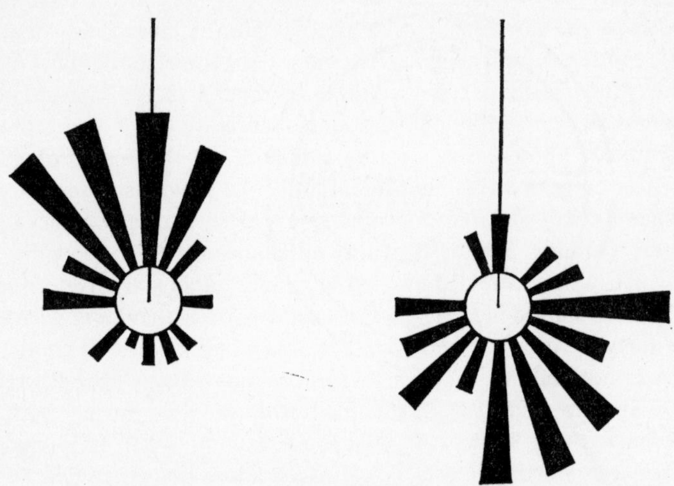

Fig. 116. Influence of clouds on the orientation of Manx shearwaters (*Puffinus puffinus*) during homing experiments.
Left: Open sky; most birds start in the right direction (marked by a vertical line) as soon as they are released.
Right: Dense clouds. Most birds lose their bearings and take the wrong direction.
The extent of the black sectors is proportionate to the number of birds flying in a given direction. After Matthews, 1953 c.

In order to check this, Kramer decided to modify his experimental conditions. His work with birds during their migratory restlessness was necessarily confined to short periods. He now trained starlings to 'reply' to light stimuli derived from a natural or artificial source by offering them food from a specific receptacle or feeder, one of a series placed around the cage. Taking food from the right receptacle was considered a positive result, taking it from the wrong one a negative result. (Of course the feeders are fashioned in such a way that the starling does not see whether they contain food or not.)

Although this is, of course, very different from the natural conditions of orientation during 'homing' experiments or migration, it shows what the bird can do.

In the first test a starling was trained to take food from a certain feeder at a definite hour. (Fig. 117). When thoroughly trained, the bird

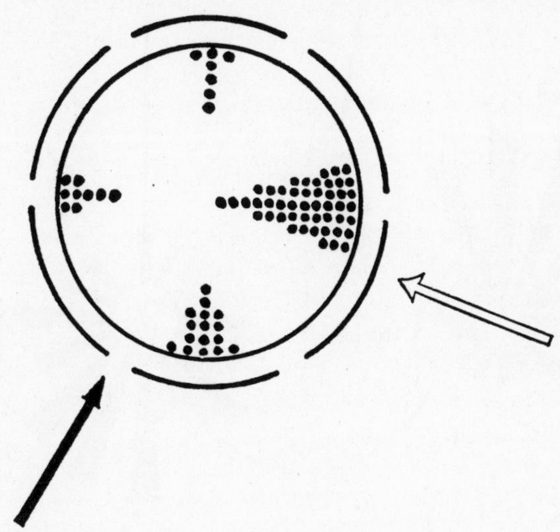

Fig. 117. The starling is capable of compensating for the sun's movement. A bird trained to fly in a given direction at a certain hour (the sun's position is marked by the hollow arrow) will find its direction at any hour of the day, even when the sun is in another place (for example, when it occupies the position marked by a solid arrow). The dots indicate successive records. After Kramer, 1952.

was tested at a different hour so the sun formed an angle with its first position. The bird responded in a positive fashion by taking food from the same feeder, which showed that it was capable of taking the sun's position into account and making the necessary correction.

Another starling was trained to follow the movement of the sun and to take food from the feeder pointing towards the sun at any time. (Fig. 118). Here, however, Kramer had the utmost difficulty in obtaining a satisfactory result, and he never got as many positive results as during other experiments. It is interesting that a bird can keep track of the sun's *position* and make the necessary corrections, yet it has much trouble 'following the sun' – a process which seems far easier to us.

A bird's ability to determine the sun's position as a conditioning signal is no more astonishing than the performance of insects. Ants

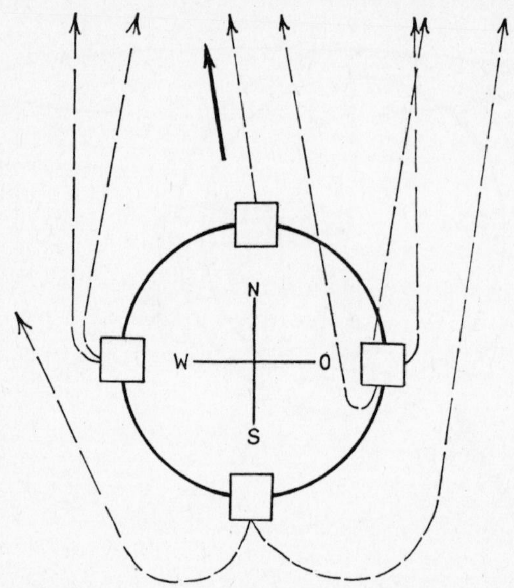

Fig. 118. Flight direction taken by carrier pigeons transported 200 miles from their dovecote. The heavy arrow indicates where their home lies. They all fly in the right direction, a fact which does not indicate that they are exploring the country. After Kramer, 1952.

plot their course according to the sun with remarkable accuracy, as Santschi discovered in 1911; and Karl von Frisch (1950) has demonstrated that bees do even better. Not only do these Hymenoptera check their bearings by the sun but they can communicate information through this medium; a special dance (*Schwanzeltanz*), oriented according to the position of the sun, tells other bees where to find abundant food. Pardi and Papi have recently brought to light similar facts pertaining to various Coleoptera (*Geotrupes sylvaticus*, Scarabeidae; *Phalaria provincialis*, Tenebrionidae; several species of Carabidae) and in the Crustacean and sand-flea (*Talitrus saltator*).

Kramer and his collaborators often repeated his first experiments which reveal that several other species, notably the barred warbler (*Sylvia nisoria*) and the red-backed shrike (*Lanius collurio*), get their bearings from the sun. (Fig. 119).This is all the more interesting since these are nocturnal migrants. U. von St. Paul (1956) undertook similar

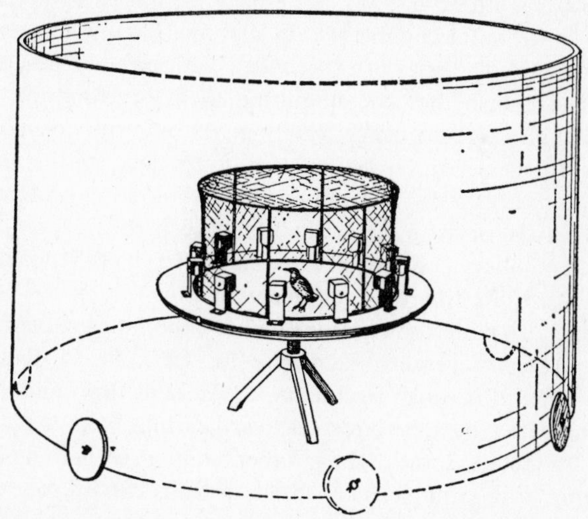

Fig. 119. Training-cage used by Kramer and his collaborators to study the orientation of birds according to natural (the sun) or artificial landmarks. 12 feeders are arranged on a lower ring and 12 covers on an upper movable ring. The circular masonite wall, which can be rotated, excludes landmarks from the bird's view. From U. von Saint Paul, 1956.

experiments with the western meadowlark (*Sturnella neglecta*) and trained birds to hunt for their food in a given compass direction. After twenty days the birds were able to choose the right direction, and most of them could compensate for the sun's movement, although one bird followed it without making the compensation.

That birds can get their bearings from the sun and compensate for its movement throughout the day implies that they have an internal clock, but to prove it one would have to stop the sun and then start it again to get the bird off schedule! As that is impossible, Kramer decided to undertake another series of experiments with an artificial sun. He put the training cage with its feeders under a circular tent where no daylight could enter and arranged an 'artificial sun' consisting of a 250-watt projector, which moved on a circular track that formed its orbit. Starlings were trained as before and responded in exactly the same way, so by varying the experimental conditions, Kramer succeeded in upsetting their amazing internal 'clock.'

Matthews's studies (1955a, b) show that the clock seems to be closely related to the rhythm of daily illumination or photoperiodism. When he started a series of experiments with pigeons, he upset their whole internal rhythm by submitting them for four–five days to irregular light-dark sequences; he then restored the normal rhythm for five to eleven days, but advanced or delayed the period of illumination artificially. During consecutive homing experiments he found that the birds' internal clock had been really upset, and this caused anomalies in homing behaviour. Hoffman (1954) got the same results from quite different experiments.

Kramer also undertook a large number of homing experiments with carrier pigeons. Several of them (Kramer, 1952, 54, 55; Kramer and St. Paul, 56a, b, see also Hoffmann, 1959a, and Pratt and Thouless, 1955) indicate that these birds get their bearings from the sun, but a number of factors, some of them rather bafflling, seem to modify their behaviour. For example, it is easier to train carrier pigeons to fly home in some directions than in others, and topographical factors have nothing to do with this. Winter also has an effect, which has not been explained (Kramer, 1954, 57; Kramer and St. Paul, 1956a). Fewer birds return home in winter than in summer, and this cannot be blamed on bad climatic conditions. (Although this is true in Germany, the same experiments in the U.S.A. [North Carolina] produced different results.)

Even more important in the framework of solar orientation is the fact that some points of the compass seem more favourable than others for homing experiments. That seems to indicate that it is easier for the bird to get its bearings from the sun in some directions than in others.

By these and other experiments Kramer and his collaborators and Matthews, who was working independently, proved that birds are able to get their bearings from the sun and to compensate for its movement throughout the day because they have a perfectly regulated internal clock.[1]

1. Hoffmann's recent experiments (1959b) reveal that starlings can even use the midnight sun.

It is, however, impossible to say objectively how the bird makes use of this solar landmark, and there are two theories.

Kramer believed that the bird finds the right direction by determining the horizontal angle (azimuth) measured on the horizon from the

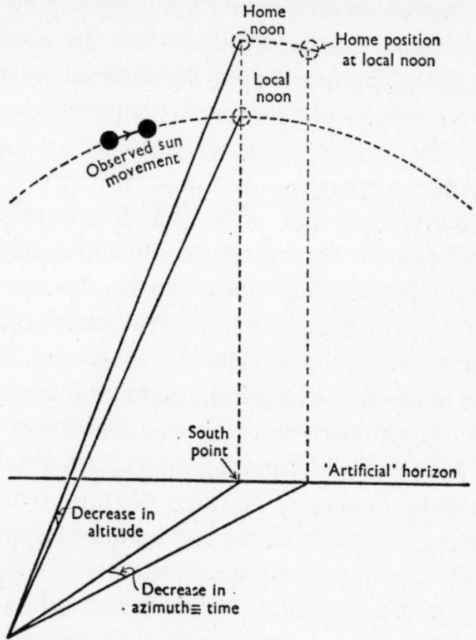

Fig. 120. Diagram illustrating the sun-arc hypotheses of navigation. Birds are released north and west of home. From Matthews, 1953 a.

sun's projection. It corrects the sun's movement by compensating this, and so it can maintain the same direction; this is a homing of Griffin's Type II. According to Kramer (1957), the sun is only a compass which enables the bird to find and maintain its direction. But no one knows how the bird determines the relationship between the point of release and its goal.

Kramer's hypotheses thus do not solve the problem entirely. Moreover, a little trigonometry shows that the movement of the sun's projection on the horizon is not uniform, so the bird has to make different corrections at different hours, and that is rather difficult to accept.

Matthews's theory, based on other elements involving the sun's position, is quite different (Fig. 120). He thinks the important factor is the *sun-arc*, representing the angle made by the plane through which the sun is moving in relation to the horizontal (in a Ptolemaic conception of the universe). This angle is constant throughout the year at a certain point and measures its latitude, if the angle of the ecliptic is considered. The higher the latitude, the greater the plane where the sun seems to be moving is slanting in relation to the horizontal. In the northern hemisphere the highest point reached each day by the sun is in the *south*. This indicates *direction*, and the point is reached at noon which indicates *time*.

In its 'home' the bird is familiar with the different solar characteristics, as its internal clock is regulated by solar rhythm. Placed in strange surroundings, the bird observes the sun and, after watching even a small part of its course, can project the whole curve. The measure of maximum altitude, the angle in relation to the horizontal, and a comparison with the circumstances at home give latitude; the sun's position in relation to its highest point and the home position, as revealed by the bird's internal clock, give details about longitude.

Kramer and Matthews multiplied their experiments in an effort to bear out their own hypotheses. This provoked an extremely interesting discussion, which has certainly cast new light on the problem; yet to be completely objective, one must admit that neither has succeeded in proving his theories by truly convincing observations or experiments. We now know that the sun plays an important rôle in the orientation of birds, especially migrants, but we know practically nothing about *how* birds get their bearings from it.

How to Conceive the Orientation of Migrants

We can now try to arrive at a synthesis of the different methods by which birds get their bearings and decide which senses guide them on their long flights.

It is certain that birds do not use *one* particular sense, but that orientation involves many different phenomena which are difficult to distinguish. Orientation ability varies widely according to systematic and biological groups; even with the individual and within the framework of a single population some birds find their way back to their nests much more easily than others.

Any theory involving the earth's magnetic field must be disregarded. Although many of these are perfectly correct from the point of view of physics, it now seems clear that no animal is sensitive to the action of this magnetic field. Not a single experiment during the past eighty years has disclosed any such sensitivity.[1]

Rejection of this theory does not imply that birds are *insensitive* to certain radiations which man cannot perceive. During the war Drost (1949) observed that migrant birds reacted to rays from radar stations installed near the ornithological station at Heligoland. He found that when rooks, flying in flocks of about fifty birds, encountered radar beams, they seemed afraid, scattered, and did not resume formation until they had emerged from the beams. Geese, gulls and some song-birds acted in the same manner, but other birds showed no reaction to the radiations.

Knorr (1954) got similar results on the east coast of the U.S.A. by using radar equipped with a wave ten cm. long and a peak power of 210 kilowatts. He reports that when he focused the beam on flocks of scaups (*Aythya* sp.) and scoters (*Melanitta* sp.), flying parallel to the shore, the flock was transformed into a 'bewildered mass of individuals which flew in circles, missed wing-beats and performed many unbirdlike gyrations.' Once beyond the beam, the flock resumed its normal behaviour.

Yet Kramer (1951b) tried in vain to make some birds react to electro-magnetic waves and finally decided they are not sensitive to such stimuli. Busnel and his collaborators (1956) also tried radar equipment, comparable to Knorr's, on European crows, but the birds did not display any significant change in behaviour.

So the question cannot be settled, but it is worth more detailed study, as these perceptions are important. At present we can merely state that in some instances birds seem to feel the effect of beams which do not influence human beings.

Certain writers claim that mysterious radiations emanate from living beings and the objects surrounding them. In 1898 Thauziès joked about this when he was discussing carrier pigeons: 'Would you believe there could be such powerful electric radiations in the four planks

1. F. A. Brown, Jr., W. J. Brett, M. F. Bennett and F. H. Barnwell (*Biol. Bull.* 118: 367–381, 1960) have, however, recently proved that common mud-snails (*Nassarius obsoletus*) of the Atlantic coasts of the U.S.A. can orient themselves by magnetic fields. This shows that new experiments will be necessary, at least with certain animals, before a definitive opinion can be obtained on the influence exerted by magnetism on living creatures.

composing a number of dovecots?' Similar explanations have been suggested for other animals, including insects, dogs and cats, but no scientific experiments have as yet thrown any light on the problem.

Thus we come back to visual landmarks in our study of orientation.

During migration birds have to solve three major problems:

1. In which direction to start;
2. How to maintain this direction during flight, or to modify it in order to arrive at the destination;
3. How to recognize their breeding area or winter quarters.

The last problem is easy, except in the case of winter quarters which a juvenile bird has never seen, because the bird's visual memory is such that it recognizes its 'home' from adjoining landmarks, the spot where it built a nest the preceding year, or where it was hatched and made its first flights. Climatic landmarks must also help, particularly for winter quarters. Furthermore, many birds do not winter in a specific place, but in the general area frequented by the species or population to which they belong. A number wander, and few show an attachment to a definite zone such as they have for the breeding area. Some, however, return to winter in the same place year after year, just as they come back to nest in the same spot (see p. xv), even to the same bush, tree or sand bank.

The other two problems are connected, and several explanations have been suggested. It might seem that experienced individuals guide young birds towards their nesting and wintering zones, so a tradition could be transmitted from one generation to the next.

This hypothesis is supported by the flights of birds such as geese and cranes, which keep their family units even when travelling in large bands. We must not forget that during migrations it is not just isolated individuals but that a whole population, or at least an important fraction of a population, is involved. Imitation is a factor in a group forming a relatively coherent whole, and it would be absurd to explain orientation mechanically, disregarding certain important psychic phenomena. In a migratory flock we may assume that the older and more experienced individuals are more or less *dominant* and that they play a leading rôle in guiding migrants.

This explanation alone, however, does not explain orientation, and it contradicts many observations. In certain species adults and young travel separately, the adults leaving before or *after* the young (p. 252). When young storks were held captive until after the departure of the adults, they started in the right direction, although they had never made the flight before.

Hence there is something other than 'experience.' Schüz's work with storks implies the existence of a hereditary instinct leading them to migrate in a certain direction, but this cannot be affirmed until further experiments have been conducted. Heredity would involve reacting in a specific way to certain environmental conditions, and here we encounter the various types of landmarks already discussed.

It seems evident that the bird which is ready to migrate turns in a *primary* direction. Rüppell's experiments proved this, and Kramer's observations of caged starlings indicate the same thing. This primary direction is probably found and maintained according to astronomical landmarks, chiefly the sun. Kramer and Matthews have demonstrated its paramount importance to the bird and how migrants can compensate in a surprising fashion for the sun's apparent movement.

Experiments with Manx shearwaters are particularly interesting, since these petrels are essentially nocturnal in their breeding, so it would seem *a priori* as if they should be capable of navigating by other than solar landmarks. One of Matthews's experiments (1953c), however, reveals that this is apparently not so. Birds captured at Skokholm were released two hours after sundown inland, or in a strange area. Night had fallen, and, although the distance back to the nest was very short, not a single shearwater returned during the night or at dawn. A very large proportion of returns was observed the next night (these birds return to their burrows when it is dark) after they had had an opportunity to get their bearings by daylight. This seems to prove that shearwaters cannot orient themselves at night, despite their largely nocturnal rhythm.

When the bird has once determined its primary direction, landmarks of many various types determine the *secondary directions*.

Some are topographic. Birds get their bearings from features in the terrain, river systems or sea-shores. That some migration routes have been followed since time immemorial is adequate proof of this. Ecological landmarks, particularly great forests, complete the bird's system of orientation.

Other landmarks are *meteorological*. Since it lives in the air, the bird knows the direction of the prevailing winds and the masses of air of different temperature and humidity, which are relatively fixed at a given period of the year. These are definite landmarks.

These meteorological landmarks also play a very important part in the orientation of marine migrants, especially during the circular flights of some Procellariiformes. The direction of the prevailing winds is fairly constant. Vleugel (1954a, 1955) has insisted on this point, on the basis of numerous observations of various song-birds, especially common chaffinches (*Fringilla coelebs*) in the Netherlands. Vleugel believes that birds rely on the wind to maintain their basic direction, even when the sun is hidden. Land-birds also use the wind when traversing expanses of water. When birds approach land, even small islands, changes occur in local meteorological conditions before land can be sighted from the altitude at which they fly.

These factors vary in importance with different species, especially the rôle played by the two groups of landmarks: astronomical and 'terrestrial' (topographical, ecological, etc.). There is not *one* orientation – there are a number. Some birds seem to have no ability to take bearings by the sun; others start immediately in the right direction. This explains the differences and apparent contradictions in various experiments. A comparison of some of Kramer's 'homing' experiments on carrier pigeons and Griffin's with gannets reveals that the former got off at once to the right start, whereas the latter 'groped' much longer, and obviously did not have a navigational system that functions over land. The same is true of the gulls with which Matthews worked. Migratory lesser black-backed gulls get their bearings much more easily and return more quickly than the more sedentary herring gulls.

Can these visual landmarks explain the sensational returns obtained in homing experiments, and do they make it possible to understand the orientation of migrants on routes thousands of miles in length? We think so in so far as astronomical landmarks are concerned. Their use still involves a large number of obscure points, but we know that birds are sensitive to them and that they get bearings from them.

Moreover, we must not be too much impressed by a few spectacular cases. As Griffin wisely remarks, the successful returns from distant points in certain homing experiments are 'lucky instances' out of a high proportion of failures. It is natural to emphasize these impressive returns, but they seem less significant when considered in relation to the many attempts that failed through the birds' inability to find their way home at all.

In migrations, too, only a fraction of the population arrives at its intended destination. That a large number of birds are lost along the way is proved by all the birds trapped or observed far outside the normal routes and by the fact that even among migrants with large broods the spring population does not show a marked increase from year to year.

Nocturnal Migrations

There remains one unknown, for many migrants fly at night, particularly song-birds (some of which are, however, capable of keeping track of their solar bearings). We might assume that birds get their bearings by day and fly at night, since observers have shown that, even when resting, migrants face in a direction approaching the one in which they are travelling. But this is a risky hypothesis.

Again we might assume that the moon serves as a nocturnal landmark. But Drost (1935) proved that it has no influence on nocturnal migrations; and the number of birds captured in banding traps at ornithological stations, which indicates the number of migrants, does not vary significantly according to the moon's phases or to the amount of light it sheds. These data were confirmed by Kramer (1952).

Some observers, especially Wojtusiak (1945), have suggested that infra-red rays, which are especially intense at night, might help in the orientation of birds whose vision would be as keen during the day as it is at night. This hypothesis has never been checked, but it is not necessary to imagine that a bird is particularly sensitive to infra-red radiation, for even human beings can find their way with relative ease on dark nights.

But these rudimentary methods would never suffice to explain the orientation of nocturnal migrants. That such flights are made by vast numbers of birds in both spring and autumn has been demonstrated in spectacular fashion by Lowery, with his telescopes focused on the lunar disk, and by Sutter with radar. The latter's pictures and a study of the films taken on the radar screen reveal that the nocturnal migrants were flying in a definite direction with no hesitation.

Experiments with nocturnal homing have recently confirmed that there is a real nocturnal orientation. Bellrose (1958a) proved this with his work on mallards (*Anas platyrhynchus*) when he took birds eleven to thirty-three miles from their haunts in the Illinois River Valley and released them at night, after attaching a tiny flashlight to the foot of each bird so it would leave a luminous trail (Figs. 121 and 122). He

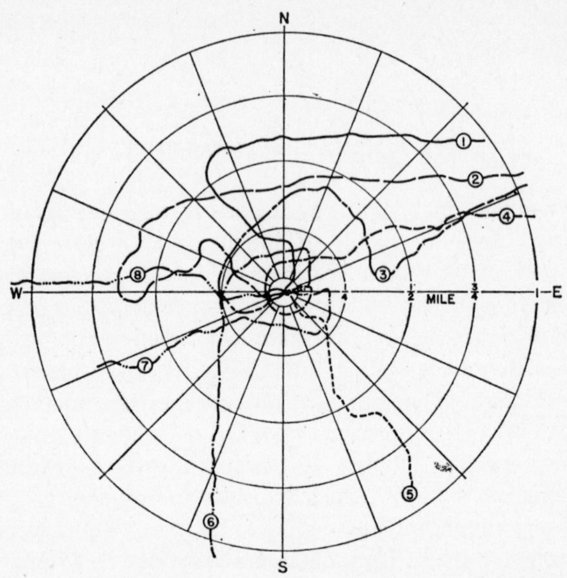

Fig. 121. The movement of eight mallards (*Anas platyrhynchus*) during the night under overcast skies within a one-mile radius of the release point. From Bellrose, 1958a.

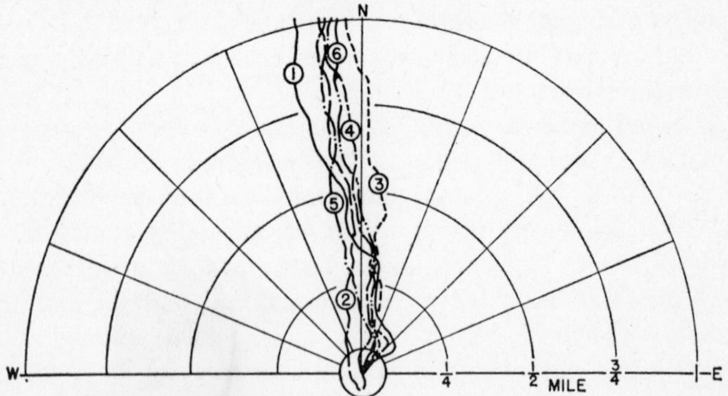

Fig. 122. The movement of six mallards during the night under clear skies within a one-mile radius of the release point. From Bellrose, 1958 a.

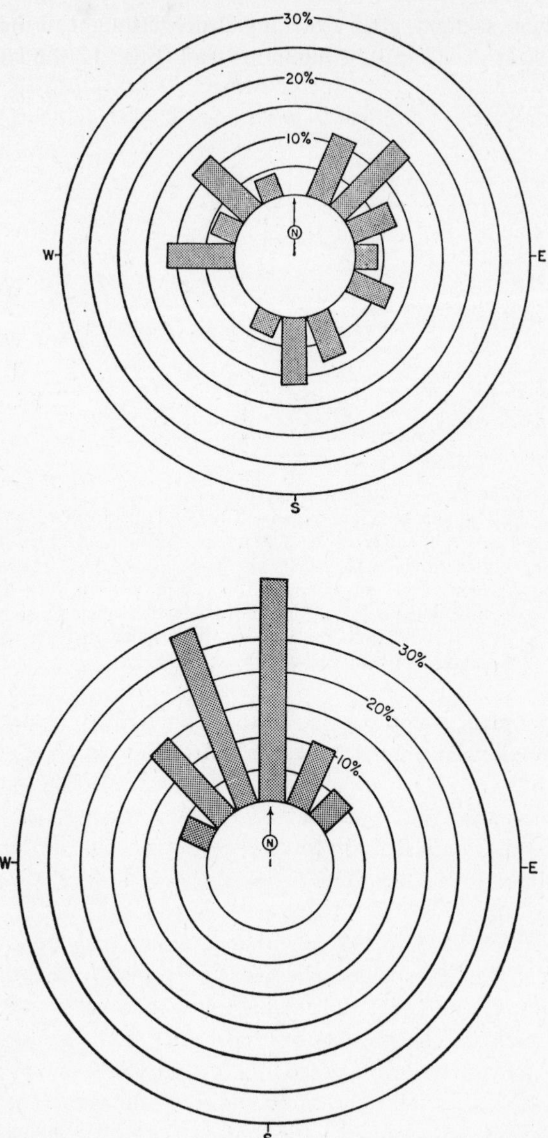

Fig. 123. The initial flight of all mallards released during the night under overcast skies (A) and under clear skies (B). From Bellrose, 1958 a.

followed the flight of the birds until they vanished on the horizon and found that the ducks flew immediately in the right direction, *provided the sky was clear*. If it was foggy, however, the birds scattered and seemed completely bewildered. Bellrose's diagrams are especially convincing (Fig. 123).

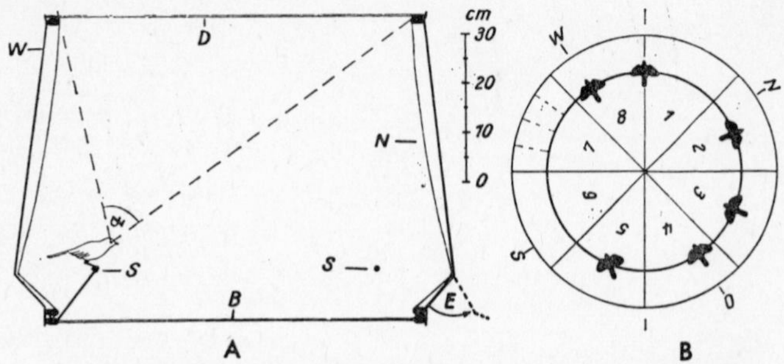

Fig. 124. Diagram of the cage used by F. Sauer to prove that migrants orient themselves by the stars. A: Side elevation. B: Ground plane. Angle of the bird's vision. B. glass floor; D: glass ceiling; E swing door entrance; N. protecting net (to keep the birds from hitting the solid wall); S. circular perch; the rear of the cage is divided into numbered sectors so that the observer can determine the bird's position. From Sauer, 1957 b.

This experiment is comparable to those conducted in broad daylight by a number of authors, including Bellrose himself. It shows that, even at night, birds which are able to get their bearings and start in the right direction when the sky is clear wander at random under a cloudy sky. The parallelism is striking. Since everything occurs as though the bird had taken its bearings from the sun, one wonders if it is guiding itself by the stars.

Sauer (1956, 1957a, b, 1958a, b) and Sauer and Sauer (1955) demonstrated this by means of experiments which were often repeated, carefully checked, and yet which seemed unbelievable.

Sauer's methods resemble those used by Kramer. A round cage, ninety cm. in diameter, was divided into sectors, so the observer could note the bird's position but the bird could see nothing save the sky; its angle of upward vision was 68° (Fig. 124). After testing the apparatus to be sure that it could not supply the birds with any other landmarks, Sauer placed in the cage blackcaps (*Sylvia atricapilla*), garden warblers (*Sylvia borin*), and lesser whitethroats (*Sylvia curruca*) during the spring and autumn migrations, the period when these birds have the 'flight fidgets' which had already served Kramer. He found that the birds got their bearings immediately, and that the blackcaps and garden warblers started south-south-west and south-west, which is normal for migrants in Germany in the autumn (Fig. 125). It was

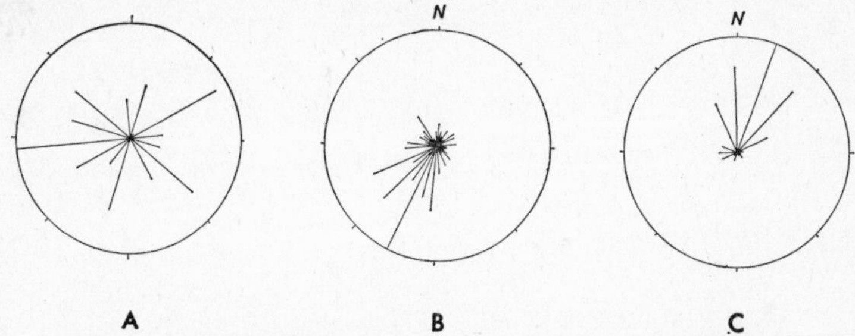

Fig. 125. Orientation of migrants by the stars. Experiments with blackcaps (*Sylvia atricapilla*) and garden warblers (*Sylvia borin*). A. Experiment under overcast skies; the bird wanders in every direction and is incapable of getting its bearings as it does when the sky is clear (for example, B and C). B. The bird's orientation in autumn. C. The bird's orientation in spring. The directions are represented by vectors whose length corresponds to the frequency in which the birds head in this direction. They correspond exactly to those the birds would take in the wild at this season. From Sauer, 1957 b.

evident that they were getting their bearings from the stars. The moon had nothing to do with this orientation; as a matter of fact, it was a hindrance, since it dimmed the constellations and was responsible for some directional errors.[1]

All of this occurred only in clear weather. As soon as dense clouds covered the sky, the birds lost their bearings and fluttered in complete bewilderment.

When Sauer repeated his work in the spring, it was again crowned with success. The blackcaps got their bearings to the north-north-east and north-east, the direction they take in Germany at that season. These experiments, comparable in every way to Kramer's on the sun's rôle in diurnal migration, show that nocturnal migrants get their bearings by the stars.

1. But migrations of tremendous magnitude take place on and around the night of the full moon, as many authors, especially Lowery and Newman have shown. And no heavy pattern of stars is visible at that time!

In order to check these surprising discoveries, Sauer decided to study the migrants' reactions to an artificial sky in the Olbers-Planetarium at the Naval School in Bremen (Fig. 126). This has a dome twenty feet in diameter, with a facsimile of the sky which can, of course, be altered at will. He placed the cage in the side of the planetarium so that only the

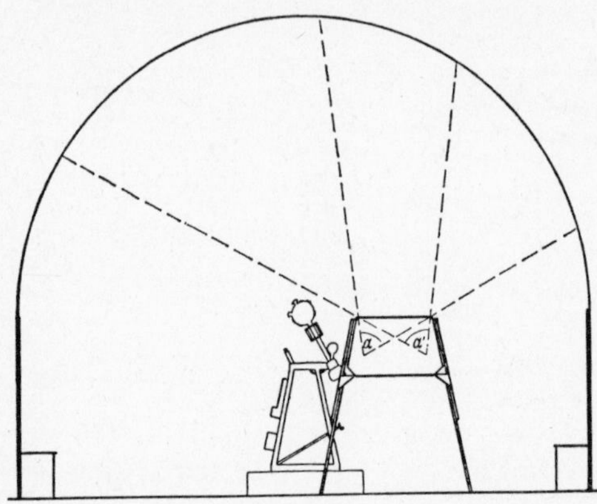

Fig. 126. Planetarium experiments. The cage is placed under the dome, so the bird can see only the artificial sky which has a diameter of six meters. From Sauer, 1957 b.

dome was visible to the birds. Again he made a number of tests to be sure they could use no landmarks other than the artificial 'stars,' but uniform diffuse lighting showed that they were wandering at random through all the sectors. In the spring of 1956 Sauer presented an artificial spring sky to a blackcap, and the bird immediately flew north-north-east to north-east (in terms of the planetarium 'sky'), which is normal at that season. The next autumn blackcaps and garden warblers, which were submitted to the same experimental conditions, headed south-west, their normal direction. Lesser whitethroats, on the other hand, headed south-east, as these 'eastern' migrants do on their post-nuptial migration. Sauer then changed the position of the 'stars' so that the latitudes represented remote subtropical and tropical regions between 35° N. and 20° N., like those which the birds traverse to reach their winter quarters.

The lesser whitethroats immediately headed 'south', which is their normal procedure when they reach southern latitudes on postnuptial migrations. True celestial navigation is involved, and the bird determines its latitude and longitude by the position of the stars, instead of merely choosing its *direction* by the sun.

Sauer next placed the birds in purely artificial conditions. By arranging the stars to simulate a season six months from the migration

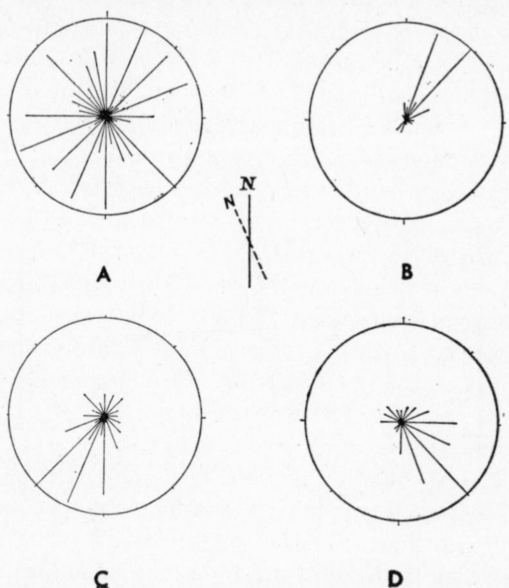

Fig. 127. Orientation of migrants by the artificial stars in the dome of a planetarium. Experiments with blackcaps (*Sylvia atricapilla*) and lesser whitethroats (*Sylvia curruca*). A. Diffuse lighting of the dome; the birds wander in all directions without being able to get their bearings. B. Orientation of a blackcap in the spring when it is placed under a spring sky. C. Orientation of a blackcap in autumn, when it is placed under an autumn sky. D. Orientation of a lesser whitethroat in the autumn under the same conditions. The birds take the same directions they would take in the wild. As in fig. 125, the directions are represented by vectors whose length is proportionate to the frequency with which the birds head in this direction.

The true north is marked by the dotted line; the north as it can be determined from the artificial dome by the unbroken line. From Sauer, 1957 b.

period he was studying (a spring sky in autumn and vice versa), he confused the birds, which took first the normal spring route and then the autumn one. When they were placed beneath a summer or winter sky, they were completely bewildered. Finally Sauer and Sauer (1959) decided to take some European migrants to their winter quarters just before the beginning of the migratory period and to show them the sky and the stars in order to see how they would react. In the autumn they carried whitethroats (*Sylvia communis*), garden warblers (*Sylvia borin*) and blackcaps (*Sylvia atricapilla*) to South-west Africa, where they repeated the experiments. They found that the birds first headed south, their normal direction in autumn, and then quieted down. The sight of the African sky, beneath which these warblers are accustomed to spend the winter, showed them that they had arrived in their winter quarters and that no further migratory restlessness was necessary.

From all these experiments it is evident that the bird gets its bearings from constellations as well as from the sun, and that it modifies its reactions to these visual stimuli in accordance with the prenuptial or postnuptial migration season. No one knows what psycho-physiological processes are involved or how the bird gets its bearings, but the fact is proved, and it is certainly the most amazing recent discovery in the field of avian orientation.

Orientation by the stars enables a bird to establish its *primary direction*, just as diurnal migrants use the sun. Other factors then modify its flight and determine secondary directions on the basis of local conditions. If geographical and topographic conditions are less important than in diurnal migrations, meteorological conditions certainly play a greater rôle.

Although we must still admit ignorance on many points about bird orientation and navigation, much has been learned during recent years, and we may be on the threshold of an explanation which will be based on facts rather than bold hypotheses. It is true that birds are sensitive to phenomena which we do not perceive; very little has been done on the physiology of their sense organs, especially of the inner ear, and a study of this subject may have some surprises in store for us.

But for the moment we had best stick to known facts. More has been learned during the last decade than in past centuries. We now know some of the landmarks which birds use, and they are highly unexpected: the sun and the stars. The future will tell us how birds perceive them, and by what process they transform these observations into practical flight directions. The orientation of migratory birds, as of many animals, is very strange, but these recent advances prove there is no need to surround it with legends.

CHAPTER 13

The Origin and Evolution of Migrations

The origin of bird migrations is such an important question that it dominates all other aspects of ornithology, but every 'solution' must remain in the realm of pure conjecture, as it cannot be substantiated by observation or experiment.

Although many theories have been suggested, this origin must be explained in relation to the adaptive power and flight ability of birds and, above all, in relation to geography and climatology as they have been since the Tertiary Period.

We know the wide range of adaptations of birds whose habitats have changed – and still keep changing. Current information, although restricted to very short periods in relation to the history of birds, gives evidence of this plasticity, and many species have moved their habitat in very recent times. In North America Snyder (*in:* 'Changes in the Fauna of Ontario,' edited by Urquhart, *Contr. Div. Zool. Paleont. Royal Ontario Museum*, Toronto, 1957) found twenty-three cases of extension of range in Ontario, fifteen of which were oriented northward (including the mourning dove, black-billed cuckoo, mockingbird, bobolink, eastern meadowlark, cowbird and cardinal). The author attributes these movements to the influence of man in settling these regions.

One of the best examples among European birds is the serin (*Serinus serinus*), whose breeding area has spread during the past century over the whole of continental Europe to Schleswig and the southern coast of the Baltic Sea. Although once a strictly Mediterranean bird, the serin is common today throughout a good part of Europe. Its Mediterranean populations have remained sedentary, but those of countries it recently invaded have become migratory probably because the more rigorous winter climate of their new home exterminated most individuals which failed to migrate.

In Scandinavia many birds have taken advantage of the milder temperatures observed since the middle of the last century (Kalela, 1950). Occasional hard winters reduce their distribution and numbers, but populations later increase and spread into even more northerly districts as soon as the temperature moderates. Such movements are performed by sedentary birds, but many migrants move farther and farther north in Finland, as, for example, the greenish warbler (*Phylloscopus trochiloides viridanus*), which advances as the average spring and summer temperature rises (Välikangas, 1951). These extensions of the breeding area are certainly linked to migrations, as has been noted in northern Europe. Otterlind (1954) shows that the phenomenon applies to other species as well. There is no doubt that contemporary faunistic changes are a simple prolongation of immigration movements which followed the last glaciation and find their chief sources in a prolonged or an abbreviated migration.

According to Otterlind, there is a balance between the reproductive instinct and spring migration. If there is overpopulation, a surplus number of birds moves north, some of them as far beyond the normal limit of the species as circumstances permit. Relatively high temperatures tend to induce the birds to go farther north, and we must not forget that in many species the young are more adventurous (Snyder, loc. cit.). Impelled by a stronger migratory urge, they tend to go farther, to settle new areas as pioneers, and to return to breed in succeeding years. In Sweden the herring gull (*Larus argentatus*) and the mute swan (*Cygnus olor*) have established breeding territories in places which they first visited as immature birds.

The contrary may also be true. An abbreviated migration due to unfavourable meteorological conditions in the spring may halt part of a population and prompt it to nest south of its normal habitat. But whether restrictions or extensions are involved, there is always an equilibrium between the migratory impulse and reproduction, and the result determines the location of the breeding range of the species.

Many similar instances could be recorded in Europe, Iceland and Greenland,[1] where climatic changes have been very apparent during

1. As the climate has grown warmer, southern Greenland has been occupied by fieldfares (*Turdus pilaris*). After a series of attempts at colonization, a real

the past seventy years (Salomonsen, 1948; Gudmundsson, 1951); this is also true of North America.

Not all changes extend the habitat, for some species tend to decline when conditions are unfavourable. Severe winters reduce breeding populations to such an extent that birds leave the most northerly portions of their range. Some of the contemporary extensions and reductions of habitat are caused by man, who, by upsetting the natural balance, helps some species to colonize new areas but hinders others.[1] But other changes are perfectly natural and are caused by spontaneous transformations in the environment. The influence of climatic evolution and natural environmental changes on the distribution of birds forms a general framework for avian migrations which must be considered as a reaction against unfavourable conditions at certain periods of the year.

We may assume, in some cases, that the birds' original home was in their present winter quarters, and that they developed a tendency to leave it in spring in order to breed in other territories. Seasonal change of weather or food supply in these newly settled regions forced the birds to migrate in autumn, and so they retreated to their former abode. Other authors think that the original home of the species was their present breeding area, and that changes in climate over long periods forced them to migrate to a new region which has become their winter quarters.

These two hypotheses are most frequently mentioned in connection with the great Quaternary 'Ice Ages,' which altered the distribution of species in northern regions of the globe. Although these glaciations were important, we must not forget that migrations occurred long before the ice sheets moved down. Palaeontology, which unfortunately furnishes little information on birds, reveals that most of the strong flying species we know today existed at the end of the Tertiary. World climates were warmer then than they are today, but in certain regions, at least, seasonal changes must have forced or stimulated migrations. Although migratory phenomena preceded the Quaternary glaciations,

---

invasion occurred in 1937 following unusual atmospheric conditions which Salomonsen (1951) described in detail. These thrushes have become established as a sedentary population in various parts of southern Greenland and breed there regularly.

1. Clearings in the great forests which covered most of Europe and North America until quite recently and cultivation of more northerly regions permit many species to advance farther north.

the latter exerted a powerful influence on them in Europe and North America, both because of climatic changes wrought by the ice and because, as the last great transforming factor, they were responsible for the current geography of avian migrations.

The great Quaternary glaciations – separated by interglacial periods when the temperature rose – prevented many birds from living in Europe and North America. The fact that bird life was much more concentrated near the equator does not mean that birds had emigrated to southerly areas. Populations in northern countries probably perished on the spot, and only a small fraction survived to retreat southward as the ice-cap advanced. These birds preserved the species link with more southern populations which were able to survive because of the difference in climate. As temperatures moderated after the final retreat of the glaciers, birds began to return to their former homes in the spring, but winter always forced them to go back to a place of refuge. Among these boreal forms were many Anseriformes – ducks, geese, swans – as well as most of the shore-birds (Charadriidae), in which speciation had occurred before the glaciations.

After the Ice Ages a number of birds of tropical origin took advantage of warm summer weather in northern countries to extend their breeding range. Although summer conditions enable them to raise their young and to find ample food in the Far North, autumn forces them to return to their ancestral home.

Migrations of birds of the northern hemisphere may thus have originated in the alternation of seasons during interglacial periods. Areas which were freed from ice and habitable at least part of the year were gradually settled. As new regions became available, vital competition for food stimulated expansion, a process which, among some species, is still continuing.

If this is true, northern migrants sprang from two distinct stocks which emigrated at the end of the last glaciation: one consisting of northern birds which sought refuge in low latitudes during glacial periods; the other, of tropical birds which took advantage of warmer weather to move farther and farther north. The theories are perfectly compatible and apply to phenomena which occurred simultaneously.

This double origin appears most clearly in North America, where the 'tropical' element is most abundant. This is due to the geography of the continent, where chains of mountains extending from north to south form no barriers to prevent northward penetration. The tropical birds include humming-birds (Trochilidae), tyrant flycatchers (Tyrannidae), American blackbirds and orioles (Icteridae) and tanagers (Thraupidae). Birds with distinct tropical affinities thus nest 'side by side' with arctic forms, such as many Charadriidae, with which they have nothing in common from the bio-geographical point of view.

The situation is quite different in the western Palearctic region, where the Mediterranean and the Sahara – both of which were formed or extended at the end of glacial periods – constitute supplementary barriers. Here tropical birds, although much less numerous, include some rather typical species, such as the bee-eater, roller, hoopoe and quail, which represent groups inhabiting tropical regions in the Old World.[1]

In the most eastern sector of the Palearctic, particularly in China, migrants of tropical origin are proportionately more abundant in their variety. Along with various shore-birds, ducks, thrushes, Sylviidae (warblers) and other little Passerines from a 'cold' region, there are migrants such as black-capped and ruddy kingfishers (*Halcyon pileata, H. coromanda*), orioles, pittas (*Pitta brachyura* breeds as far as Manchuria and eastern Siberia and winters in Malaysia), drongos (*Dicrurus leucophaeus, D. hottentotus*), minivets (*Pericrocotus ethologus, P. divaricatus*), Zosterops or white-eyes (*Zosterops japonica, Z. erythropleura*), all of which belong to tropical families which emigrated northward during the post-glacial warming-up period.

The ancestral home of migrants is often revealed by differences in behaviour. 'Tropical' birds tend to leave earlier in autumn and to return later in the spring. Their winter quarters is apt to be farther south, as they require warmer temperatures and food found chiefly in warmer areas.

The relationship between boreal migrations and Quaternary glaciations is very fragmentary. It applies only in a general fashion to the origins of avian migration and only to cold and temperate countries of the northern hemisphere. But birds migrate in other parts of the globe. The migrations of austral birds can be partially explained by antarctic glaciations, notably in the southern part of South America. Patagonia was probably covered with ice and a large part of the rest of

1. Verheyen (1947) adds to this list the peregrine falcon (*Falco peregrinus*) related to the African peregrine falcon (*F. perconfusus*), the kestrel (*Falco tinnunculus*), related to the African *F. rupicola*, the European cuckoo and swifts. Except for the cuckoo, however, these birds are much less 'tropical' than the North American genera already mentioned.

Argentina was under water. When the glaciers retreated, more and more birds emigrated south but returned north for the austral winter. This phenomenon is so old that a rather distinct Patagonian avifauna has developed, along with forms much more clearly related to neotropical examples. Outside the Americas birds belong to tropical groups which have spread south without becoming differentiated. There is no subantarctic land fauna comparable to the boreal fauna, because continental configuration in the southern hemisphere has not permitted a special avifauna to develop.

In tropical regions migrations may be regarded as reactions to a seasonal change which causes important fluctuations in the quantity of food available. Food factors are direct causes whose mechanism is in a way easier to explain.

Birds adapt themselves very gradually to different environments. At the beginning a large percentage must have perished without attempting to move away from the cold. Only a fraction of the population had any impulse to seek refuge elsewhere, but natural selection favoured the 'migrants,' and migratory tendencies developed.

Although this purely theoretical solution explains how the 'migratory' character has been maintained and developed, it does not suggest how it appeared. Did migration become an acquired characteristic after a number of generations, or is it part of the bird's inheritance? Is it due to a mutation or to a series of mutations? This is all pure hypothesis.

A sounder theory seems to be that migratory birds take the routes by which their ancestors first invaded new regions after the glacial recession. In Europe this applies particularly to migrants such as the red-backed shrike (*Lanius collurio*) and the lesser grey shrike (*Lanius minor*), which arrive in the spring from the East, after crossing Syria and Asia Minor; like the roller and the oriole (see p. 83), they detour north and south around the Alps and then spread throughout the continent.

The wheatear (*Oenanthe oenanthe leucorrhoa*), which invaded Greenland from Europe (it is unknown in the New World except in Alaska, which it reached from Siberia), migrates every year across the western Atlantic, and follows the coasts of western Europe to winter in tropical Africa. This Passerine is so small that its flight across great expanses of open ocean seems out of proportion to its strength. At rare intervals a few individuals are encountered migrating along much more accessible North American coasts, in Bermuda or Cuba, but these are birds which were carried off their course by storms.

The migrations of the wheatear are unlike those of other birds of Greenland which came from the New World and winter in North America. Occasionally a few of these lose their way and are carried to Europe by winds.

Similar instances occur among the terrestrial avifauna of Alaska and that part of eastern Siberia just across from it. Several are forms typical of the Old World; the yellow wagtail, which settled in the arctic zone of western Alaska and has developed a special race (*Motacilla flava alascensis*), the arctic warbler (*Phylloscopus borealis kennicotti*), and the wheatear migrate annually into the New World but winter in the warm regions of south-eastern Asia and even Africa. Yet a typically American thrush (*Hylocichla minima*), which has extended its breeding area to north-eastern Siberia, returns to winter in Central or South America.

Some authors have thought that certain migration routes reveal geographical conditions of another era. They believe that the numerous birds which cross the Sahara at its widest point are following the traces of remote ancestors which traversed a much greener and more fertile region. Similarly, birds migrating from India to Madagascar are believed to be 'using' the hypothetical land-bridge which may once have linked these two land masses. These explanations rest on bold and unverified hypotheses. Furthermore, so many birds traverse hostile seas or deserts that we have no reason to assume they were more hospitable at any time in the past.

Wegener's theory of continental drift may be attached to hypotheses of this kind. As Wolfson (1948) stated, migrations are due to the fact that birds *originally* nomadic between their breeding area and adjacent areas where they came at other seasons (to hunt food, for example), were gradually forced to make longer flights because of continental drift. These flights, so the theory goes, were short at first when the continents were close together but became longer, and most of the birds slowly adapted themselves to the new distribution of continental masses.

To support his theory, Wolfson cites several shore-birds, the turnstone (*Arenaria interpres*), which winters in South Africa, Australia and New Zealand, the sanderling (*Crocethia alba*), which winters in

Patagonia, South Africa and Australia, and the knot (*Calidris canutus*), which winters in South Africa, India, Australia, New Zealand and Patagonia. According to Wegener, these countries were once united, and the winter quarters of these species now represent the remains of an ancient 'Gondwana,' the ancestral home from which all these birds went north to nest, but to which they returned for refuge during the northern winter.

Wolfson also cites the migrations of the arctic tern and the Greenland wheatear, which, he believes, substantiate his strange theory.

Although Wegener's hypotheses are attractive, geologists have pointed out that they are replete with errors. Wolfson's statements are likewise indefensible, especially those pertaining to the antarctic origin of birds and the idea that Wegener's great dislocations preceded the development of the birds of today. Prevailing winds afford a better explanation for the transoceanic migrations of various birds, such as the arctic tern.

Lengthening of Migration Routes

As birds extended their breeding area northward, following the glacial recession, they also seem to have gone farther south for the winter. Today the most northern populations (or races) 'pass over' more southern populations of their own species on the way to their winter quarters (see p. 381).

The northward advance in spring may be explained by a stronger migratory impulse and by competition in the winter range from which the species is moving. Postnuptial migration towards lower and lower latitudes is more difficult to understand. Although vital competition in the original winter quarters forces birds to move farther south, there must be another cause.

We may assume that a stronger migratory impulse gradually developed in birds which moved northward to breed, and that this impetus drove them farther south in winter. Another hypothesis is that the effect of photoperiodism on the avian organism is such that the bird tried to find in the southern hemisphere the same length-of-daylight conditions as those to which it is accustomed; but this would make all migrants cross the equator so that their breeding and winter areas might be evenly distributed according to latitude, and this is true of only a few species.

Migrations and Evolution

Migration changes the rhythm of a bird's life, and it has given many birds certain morphological characters. As migratory flights require tremendous strength, the best fliers have an advantage. A comparison of birds belonging to the same systematic group shows that migrants are much stronger fliers than sedentary birds.

These morphological characters are best revealed in the shape of the wing. It is usually much more pointed among migrants than sedentary birds because the outermost primaries are the longest and the others decrease rapidly in length. This formation, which permits a swift, easy flight, is found among many powerful migrants, such as falcons, swallows, bee-eaters, terns and shore-birds. Largely sedentary groups have much less developed primaries, and the first are never the longest. Some birds in warm parts of the globe like certain Timaliidae, pittas (except a few special cases such as the fairy pitta [*Pitta brachyura*], a migratory species with pointed wings), manakins (Pipridae), sedentary forms in the South American forests, etc. are interesting in this connection.

The most valuable comparisons are, however, those between sedentary and migratory forms within a single group. Some species – often even closely related subspecies – differ considerably in their wing formula. Orioles are a good example, as Kipp showed (1942, 1958). This group is well differentiated in the tropics, where the birds are sedentary. The Indian black-headed oriole (*Oriolus xanthornus*) has a very rounded wing, with primaries only slightly longer than the secondaries. Migratory orioles leave the tropics to breed but return to them in autumn. The black-naped oriole (*Oriolus chinensis*) breeds in eastern Siberia, China and Formosa but winters in India and Ceylon. Its wing is much more pointed because the primaries are more developed. In the European golden oriole (*Oriolus oriolus*), which winters as far as South Africa, the primaries are also considerably longer than the secondaries (Fig. 128).

Along with a relative lengthening of the wing, the outermost primary tends to regress among migratory song-birds. It is frequently well-developed among sedentary birds with a rounded wing, whereas their migratory relatives have a vestigial primary that is often invisible among the coverts. Warblers of the genus *Sylvia* and thrushes of the genus *Turdus* are characteristic examples (Fig. 129).

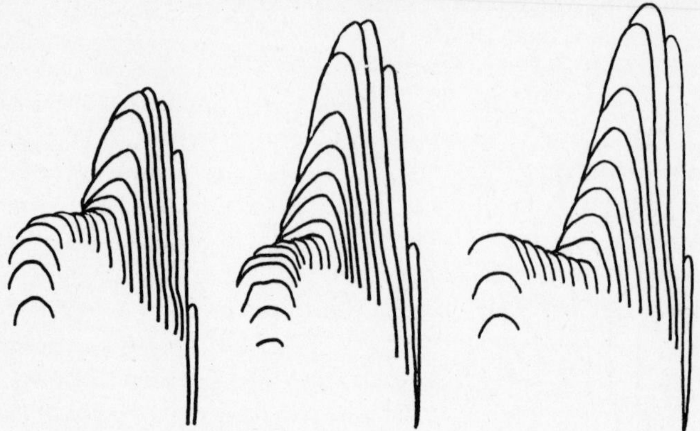

Fig. 128. Variations in the shape of the wing in Old World orioles.
Left: Black-headed oriole, *Oriolus xanthornus*, a sedentary bird.
Centre: Black-naped oriole, *Oriolus chinensis*, a migrant.
Right: Golden oriole, *Oriolus oriolus*, a bird which migrates great distances. From Kipp, 1942.

Niethammer (1937) showed that the whole wing may be longer among migratory than sedentary species, but the differences appear chiefly in its general form. That the wing surface usually tends to decrease among migrants is evident from Meinertzhagen's comparisons of larks (1951).

	Weight	*Wing length*	*Wing area*
Calendrella cinerea brachydactyla (migrant)	21 gm.	98 mm.	6160 mm.^{2}
Ammomanes deserti hijazensis (sedentary)	24 gm.	106 mm.	9160 mm.^{2}

Despite appearances, a narrow wing is much more efficient in prolonged flight than a broad one.

Countless examples could be given by examining all avian groups containing both migratory and sedentary forms. Migration has thus contributed to the modification of some populations by causing their structural characteristics to vary. Systematicians recognized this evolution by distinguishing as subspecies, and occasionally as separate species, forms which present these variations.

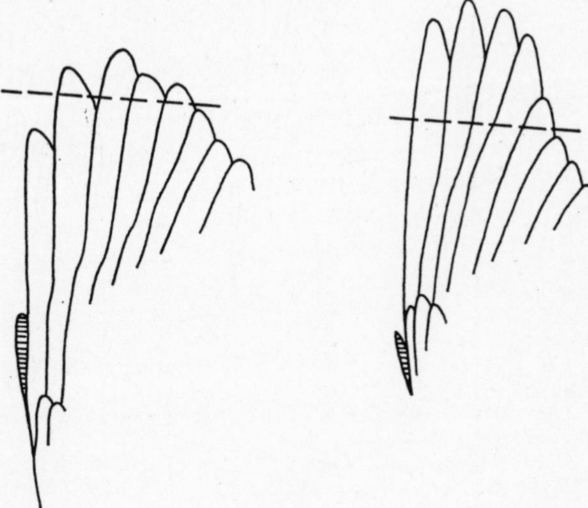

Fig. 129. Variations in the shape of the wing among thrushes (*Turdus*).

Left: Black ouzel, *Turdus serranus*, sedentary in South America.

Right: Song thrush, *Turdus philomelos*, a Palearctic migrant.

Note the development of the first outer primary (hatched) in the sedentary species.

In addition to these morphological features, the geographical races of a species often vary widely in their migration patterns. Winter quarters may differ almost as much as breeding areas. A classic example is the fox sparrow (*Passerella iliaca*), which has several distinct local races along the Pacific coast from Alaska to California (Fig. 130). All the northern races are migratory, but Swarth (1920) found that each one behaves like a separate entity and migrates independently. The most northern populations are the most migratory, with winter quarters actually farther south than those of more southern races. Hence they perform a 'leapfrog migration' over their relatives on their semi-annual migrations. Winter quarters remain separate, and the most northern races (*unalaschensis*, *insularis*, *sinuosa*) probably fly over the eastern Pacific and do not touch the coast again

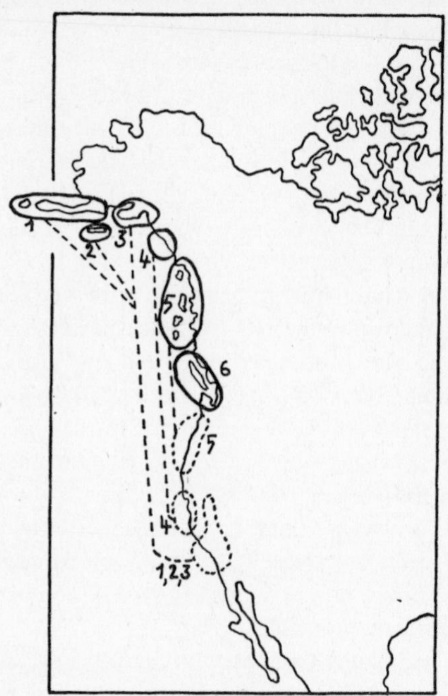

Fig. 130. Geographical variations in winter quarters among races of the fox sparrow (*Passerella iliaca*)
1. *P. i. unalaschcensis*, 2. *P. i. insularis*, 3. *P. i. sinuosa*, 4. *P. i. annectens*, 5. *P. i. townsendi*, 6. *P. i. fuliginosa*. From Swarth, 1920.

until they reach the latitude of winter quarters. In principle at least, they never mingle with other races.[1]

Many other examples could be cited, especially among shore-birds. Salomonsen (1955) showed that the ringed plover (*Charadrius hiaticula*) has a marked leapfrog migration, for the most northern

1. It should be noted that birds do not winter in such separate regions because of vital competition. Migratory races winter in areas, especially in California, where sedentary races live all year. A different migratory impulse is thus involved, one which becomes stronger among birds that nest far to the north.

populations winter in Central and South Africa, those from southern Sweden go to West Africa, Danish birds migrate south to western Europe, and most English birds are sedentary (Fig. 131). Salomonsen also found a cline in wing length, the most northern populations having the shortest wing, the Danish birds a longer wing, and British birds the longest. This contradicts Bergmann's rule as far as the breeding range is concerned, but agrees with it about winter quarters. As Salomonsen said: 'The only explanation of this phenomenon is that adaptive selection in the wintering grounds is responsible for the variation.' He thus agrees with Hemmingsen (1951b), who stated that Bergmann's rule applies to migratory species, provided the winter quarters, not the reproductive area, is considered.

Cold climate in winter quarters is said to be responsible for the larger size of northern populations of a species. Williamson (1958a), however, observed that this does not always apply, and he cites the Greenland wheatear (*Oenanthe oenanthe leucorrhoa*), which is the largest and most northern representative of the species. He suggests that in this case selection is most rigorous during the migratory period when the largest individuals have an advantage. As overseas flights exhaust migrants and cause them to lose considerable weight (see p. 245), the largest birds, and those with the longest wings, survived best during the evolutionary process. Hence a population may be affected by a number of different influences.

The winter quarters of the western fox sparrow is along the Pacific coast, but in other cases winter quarters form a real mosaic. This is true of some Eurasian nesting birds distributed over a vast area, like the red-backed shrike, where every race migrates in a slightly different fashion, sometimes even to different continents (Africa, South-east Asia).

Although starlings form separate populations, even local races, their winter quarters are superimposed on one another to a considerable degree. A number of recoveries of banded birds show, however, that they remain fairly distinct. As flocks of wintering starlings do not mingle with those from other regions, it is apparent that different races can evolve and maintain their identity in a single winter range.

Other migrants, such as European black-headed gulls, mingle much more freely. This mingling during flights, which resemble a winter dispersion rather than real migrations, prevents segregation which might lead to racial differentiation. In some migrants different

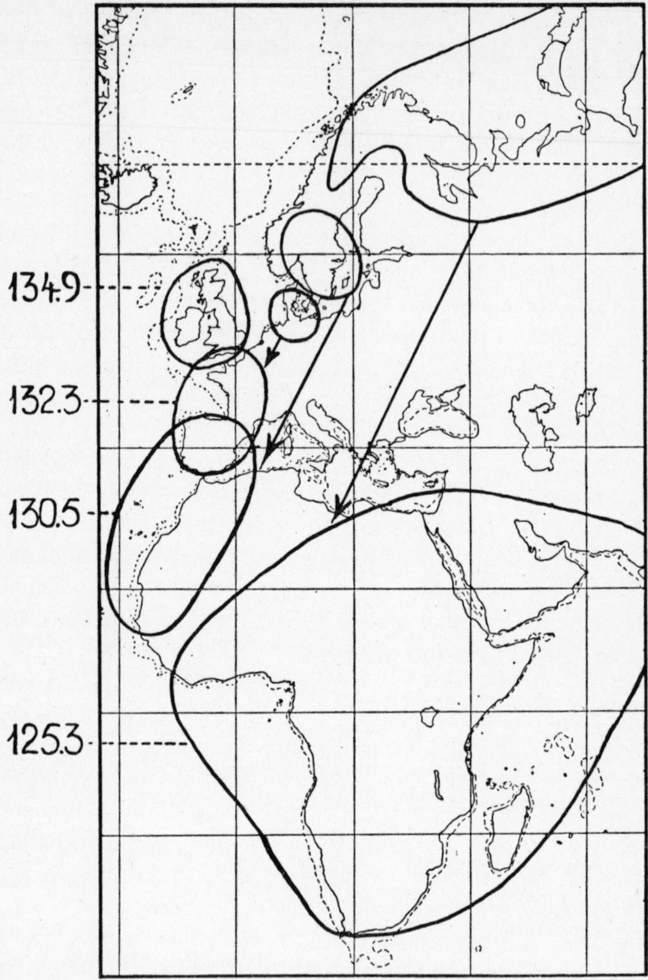

Fig. 131. Breeding areas and winter quarters of several populations of the ringed plover (*Charadrius hiaticula*), based partly on recoveries of banded birds. Breeding areas and corresponding winter quarters are connected by arrows; the British population is resident. Figures at the left give the average wing length of the population wintering in the area in question. From Salomonsen, 1955.

geographical races, although separated in their reproductive areas, are very closely associated in winter quarters. Wallace (1955) found that in Kenya eight subspecies of blue-headed wagtails (*Motacilla flava*) were sometimes seen in a single flock (*flavissima*, *beema*, *cinereocapilla*, *thunbergi*, *feldegg* and *leucocephala*)! Each subspecies shows slight ecological preferences which may be sufficient to keep the flocks separate.

Thus every stage is found in winter quarters between a complete mingling of populations and strict segregation. Salomonsen (1955), who termed these extremes *synhiemy* and *allohiemy*, has insisted on the importance of migration in avian evolution. He established the evolutionary significance of certain controlling factors which are frequently overlooked because of the emphasis placed on environment in breeding areas.

A number of species can be divided into three groups – sedentary, migratory and partially migratory populations. A phenomenon of much interest is the formation of physiological 'races' which have not yet had time to acquire marked structural differences. Although they cannot be recognized taxonomically, they are valid races which might be placed beside morphologically distinct forms, if any useful purpose could be derived from this procedure.

Other races have had the opportunity and the time to become distinct from the morphological point of view. Some criteria are due to geographical segregation; others, like the wing formula, are linked to migration. This character reveals an aptitude for long flight that increases as the migratory distance lengthens. Differentiation evidently occurred more easily when populations were separated in both winter quarters and the breeding area, since this gave natural selection a freer rein throughout the whole life cycle.

Migration, like other biological factors, is thus an agent which has played a very important part in avian evolution. Although similar phenomena doubtless affect certain insects and marine animals, little is known about them.

Migration has made possible the colonization of areas by species which could not survive in the region throughout the whole year. Occasionally birds linger in places along their migration routes, establish breeding colonies and then become sedentary. Meinertzhagen (1919) thus explains the presence of hooded crows (*Corvus cornix*) in Egypt and the Persian Gulf.

European bee-eaters migrated to South Africa, where they established a colony of birds completely isolated from their relatives in the northern hemisphere. The white storks, which now nest in South Africa, may have been responsible for a similar evolution, along with shore-birds like *Tringa hypoleucos*. In certain cases this would explain the presence in warm regions of sedentary races of species that breed mainly in more northern climes. They may have settled permanently in what was originally only a winter area or a relay station on a long migration.

Occasionally invasions seem to have 'taken' in the same way, as in the case of certain sand-grouse and cross-bill populations, which may have gone to the Mediterranean, settled there and lost contact with their relatives. However, such periodic invasions seldom lead to any lasting extension of habitat, as displaced populations usually die out.[1]

1. Bird migrations have doubtless exerted a considerable influence on the distribution of certain plants by disseminating seeds over a vast region. This is particularly true of aquatic plants, for ducks and shore-birds often have on their feet dry mud containing small seeds which are thus carried a great distance. Charles Darwin showed this a century ago. It is also true of aquatic Crustacea and even of small adult molluscs (including *Vitrina pellucida*).

Doctors have found that migrants may have an important part in the spread of epidemics. Recent research has shown that they play an essential rôle as a circulating virus reservoir available to mosquitoes or as tick hosts. This would explain the appearance of scattered centres of infection. Viruses could be easily transported by swallows, which live near man, and by shore-birds which could infect mosquitoes. In the western hemisphere diseases of domestic animals and Saint Louis encephalitis are among those that could be carried by migrant birds, which thus have an important influence on epidemiology.

CONCLUSION

Since the dawn of history man has been fascinated by the disappearance and return of birds and has invented countless legends and theories to account for them. In the past fifty years significant strides have been made towards solving these mysteries, but what we have learned about orientation, the physiology of the migratory impulse and the fundamental causes of migration is still like a few guide posts planted in an almost virgin forest.

Nevertheless, the results recently obtained give us cause to hope that much more will be discovered within the next few years. Hasty generalizations must be avoided, and the application to all birds of what is known about the behaviour of a few species could lead to errors that would impede further study. Furthermore, the migratory phenomenon is certainly not unique, and it must have appeared many times during the course of avian evolution because we are in the presence of a vast number of convergences which are not all governed by the same laws.

Birds are characterized by psychological behaviour that is usually stereotyped and set in the framework of a species or a systematic group. When they are confronted by unforeseen circumstances, their habits usually do not permit quick adaptation. It is evident from experiments and observations pertaining to the biology of reproduction that in most cases the bird reacts like a well-regulated machine, one which requires definite combinations in order to function. From this point of view the bird's behaviour is much more inflexible than that of a mammal, which is more subtle in its reactions.

It would, however, be a mistake to extend these conclusions to relationships between birds and their physical environment. The study of ecology shows that birds reveal extraordinary gifts of adaptation. Some types, often archaic forms, are closely linked to a definite biotope and die out rather than adapt themselves to a natural or artificial evolution inside a new environment. But the majority adapt themselves to change and can modify their feeding requirements sufficiently to settle in alien biotopes.

Migrations must be considered in the framework of ecology, of which they constitute only one aspect. They represent a reaction of the animal to changing environmental factors, a reaction whose origin and relative stability we do not know, but which is a plain fact. Behaviour varies according to the types of birds, and very slight influences may transform it completely. Here again unknown factors are involved.

Subtle variations occur in groups and species, but migration cannot be regarded as a characteristic of species – it belongs in the framework of *populations*. Every group of individuals in a given avian species, and inhabiting an area determined by geography, climate, food and doubtless other elements, migrates independently and in a manner often different from that of other populations. Here we agree with Isakov (1949), who stated that every avian species forms a mosaic of elementary populations, some of whose members breed side by side, migrate together, and even spend the winter in the same district.[1] The existence of these micropopulations, which also occur among some species of fishes, alone can explain migration among birds.

Perceptible differences occasionally occur within a single population. In partial migrations some individuals are sedentary, whereas others – even from the same brood – leave to avoid the cold, drought or rain season which their relatives withstand easily. These differences are determined by age, sex, and also by the 'mood' of the individual, a term which designates the bird's physiological state.

All of this reveals that we must be on guard against the over-simplified explanations which have been advanced ever since mankind became interested in ornithology. Migrations, like birds themselves, are multiple and involve a number of very different elements which cannot be reduced to a rigid formula.

1. Austin's work at Cape Cod (1951) shows that this is true of the common tern (*Sterna hirundo*). He calls the phenomenon *group adherence* and shows by recoveries of banded birds that the young migrate together the first year, and that this association seems to last throughout life. Serventy (*in litt.*) found the same to be true of the Australasian gannet (*Morus serrator*). Ducks and many other groups have the same pattern.

Bibliography

THE LIST of works cited below contains only a fraction of the articles and reports devoted to bird migrations. A complete bibliography would fill a volume.

We have not included the classical monographs dealing with various parts of the world, although they are full of interesting information. A. C. Bent's *Life Histories of North American birds* (1919–1958), D. A. Bannerman's *Birds of Tropical West Africa*, which covers Africa and the numerous European faunas, are two of these indispensable books.

A letter follows the publication date when the author published more than one work during the same year. This makes it possible to give a precise bibliographical reference.

AHLQVIST, H., and Pontus PALMGREN

1935. Ett försök att utröna sambandet mellan burfaglars flyttningsoro och väderlekslaget. *Ornis fenn.* 12:44–54.

ALDRICH, John W., and others

1949. Migration of some North American waterfowl. *U.S. Fish and Wildlife Service, Special Scientific Report* (*Wildlife*) No. 1, pp. 1–48.

ALEXANDER, Wilfred Backhouse

1938. Homing experiments with wild birds. *Proc. 8th International Ornithological Congress* (Oxford 1934), pp. 560–7.

——, and R. S. R. FITTER

1955. American land birds in Western Europe. *Brit. Birds* 48:1–14.

ALLARD, H. A.

1928. Bird migration from the point of view of light and length of day changes. *Amer. Nat.* 62:385–408.

ALLEN, Elsa Guerdrum

1951. The history of American ornithology before Audubon. *Trans. Amer. Phil. Soc.*, new ser., 41(3):387–591.

ALLEN, William H.

1948. Bird migration and magnetic meridians. *Science* 108:708.

AMADON, Dean

1948. Continental drift and bird migration. *Science* 108:705–7.

1949. Comments on recent literature. *Wilson Bull.* 61:237–8.

1953. Migratory birds of relict distribution: some inferences. *Auk* 70:461–9.

ANDERSSON, Tore

1954. Simflyttning hos skäggdopping (*Podiceps cristatus*) och grahakedopping (*P. griseigena*). *Vår Fågelv.* 13:133–42.

ANGOT, Michel
1954. Notes sur quelques oiseaux de l'archipel de Kerguelen. *Oiseau. Rev. Fr. Orn.* 24:123–7

ARELLANO, Marcos, and Paulino M. ROJAS
1956. Aves acuaticas migratorias en Mexico. Mexico: *Inst. Mex. Recursos Naturales Renovables.*

ARNHEM, R.
1957. Du comportement des oiseaux adultes vis à vis de leurs jeunes bagués au nid. *Gerfaut* 47:237–40.

ARNOULD-TAYLOR, W. E., and A. M. MALEWSKI
1955. The factor of topographical cues in bird homing experiments. *Ecology* 36:641–6.

AUDUBON, John James
1831–49. Ornithological biography. Edinburgh: Black.

AUSTIN, Oliver L., Jr.
1928. Migration-routes of the Arctic Tern (*Sterna paradisaea Brünnich*) *Bull. N. E. Bird-Banding Assoc.* 4:121–5.
1957. Notes on banding birds in Antarctica, and on the Adelie Penguin colonies of the Ross Sea Sector. *Bird-Banding* 28:1–26.

AUSTIN, Oliver L., Sr.
1951. Group adherence in the Common Tern. *Bird-Banding* 22:1–15.
1953. The migration of the Common Tern (*Sterna hirundo*) in the Western Hemisphere. *Bird-Banding* 24:39–55.

AVERILL, Charles K.
1925. The outer primary in relation to migration in the ten-primaried Oscines. *Auk* 42:353–8.
1927. Emargination of the long primaries in relation to power of flight and migration. *Condor* 29:17–18.

BAGG, Aaron M., W. W. H. GUNN, D. S. MILLER, J. T. NICHOLS, Winnifred SMITH, and F. P. WOLFARTH
1950. Barometric pressure-patterns and spring bird migration. *Wilson Bull.* 62:5–19.

BAIRD, James, Aaron BAGG, Ian C. T. NISBET, and Chandler S. ROBBINS
1959. Operation recovery report on mist-netting along the Atlantic Coast in 1958. *Bird-Banding* 30:143–71.

——, and Ian C. T. NISBET
1960. Northward fall migration on the Atlantic Coast and its relation to offshore drift. *Auk* 77:119–49.

——, Chandler S. ROBBINS, Aaron BAGG, and John V. DENNIS
1959. 'Operation Recovery'—the Atlantic coastal netting project. *Bird-Banding* 29:137–68.

BAIRD, Spencer F.
1866. The distribution and migrations of North American birds. *Amer. J. Sci.* 41(2):78–90, 184–92, 337–47.

BAKER, John R., Alan John MARSHALL, and T. H. HARRISON
1940. The seasons in a tropical rain-forest (New Hebrides). Part 5. Birds (Pachycephala). *J. Linn. Soc.* (Zool.) Lond. 41:50–70.

BALDWIN, S. Prentiss, and S. Charles KENDEIGH
1932. Physiology of the temperatures of birds. *Sci. Publ. Cleveland Mus. nat. Hist.* 3:1–196.
1938. Variations in the weight of birds. *Auk* 55:416–67.

BALL, Stanley C.
1952. Fall bird migration on the Gaspé Peninsula. *Bull. Peabody Mus.* 7:1–211.

BANZHAFT, W.
1935. Zum Zug der deutschen Fischadler (*Pandion haliaetus*). *Vogelzug* 6:183–5.

BARNES, J. A. G.
1953. The migrations of the Lesser Black-backed Gull. *Brit. Birds* 46:238–52.

BARTHOLOMEW, George A., Thomas R. HOWELL, and Tom J. CADE
1957. Torpidity in the White-throated Swift, Anna Hummingbird, and Poor-will. *Condor* 59:145–55.

BARTSCH, Paul
1952. A note on the first bird-banding in America. *Bird-Banding* 23:59–60.

BAUGHMAN, J. L.
1947. A very early notice of hawk migration. *Auk* 64:304.

BEEBE, William
1947. Avian migration at Rancho Grande in north-central Venezuela. *Zoologica* 32:153–68.

BEECHER, William John
1951. A possible navigation sense in the ear of birds. *Amer. Midl. Nat.* 46:367–84.
1952. The unexplained direction sense of vertebrates. *Sci. Mon.* 75:19–25.
1954. On Coriolis force and bird navigation. *Sci. Mon.* 79:27–31.

BELLROSE, Frank C.
1957. A spectacular waterfowl migration through Central North America. *Biol. Notes No.* 36, *State of Illinois Dept. Reg. Education. Nat. Hist. Survey Division* 1–24.
1958a. Celestial orientation by wild Mallards. *Bird-Banding* 29:75–90.
1958b. The orientation of displaced waterfowl in migration. *Wilson Bull.* 70:20–40.

——, and James G. SIEH
1960. Massed waterfowl flights in the Mississippi Flyway, 1956 and 1957. *Wilson Bull.* 72:28–59.

BENOIT, Jacques
1950. Reproduction: Caractères sexuels et hormones. Déterminisme du cycle sexuel saisonnier. In *Traité de Zoologie by* P. P. Grassé (Paris: Masson), 15:384–478.

——, and I. ASSENMACHER
1955. Le contrôle hypothalamique de l'activité préhypophysaire gonadotrope. *J. Physiol. Path. gén.* 47:427–567.

BERGMANN, Göran

1950. Zur Zugphysiologie der Drosseln (*Turdus pilaris* L., *T. merula* L. and *T. musicus* L.). Über Blutzuckerspiegel. Körpertemperatur und Einwirkung von Adrenalin. *Soc. Scient. Fenn. Comm. Biol.* 10(16):1–20.

BERLIOZ, Jacques
1950. Caractères généraux et origines des migrations. In *Traité de Zoologie*, by P. P. Grassé (Paris: Masson) 15:1074–88.

BERNDT, Rudolf, and Peter DANCKER
1960. Analyse der Wanderungen von *Garrulus glandarius* in Europa von 1947 bis 1957. *Proc. 12th International Ornithological Congress* (Helsinki, 1958), 97–109.

BERNIS, Francisco
1959. La migracion de las cigueñas españolas y de las otras cigueñas 'occidentales'. *Ardeola* 5:9–80.
1960. About wintering and migration of the Common Crane (*Grus grus*) in Spain. *Proc. 12th International Ornithological Congress* (Helsinki, 1958), 110–17.

BESSERER, Ingeburg, and Rudolf DROST
1935. Ein Beitrag zum Kapital 'Vogelzug und Elektrizität' *Vogelzug* 6:1–5.

BIERMAN, W. H., and K. H. VOOUS
1950. Birds observed and collected during the whaling expeditions of the 'Willem Barendsz' in the Antarctic, 1946–47 and 1947–48. *Ardea* 37, Suppl.: 1–123.

BISSONNETTE, Thomas Hume
1930. Studies on the sexual cycle in birds. I. Sexual maturity, its modification and possible control in the European Starling (*Sturnus vulgaris* L.). *Amer. J. Anat.* 45:289–305.
1931. Studies on the sexual cycle of birds. IV. Experimental modification of the sexual cycle in males of the European Starling (*Sturnus vulgaris* L.) by changes in the daily period of illumination and of muscular work. *J. exp. Zool.* 58:281–320.
1932. Light or exercise as factors in sexual periodicity in birds? *Science* 76:253–5.
1937. Photoperiodicity in birds. *Wilson Bull.* 49:241–70.

BLANCHARD, Barbara D., afterwards: BLANCHARD OAKESON, Barbara
1941. The White-crowned Sparrows (*Zonotrichia leucophrys*) of the Pacific seaboard: environment and annual cycle. *Univ. Calif. Publ. Zool.* 46:1–178.
1942. Migration in Pacific Coast White-crowned Sparrows. *Auk* 59:47–63.
1949. Des phénomènes physiologiques concomitants de la migration chez *Zonotrichia leucophrys*. *C.R. 13ème Congr. Int. Zool.* (Paris, 1948) pp. 400–1.
1953. Cyclic changes in liver and spleen weights in migratory White-crowned Sparrows. *Condor* 55:1–16.
1956. Liver and spleen weight cycles in non-migratory White-crowned Sparrows. *Condor* 58:45–50.

BODENSTEIN, Günther

1937. Von den Wanderungen der Seemöven (*Larus hyperboreus*, *L. marinus*, *L. argentatus*, *L. fuscus* and *L. canus*) der östlichen Ostsee, nach Beringungsergebnissen. *Schr. phys.-ökon. Ges. Königsb.* 69:223–34.

——, and Ernst SCHÜZ

1937. Rossittener Heringsmöve (*Larus f. fuscus*) am Viktoria-See Ostafrika). *Vogelzug* 8:61–2.

1944. Vom Schleifenzug des Prachttauchers (*Colymbus arcticus*). *Orn. Mber.* 52:98–105.

BOGERT, Cardine

1937. Birds collected during the Whitney South Sea Expedition. 34. The distribution and the migration of the Long-tailed Cuckoo (*Urodynamis taitensis* Sparrman). *Amer. Mus. Novit.* 933:1–12.

BONHAM, L. L. and L. V. BLAKE

1956. Radar echoes from birds and insects. *Sci. Mon.* 82:204–9.

BONT, A. F. de

1947. Le métabolisme des graisses chez les oiseaux migrateurs et sédentaires. *Gerfaut* 37:57–62.

1957. Notes sur l'hirondelle de cheminée, *Hirundo r. rustica* (L.), dans son quartier d'hiver. *Gerfaut* 47:127–33.

1960. Résultats du baguage d'oiseaux au Congo belge et au Ruanda-Urundi. *Gerfaut* 50:41–7.

BOUBIER, Maurice

1919. Les cinq éventails de migration des oiseaux de la faune paléarctique. *Bull. Soc. zool. Genève* 2:216–28.

BOUET, Georges

1935. Le problème de la migration des Cigognes blanches (*Ciconia ciconia ciconia* L.) de l'Afrique du Nord. *Oiseau. Rev. Fr. Orn.* 5:108–15.

1938a. Le problème de la migration des Cigognes blanches (*Ciconia ciconia ciconia* L.) de l'Afrique du Nord. *Proc. 8th International Ornithological Congress* (Oxford, 1934), 671–7.

1938b. Nouvelles recherches sur les Cigognes blanches de l'Afrique du Nord. Densité du peuplement des cigognes nichant au Maroc et en Tunisie. Migrations des cigognes nord-africaines. *Oiseau. Rev. Fr. Orn.* 8:20–45.

1950. La vie des cigognes. Paris: Braun.

1951. Les Cigognes blanches de l'Afrique du Nord et leurs migrations. *Proc. 10th International Ornithological Congress* (Uppsala, 1950), pp. 341–3.

BOULIÈRE, François

1948. Spring migration of the Swift. *Bird Notes* 23:77–80.

1949. Conceptions récentes sur la biologie des migrations aviennes. *C.R. 13ème Congr. Int. Zool.* (Paris, 1948), pp. 376–9.

1950. Physiologie des migrations. In *Traité de Zoologie* by P. P. Grassé (Paris: Masson), 15:1089–99.

BOYD, Hugh

1954. The 'wreck' of Leach's Petrels in the autumn of 1952. *Brit. Birds* 47:137–63.

BRACKBILL, Hervey

1956. Unstable migratory behavior in a Mockingbird. *Bird-Banding* 27:128.

BREWSTER, William

1886. Bird migration. *Mem. Nuttall Ornith. Club* No. 1.

BRICKENSTEIN-STOCKHAMMER, Caroline, and Rudolf DROST

1956. Über den Zug der europäischen Grasmücken *Sylvia a. atricapilla, borin, c. communis* und *c. curruca* nach Beringungsergebnissen. *Vogelwarte* 18:197–210.

BROEKHUYSEN, Gerrit Jeronimo

1955–6. Occurrence and movement of migratory species in Rhodesia and Southern Africa during the period 1950–53. *Ostrich* 26:99–114, 27:159–67.

1956. Moult adaptation in relation to long-distance migration. *Nature* 178:489–90.

BROLEY, Charles L.

1947. Migration and nesting of Florida Bald Eagles. *Wilson Bull.* 59(2):3–20.

BROOKS, Allan

1939. Migrations of the Skua family. *Ibis* 324–8.

BROOKS, S. C.

1934. Oceanic currents and the migration of pelagic birds. *Condor* 36(5):185–90.

BROUN, Maurice

1949. Hawks aloft: the story of Hawk Mountain. (New York: Dodd, Mead).

1951. Hawks and the weather. *Atlantic Naturalist* (Jan.–Feb.), pp. 105–12.

BROWN, Frank A., Jr., and Marie ROLLO

1940. Light and moult in Weaver Finches. *Auk* 57:485–98.

BROWNLOW, Henry Guy

1952. The design, construction and operation of Heligoland traps. *Brit. Birds* 45:387–99.

BRUNER, S. C.

1941. Calendario de la migracion de las aves en Cuba occidental. *Mem. Soc. Cubana Hist. Nat.* 15:319–25.

BULLIS, Harvey R., Jr.

1954. Trans-gulf migration, spring 1952. *Auk* 71:298–305.

——, and Frederick C. LINCOLN

1952. A trans-gulf migration. *Auk* 69:34–9.

BULLOCK, Dillman S.

1949 North American bird migrants in Chile. *Auk* 66:351–4.

BULLOUGH, W. S.

1942. The reproductive cycles of the British and continental races of the Starling (*Sturnus vulgaris* L.) *Phil. Trans.* ser. B 231:165–246.

1943. Autumn sexual behaviour and the resident habit of many British Birds. *Nature* 151:531.

1945. Endocrinological aspects of bird behaviour. *Biol. Rev.* 20:89–99.

BURCKHARDT, Dieter

1948. Sammelbericht über den Frühlingszug und die Brutperiode 1948. *Orn. Beob.* 45:205–27.

BURGER, J. Wendall

1949. A review of experimental investigations on seasonal reproduction in birds. *Wilson Bull.* 61:211–30.

BURR, Friedrich

1936. Über die jahreszeitliche Verbreitung des Maüsebussards (*Buteo b. buteo*) L. mit besonderem Vergleich einzelner Populationen. *Vogelzug* 7:17–34.

1954. Der Seidenschwanz (*Bombycilla garrulus*) in Deutschland 1946–1954. *Orn. Mitt.* 6:245–55.

BUSNEL, René G., J. GIBAN, P. GRAMET, and F. PASQUINELLY

1956. Absence d'action des ondes du radar sur la direction de vol de certains oiseaux. *C. R. Soc. Biol. Paris*, 150:18–20.

BUSS, Irven O.

1946. Bird detection by radar. *Auk* 63(3):315–18.

CADE, Tom J.

1955. Experiments on winter territoriality of the American Kestrel, *Falco sparverius*. *Wilson Bull.* 67:5–17.

CARRICK, Robert

1956. The Australian bird-banding scheme. *C.S.I.R.O. Wildlife Research* 1:26–30.

1959. The contribution of banding to Australian bird ecology. *In* Biogeography and Ecology in Australia. *Monographiae biologicae* 8:369–82.

——, W. R. WHEELER, and M. D. MURRAY

1957. Seasonal dispersal and mortality in the Silver Gull, *Larus novae hollandiae* Stephens, and Crested Tern, *Sterna bergii* Lichtenstein, in Australia. *C.S.I.R.O. Wildlife Research* 2:116–44.

CASAMAJOR, Jean

1926. Le mystérieux 'sens de l'espace' chez les Pigeons voyageurs. *Nature*, Paris, No. 2748:366–7.

CHAPIN, James Paul

1932. The birds of the Belgian Congo. Part I. *Bull. Amer. Mus. nat. Hist.* 65:(322–62).

1954. The African River Martin and its migration. *Ann. Mus. Congo Belge. Sci. Zool.*, new ser., 1:9–15.

CHAPMAN, Frank M.

1916. The travels of birds. New York: Appleton.

1926. The distribution of bird-life in Ecuador. *Bull. Amer. Mus. nat. Hist.* 55.

CLAPAREDE, E.
1903. La faculté d'orientation lointaine (sens de direction—sens de retour). *Arch. Psych.* 2:133–80.

CLARK, William C., and E. W. DAWSON
1957. The Trans-Tasman dispersal of the White-fronted Tern (*Sterna striata, Gm*). *Notornis* 7:65–9.

CLARKE, William Eagle
1912. Studies in bird migration. London: Gurney and Jackson. 2 vols.

COLE, L. J.
1933. The relation of light periodicity to the reproductive cycle migration and distribution of the Mourning Dove (*Zenaidura macroura carolinensis*). *Auk* 50:284–96.

COOCH, Graham
1955. Observations on the autumn migration of Blue Geese. *Wilson Bull.* 67:171–4.

COOKE, May Thacher
1937. Flight speed of birds. *U.S. Dept. Agr. Circ.* No. 428:1–13.
1940. Notes on speed of migration. *Bird-Banding* 11:21.
1941. Banded birds recovered in El Salvador. *Auk* 58:589–90.
1945. The Kittiwake as a transatlantic bird. *Bird-Banding* 16:58–62.

COOKE, Wells W.
1904a. The effect of altitude on bird migration. *Auk* 21:338–41.
1904b. Distribution and migration of North American Warblers. *U.S. Dept. Agr. Div. Biol. Survey Bull.* 18:1–142.
1905. Routes of bird migration. *Auk* 22:1–11.
1906. Distribution and migration of North American Ducks, Geese, and Swans. *U.S. Dept. Agr. Bur. Biol. Survey Bull.* 26:1–90.
1910. Distribution and migration of North American shorebirds. *U.S. Dept. Agr. Bur. Biol. Survey Bull.* 35:1–110.
1913. Distribution and migration of North American Herons and their allies. *U.S. Dept. Agr. Biol. Survey Bull.* 45:1–70.
1914. Distribution and migration of North American Rails and their allies. *U.S. Dept. Agr. Bull.* 128:1–50.
1915a. The Yellow-billed Loon: a problem in migration. *Condor* 17:213–14.
1915b. Bird migration. *U.S. Dept. Agr. Bull.* 185:1–47.
1915c. Distribution and migration of North American Gulls and their allies. *U.S. Dept. Agr. Bull.* 292:1–70.

COOMBES, Robert Armetage Hamilton
1950. The moult migration of the Sheld-duck. *Ibis* 92(3):405–18.

CORNWALLIS, Richard Kinnehan
1956. Autumn migration on the east coast of Britain in relation to weather. *Ardea* 44:224–31.
1957. The pattern of migration in 1955 at the east coast bird observatories. *Brit. Birds* 50:105–18.

CREUTZ, Gerhard
1941. Vom Zug des Grauen Fliegenschnäppers, *Muscicapa striata striata* (Pallas). *Vogelzug* 12:1–14.

1949. Verfrachtungen mit Kohl- und Blaumeisen (*Parus m. major* L. und *Parus c. caeruleus* L.). *Vogelwarte* 15:78–93.

CROZIER, W. J., and Ernst WOLF

1944a. Theory and measurement of visual mechanisms. -X. Modifications of the Flicker response contour and significance of the avian pecten. *J. gen. Physiol.* 27:287–313.

1944b. Flicker response contours for the sparrow and theory of the avian pecten. *J. gen. Physiol.* 27:315–24.

CULBERTSON, A. E.

1946. Occurrences of Poor-wills in the Sierran foothills in winter. *Condor* 48:158–9.

CURRY-LINDAHL, Kai

1953. Fysiologiska och klimatologiska factorer kring fagelflyttningen i Centralafrika. *Stat. Naturvet. Forsk. Arsbok.* 1951–52:143–9.

1956. Svenska faglar i Kongo. 7th Rapport annuel IRSAC, 1954:127–8.

1958. Internal timer and spring migration in an equatorial migrant. The Yellow Wagtail (*Motacilla flava*). *Arkiv. Zool.* 11 (33): 541–57.

DARLINGTON, Arnold

1951. The use of mobile observers in the study of patterns of migration. *Brit. Birds* 44:152–7.

DARLINGTON, Philip J., Jr.

1957. Zoogeography: the geographical distribution of animals. New York (John Wiley & Sons).

DATHE, Heinrich, and Joachim PROFFT

1938. Zum Zug des Kranichs (*Megalornis g. grus*) in Deutschland. *Vogelzug* 9:1–2.

DAVIS, David E.

1937. A cycle in Northern Shrike emigrations. *Auk* 54:43–9.

DAVIS, John, and Laidlaw WILLIAMS

1957. Irruptions of the Clark Nutcracker in California. *Condor* 59:297–307.

DAVIS, Leverett, Jr.

1948. Remarks on 'The physical basis of bird navigation'. *J. appl. Physics* 19:307–8.

DAVIS, T. A. W.

1954. Notes on northern migrants observed inland in British Guiana. *Ibis* 96:441–8.

DEELDER, C. L.

1949. On the autumn migration of the Scandinavian Chaffinch (*Fringilla c. coelebs* L.). *Ardea* 37:1–88.

1952. Some historical data on the relation between wind direction and migration of Chaffinches (*Fringilla coelebs* L.). *Ardea* 40:63–6.

——, and Lukas TINBERGEN

1947. Waarnemingen over de vlieghoogte van trekkende Vinken,

Fringilla coelebs L., en Spreeuwen, *Sturnus vulgaris* L. *Ardea* 35:45–78.

DELACOUR, Jean

1929. Les oiseaux migrateurs de l'Indochine française. *J. Orn. Festschr. Hartert*:71–82.

DEMENTIEV, Georges P.

1946. Les migrations transatlantiques de la Mouette tridactyle *Rissa tridactyla tridactyla* L. *Oiseau Rev. Fr. Orn.* 16:37–41.

1947. (Editor.) Seasonal distributions and migrations of birds as shown by banding results in USSR. *Trudy Byuro Kolts.* 1:1–99. (In Russian.)

1948. (Editor.) Seasonal distribution and migrations of birds as shown by banding results in USSR. *Trudy Byuro Kolts.* 2:1–269. (In Russian.)

1955. (Editor.) Migrations of Kittiwakes (*Rissa tridactyla* L.) as shown by banding results in USSR. *Trudy Byuro Kolts.* 8:22–32. (In Russian.)

——, and V. N. WUCZETICZ

1947. Seasonal distribution and migrations of Gulls as shown by banding results in USSR. *Trudy Byuro Kolts.* 1:1–31. (In Russian.)

DENNLER de la TOUR, G.

1957. El problema de la migracion de las aves considerado desde de la plata forma interamericana. *An. Parques nac.* 6:25–82.

DENNIS, John V.

1954. Meteorological analysis of occurrence of grounded migrants at Smith Point, Texas, April 17–May 17, 1951. *Wilson Bull.* 66:102–11.

DESSELBERGER, Hermann, and Georg STEINBACHER

1934. Weibliches Sexualhormon und Vogelzug. II. Kritische Bemerkungen zu der Arbeit von H. Schildmacher 'Zur Physiologie des Zugtriebes'. *Vogelzug* 5:169–72.

DEVLIN, Joseph M.

1954. Effects of weather on nocturnal migration as seen from one observation point at Philadelphia. *Wilson Bull.* 66:93–101.

DICKEY, Donald R., and A. J. VAN ROSSEM

1938. The Birds of El Salvador. *Field Mus. Nat. Hist. Zool.* ser. 23.

DIJKGRAAF, S.

1946. Over het orientatie probleem bij vogels. *Proc. Kon. Nederl. Akad. Wetensch.* 49:690–8.

DIRCKSEN, Rolf

1932. Die Biologie des Austernfischers, der Brandseeschwalbe und der Kustenseeschwalbe. *J. Orn.* 80:427–521.

DIXON, C. C.

1933. Some observations on the Albatrosses and other birds of the Southern Oceans. *Trans. roy. Canadian Inst.* 19:117–39.

DOBBEN, W. H. van

1953. Bird migration in the Netherlands. *Ibis* 95:212–34.

——, and M. F. Mörzer Bruyns
1939. Zug nach Alter und Geschlect an niederländischen Leuchttürmen. *Ardea* 28:61–79.

——, and G. F. Makking
1933. Der Einfluss der Leitlinien auf die Richtung des Herbstzuges am niederländischen Wattenmeer. *Ardea* 22:30–48.

Donker, J. K.
1959. Migration and distribution of the Wigeon, *Anas penelope* L. in Europe, based on ringing results. *Ardea* 47:1–27.

Dorst, Jean
1958. Observations ornithologiques à bord des navires météorologiques français dans l'Atlantique Nord. *Oiseau. Rev. Fr. Orn.* 28:309–23.

Douaud, Joseph
1957. Les migrations au Togo (Afrique occidentale). *Alauda* 25:241–66.

Downes, M. C., A. M. Gwynn, and P. F. Howard
1954. Banding of Giant Petrels at Heard and Macquarie Islands. *Emu* 54:257–62.

Drost, Rudolf
1925. Eine gewaltige Zugnacht auf Helgoland als Folge ungünstiger Wetterverhältnisse im Frühjahr 1924. *Orn. Mber.* 33:11–13.
1930a. Vom Zug der Amsel (*Turdus m. merula* L.). *Vogelzug* 1:74–85.
1930b. Zum Zug deutscher Stelzen (*Motacilla* L.). *Vogelzug* 1:86–8.
1930c. Zum Zuge der Ringdrossel (*Turdus torquatus torquatus* L.). *Vogelzug* 1:113–17.
1931. Zug gegen den Wind bei Finkenvögeln. *Vogelzug* 2:113–15.
1932. Wanderungen deutscher Kohlmeisen und Blaumeisen (*Parus m. major* L. und *Parus c. caeruleus* L.). *Vogelzug* 3:169–73.
1935. Vogelzug und Mondlicht. *Vogelzug* 6:26–33.
1940. Massenzug des Wespenbussards (*Pernis a. apivorus* L.) auf Helgoland. *Vogelzug* 11:191–2.
1941. Zug einer kastrierten Amsel (*Turdus m. merula* L.). *Vogelzug* 12:163.
1949. Zugvögel perzipieren Ultrakurzwellen. *Vogelwarte* 15:57–9.
1956. Geschichte der Vogelwarte Helgoland. *In* Natur und Jagd in Niedersachsen, Festschrift zum 70. Geburtstag H. Weigold. Suppl. *Beitr. Naturk. Niedersachs.*: 12–32.

——, and Lothar Schilling
1940a. Über den Lebensraum deutscher Silbermöwen, *Larus a. argentatus* Pontopp., auf Grund von Beringungsergebnissen. *Vogelzug* 11:1–22.
1940b. Über den Zug des Trauerfliegenschnäppers, *Muscicapa hypoleuca* (Pall.). *Vogelzug* 11:71–85.

——, and Ernst Schüz
1932. Vom Zug des Rotkehlschens *Erithacus r. rubecula* (L.) *Vogelzug* 3:164–9.
1940. Über den Zug der europäischen Bachstelzen (*Motacilla a. alba* L. und *M. a. yarellii* Gould). *Vogelzug* 11:145–61.

1952. Europäische Rauchschwalben (*Hirundo rustica*) in Afrika. *Vogelwarte* 16:95–8.

——, and Marianne STANISLAUS

1938. Sur la migration des Pouillots véloce, chantre et siffleur, *Phylloscopus collybita* (Vieillot), *trochilus* (L.) et *sibilatrix* (Bechstein). *Alauda* 10:264–78.

DUBIEF, Jean

1952. Les Cigognes et le Sahara. *Bull. Liaison saharienne*, No. 11:2–10.

DUNNET, G. M.

1956a. Arctic Tern, *Sterna macrura Naum*, banded in Russia and recovered in Western Australia. *C.S.I.R.O.*, *Wildlife Research* 1:134.

1956b. Common Tern, *Sterna hirundo hirundo* in Western Australia. *W. Aust. Nat.* 5:86–8.

EATON, Richard Jefferson

1933–4. The migratory movements of certain colonies of Herring Gulls (*Larus argentatus smithsonianus* Coues) in eastern North America. *Bird-Banding* 4:165–76 and 5:1–19, 70–84.

EDELSTAM, Carl, and Johannes SNELLMAN

1953. Vädrets betydelse för uppträdandet av sällsynta fagelgäster. 1:De fennoskandiska fynden av Lanius sensator. *Vår Fågelv.* 12:8–22.

EICHLER, Wolfdietrich

1934. Vom Zuge der Singdrossel (*Turdus ph. philomelos* Brehm). *Vogelzug* 5:135–43.

EIFRIG, G.

1924. Is photoperiodism a factor in the migration of birds? *Auk* 41:439–44.

EISENMANN, Eugene

1951. Northern birds summering in Panama. *Wilson Bull.* 63:181–5.

EKLUND, Carl R.

1959. Antarctic ornithological studies during the I.G.Y. *Bird-Banding* 30:114–18.

ELGOOD, J. H.

1959. Bird migration at Ibadan, Nigeria. *Ostrich*, Suppl. 3 (*Proc. 1st. Pan. Afr. Orn. Congr.*):306–16.

ELIASSON, Einar

1958. The water-loss of wind-drifted migratory birds. *Abst. Papers 12th International Ornithological Congress* (Helsinki, 1958) 7.

ELLIOTT, H. F. I.

1953. The fauna of Tristan da Cunha. *Oryx* 2:41–53.

ELLIOTT, John J.

1939. Wintering Tree-Swallows at Jones Beach fall and winter of 1937 and 1938. *Bird Lore* 41:11–16.

ELLIS, D. V.

1956. Observations on the migration, distribution and breeding of birds in the Canadian Arctic during 1954 and 1955. *Dansk orn. Foren. Tidsskr.* 50:207–30.

ERARD, Christian

1958. Sur les zones de reproduction et d'hivernage et les migrations du Goéland railleur *Larus genei* Brême. *Alauda* 26:86–104.

EYSTER, Marshall B.

1952. Mechanically recorded nocturnal unrest in captive song birds. *Abst. Papers AOU* 70 *Stat. meeting* 1952, 3.

1954. Quantitative measurement of the influence of photoperiod, temperature and season on the activity of captive songbirds. *Ecol. Monogr.* 24:1–28.

FALLA, R. A.

1934. The distribution and breeding habits of Petrels in northern New Zealand. *Rec. Auckland Inst. Mus.* 1:245–60.

1936. Arctic birds as migrants in New Zealand. *Rec. Auckland Inst. Mus.* 2:3–14.

FARNER, Donald S.

1950. The annual stimulus for migration. *Condor* 52:104–22.

1955. The annual stimulus for migration: experimental and physiologic aspects. *In* Recent studies in avian biology, pp. 198–237. *Univ. Ill. Bull.* (Urbana).

1960. Metabolic adaptations in migration. *Proc.* 12*th International Ornithological Congress* (Helsinki, 1958), pp. 197–208.

——, and L. R. MEWALDT

1953a. The recording of diurnal activity patterns in caged birds. *Bird-Banding* 24:55–65.

1953b. The relative roles of diurnal periods of activity and diurnal photoperiods in gonadal activation in male *Zonotrichia leucophrys gambelii. Experientia* 9:219–21.

1955. The natural termination of the refractory period in the White-crowned Sparrow. *Condor* 57:112–16.

——, L. R. MEWALDT, and J. R. KING

1954. The diurnal activity patterns of caged migratory White-crowned Sparrows in late winter and spring. *J. comp. physiol. Psychol.* 47:148–53.

FELL, H. Barraclough

1947. The migration of the New Zealand Bronze Cuckoo *Chalcites lucidus lucidus* (Gmelin). *Trans. roy. Soc. N. Z.* 76:504–15.

FISCHER, Richard B., and Geoffrey GILL

1946. A cooperative study of the White-throated Sparrow. *Auk* 63:402–18.

FISHER, James

1952. The Fulmar. London: Collins

——, and Ronald M. LOCKLEY

1954. Sea-birds. London (Collins).

FOG, Jorgen, and Kay W. PETERSEN

1957. Om Natravne (*Caprimulgus europaeus* L.) i dvale. *Dansk orn. Foren. Tidsskr.* 51:1–6.

FORMOSOV, A. N.

1933. The crop of Cedar nuts, invasions into Europe of the Siberian Nutcracker (*Nucifraga caryocatactes macrorhynchus*) and fluctuations in number of the Squirrel (*Sciurus vulgaris* L.). *J. Anim. Ecol.* 2:70–81.

1960. La production de graines dans les forêts de conifères de la taïga de l'U.R.S.S. et l'envahissement de l'Europe occidentale par certaines espèces d'oiseaux. *Proc.* 12*th International Ornithological Congress* (Helsinki, 1958), pp. 216–29.

FORSTER, G. H.

1955. Thermal air currents and their use in bird-flight. *Brit. Birds* 48:241–53.

FOX, F. W.

1940. Observations on the 'homing instinct' of Cowbirds (*Molothrus ater*). *Bird-Banding* 11:23.

FRANZ, Jost

1947. Jahres—und Tagesrhythmus einiger Vögel in Nordfinnland. *Z. Tierpsych.* 6:309–29.

FRANZISKET, Ludwig

1951. Über die Ursachen des Formationsfluges. *Vogelwarte* 16:48–55.

1952. Bemerkungen zum Selektionsvorteil des Schwarmzuges. *Vogelwarte* 16:119–21.

FRISCH, Karl von

1950. Bees: their vision, chemical senses and language. Ithaca: *Cornell Univ. Press.*

FRITH, H. J.

1957. Breeding and movements of Wild Duck in inland New South Wales. *C.S.I.R.O. Wildlife Research* 2:19–31.

1959. Ecology of Wild Ducks in inland Australia. *In* Biogeography and ecology in Australia. *Monographiae biologicae* 8:383–95.

GAIN, Louis

1914. La vie et les moeurs du Pingouin Adelie. 9*th International Zoological Congress* (Monaco, 1913), pp. 501–21.

GATKE, Heinrich

1891. Die Vogelwarte Helgoland. Braunschweig: J. H. Meyer.

1895. Heligoland as an ornithological observatory: the results of fifty years' experience. Edinburgh.

GAVRIN, V. F.

1957. Seasonal migrations of birds in the Bieloviez forest and its surroundings. Trudy 2. *Pribalt. Orn. Konf.* (*Acad. Sci. USSR*), pp. 108–30. (In Russian.)

G(EROUDET), P(aul)

1954. Des oiseaux migrateurs trouvés sur le glacier de Khumbu dans l'Himalaya. *Nos Oiseaux* 22:254.

GEYR VON SCHWEPPENBURG, Hans
1929. 'Zugstrassen.' Leitlinien. *Jour. Orn. Festschrift Hartert*, pp. 17–32.
1934. Warum kein Kranichzug am Bosporus. *Jour. Orn.* 82:579–93.
1936. Storchzug und Mittelmeer. *Jour. Orn.* 84:339–51.
1943. Mauserzug—Zwischenzug. *Vogelzug* 14:73–6.
1949a. Zur Theorie der Zugrichtung. *Ardea* 36:219–57.
1949b. Zuggeselligkeit. *In* Ornithologie als biologische Wissenschaft, pp. 261–8. Heidelberg: Winter.
1952. Vorteile der Zuggeselligkeit. *Vogelwarte* 16:116–19.

GIBAN, J.
1947. Données fournies par le baguage sur la biologie du Freux (*Corvus frugilegus* L.) en France et sur la migration de l'espèce en Europe occidentale. *Ann. Epiphyties*, N.S. 13:19–41.

GIESBERG, Hermann, and R. STADIE
1934. Ueber experimentelle Auslösung des Zugtriebes durch weibliches Sexualhormon. *Vogelzug* 5:173–6.

GILBERT, P. A.
1934–35. The seasonal movements and migrations of birds in eastern New South Wales. *Emu* 34:101–5, 200–9; 35:17–27.

GILLESPIE, John A.
1930. Homing instinct in Cowbirds. *Bird-Banding* 1:42.
1934. The homing instinct in the Rough-winged Swallow. *Bird-Banding* 5:43–4.

GLOVER, Brian
1952. Movements of birds in South Australia. *S. Austr. Orn.* 20:82–91.
1956a. Movements of birds in South Australia. Part II. *S. Austr. Orn.* 22:6–8.
1956b. Movements of birds. Part III. In other States. *S. Austr. Orn.* 22:25–8.

GOETHE, Friedrich, and Rudolf KUHK
1951. Beringungs—Ergebnisse an deutschen Adlern, Weihen, Milanen und Wespenbussarden (*Aquila*, *Circus*, *Milvus*, *Haliaaetus*, *Pernis*, *Pandion*). *Vogelwarte* 16:69–76.
1952. Beringungs—Ergebnisse an deutschen Wanderfalken (*Falco peregrinus*) und Baumfalken (*F. subbuteo*). *Vogelwarte* 16:104–8.

GOLDSMITH, Timothy H., and Donald R. GRIFFIN
1956. Further observations of homing terns. *Biol. Bull.* 111:235–9.

GOODBODY, Ivan M.
1956. Autumn migration on the Kintyre peninsula. *Brit. Birds* 49:417–31.

GOODWIN, Derek
1949. Notes on the migration of birds of prey over Suez. *Ibis* 91:59–63.

GOULD, John
1861. A Monograph of the Trochilidae. London.

GRABER, Richard R., and William W. COCHRAN
1959. An audio technique for the study of nocturnal migration of birds. *Wilson Bull.* 71:220–36.

GREENWAY, James C., Jr.
1958. Extinct and vanishing birds of the world. New York (Amer. Com. Int. Wildlife Protection).
GRIFFIN, Donald R.
1940. Homing experiments with Leach's Petrels. *Auk* 57:61–74.
1943. Homing experiments with Herring Gulls and Common Terns. *Bird-Banding* 14:7–33.
1944. The sensory basis of bird navigation. *Quart. Rev. Biol.* 19:15–31.
1952a. Bird navigation (appendix by E. MAYR). *Biol. Rev.* 27:359–400.
1952b. Airplane observations of Homing Pigeons. *Bull. Mus. comp. Zool. Harv.* 107:411–40.
1952c. Radioactive tagging of animals under natural conditions. *Ecology* 33:329–35.
1953. Sensory physiology and the orientation of animals. *Amer. Scient.* 41:209–44, 281.
1955. Bird navigation. *In* Recent studies in avian biology. *Univ. Ill. Bull.* (Urbana) pp. 154–97.
——, and Timothy H. GOLDSMITH
1955. Initial flight directions of homing birds. *Biol. Bull.* 108:264–76.
——, and Raymond J. HOCK
1948. Experiments on bird navigation. *Science* 107:347–9.
1949. Aeroplane observations of homing birds. *Ecology* 30:176–98.
GRINNELL, Joseph
1931. Some angles in the problem of bird migration. *Auk* 48:22–32.
GRISCOM, Ludlow
1932. The distribution of bird-life in Guatemala. *Bull. Amer. Mus. nat. Hist.* 64.
——, Alexander SPRUNT, Jr., and others
1957. The Warblers of America. New York (Devin-Adair Co.).
GRITTNER, Ilse
1941. Zugverhältnisse des europäischen Stieglitzes, *Carduelis carduelis* (L.). *Vogelzug* 12:56–73.
GROEBBELS, Franz
1928. Zur Physiologie des Vogelzuges. *Verh. Orn. Ges.* Bayern 18:44–74
1931a. Physiologische und histophysiologische Untersuchungen an Helgoländer Zugvögeln. *Proc. 7th International Ornithological Congress* (Amsterdam, 1930) pp. 152–5.
1931b. Weitere Untersuchungen über die Körpertemperatur der Zugvögel am Leuchtturm. *Vogelzug* 2:167–9.
GROSKIN, Horace
1945. Chimney Swifts roosting at Ardmore, Pennsylvania. *Auk* 62:361–70.
GROSS, Alfred Otto
1931. Snowy Owl migration 1930–31. *Auk* 48:501–11.
1940. The migration of Kent Island Herring Gulls. *Bird-Banding* 11:129–55.
1947. Cyclic invasions of the Snowy Owl and the migration of 1945–46.

Auk 64:584–601.

GROTE, Hermann

1930. Wanderungen und Winterquartiere der paläarktischen Zugvögel in Afrika. *Mitt. zool. Mus. Berl.* 16:1–116.

1931. Weitere Mitteilungen über paläarktische Zugvögel in Afrika. *Mitt. zool. Mus. Berl.* 17:406–14.

1936. Die Winterquartiere von Nachtigall und Sprosser. *Orn. Mber.* 44:97–100.

1939. Über Wanderungen des Rauhfusshühner (*Tetraonidae*) in Russland. *Vogelzug* 10:59–63.

1940. Manifestations migratoires chez des oiseaux soi-disant sédentaires. *Gerfaut* 30:14–28.

GUDMUNDSSON, Finnur

1951. The effects of the recent climatic changes on the bird life of Iceland. *Proc. 10th International Ornithological Congress* (Uppsala, 1950) pp. 502–14.

GUIRTCHITCH, Grégoire de

1933. Passage de Hérons pourprés à Sfax (Tunisie). *Oiseau Rev. Fr. Orn.* 3:838.

GUNN, William Walker Hamilton, and A. M. CROCKER

1951. Analysis of unusual bird migration in North America during the storm of April, 4–7, 1947. *Auk* 68:139–63.

HAARTMANN, Lars von

1939. Über den Herbstzug von *Numenius a. arquata* (L.) und die Witterung. *Ornis. fenn.* 16:52–67.

——, and Göran BERGMAN

1943. Der Herbstzug an zwei Orten in Südfinnland und seine Abhängigkeit von äusseren Faktoren. *Acta zool. fennica* 39:1–33.

HAMILTON, William J., III

1959. Aggressive behavior in migrant Pectoral Sandpipers. *Condor* 61:161–79.

HANN, Harry W.

1939. The relation of castration to migration in birds. *Bird-Banding* 10:122–4.

HANSSON, Göran, and Lars WALLIN

1958. Invasionen av sidensvans (*Bombycilla garrulus*) 1956–57. *Vår Fågelv.* 17:206–41.

HARPER, W. P.

1959. Roosting movements of birds and migration departures from roosts as seen by radar. *Ibis* 101:201–8.

HARRISON, Jeffery G.

1954. The effect of wind on diurnal spring migrants crossing the mouth of the Elbe. *Bull. Brit. Orn. Cl.* 74:14–21.

HARRISSON, T. H.

1931a. On the normal flight speeds of birds. *Brit. Birds* 25:86–96.

1931b. The altitude of bird migration. *Nature* 127:781–2.

Harrisson, Tom
1960. Regularity of migrant dates in Central Borneo. *Ibis* 102:472.
Hartley, P. H. Trahair
1935. A contribution to the study of sea-bird movements. *Brit. Birds* 29:203–10.
Haverschmidt, François
1936. Terugmeldingen van in Nederland geringde Ooievars (*Ciconia c. ciconia* (L.)). *Ardea* 25:112–27.
1950. Bemerkungen über den Weissen Storch (*Ciconia ciconia* (L.)) im nördlichen Zugscheidegebiet. *Orn. Beob.* 47:73–9.
1955. North American shore birds in Surinam. *Condor* 57:366–8.
Hawksley, Oscar
1949. Transatlantic Arctic Tern recoveries. *Bird-Banding* 20:185–6.
Heidemann, J.
1935. Vom Zug des Turmfalken (*Falco t. tinnunculus*) Wanderfalken (*Falco peregrinus*) und Baumfalken (*Falco s. subbuteo*) *Vogelzug* 6:11–26.
Heim de Balsac, Henri, and Tristran Heim de Balsac
1949–51. Les migrations des oiseaux dans l'ouest du continent africain. *Alauda* 17–18:129–43, 206–21; 19:19–39, 97–112, 157–71, 193–210.
Heinroth, Oskar, and Käthe Heinroth
1941. Das Heimfinde-Vermögen der Brieftauben. *J. Orn.* 89:213–56.
Hemmingsen, Axel M.
1951a. Observations on the migration of the Eastern White Stork (*Ciconia ciconia boyciana* Swinhoe). *Proc. 10th International Ornithological Congress* (Uppsala, 1950) pp. 351–3.
1951b. Observations on birds in North-Eastern China, especially the migration at Pei-tai-ho Beach. I General Part. *Spolia Zool. Mus. Hauniensis. Skrifter Univ. Zool. Mus. Kopenhavn* 11:1–227.
Helms, Carl W.
1959. Song and Tree Sparrow weight and fat before and after a night of migration. *Wilson Bull.* 244–53.
——, and William H. Drury, Jr.
1960. Winter and migratory weight and fat field studies on some North American Buntings. *Bird-Banding* 31:1–40.
Hempel, Christine
1957. Vom Zug des Steinschmätzers (*Oenanthe oenanthe*). *Vogelwarte* 19:25–36.
——, and Waltraud Reetz
1957. Der Zug von Hausrotschwanz (*Phoenicurus ochruros gibraltariensis*) und Gartenrotschwanz (*Ph. phoenicurus*) nach Beringungsergebnissen. *Vogelwarte* 19:97–119.
Hickey, Joseph J.
1956. Autumnal migration of Ducks banded in Eastern Wisconsin. *Trans. Wis. Acad. Sci. Arts Lett.* 45:59–76.
Hindwood, K. A.
1946. The White-fronted Tern (*Sterna striata*) in Australia. *Emu*

45:179–200.
1948. Migration of two species of Honeyeaters. *Emu* 47:391–3.
1956. The migration of the White-naped and Yellow-faced Honeyeaters. *Emu* 56:421–5.
1958. The Arctic Tern in Australia. *Emu* 58:259–63.

HITCHCOCK, Harold Bradford
1952. Airplane observations of homing Pigeons. *Proc. Amer. Phil. Soc.* 96:270–89.
1955. Homing flights and orientation of Pigeons. *Auk* 72:355–73.

HITCHCOCK, W. B., and R. CARRICK
1958. First report of banded birds migrating between Australia and other parts of the world. *C.S.I.R.O. Wildlife Research* 3:54–70.

——, and N. J. FAVALORO
1951. Victorian records of *Sterna striata* Gm. and *Sterna hirundo longipennis* Nordm. *Mem. Nat. Mus. Vict.* 17:207–14.

HOBBS, J. N.
1959. Migratory movements of the Swamp Harrier. *Emu* 59:87–8.

HOCHBAUM, Hans Albert
1955. Travels and traditions of Waterfowl. Minneapolis (Univ. Minnesota Press).

HODGE, C. F.
1894. The method of homing Pigeons. *Pop. Sci. Mon.* 44:758–75.

HOFFMANN, Klaus
1953. Die Einrechnung der Sonnenwanderung bei der Richtungsweisung des sonnenlos aufgezogenen Stares. *Naturwiss* 40:148.
1954. Versuche zu der im Richtungsfinden der Vögel enthaltenen Zeitschätzung. *Z. Tierpsychol.* 11:453–75.
1959a. Ueber den Einfluss verschiedener Faktoren auf die Heimkehrleistung von Brieftauben. *J. Orn.* 100:90–102.
1959b. Die Richtungsorientierung von Staren unter der Mitternachtssonne. *Z. vergl. Physiol.* 41:471–80.

HOFFMANN, Luc
1954. Premiers résultats de l'étude des migrations des Flamants de Camargue. *Alauda* 22:40–3.
1957. Le passage d'automne du Chevalier sylvain (*Tringa glareola*) en France méditerranéenne. *Alauda* 25:30–42.

HOLGERSEN, Holger
1938. Vom Zuge der norwegischen Heringsmöwen (*Larus fuscus intermedius* Schiöl.). *Vogelzug* 9:22–7.
1953. Banding shorebirds in Southern Norway. *Bird-Banding* 24:47–153.

HOWELL, Thomas R., and George A. BARTHOLOMEW
1959. Further experiments on torpidity in the Poor-will. *Condor* 61:180–5.

HUDSON, W. H.
1872. On the birds of the Rio Negro of Patagonia. *Proc. zool. Soc. Lond.* pp. 534–50.

HUGUES, A.
1907. Le jeûne chez le Martinet. *Bull. Soc. zool. Fr.* 32:106–8.

HURZELER, Ernst
1950. Kranichzug 4300 m. hoch über den Kanal. *Orn. Beob.* 47:172.

IRVING, Laurence
1960. Birds of Anaktuvuk Pass, Kobuk, and Old Crow. A study in Arctic adaptation. *U.S. Nat. Mus. Bull.* 217:1–409.

ISAKOV, I. A.
1949. (Editor.) The problem of elementary populations in birds. *Izvestia* (*Acad. Sci. USSR*) *Biol.* ser. No. 1:54–70. (In Russian.)
1957. (Editor.) Seasonal migrations of the Common Heron (*Ardea cinerea* L.) as shown by banding results in USSR. *Trudy Byuro Kolts.* 9:46–85. (In Russian.)

ISING, Gustaf
1946. Die physikalische Möglichkeit eines tierischen Orientierungssinnes auf Basis der Erdrotation. *Ark. Mat. Astr. Fys.* 32 A, No. 18:1–23.

JAEGER, Edmund C.
1948. Does the Poor-will 'hibernate'? *Condor* 50:45–6.
1949. Further observations on the hibernation of the Poor-will. *Condor* 51:105–9.

JANY, Eberhard
1959. Die Wanderungen der Wüstengrasmücke (*Sylvia deserticola* Tristram). *Bonn. Zool. Beitr.* 10:68–74.

JENNER, Charles E., and William L. ENGELS
1952. The significance of dark period in the photoperiodic response of male Juncos and White-throated Sparrows. *Biol. Bull.* 103:345–55.

JESPERSEN, Poul
1930. Ornithological observations in the North Atlantic Ocean. Danish 'Dana' Exp., 1920–22. *Dana Rep.* No. 7:1–36.
1951. La migration des Cigognes blanches (*Ciconia ciconia* (L.)) en Afrique du Nord. *Proc. 10th International Ornithological Congress* (Uppsala, 1950) pp. 344–50

JOUANIN, Christian
1952. Une invasion de Pétrels cul-blanc. *Oiseau Rev. Fr. Orn.* 22: 322–5.
1953. Note complémentaire sur les Oceanodroma leucorhoa (Vieillot) échoués en France en automne 1952. *Oiseau Rev. Fr. Orn.* 23:240–42.
1957. L'irruption en France de Mouettes tridactyles en février 1957. *Oiseau Rev. Fr. Orn.* 27:363–77.

——, and Patrice PAULIAN
1954. Migrateurs continentaux dans les îles Nouvelle Amsterdam et Kerguelen. *Oiseau Rev. Fr. Orn.* 24:136–42.

Kalela, Olavi
1950. Zur säkularen Rhythmik der Arealverängerungen europäischer Vögel und Säugetiere, mit besonderer Berücksichtigung der Uberwinterungsverhältnisse als Kausalfaktor. *Ornis fenn.* 27:1–30.

Keast, Allen
1958. Seasonal movements and geographic variations in the Australian Wood-Swallows (*Artamidae*). *Emu* 58:207–18.

Kemper, Charles A.
1958. Bird destruction at a TV tower. *Audubon Mag.* 60:270–1, 290–3.

Kendeigh, S. Charles
1934. The rôle of environment in the life of birds. *Ecol. Monogr.* 4:299–417.

Kenyon, Karl W., and Dale W. Rice
1958. Homing of Laysan Albatrosses. *Condor* 60:3–6.

Kessel, Brina
1953. Distribution and migration of the European Starling in North America. *Condor* 55:49–67.

King, James R., and Donald S. Farner
1956. Bioenergetic basis of light-induced fat deposition in the White-crowned Sparrow. *Proc. Soc. exp. Biol. N. Y.* 93:354–9.
1959. Premigratory changes in body weight and fat in wild and captive male White-crowned Sparrows. *Condor* 61:315–24.

Kipp, Friedrich A.
1936. Studien über den Vogelzug in Zusammenhang mit den Flügelbau und Mauserzyklus. *Mitt. Vogelw.* 49–80.
1942. Ueber Flügelbau und Wanderzug der Vögel. *Biol. Zbl.* 62:289–99.
1943. Beziehungen zwischen dem Zug und der Brutbiologie der Vögel. *J. Orn.* 91:144–53.
1955. Voraussetzungen und Folgeerscheinungen der Fernwanderungen bei Zugvögeln. *Acta II Congr. Int. Orn.* (Basel 1954) pp. 643–8.
1958. Zur Geschichte des Vogelzuges auf der Grundlage der Flügelanpassungen. *Vogelwarte* 19:233–42.

Kirchner, Heinrich
1937. Beitrag zur Vergesellschaftung ziehender Limicolen. *Vogelzug* 8:14–18.

Knabe, G.
1938. Ostpreussische Fischreihersiedlungen und der Zug ostpreussischer Fischreiher (*Ardea cinerea*) auf Grund sechsjähriger Bestandsaufnahmen und Beringungsergebnisse nach dem Stand vom 1 Oktober 1937. *Schr. phys.-ökon. Ges. Königsb.* 70:9–52.

——, and H. Ringleben
1938. Beringte Fischreiher (*Ardea c. cinerea* L.) aus Europa in Afrika. *Schr. phys.-ökon. Ges. Königsb.* 70:217–24.

Knorr, O. A.
1954. The effect of radar on birds. *Wilson Bull.* 66:264.

KOCH, J. C.
1934. Vogelzug unter Einfluss von Leitlinie und Windrichtung. *Vogelzug* 5:45–52.
KORTRIGHT, Francis H.
1942. The Ducks, Geese and Swans of North America. Harrisburg (Stackpole Co.) and Washington Wildlife Management Institute.
KOSKIMIES, Jukka
1948. On temperature regulation and metabolism in the Swift (*Micropus a. apus* L.) during fasting. *Experientia* 4:274–6.
1950. The life of the Swift (*Micropus apus* L.), in relation to the weather. *Ann. Acad. Sci. Fenn.* Ser. A. 4. Biol. 15:1–151.
KRAMER, Gustav
1947–48. Neue Beiträge zur Frage der Fernorientierung der Vögel. *Orn. Ber.* 1:228–38.
1949. Ueber Richtungstendenzen bei der nächtlichen Zugunruhe gekäfigter Vögel. *In* Ornithologie als biologische Wissenschaft. Heidelberg (Carl Winter): 269–83.
1950a. Orientierte Zugaktivität gekäfigter Singvögel. *Naturwiss.* 37:188.
1950b. Weitere Analyse der Faktoren, welche die Zugaktivität des gekäfigten Vogels orientieren. *Naturwiss.* 37:377–8.
1951a. Eine neue Methode zur Erforschung der Zugorientierung und die bisher damit erzielten Ergebnisse. *Proc. 10th International Ornithological Congress* (Uppsala, 1950) pp. 269–80.
1951b. Versuche zur Wahrnehmung von Ultrakurzwellen durch Vögel. *Vogelwarte* 16:55–9.
1952. Experiments on bird orientation. *Ibis* 94:265–85.
1953a. Wird die Sonnenhöhe bei der Heimfindeorientierung verwertet? *J. Orn.* 94:201–19.
1953b. Die Sonnenorientierung der Vögel. *Zool. Anz.* 17 Suppl. Verh. Dtsch. zool. Ges. Freiburg 1952. 72–84.
1954. Einfluss von Temperatur und Erfahrung auf das Heimfindevermögen von Brieftauben. *J. Orn.* 95:343–7.
1955. Ein weiterer Versuch die Orientierung von Brieftauben durch jahreszeitliche Änderung der Sonnenhöhe zu beeinflussen. Gleichzeitig eine Kritik der Theorie des Versuchs. *J. Orn.* 96:173–85.
1957. Experiments on bird orientation and their interpretation. *Ibis* 99:196–227.
1959. Recent experiments on bird orientation. *Ibis* 101:399–416.
——, J. G. PRATT, and Ursula von SAINT PAUL
1956. Directional differences in Pigeon homing. *Science* 123:329–30.
1957. Two-direction experiments with homing pigeons and their bearing on the problem of goal orientation. *Amer. Nat.* 91:37–48.
——, and E. RIESE
1952. Die Dressur von Brieftauben auf Kompassrichtung im Wahlkäfig. *Z. Tierpsychol.* 9:245–51.
——, and Ursula von SAINT PAUL

1950. Ein wesentlicher Bestandteil der Orientierung der Reisetaube: die Richtungsdressur. *Z. Tierpsychol.* 7:620–31.

1952. Heimkehrleistungen von Brieftauben ohne Richtungsdressur. *Zool. Anz.* 16 Suppl. Bd.: 172–8.

1954. Das Heimkehrvermögen gekäfigter Brieftauben. *Orn. Beob.* 51:4–12.

1956a. Weitere Erfahrungen über den 'Wintereffekt' beim Heimfindevermögen von Brieftauben. *J. Orn.* 97:353–70.

1956b. Ueber das Heimfinden von Käfigtauben über Kurzstrecken. *J. Orn.* 97:371–6.

——, and Heinrich SEILKOPF

1950. Heimkehrleistungen von Reisetauben in Abhängigkeit vom Wetter, insbesondere vom Wind. *Vogelwarte* 15:242–7.

KRÄTZIG, Heinrich

1936a. Der Frühsommerzug des Stars auf der Windenburger Ecke. *Vogelzug* 7:1–16.

1936b. Beiträge zum Zug der osbaltischen Stare. *Vogelzug* 7:112–22.

——, and Ernst SCHÜZ

1936. Ergebnis der Versetzung ostbaltischer Stare ins Binnenland. *Vogelzug* 7:163–75.

KÜCHLER, Werner

1935. Jahreszyklische Veränderungen im histologischen Bau der Vogelschildrüse. *J. Orn.* 83:414–61.

KÜHK, Rudolf

1942. Ueber Massenzug des Wespenbussards, *Pernis apivorus* (L.) in Mecklenburg, Oldenburg und der Eifel. *Vogelzug* 13:57–8.

1948. Wirkung der Regen—und Kälteperiode 1948 auf den Mauersegler, *Micropus apus* (L.). *Vogelwarte* 1:28–30.

——, and Ernst SCHÜZ

1956. Zehn Jahre Vogelwarte Radolfzell-Rossitten der Max-Planck-Gesellschaft. *Vogelwarte* 18:214–22.

KULLENBERG, Bertil

1947. Ueber Verbreitung und Wanderungen von vier *Sterna*-Arten. *Ark. Zool.* 38 A 17:1–80

1956. On the migration of palaearctic birds across the Central and Western Sahara. *Ark. Zool.* (2) 9:305–27.

KUMARI, Erik V.

1957. On the theory of flyways and migrations along wide front. Trudy 2. *Pribalt. Orn. Konf.* (*Acad. Sci. USSR*) pp. 4–26. (In Russian.)

1958. Visible migration in the east Baltic area. *Ibis* 100:503–14.

KURODA, Nagahisa

1954. Eine kurze Übersicht über die Vogelberingung in Japan. *Vogelwarte* 17:201–5.

1955. Observations on pelagic birds of the Northwest Pacific. *Condor* 57:290–300.

1957. A brief note on the pelagic migration of the Tubinares. *Misc. Reports Yamashina's Inst. Orn. Zool.* No. 11:436–49.

LACK, David

1944. The problem of partial migration. *Brit. Birds* 37:122–30, 143–50.

1953. The life of the Robin. London (Penguin Books). Revised edition.

1954. The natural regulation of animal numbers. Oxford (Clarendon Press).

1956. Swifts in a Tower. London (Methuen & Co.).

1958a. The return and departure of Swifts, *Apus apus* (L.), at Oxford. *Ibis* 100:477–502.

1958b. Migrational drift of birds plotted by radar. *Nature* 183:221–3.

1959a. Watching migration by radar. *Brit. Birds* 52:258–67.

1959b. Migration across the North Sea studied by radar. Part I. Survey through the year. *Ibis* 101:209–34.

1959c. Migration across the sea. *Ibis* 101:374–99.

1960a. The influence of weather on passerine migration. A review. *Auk* 77:171–209.

1960b. The height of bird migration. *Brit Birds* 53:5–10.

1960c. Migration across the North Sea studied by radar. Part 2. The spring departure 1956–59. *Ibis* 102:26–57.

——, and Elizabeth LACK

1953. Visible migration through the Pyrenees: an autumn reconnaissance. *Ibis* 95:271–309.

——, and Ronald M. LOCKLEY

1938. Skokholm bird homing experiments. I. 1936–37. Puffins, Storm-petrels and Manx Shearwaters. *Brit. Birds* 31:242–8.

LAVAUDEN, Louis

1929. Les migrations des oiseaux à Madagascar. *J. Orn.* Festschr. Hartert pp. 230–5.

LAW, P. G., and T. BURSTALL

1953. A.N.A.R.E.—Interim Reports No. 7 Heard Island. Antarctic Div. Dept. of external affairs, Melbourne. pp. 1–32.

LAWRENCE, Louise de Kiriline

1958. On regional movements and body weight of Black-capped Chickadees in winter. *Auk* 75:415–43.

LEBRET, T.

1947. The migration of the Teal, *Anas crecca crecca* (L.) in Western Europe. *Ardea* 35:79–131.

LENNERSTEDT, Ingvar

1958. En invasion av kentska tärnor (*Sterna sandvicensis*) pa Västkusten 1956. *Vår Fågelv.* 17:28–44.

LEWIS, Harrison F.

1937. Migrations of the American Brant (*Branta bernicla hrota*). *Auk* 54:73–95.

1939. Reverse migration. *Auk* 56:13–27.

LIBBERT, Walter

1936. Der Zug des Kranichs (*Grus grus grus*). *J. Orn.* 84:297–337.

1948. Zum Herbstdurchzug des Kranichs (*G. grus*) in Nordafrika. *Vogelwarte* 15:36–7.

1957. Massenzug des Kranichs (*Grus grus*) im Herbst 1955 und seine Ursachen, *Vogelwarte* 19:119–32.

LINCOLN, Frederick C.

1917. Bohemian Waxwing (*Bombycilla garrula*) in Colorado. *Auk* 34:341.

1926. The migration of the Cackling Goose. *Condor* 28:153–7.

1928. The migration of young North American Herring Gulls. *Auk* 45:49–59.

1930. Migratory status of Mourning Doves is proved by banding. *U.S. Dept. Agr. Yearbook* for 1930 pp. 386–8.

1935a. The Waterfowl flyways of North America. *U.S. Dept. Agr. Circ.* No. 342:1–12.

1935b. The migration of North American birds. *U.S. Dept. Agr. Circ.* No. 363:1–72.

1939. The migration of American birds. New York (Doubleday, Doran & Co.).

1944. Chimney Swift's winter home discovered. *Auk* 61:604–9.

1950. Migration of birds. *U.S. Dept. Interior Fish and Wildlife Serv. Circ.* No. 16.

1952. Migration of birds. New York (Doubleday & Co.).

LINDSDALE, Jean M., and E. L. SUMNER, Sr.

1934. Variability in weight in the Golden-crowned Sparrow. *Univ. Calif. Publ. Zool.* 40:309–20.

LIVERSIDGE, R.

1959. The place of South Africa in the distribution and migration of ocean birds. *Ostrich* Suppl. 3 (*Proc. 1st Pan Afr. Orn. Congr.*) pp. 47–67.

LOCKLEY, Ronald M.

1942. Shearwaters. London (J. M. Dent & Sons).

1948. Bird migration stations in Britain. *New Nat.* 1:165–71.

1953. On the movements of the Manx Shearwater at sea during the breeding season. *Brit. Birds* 46 (suppl): 1–48.

——, and Rosemary RUSSEL

1953. Bird ringing. London (Crosby Lockwood & Son).

LOETSCHER, Frederick W., Jr.

1955. North American migrants in the State of Veracruz, Mexico: a summary. *Auk* 72:14–54.

LOFTS, B., and Alan John MARSHALL

1957. The interstitial and spermatogenetic tissue of autumn migrants in Southern England. *Ibis* 99:621–7.

1960. The experimental regulation of Zugunruhe and the sexual cycle in the Brambling *Fringilla montifringilla*. *Ibis* 102:209–14.

LOOMIS, Leverett Mills

1921. Remarks on the migration of Southern Hemisphere Albatrosses and Petrels. *Auk* 38:527–31.

LORENZ, Konrad

1932. Beobachtungen an Schwalben anlässlich der Zugkatastrophe im September 1931. *Vogelzug* 3:4–10.

Lowery, George H., Jr.
1943. The dispersal of 21,414 Chimney Swifts banded at Baton Rouge, Louisiana, with notes on probable migration routes. *Proc. La. Acad. Sci.* 7:56–74.
1945. Trans-Gulf spring migration of birds and the coastal hiatus. *Wilson Bull.* 57:92–121.
1946. Evidence of Trans-Gulf migration. *Auk* 63:175–211.
1951. A quantitative study of the nocturnal migration of birds. *Publ. Mus. nat. Hist. Univ. Kans.* 3 No. 2:361–472.
——, and Robert J. Newman
1954. The birds of the Gulf of Mexico. *In* Gulf of Mexico, its origin, waters and marine life. *Fishery Bull.* 89 *U.S. Fish and Wildlife Serv.* Vol. 55:519–40.
1955. Direct studies of nocturnal bird migration. *In* Recent studies in avian biology. *Univ. Ill. Bull.* (Urbana) pp. 238–63.
Ludwig, Frederick B.
1942. Migration of Caspian Terns banded in the Great Lakes area. *Bird-Banding* 13:1–9.
Lyon, F.
1935. Homing instinct of Cowbirds. *Inland Bird Band. News* 7:7.

MacArthur, Robert H.
1959. On the breeding distribution pattern of North American migrant birds. *Auk* 76:318–25.
MacAtee, W. L.
1947. Torpidity in Birds. *Amer. Midl. Nat.* 38:191-206.
——, and Thomas D. Burleigh, George H. Lowery, Jr., and Herbert L. Stoddard
1944. Eastward migration through the Gulf States. *Wilson Bull.* 56:152–60.
MacCabe, Robert A.
1947. The homing of transplanted young Wood Ducks. *Wilson Bull.* 59:104–9.
MacCartan, Leontia
1958. The wreck of Kittiwakes in early 1957. *Brit. Birds* 51:253–66.
MacClure, Howe Elliot, and Masashi Yoshii
1957. The arrival of continental migrants in western Japan. *Auk* 74:359–70.
MacGill, A. R.
1947. Migrating Honeyeaters. *Emu* 47:56–7.
Mackintosh, Duncan Robert
1949. The use of thermal currents by birds on migration. *Ibis* 91:55–9.
Mackworth-Praed, Cyril Winthrop, and C. H. B. Grant
1952–55. Birds of Eastern and North Eastern Africa. London, New York, Toronto (Longmans, Green & Co.).
MacLean, Ivor, and Kenneth Williamson
1958a. Waders at Ocean Weather Ships in 1956. *Brit. Birds* 51:152–6.

1958b. Migrant land-birds in the Western approaches. *Brit. Birds* 51:351–3.

MAGEE, M. J.

1934. The distribution of Michigan recovered Eastern Evening Grosbeaks near the Atlantic Seaboard. *Bird-Banding* 5:175–81.

MALBRANT, René

1949. Les migrations de la Cigogne blanche en Afrique équatoriale française. *Oiseau Rev. Fr. Orn.* 19:113–17.

MARSHALL, Alan John

1951. The refractory period of testis rhythm in birds and its possible bearing on breeding and migration. *Wilson Bull.* 63:238–61.

1952. The condition of the interstitial and spermatogenetic tissue of migratory birds on arriving in England in April and May. *Proc. zool. Soc. Lond.* 122:287–95.

1960. The rôle of the internal rhythm of reproduction in the timing of avian breeding seasons, including migration. *Proc. 12th International Ornithological Congress* (Helsinki, 1958) pp. 475–82.

——, and D. L. SERVENTY

1956a. Moult adaptation in relation to long-distance migration in Petrels. *Nature* 177:943.

1956b. The breeding cycle of the Short-tailed Shearwater, *Puffinus tenuirostris* (Temminck), in relation to trans-equatorial migration and its environment. *Proc. zool. Soc. Lond.* 127:489–510.

1959. The experimental demonstration of an internal rhythm of reproduction in a trans-equatorial migrant (the Short-tailed Shearwater, *Puffinus tenuirostris* (Temminck). *Nature* 184: 1704–5.

——, and M. C. WILLIAMS

1959. The pre-nuptial migration of the Yellow Wagtail (*Motacilla flava* L.) from latitude 0.04′ N. *Proc. zool. Soc. Lond.* 132:313–20.

MARSHALL, F. H. A.

1936. Sexual periodicity and the causes which determine it. *Philos. Trans.* ser. B. 226:423–56.

MARSHALL, Joe T., Jr.

1955. Hibernation in captive Goatsuckers. *Condor* 57:129–34.

MASCHER, Jan W.

1955. Vädrets inverkan pa varsträckets forlopp i Mälardalen 1953. *Vår Fågelv.* 14:96–112.

MATTHEWS, Geoffrey V. T.

1948. Bird navigation. *New Nat.* 1:146–55.

1951a. The experimental investigation of navigation in homing Pigeons. *J. exp. Biol.* 28:508–36.

1951b. The sensory basis of bird navigation. *J. Inst. Navig.* 4:260–75.

1952a. The relation of learning and memory, to the orientation and homing of Pigeons. *Behaviour* 4:202–21.

1952b. An investigation of homing ability in two species of Gulls. *Ibis* 94:243–64.

1953a. Sun navigation in homing Pigeons. *J. exp. Biol.* 30:243–67.

1953b. The orientation of untrained Pigeons: a dichotomy in the homing process. *J. exp. Biol.* 30:268–76.

1953c. Navigation in the Manx Shearwater. *J. exp. Biol.* 30:370–96.

1953d. Recent developments in the study of bird navigation. *J. Inst. Navig.* 6:264-70.

1955a. An investigation of the 'chronometer' factor in bird navigation. *J. exp. Biol.* 32:39–58.

1955b. Bird navigation. Cambridge (Univ. Press) (*Cambridge monographs in experimental biology No.* 3).

MAYAUD, Noël

1952. Migration de *Turdus viscivorus* (L.) et particularités de sa reproduction. *Alauda* 20:31–8.

1954. Sur les migrations et l'hivernage de *Larus melanocephalus* Temminck. *Alauda* 22:225–45.

1955. Coup d'oeil sur les reprises en France de Buses variables, *Buteo buteo* (L.). *Alauda* 23:225–48.

1956a. Nouvelles données sur *Larus melanocephalus* Temminck. *Alauda* 24:123–31.

1956b. Etude sur la migration et les zones d'hivernage des Sternes caspiennes, *Hydroprogne caspia* (Pallas), d'Eurasie. *Alauda* 24:206–18.

1957. La migration 'en boucle' du Faucon kobez, *Falco vespertinus* (L.), en Afrique du Nord et Méditerranée. *Alauda* 25:24–9.

MAYR, Ernst

1942. Systematics and the origin of species. New York (Columbia Univ. Press).

1957. On the origin of bird migration in the Pacific. *Proc. 7th Pacif. Sci. Congr.* 4:387–94.

——, and Wilhelm MEISE

1930. Theoretisches zur Geschichte des Vogelzuges. *Vogelzug* 1:149–72.

MEINERTZHAGEN, Richard

1919. A preliminary study of the relation between geographical distribution and migration with special reference to the Palaearctic region. *Ibis* 379–92.

1920. Some preliminary remarks on the altitude of the migratory flight among birds with special reference to the Palaearctic region. *Ibis* 920–36.

1921. Some preliminary remarks on the velocity of migratory flight among birds with special reference to the Palaearctic region. *Ibis* 228–38.

1951. Review of the Alaudidae. *Proc. zool. Soc. Lond.* 121:81–132.

1955. The speed and altitude of bird flight (with notes on other animals). *Ibis* 97:81–117.

1956. Birds in Greenland. *Bull. Brit. Orn. Cl.* 76:17–22.

MEISE, Wilhelm

1933. Kinaesthetisches Gedächtnis und Fernorientierung der Vögel. *Vogelzug* 4:101–13.

MENNER, Erich

1938. Die Bedeutung des Pecten im Auge des Vogels für die Wahrnehmung von Bewegungen, nebst Bemerkungen über seine Ontogenie und Histologie. *Zool. Jahr. Abt. allg. Zool. Physiol. Tiere.* 58:481–538.

MENNIG, S.

1939. A propos de l'engourdissement des Hirondelles. *Gerfaut* 29:107.

MERKEL, Friedrich Wilhelm

1937. Zur Physiologie des Vogelzugtriebes. *Zool. Anz.* 117:297–308.

1938. Zur Physiologie der Zugunruhe bei Vögeln. *Ber. Ver. schles. Orn.* 23, Sonderheft 1–72.

1940. Neuere Untersuchungen über die Ursachen des Vogelzug-Triebes. *Natur u. Volk* 70:167–78.

1956. Untersuchungen über tages—und jahres—periodische Aktivitätsänderungen bei gekäfigten Zugvögeln. *Z. Tierpsychol.* 13:278–301.

1958a. Untersuchungen zur künstlichen Beeinflussung der Aktivität gekäfigter Zugvögel. *Vogelwarte* 19:173–85.

1958b. Untersuchungen über Tages—und Jahres periodische Änderungen im Energiehaushalt gekäfigter Zugvögel. *Z. vergl. Physiol.* 41:154–78.

1960. Zur Physiologie der Zugunruhe nächtlich ziehender Kleinvögel: eine Arbeitshypothese. *Proc. 12th International Ornithological Congress* (Helsinki, 1958) pp. 507–12.

——, and H. G. FROMME

1958. Untersuchungen über das Orientierungsvermögen nächtlich ziehender Rotkehlchen (*Erithacus rubecula* L.). *Naturwiss.* 45: 499–500.

MIDDENDORFF, A. von

1855. Die Isepiptesen Russlands. Grundlagen zur Erforschung der Zugzeiten und Zugrichtungen der Vögel Russlands. *Mém. Acad. Imp. Sci. St Pétersbourg* 6 ser. Part 2, Sci. nat. 8:1–143.

MILDENBERGER, Heinz

1950. Messungen von Höhe und Geschwindigkeit ziehender Vögel (*Columba palumbus, Corvus frugilegus, Grus grus*). *Bonn. Zool. Beitr.* 1:55–7.

MILLER, Alden Holmes

1948a. The refractory period in light-induced reproductive development of Golden-crowned Sparrows. *J. exp. Zool.* 109:1–11.

1948b. Potentiality for testicular recrudescence during the annual refractory period of the Golden-crowned Sparrow. *Science* 109:546.

1950. Temperatures of Poor-wills in the summer seasons. *Condor* 52:41–2.

1951. Further evidence on the refractory period in the reproductive cycle of the Golden-crowned Sparrow, *Zonotrichia coronata. Auk* 68:380–3.

1954. The occurrence and maintenance of the refractory period in

Crowned Sparrows. *Condor* 56:13–20.
1957. Migratory flight of a *Zonotrichia* at 10,000 feet above ground level. *Condor* 59:209–10.

MISKIMEN, Mildred
1955. Meteorological and social factors in autumnal migration of Ducks. *Condor* 57:179–84.

MISONNE, Xavier
1953. Les grands quartiers d'hiver du Sud-Est de la Mer Caspienne. *Gerfaut* 43:103–27.
1954. Note complémentaire sur les oiseaux de la côte Caspienne. *Gerfaut* 44:88–91.
1955. La migration d'automne dans le Kurdistan oriental. *Gerfaut* 45:33–67.

MONTGOMERY, K. C., and Eric G. HEINEMANN
1952. Concerning the ability of homing Pigeons to discriminate patterns of polarized light. *Science* 116:454–6.

MOREAU, Reginald Ernest
1931. Equatorial reflections on periodism in birds. *Ibis* 553–70.
1938. Bird migration over the north-western part of the Indian Ocean, the Red Sea, and the Mediterranean. *Proc. zool. Soc. Lond.* 108 A:1–26.
1952. The place of Africa in the palaearctic migration system. *J. Anim. Ecol.* 21:250–71.
1953. Migration in the Mediterranean area. *Ibis* 95:329–64.
1956. The Iberian peninsula and migration. *Bird Study* 3:1–25.
1959. Les problèmes de la migration à travers le Maroc. *Alauda* 27:81–96.

——, A. L. WILK, and William ROWAN
1947. The moult and gonad cycles of three species of birds at five degrees south of the Equator. *Proc. zool. Soc. Lond.* 117:345–64.

MORLEY, Averil
1943. Sexual behaviour in British birds from October to January. *Ibis* 85:132–58.

MULLER, Horst
1959. Die Zugverhältnisse der europäischen Brandseeschwalben (*Sterna sandvicensis*) nach Beringungsergebnissen. *Vogelwarte* 20:91–115.

MURPHY, Robert Cushman
1936. Oceanic birds of South America. New York (Macmillan; Amer. Mus. Nat. Hist. 2 vols.

——, and William VOGT
1933. The Dovekie influx of 1932. *Auk* 50:325–49.

NATORP, Otto
1932. Rückzugbeobachtung im Frühjahr 1931. *Vogelzug* 3:72–4.

NICE, Margaret M.
1937. Studies in the life history of the Song Sparrow. *Trans. Linn. Soc. New York* 4:6:1–247.

NIETHAMMER, Günther

1937. Über die Beziehungen zwischen Flügellänge und Wanderstrecke bei einigen europäischen Singvögeln. *Arch. Naturgesch.* 6:519–25.

——, and J. LAENEN

1954. Hivernage au Sahara. *Alauda* 23:25–31.

NISBET, Ian Christopher Thomas

1957. Passerine migration in South Scandinavia in the autumn of 1954. *Ibis* 99:228–68.

NORRIS, Robert A., Clyde E. CONNELL, and David W. JOHNSTON

1957. Notes on fall plumages, weights and fat condition in the Ruby-throated Hummingbird. *Wilson Bull.* 69:155–63.

OAKESON.—Formerly BLANCHARD, Barbara. See BLANCHARD, Barbara D.

OBERHOLSER, H.

1923a. The migration of North American birds. 21. Orchard Oriole. *Bird Lore* 25:119–20.

1923b. The migration of North American birds. 22. Bullock's Oriole and Hooded Orioles. *Bird Lore* 25:243–4.

1923c. The migration of North American birds. 23. Scott's Oriole and Audubon's Oriole. *Bird Lore* 25:388–9.

ODUM, Eugene P.

1949. Weight variations in wintering White-throated Sparrows in relation to temperature and migration. *Wilson Bull.* 61:3–14.

1958. The fat deposition picture in the White-throated Sparrow in comparison with that in long-range migrants. *Bird-Banding* 29:105–8.

1960. Lipid deposition in nocturnal migrant birds. *Proc. 12th International Ornithological Congress* (Helsinki, 1958) pp. 563–76.

——, and Jesse D. PERKINSON, Jr.

1949. The relation of lipid metabolism to migration in birds. *J. Tenn. Acad. Sci.* 24:169.

——, and James C. MAJOR

1956. The effect of diet on photoperiod-induced lipid deposition in the White-throated Sparrow. *Condor* 58:222–8.

OHLENDORF, Albert

1933. Wie vollzieht sich zeitlich der Abzug der jungen und alten Störche (*Ciconia c. ciconia* L.)? *Vogelzug* 4:118–24.

OLIVARES, Antonio

1959. Aves migratorias en Colombia. *Rev. Acad. Colomb.* 10, No. 41:371–442.

OLIVER, W. R. B.

1955. New Zealand birds. Wellington (Reed), 2nd edition.

OLSSON, Viking

1958. Dispersal, migration, longevity and death causes of *Strix aluco*, *Buteo buteo*, *Ardea cinerea* and *Larus argentatus*. *Acta Vertebratica* 1, No. 2:91–189.

OORDT, G. J. van

1949. Vogeltrek. Leiden (Brill), 3rd ed.

1959. The reactions of the gonads to lengthening days in northern birds migrating far beyond the Equator. *Ostrich*, Suppl. 3 (*Proc. 1st Pan. Afr. Orn. Congr.*) pp. 342–5.

——, and J. P. KRUIJT

1953. On the pelagic distribution of some Procellariiformes in the Atlantic and southern oceans. *Ibis* 95:615–37.

ORGEL, Arthur R., and James C. SMITH

1954. Test of the magnetic theory of homing. *Science* 120:891–2.

OTTERLIND, Gunnar

1954. Flyttning och utbredning. Ett bidrag till kännedomen om den skandinaviska fagelfaunans utbredningsdynamik. *Vår Fågelv.* 13:1–31, 83–113, 147–67, 245–61.

PACKARD, Fred Mallery

1946. Midsummer wandering of certain Rocky Mountain birds. *Auk* 63:152–8.

PAIGE, S.

1948. On continental drift and bird migration. *Science* 108:711.

PALMGREN, Pontus

1935. Ein einfacher Apparat zur Registrierung der Intensitäts—variation der Zugunruhe bei gekäfigten Zugvögeln. *Ornis fenn.* 12:55–8.

1936. Warum ziehen die Vögel des Nachts? *Ornis fenn.* 13:41–9.

1937. Auslösung der Frühlingszugunruhe durch Wärme bei gekäfigten Rotkehlchen, *Erithacus rubecula* (L.). *Ornis fenn.* 14:71–3.

1938. Studien über den zeitlichen Ablauf der Zugerregung bei gekäfigten Kleinvögeln. I. *Ornis fenn.* 15:1–16.

1943. Eine Anlage für Registrierung der Tagesrhythmik bei Käfigvögeln. *Vogelzug* 14:12–18.

1949a. On the diurnal rhythm of activity and rest in birds. *Ibis* 91: 561–76.

1949b. Studien über die Tagesrhythmik gekäfigter Zugvögel. *Z. Tierpsychol.* 6:44–86.

PANOUSE, Jean B.

1949. Les migrations des cigognes marocaines. *Bull. Soc. Sci. Nat. Maroc* 29:217–27.

1951. Sur les migrations des Cigognes blanches d'Europe occidentale et du Maroc. *C. R. Acad. Sci.* 232:557–9.

PAULIAN, Patrice

1953. Pinnipèdes, cétacés, oiseaux des îles Kerguelen et Amsterdam. *Mém. Inst. Sci. Madagascar* A 8:111–234.

1956. Addition à l'avifaune de l'île Amsterdam. *Oiseau Rev. Fr. Orn.* 26:65–6.

PEARSON, Olivier P.

1950. The metabolism of Hummingbirds. *Condor* 52:145–52.

PEIPONEN, Valto

1957. Wechselt der Birkenzeisig. *Carduelis flammea* (L.), sein Brutgebiet während des Sommers? *Ornis fenn.* 34:41–64.

PERDECK, A. C.

1958. Two types of orientation in migrating Starlings, *Sturnus vulgaris* (L.), and Chaffinches, *Fringilla coelebs* (L.), as revealed by displacement experiments. *Ardea* 46:1–37.

PETERSON, Roger T., and James FISHER

1955. Wild America. Boston (Houghton Mifflin Co.).

PHILIPPI, Rodolfo

1940. Aves migratorias Norte-americanas que visitan Chile. *Bol. Mus. Nac. Hist. Nat. Santiago* 18:65–85.

PICHON, Robert, and Marcel BON SAINT COME

1952. Note complémentaire sur l'avifaune des Antilles françaises. *Oiseau Rev. Fr. Orn.* 22:113–19.

PLATT, C. S., and Robert S. DARE

1945. The homing problem in Pigeons. *Science* 101:439–40.

POLIVANOV, V. M.

1957. Seasonal distribution and some notes on the biology of the Starling (*Sturnus vulgaris* L.) as shown by banding results. *Trudy Byuro Kolts.* 9:215–41. (In Russian.)

PRATT, J. G.

1953. The homing problem in Pigeons. *J. Parapsychol.* 17:34–60.

1955. An investigation of homing ability in Pigeons without previous homing experience. *J. exp. Biol.* 32:70–83.

——, and R. H. THOULESS

1955. Homing orientation in pigeons in relation to opportunity to observe the sun before release. *J. exp. Biol.* 32:140–57.

——, and H. G. WALLRAFF

1958. Zwei—Richtungs—Versuche mit Brieftauben: Lanstreckenflüge auf der Nord-Süd-Achse in West-Deutschland. *Z. Tierpsychol.* 15:332–9.

PRECHT, H., and others

1956. Einige Versuche zum Heimfindevermögen von Vögeln. *J. Orn.* 97:377–83.

PREVOST, Jean, and R. VINCENT

1957. Baguage du Manchot Empereur. Solution pour une étude éthologique. *Oiseau Rev. Fr. Orn.* 27:150–4.

PRILL, A. G.

1931. A land migration of Coots. *Wilson Bull.* 43:148–9.

PROMPTOV, A. N.

1934. (Editor.) The evolutionary significance of bird migration. *Zool. Journ.* 13:409–36. (In Russian; German summary).

1949. (Editor). Seasonal migration of birds as a physiological problem. *Izvestia* (*Acad. Sci. USSR*), Ser. Biol. pp. 30–9. (In Russian.)

PUMPHREY, R. J.

1948. The sense organs of birds. *Ibis* 90:171–99.

PUTZIG, P.

1937. Von der Beziehung des Zugablaufs zum Inkretdrüsensystem. *Vogelzug* 8:116–30.

1938a. Beobachtungen über Zugunruhe beim Rotkehlchen (*Erithacus rubecula*). *Vogelzug* 9:10–14.

1938b. Über das Zugverhalten umgesiedelter englischer Stockenten (*Anas p. platyrhyncha* L.). *Vogelzug* 9:139–45.

1938c. Weitere Versuche über die Beziehungen der Keimdrüsen zum Zugverhalten. *Vogelzug* 9:189–200.

1938d. Der Frühwegzug des Kiebitzes (*Vanellus vanellus* L.) unter Berücksichtigung anderer Limicolen. Seine Physiologie und Bedeutung für das Problem Zugtriebauslösung. *J. Orn.* 86: 123–65.

1938e. Die Wanderungen des Eichelhähers (*Garrulus glandarius* L.) im Lichte neuerer Ergebnisse. *Schr. phys.-ökon. Ges. Königsb.* 70:189–216.

1939a. Keimdrüsen und Heimzug. *Ber. Ver. Schles. Orn.* 24:36–41.

1939b. Beiträge zur Stoffwechselphysiologie des Zugvogels. *Vogelzug* 10:139–54.

PYNNÖNEN, Alpi

1957. Über die Orientierung beim Zug einiger Stelzvögel. *Ann. Zool. Soc. Zool. Bot. Fennicae* 'Vanano' 18 No. 8:1–23.

RABAUD, Etienne

1928. How animals find their way about. A study of distant orientation and place recognition. London.

RAND, Austin L.

1936. The distribution and habits of Madagascar birds. *Bull. Amer. Mus. nat. Hist.* 72:143–499.

RANKIN, M. Neal, and Eric A. G. DUFFEY

1948. A study of the bird life of the North Atlantic. *Brit. Birds* 41 (suppl.) 1–42.

RAUTENBERG, Werner

1957. Vergleichende Untersuchungen über den Energiehaushalt des Bergfinken (*Fringilla montifringilla* L.) und des Haussperlings (*Passer domesticus* L.) *J. Orn.* 98:36–64.

RAWSON, Kenneth S.

1954. Sun compass orientation and endogenous activity rhythms of the Starling (*Sturnus vulgaris* L.). *Z. Tierpsychol.* 11:446–52.

——, and Anne M. RAWSON

1955. The orientation of Homing Pigeons in relation to change in sun declination. *J. Orn.* 96:168–72.

RAYNOR, Gilbert Sidney

1956. Meteorological variables and the northward movement of nocturnal land bird migrants. *Auk* 73:153–75.

REINIKAINEN, Antti

1937. The irregular migrations of the Crossbill, *Loxia c. curvirostra*, and their relation to the cone-crop of the conifers. *Ornis fenn.* 14:55–64.

REITZ, R.
1954. Birds meet with disaster at the Brunswick Naval Air Station. *Bull. Me. Aud. Soc.* 10:61–2.
RENDAHL, Hialmar
1960. Über den Zug der nordischen Sylviinen. *Vogelwarte* 20:222–32.
——, and Greta VESTERGREN
1958. Über die Zugverhältnisse bei schwedischen Gartenrotschwänzen (*Ph. phoenicurus* L.). *Vogelwarte* 19:256–65.
RIABOV, V. F.
1955. (Editor.) Bird Banding in USSR. *Trudy Byuro Kolts.* 8:5–10. (In Russian.)
——, and T. P. SCHEVAREVA
1955. (Editor.) Results of banding of Rooks. *Trudy Byuro Kolts.* 8:104–22. (In Russian.)
RICHDALE, Lancelot Eric
1951. Banding and marking Penguins. *Bird-Banding* 22:47–54.
RIDDLE, Oscar, Guinevere C. SMITH, and Francis C. BENEDICT
1932. The basal metabolism of the Mourning Dove and some of its hybrids. *Amer. J. Physiol.* 101:260–7.
RILEY, Gardner M.
1940. Light versus activity as a regulator of the sexual cycle in the House Sparrow. *Wilson Bull.* 52:73–86.
ROBERTS, B. B.
1932. On the normal flight-speed of birds. *Brit. Birds* 25:220–2.
ROBERTS, Brian
1940. The life cycle of Wilson's Petrel, *Oceanites oceanicus* (Kuhl). *Sci. Rep. Brit. Graham Land Exp.* 1934–37. 1, No. 2:141–94.
ROBERTSON, J. S.
1957. Migrating Shearwaters. *Emu* 57:191–7.
1958. Yellow-faced Honeyeater migration. *Emu* 58:370–4.
ROLLO, Marie
1941. Photoperiodism and migration. *Bird-Banding* 12:161–4.
——, and L. V. DOMM
1943. Light requirements of the Weaver Finch. I. Light period and intensity. *Auk* 60:357–67.
ROUGEOT, Pierre Claude
1959. Sur la migration du Fou du Cap, *Morus capensis* Falk (1823), le long des côtes du Gabon. *Ostrich*, Suppl. 3 (*Proc. 1st Pan. Afr. Orn. Congr.*) pp. 331–2.
ROUX, Francis
1959. Captures de migrateurs paléarctiques dans la Basse Vallée du Sénégal. *Bull. Mus. Paris* 2ème ser. 31:334–40.
ROWAN, William
1926. On photoperiodism, reproductive periodicity, and the annual migrations of birds and certain fishes. *Proc. Boston Soc. Nat. Hist.* 38:147–89.
1927. Migration and reproductive rhythm in birds. *Nature* 119:351–2.
1929. Experiments in bird migration. I. Manipulation of the repro-

ductive cycle: Seasonal histological changes in the gonads. *Proc. Boston Soc. Nat. Hist.* 39:151–208.

1930. Experiments in bird migration. II. Reversed migration. *Proc. Nat. Acad. Sci.* 16:520–5.

1931. The riddle of migration. Baltimore (Williams and Wilkins Co.).

1932. Experiments in bird migration. III. The effects of artificial light, castration and certain extracts on the autumn movement of the American Crow (*Corvus brachyrhynchos*). *Proc. Nat. Acad. Sci.* 18:639–54.

1946. Experiments in bird migration. *Trans. roy. Soc. Can.* (3) 40, 5:123–35.

——, and A. M. Batrawi

1939. Comments on the gonads of some European migrants collected in East Africa immediately before their spring departure. *Ibis* 58–65.

Rudebeck, Gustaf

1950. Studies on bird migration. *Vår Fågelv.* Suppl. 1:1–148.

1956. Some aspects of bird migration in the Western palaearctic region. *In* Bertil Hanström. Zoological papers in honour of his sixty-fifth birthday. Lund, pp. 257–68.

Rüppell, Werner

1931. Zug der jungen Störche (*Ciconia c. ciconia* L.) ohne Führung der Alten? *Vogelzug* 2:119–22.

1934a. Versuche zur Ortstreue und Fernorientierung der Vögel. II. Verfrachtungsversuche am Star (*Sturnus vulgaris* L.) u.a. Art von W. Schein. Winsen. *Vogelzug* 5:53–9.

1934b. Versuche zur Ortstreue und Fernorientierung der Vögel. III. Heimfinde-Versuche mit Rauchschwalben (*Hirundo rustica* L.) und Mehlschwalben (*Delichen urbica*) von H. Warnat (Berlin-Charlottenburg). *Vogelzug* 5:161–6.

1935. Heimfindeversuche mit Staren 1934. *J. Orn.* 83:462–524.

1936. Heimfindeversuche mit Staren und Schwalben 1935. *J. Orn.* 84:180–98.

1937. Heimfindeversuche mit Staren, Rauchschwalben, Wendehälsen, Rotrückwürgern und Habichten (1936). *J. Orn.* 85: 120–35.

1938a. Heimfindeversuche mit Staren und Schwalben 1934. Eine Zusammenfassung. *Proc. 8th International Ornithological Congress* (Oxford, 1934) pp. 529–35.

1938b. Planbeobachtung und Beringung von *Larus ridibundus* in europäischen Winterquartieren. *C.R. 9ème Congrès Ornithologique International* (Rouen, 1938) pp. 271–8.

1940. Neue Ergebnisse über Heimfinden beim Habicht. *Vogelzug* 11:58–64.

1942. Versuch einer neuen Storchzugkarte. *Vogelzug* 13:35–9.

1944. Versuche über Heimfinden ziehender Nebelkrähen nach Verfrachtung. *J. Orn.* 92:106–32.

1948. Heimkehr verfrachteter Habichte (*Accipiter gentilis*) aus 300 und 600 km Entfernung. *Vogelwarte* 15:39.

——, and Alfred SCHIFFERLI

1939. Versuche über Winter-Ortstreue an *Larus ridibundus* und *Fulica atra*. 1935. *J. Orn.* 87:224–39.

——, and Ernst SCHÜZ

1948. Ergebnis der Verfrachtung von Nebelkrähen (*Corvus corone cornix*) während des Wegzuges. *Vogelwarte* 15:30–6.

RYDZEWSKI, Wladyslaw

1951. A historical review of bird marking. *Dansk. orn. Foren. Tidsskr.* 45:61–95.

1956. The nomadic movements and migrations of the European Common Heron, *Ardea cinerea* L. *Ardea* 44:71–188.

SABINE, Winifred S.

1955. The winter society of the Oregon Junco: the flock. *Condor* 57:88–111.

SAINT PAUL, Ursula von

1953. Nachweis der Sonnerorientierung bei nächtlich ziehenden Vögeln. *Behaviour* 6:1–7.

1956. Compass directional training of Western Meadowlarks (*Sturnella neglecta*). *Auk* 73:203–10.

1958. Neue experimentelle Ergebnisse über Fernorientierung der Tiere. *Vogelwarte* 19:193–8.

SALOMONSEN, Finn

1948. The distribution of birds and the recent climatic change in the North Atlantic area. *Dansk. orn. Foren. Tidsskr.* 42:85–99.

1951. The immigration and breeding of the Fieldfare (*Turdus pilaris* L.) in Greenland. *Proc. 10th International Ornithological Congress* (Uppsala, 1950) pp. 515–26.

1953. Fugletraekket og dets gåder. Copenhagen (Ejnar Munksgaard).

1955. The evolutionary significance of bird-migration. *Dan. Biol. Medd.* 22 No. 6:1–62.

——, and GITZ-JOHANSEN

1950–51. Grønlands Fugle. The birds of Greenland. Copenhagen (Ejnar Munksgaard). 3 vols.

SAPIN-JALOUSTRE, Jean

1952. Découverte et description de la rookery de Manchot Empereur (*Aptenodytes forsteri*) de Pointe Géologie (Terre Adélie). *Oiseau Rev. Fr. Orn.* 22:143–84, 225–60.

SAUER, Franz

1956. Zugorientierung einer Mönchsgrasmücke (*Sylvia a. atricapilla* L.) unter künstlichem Sternenhimmel. *Naturwiss.* 43:231–2.

1957a. Astronavigatorische Orientierung einer unter künstlichem Sternenhimmel verfrachteten Klappergrasmücke, *Sylvia c. curruca* L. *Naturwiss.* 44:71.

1957b. Die Sternorientierung nächtlich ziehender Grasmücken (*Sylvia atricapilla, borin* und *curruca* L.) *Z. Tierpsych.* 14:29–70.

1958a. Zur Sternenorientierung nächtlich ziehender Grasmücken. *Zool. Anz.* 21 Suppl. *Verhandl. Deutsch. Zool. Ges. Graz* 1957. pp. 280–8.

1958b. Celestial navigation by birds. *Sci. Amer.* 199:42–7.

——, and Eleonore SAUER

1955. Zur Frage der nächtlichen Zugorientierung von Grasmücken. *Rev. Suisse Zool.* 62:250–9.

1959. Nächtliche Zugorientierung europäischer Vögel in Südwestafrika. *Vogelwarte* 20:4–31.

1960. Zugvögel aus der paläarktischen und afrikanischen Region in Südwestafrika. *Bonn Zool. Beitr.* 11:41–86.

SAUNDERS, Aretas A.

1959. Forty years of spring migration in Southern Connecticut. *Wilson Bull.* 71:208–19.

SCHENK, Jakab

1924. Az erdei szalonka vonulása Európában. Der Zug der Waldschnepfe in Europa. *Aquila* 30–1:26–120.

1925. The migration of the Woodcock in Europe. *Brit. Birds* 19:34–44.

SCHEVAREVA, T. P.

1955. (Editor.) Studies of some aspects of the biology of the Mediterranean Gull (*Larus melanocephalus* Temm.) through banding. *Trudy Byuro Kolts.* 8:47–90. (In Russian.)

1957. (Editor.) Summary of bird banding for the years 1925–54. *Trudy Byuro Kolts.* 9:5–45. (In Russian.)

SCHIFFERLI, Alfred

1936. Transportversuche mit Futterplatzvögeln im Herbst und Winter. *Orn. Beob.* 34:1–8.

1942. Verfrachtungsversuch mit Alpenseglern (*Micropus melba melba* L.) Solothurn-Lissabon. *Orn. Beob.* 39:145–50.

1960. Ringfundmeldungen lassen Schleifenzug bei der mitteleuropäischen Wachtel, *Coturnix coturnix*, Vermuten. *Proc. 12th International Ornithological Congress* (Helsinki, 1958) pp. 651–6.

SCHILDMACHER, Hans

1932. Über den Zug der Nebelkrähe (*Corvus cornix* L.) im Nordseegebiet. *Vogelzug* 3:74–9.

1933. Zur Physiologie des Zugtriebes. I. Versuche mit weiblichen Sexualhormon. *Vogelzug* 4:21–4.

1934. Zur Physiologie des Zugtriebes. II. Weitere Versuche mit weiblichen Sexualhormon. *Vogelzug* 5:1–9.

1937. Zur Physiologie des Zugtriebes. III. Versuche mit künstlich verlängerter Tagesdauer. *Vogelzug* 8:107–14.

1938a. Zur Auslösung der Frühlings-Zugunruhe durch Wärme bei gekäfigten Rotkehlchen *Erithacus r. rubecula* (L.). *Vogelzug* 9:7–10.

1938b. Zur Physiologie des Zugtriebes. IV. Weitere Versuche mit künstlich veränderter Belichtungszeit. *Vogelzug* 9:146–52.

1951. Untersuchungen zur Zugdisposition der Zugvögel. *In* Die Wissenschaft vom Vögel und unsere Volkswirtschaft. Kulturbund zur demokratischen Erneuerung Deutschlands. Zentralkommission Ornithologie und Vogelschutz (Berlin) pp. 34–41.

SCHMIDT-KOENIG, Klaus

1958. Experimentelle Einflussnahme auf die 24—Stunden-Periodik bei Brieftauben und deren Auswirkungen unter besonderer Berücksichtigung des Heimfindevermögens. *Z. Tierpsychol.* 15:301–31.

SCHOLANDER, P. F., Raymond HOCK, Vladimir WALTERS, Fred JOHNSON, and Laurence IRVING

1950. Heat regulation in some arctic and tropical mammals and birds. *Biol. Bull.* 99:237–58.

SCHOLANDER, Susan Irving

1955. Land birds over the Western North Atlantic. *Auk* 72:225–39.

SCHREIBER, Bruno, Torquato GUALTIEROTTI, and Danilo MAINARDI

1955. Effetto di accelerazioni centripete e tangenziali sui potenziali cerebellari del Piccione normale e viaggiatore. *R.C. 1st Lombardo Sci. Lett., Classe di Scienze* 88:860–84.

SCHUSTER, Ludwig

1953. Über den Einzug der Rauchschwalbe im Frühjahr. *Vogelw.* 74:211–15.

SCHÜZ, Ernst

1932. Frühsommerzug bei Star und Kiebitz. *Vogelzug* 3:49–57.

1934. Vom Zug der schwarzrückigen Heringsmöwen (*Larus f. fuscus*). *Vogelzug* 5:123–34.

1935a. Von den Wanderungen der Dohle (*Coloeus monedula*). *Vogelzug* 6:33–9.

1935b. Vom Zug des Polar-Seetauchers (*Colymbus a. arcticus*). *Vogelzug* 6:113–18.

1937. Ringfunde europäischer Rauchschwalben (*Hirundo r. rustica* L.) in Afrika. *Orn. Mber.* 45:136–44.

1938. Auflassung ostpreussischer Jungstörche in England 1936. *Vogelzug* 9:65–70.

1940. Vom Zugbild des Schwarzstörches (*Ciconia nigra*). *Vogelzug* 11:23–31.

1948. Störche als Eingeborenen—Beute. *Vogelwarte* 15:8–18.

1949. Die Spät-Auflassung ostpreussischer Jungstörche in West-Deutschland durch die Vogelwarte Rossitten 1933. *Vogelwarte* 15:63–78.

1950a. Verfrachtete Zwischen-Stare kehren zum Teil in das Gebiet ihrer Jahresverbreitung zurück. *Vogelwarte* 15:192–4.

1950b. Zur Frage der angeborenen Zugwege. *Vogelwarte* 15:219–26.

1951. Überblick über die Orientierungsversuche der Vogelwarte Rossitten (jetzt: Vogelwarte Radolfzell). *Proc. 10th International Ornithological Congress* (Uppsala, 1950) pp. 249–68.

1952. Vom Vogelzug. Grundriss der Vogelzugskunde. Frankfurt am Main (Schöps).

1953. Die Zugscheide des Weissen Störches nach den Beringungs-Ergebnissen. *Bonn. Zool. Beitr.* 4:31–72.

1955. Vom Zug des Weissstörches im Raum Syrien bis Ägypten.

Vogelwarte 18:5–13.

1956. Vom Frühjahrs-Durchzug der Wiesenstelze (*Motacilla flava*) an der Südküste des Kaspischen Meeres. *Vogelwarte* 18:169–77.

1959a. Die Vogelwelt des Südkaspischen Tieflandes. Stuttgart (E. Schweizerbart'sche Verlagsbuchhandlung).

1959b. Problems about the White Stork, *Ciconia ciconia* (L.), in Africa seen from a European viewpoint. *Ostrich*, Suppl. 3 *Proc. 1st Pan Afr. Orn. Congr.*) pp. 333–41.

——, and R. Böhringer

1950. Vom Zug des Weiss-Störches in Afrika und Asien nach den Ringfunden bis 1949. *Vogelwarte* 15:160–87.

——, and Hugo Weigold

1931. Atlas des Vogelzugs nach den Beringunsergebnissen bei paläarktischen Vögeln. Berlin (R. Friedländer & Sohn).

Sedgwick, Eric H.

1949. Bird movements in the Wheat-belt of Western Australia. *W. Austr. Nat.* 2:25–33.

Seibert, Henri C.

1949. Differences between migrant and non-migrant birds in food and water intake at various temperatures and photoperiods. *Auk* 66:128–53.

Seilkopf, Heinrich

1952. Zugvögel als Wetterpropheten? *Orn. Mitt.* 4:233–4.

Semenov, S. M., and B. V. Sabinevskii

1957. (Editor.) Seasonal distribution and migrations of the Slender-billed Gull (*Larus genei* Br.) as shown by the banding results and observations. *Trudy Byuro Kolts.* 9:86–132. (In Russian.)

Serventy, D. L.

1937. Local migration in the Perth district, Western Australia. *Emu* 37:90–4.

1951. Observations on migration in the Timor Sea in 1949. *Emu* 51:134.

1952. Movements of the Wilson Storm-Petrel in Australian Seas. *Emu* 52:105–16.

1953a. Movements of pelagic sea-birds in the Indo-Pacific region. *Proc. 7th Pacific Science Congr.* 4:394–407.

1953b. The southern invasion of northern birds during 1952. *W. Austr. Nat.* 3 (8):177–96.

1957. The banding programme of *Puffinus tenuirostris* (Temminck) I. First Report. *C.S.I.R.O. Wildlife Research* 2:51–9.

1958. Recent Studies on the Tasmanian Mutton-bird. *Aust. Mus. Mag.* 12:327–32.

——, and A. J. Marshall

1957. Breeding periodicity in Western Australian birds: with an account of unseasonal nestings in 1953 and 1955. *Emu* 57:99–126.

——, and H. M. Whittell

1951. A handbook of the birds of Western Australia. Perth (Paterson Brokensha) 2nd ed.

SIEBENALER, J. B.
1954. Notes on autumnal trans-Gulf migration of birds. *Condor* 56:43–8.

SHANK, Max C.
1959. The natural termination of the refractory period in the Slate-colored Junco and in the White-throated Sparrow. *Auk* 76:44–54.

SHARLAND, Michael
1958. The Swamp Harrier as a migrant. *Emu* 58:75–80.

SHARLAND, R. E., and B. J. HARRIS
1959. West African bird-ringing report for 1958. A. Nigeria; B. Ghana. *Niger. Field* 24:72–5.

SHELFORD, V. E.
1945. The relation of Snowy Owl migration to the abundance of the Collared Lemming. *Auk* 62:592–6.

SIBSON, R. B.
1951. Some aspects of bird migration in New Zealand. *Proc. 10th International Ornithological Congress* (Uppsala, 1950) pp. 320–5.

SIIVONEN, Lauri
1936. Die Stärkevariation des nächtlichen Zuges bei *Turdus ph. philomelos* Brehm und *T. musicus* L. auf Grund der Zuglaüte geschätzt und mit der Zugunruhe einer gekäfigten Singdrossel verglichen. *Ornis. fenn.* 13:59–63.
1941. Über die Kausalzusammenhänge der Wanderungen beim Seidenschwanz, *Bombycilla g. garrulus* (L.). *Ann. Zool. Soc. Zool. Bot. fenn.* 'Vanamo' 8 No. 6:1–40.

——, and Pontus PALMGREN
1936. Über die Einwirkung der Temperatursenkung auf die Zugstimmung bei einer gekäfigten Singdrossel (*Turdus ph. philomelos* Brehm). *Ornis fenn.* 13:64–7.

SIMMONS, K. E. L.
1954. Fieldnotes on the behaviour of some Passerines migrating through Egypt. *Ardea* 42:140–51.

SIMMS, Eric
1952. Bird migrants. Some aspects and observations. London (Cleaver-Hume Press).

SKINNER, B. F.
1950. Are theories of learning necessary? *Psychol. Rev.* 57:193–216.

SKUTCH, Alexandre F.
1950. The nesting seasons of Central American birds in relation to climate and food supply. *Ibis* 92:185–222.

SLADEN, William J. Lambart
1952. Notes on methods of marking Penguins. *Ibis* 94:541–3.

——, and W. L. N. TICKELL
1958. Antarctic bird-banding by the Falkland Islands dependencies survey, 1945–57. *Bird-Banding* 29:1–26.

SLEPIAN, Joseph
1948. 'Physical basis of bird navigation'. *J. Appl. Phys.* 19:306.

SLIWINSKY, Ursula

1938. Isopiptesen einiger Vogelarten in Europa. *Zool. Polon.* 2:249–87.

SMITH, W. John

1959. Movements of Michigan Herring Gulls. *Bird-Banding* 30: 69–104.

SNYDER, Dorothy E.

1953. A great flight of Dovekies (*Plautus alle*). *Auk* 70:87–8.

SNYDER, L. L.

1947. The Snowy Owl migration of 1945–46. *Wilson Bull.* 59:74–8.

SORENSEN, J. H.

1954. Royal Albatross A 99 (*Diomedea epomophora epomophora*). *Notornis* 6:25–7.

SOUTHERN, Henry Neville

1938a. The spring migration of the Swallow over Europe. *Brit. Birds* 32:4–7.

1938b. The spring migration of the Willow-Warbler over Europe. *Brit. Birds* 32:202–6.

1939. The spring migration of the Redstart over Europe. *Brit. Birds* 33:34–8.

1941. The spring migration of the Red-backed Shrike over Europe. *Brit. Birds* 35:114–19.

SOUTHERN, William E.

1959. Homing of Purple Martins. *Wilson Bull.* 71:254–61.

SPAEPEN, J.

1957. De trek van de kleine Gele Kwikstaart, *Motacilla flava* (L.) *Gerfaut* 47:17–43.

——, and P. DACHY

1952. Le problème de l'orientation chez les oiseaux migrateurs. II. Expériences préliminaires effectuées sur des Martinets noirs, *Apus apus* (L.). *Gerfaut* 42:54–9.

1953. Het orientatieprobleem big de trekvogels. III. Verdere homingproeben met Gierzwaluwen (*Apus apus* L.). *Gerfaut* 43:327–32.

——, and H. FRAGNIÈRE

1952. Le problème de l'orientation chez les oiseaux migrateurs. I. Expériences préliminaires effectuées sur des Martinets alpins, *Apus melba* (L.). *Gerfaut* 42:49–54.

SPEIRS, J. Murray

1953. Winter distribution of Robins east of the Rocky Mountains. *Wilson Bull.* 65:175–83.

SPENCER, Robert

1958. Report on bird ringing for 1957. *Brit. Birds* 51, Suppl.: 449–87.

1959. Progress and prospects in ringing. *Ibis* 101:416–24.

SPRUCE, Richard

1908. Notes of a botanist on the Amazon and Andes. London (Macmillan). 2 vols.

SPRUNT, Alexander, Jr.

1951. Some observations on the fall migration at Dry Tortugas, Florida. *Auk* 68:218–26.

STADIE, R.
1938a. Experimentelle Untersuchungen über den Wandertrieb gekäfigter Gartenrotschwänze, *Phoenicurus ph. phoenicurus* (L.). *Ber. Ver. schles. Orn.* 23:65–80.
1938b. Licht- und Schattenseiten des zugphysiologischen Experiments. *C.R. 9ème Congrès Ornithologique International* (Rouen, 1938) pp. 343–54.

STANFORD, Walter Power
1953. Winter distribution of the Grey Phalarope, *Phalaropus fulicarius*. *Ibis* 95:483–91.

STEIN, P. A. S., and K. WODZICKI
1955. Dispersal of New Zealand Gannets. *Notornis* 6:58–64.

STEINBACHER, Georg
1933. Weibliches Sexualhormon und Vogelzug. *Orn. Mber.* 47:82–4.

STEINBACHER, Joachim
1937. Vögel halten Winterschlaf? *Natur u. Volk* 67:450–2.
1951. Vogelzug und Vogelzugforschung. Frankfurt am Main (Waldemar Kramer).

STEVENS, O. A.
1957. Fall migration and weather with special reference to Harris' Sparrow. *Wilson Bull.* 69:39–77.

STEWART, Duncan, Jr.
1934. Anorthoclase crystals as an index of the migration of Penguins. *Amer. J. Sci.* (5) 27:454–6.

STEWART, Paul A.
1958. Local movements of Wood Ducks (*Aix sponsa*). *Auk* 75:157–68.

STEWART, Robert E.
1954. Migratory movements of the Northern Clapper Rail. *Bird-Banding* 25:1–5.

——, Aeldred D. GEIS, and Charles D. EVANS
1958. Distribution of populations and hunting kill of the Canvasback. *J. Wildlife Mgmt.* 22:333–70.

STICKNEY, Eleanor Herrick
1943. Northern shore birds in the Pacific. *Amer. Mus. Novit.* No. 1248:1–9.

STIMMELMAYER, Anton
1933. Zur Kritik über die Alex Stimmelmayer'sche Reaktionshypothese. *Verh.-orn. Ges. Bayern* 20:162–9.

STONEHOUSE, Bernard
1958. Notes on the ringing and the breeding distribution of the Giant Petrel, *Macronectes giganteus*. *Ibis* 100:204–8.

STORER, John Humphreys
1948. The flight of birds. *Bull. Cranbrook Inst. Sci.* No. 28:1–94.

STORR, G. M.
1958. Migration routes of the Arctic Tern. *Emu* 58:59–62.

STRESEMANN, Erwin
1927. Die Wanderungen der Rotschwanz-Würger (Formenkreis *Lanius cristatus*). *J. Orn.* 75:68–85.

1934. Aves. *In* Handbuch der Zoologie, 7, 2 Berlin (Walter de Gruyter). *Migrations*: 658–711.
1940. Zeitpunkt und Verlauf der Mauser bei einigen Entenarten. *J. Orn.* 88:288–333.
1941. Die Vögel von Célèbes. *J. Orn.* 89:(69–100).
1944a. Der zeitliche Ablauf des Frühjahrszuges beim Neuntöter, *Lanius Collurio. Orn. Mber.* 52:1–8.
1944b. Der zeitliche Ablauf des Frühjahrszuges beim Kappenammer, *Emberiza melanocephala* Scop. *Orn. Mber.* 52:85–92.
1944c. Die Wanderungen der Blauracke (*Coracias garrulus*). *Orn. Mber.* 52:132–46.
1944d. Die Wanderungen des Schmutzgeiers (*Neophron percnopterus*). *Orn. Mber.* 52:146–52.
1947. Der zeitliche Ablauf des Frühjahrszuges bei Nachtigall und Sprosser. *Orn. Ber.* pp. 3–10.
1948. Die Wanderungen des Pirols (*Oriolus oriolus*) *Orn. Ber.* pp. 126–42.
1955. Die Wanderungen des Waldlaubsängers (*Phylloscopus sibilatrix*). *J. Orn.* 96:153–67.

SUDILOVSKAIA, A. M.
1935. Contribution à la connaissance des migrations du Syrrhaptes paradoxus Pallas. *Oiseau Rev. Fr. Orn.* 5:219–35.

SUFFERN, C.
1949. Pressure patterns in bird migration. *Science* 109:209.

SUTTER, Ernst
1948. Über den Herbstzug der Krähen in der Schweiz und in Süddeutschland. *Orn. Beob.* 45:135–50.
1950. Über die Flughöhe ziehender Vögel. *Orn. Beob.* 47:174.
1957a. Radar als Hilfsmittel der Vogelzugforschung. *Orn. Beob.* 54:70–96.
1957b. Radar—Beobachtungen über den Verlauf des nächtlichen Vogelzuges. *Rev. Suisse Zool.* 64:294–303.

SVÄRDSON, Gunnar
1953. Visible migration within Fenno-scandinavia. *Ibis* 95:181–211.
1957. The 'invasion' type of bird migration. *Brit. Birds* 50:314–43.

SWARTH, H. S.
1920. Revision of the avian genus Passerella, with special reference to the distribution and migration of the races in California. *Univ. Calif. Publ. Zool.* 21:75–224.

TABER, William Brewster
1930. The fall migration of Mourning Doves. *Wilson Bull.* 42:17–28.

TAMANTSEVA, L. S., and T. P. SCHEVAREVA
1957. (Editor.) On the biology of the Pintail and the Mallard. *Trudy* 2. *Pribalt. Orn. Konf.* (*Acad. Sci. USSR*). pp. 27–54. (In Russian.)

TAYLOR, J. Sneyd
1954. Notes on some local migrants. *Ostrich* 25:13–18.

TEDD, J. G., and David LACK
1958. The detection of bird migration by high-power radar. *Proc. roy. Soc.* B. 149:503–10.
TEPLOVA, E. N.
1957. (Editor.) Results of the banding of Wigeons (*Anas penelope* L.) in USSR. *Trudy Byuro Kolts.* 9:144–61. (In Russian.)
THAUZIES, A.
1898. L'orientation. *Rev. Sci.* 4th ser. 9:392–7.
THOMSON, Arthur Landsborough
1923. The migrations of some British Ducks: Results of the marking method. *Brit. Birds* 16:262–76.
1924. The migrations of the Herring-gull and Lesser Black-backed Gull: Results of the marking method. *Brit. Birds* 18:34–44.
1926. Problems of bird-migration. London (Witherby).
1931. On 'abmigration' among the Ducks: an anomaly shown by the results of bird-marking. *Proc. 7th International Ornithological Congress* (Amsterdam, 1930) pp. 382–8.
1939. The migration of the Gannet: Result of marking in the British Isles. *Brit. Birds* 32:282–9.
1940. Some remarks on periodicity in the life of birds. *Bull. Brit. Orn. Cl.* 60:31–9.
1949a. Bird migration. A short account. London (Witherby) 3rd edition.
1949b. Report of the bird-ringing Committee. Progress for 1948. *Brit. Birds* 42:175–80.
1950. Factors determining the breeding seasons of birds: an introductory review. *Ibis* 92:173–84.
1951. Reproduction, migration and moult: Factors controlling the annual cycle in birds. *Proc. 10th International Ornithological Congress* (Uppsala, 1950) pp. 241–4.
1953a. The migrations of British Auks (*Alcidae*) as shown by the results of marking. *Brit. Birds* 46:3–15.
1953b. The migration of British Warblers (*Sylviidae*) as shown by the results of ringing. *Brit. Birds* 46:441–50.
1953c. The study of the visible migration of birds: an introductory review. *Ibis* 95:165–80.
1956. The migrations of British Chats (*Oenanthe, Saxicola, Phoenicurus*) as shown by the results of ringing. *Brit. Birds* 49:63–73.
1958a. The migrations of British Hawks (*Accipitridae*) as shown by ringing results. *Brit. Birds* 51:85–93.
1958b. The migrations of British Falcons (*Falconidae*) as shown by ringing results. *Brit. Birds* 51:179–88.
1959. The British contribution to the study of bird migration. *Ibis* 101:82–9.
THORPE, William Homan
1949. Recent biological evidence for the methods of bird orientation. *Proc. Linn. Soc. Lond.* 160:85–94.
——, and D. H. WILKINSON

1946. Ising's theory of bird orientation. *Nature* (London) 158:903–4.

TICEHURST, Norman Frederick

1939. The migratory status of the Heron in Great Britain. *Brit. Birds* 32:242–6.

TINBERGEN, Lukas

1941. Over de Trekwegen van Vinken (*Fringilla coelebs* L.). *Ardea* 30:42–73.

1949. Vogels onderweg. Vogeltrek over Nederland in samenhang met landschap, weer and wird. Amsterdam (Scheltema and Holkema).

1950. Der geheime Finkenzug. *Orn. Beob.* 47:164–70.

TORDOFF, Harrison B., and Robert M. MENGEL

1956. Studies of birds killed in nocturnal migration. *Publ. Mus. nat. Hist. Univ. Kans.* 10:1–44.

TOSCHI, Augusto

1938. Risultati delle ricerche sulla migrazione dello storno (*Sturnus vulgaris* L.) in Italia. *C.R. 9ème Congrès International Ornithologique* (Rouen, 1938) pp. 395–403.

1939. La migrazione degli Uccelli. Bologna (Suppl. *Ric. Zool. appl. Caccia*).

1956. Esperienze sul comportamento di quaglie (*Coturnix c. coturnix*) a migrazione interrota. *Ric. Zool. appl. Caccia* 27:1–275.

TREUS, V. D.

1957. (Editor.) Seasonal distribution and migrations of the Gadwall (*Anas strepera* L.) as shown by the banding results. *Trudy Byuro Kolts.* 9:162–86. (In Russian.)

1957. (Editor.) Seasonal distribution and migrations of Shovelers (*Anas clypeata* L.) as shown by the banding results. *Trudy Byuro Kolts.* 9:187–207. (In Russian.)

TSCHUSI ZU SCHMIDHOFFEN, U.

1909. Der Zug des Steppenhuhnes, *Syrrhaptes paradoxus*, nach dem Westen 1908; mit Berücksichtigung der früheren Züge. *Hermanstadt Verh. Mitt. siebenb. Ver. Naturw.* 58:1–41.

TUGARINOW, A.

1931. Die Wanderungen der nordasiatischen Vögel. *Vogelzug* 2:55–66.

TUNMORE, B. G.

1960. A contribution to the theory of bird navigation. *Proc. 12th International Ornithological Congress* (Helsinki, 1958) pp. 718–723.

ULFSTRAND, Staffan

1960. Some aspects on the directing and releasing influence of wind conditions on visible bird migration. *Proc. 12th International Ornithological Congress* (Helsinki, 1958) pp. 730–6.

URQUHART, F. A.

1958. A discussion of the use of the word 'migration' as it relates to a proposed classification for animal movements. *Contr. Royal Ontario Museum Div. of Zool. and Paleont.* No. 50:1–11.

VALIKANGAS, Ilmari
1933. Finnische Zugvögel aus englischen Vogeleiern. *Vogelzug* 4:159–66.
1951. The expansion of the Greenish Warbler (*Phylloscopus trochiloides viridanus* Blyth) in the Baltic area, especially in Finland towards north and north-west and its causes. *Proc. 10th International Ornithological Congress* (Uppsala, 1950) pp. 527–31.

VALVERDE, José A.
1952. Le passage des Grues cendrées en Castille. *Nos Oiseaux* 21: 196–8.
1955–56. Essai sur l'Aigrette garzette (*Egretta g. garzetta*) en France. *Alauda* 23:145–71; 254–79; 24:1–36.
1957. Aves del Sahara español. Madrid (*Inst. est. afr. Consejo sup. Invest. Cien.*)

——, and P. WEICKERT
1956. Sobre la migracion de varias garzas españolas. *Grupo Cien. Nat. Aranzadi* (*San Sebastian*) *Publ.* 10.

VARIAN, Russell H.
1948. Remarks on 'A preliminary study of a physical basis of bird navigation'. *J. appl. Phys.* 19:306–7.

VERHEYEN, René
1947. Un aperçu général du problème de la migration des oiseaux. *Gerfaut* 37:1–14.
1950a. La Cigogne blanche dans son quartier d'hiver. *Gerfaut* 40:1–17.
1950b. Etude relative à la migration et aux quartiers d'hiver du Faucon hobereau (*Falco subbuteo* L.) *Gerfaut* 40:142–52.
1951a. Particularités relatives à la migration et au quartier d'hiver du Coucou d'Europe (*Cuculus canorus* L.). *Gerfaut* 41:44–61.
1951b. La migration de la Pie-grièche écorcheur, *Lanius c. collurio* L. *Gerfaut* 41:111–39.
1952a. Nos Hirondelles (*Riparia riparia*, *Delichon urbica*, *Hirundo rustica*) dans leurs quartiers d'hiver. *Gerfaut* 42:92–124.
1952b. Essai sur l'origine des communautés migratrices. *Gerfaut* 42:328–37.
1953. Exploration du Parc National de l'Upemba (Mission G. F. de Witte)—Oiseaux. Brussels, *Inst. Parcs Nat. Congo belge* No. 19:(107–10).
1954. Sur la migration de la population européenne du Combattant *Philomachus pugnax* (L.). Brussels, *Volume Jubilaire Victor van Straelen* 2:1011–25.
1955a. Les Linottes. *Carduelis cannabina* (L.), nicheurs et visiteurs d'hiver en Belgique. *Gerfaut* 45:5–25.
1955b. Over de trek von den Groenvink, *Chloris chloris* (L.), in en door België. *Gerfaut* 45:173–84.
1955c. Over de trek von de Sperwer, *Accipiter nisus* (L.), in België. *Gerfaut* 45:285–93.
1956. Note sur les déplacements saisonniers des Bergeronnettes grises, *Motacilla alba* L. *Gerfaut* 46:307–10.

1957. Over de verplaatsingen van de Boomus, *Passer montanus* (L.), in en door België. *Gerfaut* 47:161–70.

——, and Géo Le Grelle
1952. Interprétation des résultats de baguage relatifs au Héron cendré (*Ardea cinerea*) au Vanneau (*Vanellus vanellus*) et à la Mouette rieuse (*Larus ridibundus*). *Gerfaut* 42:214–22.

Verwey, Jan
1953. Over het orienteringsvermogen van vogels en zeedieren. *Ardea* 41:271–90.
1958. Orientation in migrating marine animals and a comparison with that of other migrants. *Arch. neerl. Zool.* 13 Suppl. 1:418–45.
1959. Über das Heimfinden von Vögeln aus unbekannter Gegend. *Vogelwarte* 20:1–4.

Vietinghoff-Riesch, Arnold von
1955. Verbreitung und Zug der Rauchschwalbe (*Hirundo rustica*). *Bonn. zool. Beitr. Sonderband*: 1–145.

Viguier, C.
1882. Le sens de l'orientation et ses organes. *Rev. Philos.* 14:1–36.

Vilks, K., and N. von Trausehe
1933. Ergebnisse der Beringung von Staren (*Sturnus vulgaris*) in Lettland. *Vogelzug* 4:113–18.

Vleugel, D. A.
1950. Windrichtung und Zugstärke beim Buchfinken (*Fringilla coelebs* L.) *Orn. Beob.* 47:158–64.
1952. Über die Bedeutung des Windes für die Orientierung ziehender Buchfinken, *Fringilla coelebs* L. *Orn. Beob.* 49:45–53.
1954a. De voorkeur von trekkende, zich op en wind oriënterende Botvinken (*Fringilla coelebs* L.) voor tegenwind. *Gerfaut* 44:259–77.
1954b. Waarnemingen over de nachttrek van lijsters (*Turdus*) en hun waarschijnlijke oriëntering. *Limosa* 27:1–19.
1955. Über die Unzulänglichkeit der Visierorientierung für das Geradeausfliegen, insbesondere beim Zug des Buchfinken (*Fringilla coelebs* L.) *Ornis fenn.* 32:33–40.
1960. On the temporal pattern of nocturnal migration in Thrushes. *Auk* 77:10–18.

——, and Wolfgang von Westernhagen
1957. Formen des Zuges in abweichender Richtung unter dem Einfluss geographischer Faktoren. *Dansk. orn. Foren. Tidsskr.* 51:176–90.

Voous, K. H.
1953. Vogeltrek op de Nederlandse Benedenwindse Eilanden. In *West-ind. Gids.* The Hague (Martinus Nijhoff). 33:(183–90).

Vrydagh, J. M.
1951. Comportement des Hirondelles de cheminée (*Hirundo rustica* L.) dans leur quartier d'hiver, au nord du Congo belge. *Gerfaut* 41:177–95.

Wagner, Helmuth O.

1930. Über Jahres- und Tagesrhythmus bei Zugvögeln. *Z. vergl. Physiol.* 12:703–23.
1936. Über den Jahresrhythmus verschiedener Grasmücken (*Sylvia*) in Mexico. *Vogelzug* 7:109–12.
1937. Der Einfluss von Aussenfaktoren auf den Tagesrhythmus während der Zugphase. *Vogelzug* 8:47–54.
1955. Notes on an analysis of the annual rhythm of migratory birds. *Acta 11th International Ornithological Congress* (Basle, 1954) pp. 658–61.
1956. Über Jahres- und Tagesrhythmus bei Zugvögeln. II. Mitteilung. *Z. Tierpsychol.* 13:82–92.
1957a. The technical basis of experimental research on bird migration. *Ibis* 99:191–5.
1957b. Vogelzug, Umweltreize und Hormone. *Verh. Dtsch. Zool. Ges.* 1957:289–98.
1958. Gemischte Vogelverbände in Mexiko, insbesondere das Verhalten nordischer Zugvögel. *Z. Tierpsychol.* 15:178–90.

——, and Hans Schildmacher
1937. Über die Abhängigkeit des Einsetzens der nächtlichen Zugunruhe verfrachteter Vögel von der geographischen Breite. *Vogelzug* 8:18–19.

——, and Ingeborg Thomas
1957. Die hormonale Blockierung des Zugimpulses der Vögel während der Fortpflanzungszeit. *Z. vergl. Physiol.* 40:73–84.

Wallace, Donald Ian Mackenzie
1955. The mixing of the races of the Yellow Wagtail in Kenya. *Brit. Birds* 48:337–40.

Wallace, George J.
1958. Notes on North American migrants in Colombia. *Auk* 75:177–82.

Wallgren, Henrik
1955. Der Vogelzug als Anpassungsphänomen. *Vogelwarte* 18:61–6.

Warga, Kálmán
1939. Die *Bombycilla g. garrulus*—Invasion in den Jahren 1931/32 und 1932/33 und die Ergebnisse der Beringsversuche. *Aquila* 42–45 (1935–38):490–528.

Waterhouse, M. J.
1949. Rook and Jackdaw migrations observed in Germany, 1942–45. *Ibis* 91:1–16.

Watson, Ina
1955. Migratory flight of Honeyeaters. *Emu* 55:312–13.

Watson, John Forbes, and K. S. Lashley
1915. An historical and experimental study of homing in birds. *Pap. Carnegie Inst. Wash., Dept. Marine Biol.* 7:1–60.

Watzka, Max
1934. Physiologische Veränderungen der Schildrüse. *Z. Mikro. Anat. Forsch.* 36:67–86.

Weaver, Richard Lee
1940. The Purple Finch invasion of Northeastern United States and

the Maritime Provinces. *Bird-Banding* 11:79–105.

WEIGOLD, Hugo

1924. Das Wetter und der Herbstzug der Waldschnepfe. *J. Orn.* 72:416–21.

1930. Der Vogelzug auf Helgoland, graphisch dargestellt. Abh. Vogelzugsforsch. Helgoland. No. 1

WESTERNHAGEN, Wolfgang von

1954. Hochziehende Finken auch im norddeutschen und dänischen Küstengebiet. *Ardea* 42:336–7.

1955. Zuggeselligkeit bei Greifvögeln. *Vogelwarte* 18:15–19.

WETMORE, Alexander

1926a. The migrations of birds. Cambridge (Harvard Univ. Press).

1926b. Observations on the birds of Argentina, Paraguay, Uruguay, and Chile. *U.S. Nat. Mus. Bull.* 133:1–448 (19–22).

WICHERT, Ernst

1956. Beitrag zur Frage der Zugscheide des Weissen Storches nach Ergebnissen an Bersenbrücker Störchen. *Orn. Mitt.* 8:107–8.

WILKINSON, Denys Haigh

1949. Some physical principles of bird orientation. *Proc. Linn. Soc. Lond.* 160:94–9.

1950. Flight recorders. A technique for the study of bird navigation. *J. exp. Biol.* 27:192–7.

1952. The random element in bird 'navigation'. *J. exp. Biol.* 29:532–60.

WILLIAMS, George G.

1945. Do birds cross the Gulf of Mexico in spring? *Auk* 62:98–111.

1947. Lowery on trans-Gulf migrations. *Auk* 64:217–38.

1950a. Weather and spring migration. *Auk* 67:52–65.

1950b. The nature and causes of the 'Coastal hiatus'. *Wilson Bull.* 62:175–82.

WILLIAMSON, Kenneth

1952. Migrational drift in Britain in autumn 1951. *Scot. Nat.* 64:1–18.

1953. Redwing passage in autumn at Fair Isle. *Bull. Brit. Orn. Cl.* 73:18–23.

1954a. 'Northern Chiffchaffs' and their area of origin. *Brit. Birds* 47:49–58.

1954b. The migration of the Iceland Merlin. *Brit. Birds* 47:434–41.

1954c. American birds in Scotland in autumn and winter, 1953–54. *Scot. Nat.* Vol. 66:13–29. See also *Ibid* 66:197–204.

1954d. A synoptic study of the 1953 Crossbill irruption. *Scot. Nat.* 66:155–69.

1955a. Migrational Drift. *Acta 11th International Ornithological Congress* (Basle, 1954) pp. 179–86.

1955b. Migrational drift and the Yellow Wagtail complex. *Brit. Birds* 48:382–403.

1956. The autumn immigration of the Greenland Redpoll (*Carduelis flammea rostrata* [Coues]) into Scotland. *Dansk. orn. Foren. Tidsskr.* 50:125–33.

1958a. Bergmann's rule and obligatory overseas migration. *Brit. Birds* 51:209–32.

1958b. Autumn immigration of Redwings, *Turdus musicus*, into Fair Isle. *Ibis* 100:582–604.

1959. The September drift—movements of 1956 and 1958. *Brit. Birds* 52:334–77.

——, and Alec BUTTERFIELD

1954. The spring migration of the Willow Warbler in 1952. *Brit. Birds* 47:177–97.

——, and Peter DAVIS

1956. The autumn 1953 invasion of Lapland Buntings and its source. *Brit. Birds* 49:6–25.

WIMSATT, William A.

1940. Homing instinct and prolificacy in the Duck Hawk. *Auk* 57:107–9.

WING, Leonard

1941. Size of bird flocks in winter. *Auk* 58:188–94.

WODZICKI, Kazimierz

1938. Nouvelles expériences sur le sens de l'orientation chez les oiseaux. *C.R. 9ème Congrès Ornithologique International* (Rouen, 1938) pp. 437–44.

——, Wlodzimierz PUCHALSKI, and Helmut LICHE

1938. Untersuchungen über die Orientation und Geschwindigkeit des Fluges bei Vögeln. III. Untersuchungen an Störchen (*Ciconia c. ciconia* L.) *Acta orn. Warsz.* 2:239–58.

1939. Untersuchungen über die Orientierung und Geschwindigkeit des Fluges bei Vögeln. V. Weitere Versuche an Störchen. *J. Orn.* 87:99–114.

——, and Peter STEIN

1958. Migration and dispersal of New Zealand Gannets. *Emu* 58: 289–312.

WOJTUSIAK, Roman J.

1946. Hypothesis of sensibility to infra-red rays as an attempt to explain some problems of orientation of animals. *C.R. mens. classe Sci. math. nat. Acad. Polon. Sci. Lett.* pp. 28–9.

1949. Polish investigations on homing in birds and their orientation in space. *Proc. Linn. Soc. Lond.* 160:99–108.

WOLFSON, Albert

1940. A preliminary report on some experiments on bird migration. *Condor* 42:93–9.

1941. Light versus activity in the regulation of the sexual cycles of birds: the rôle of the hypothalamus. *Condor* 43:125–36.

1942. Regulation of spring migration in Juncos. *Condor* 44:237–63.

1945. The rôle of the pituitary, fat deposition and body weight in bird migration. *Condor* 47:95–127.

1948. Bird migration and the concept of continental drift. *Science* 108:23–30.

1952a. The occurrence and regulation of the refractory period in the gonadal and fat cycles of the Junco. *J. exp. Zool.* 121:311–25.

1952b. Day length, migration and breeding cycles in birds. *Sci. Mon. N.Y.* 74:191–200.

1953. Gonadal and fat response to a 5:1 ratio of light to darkness in the White-throated Sparrow. *Condor* 55:187–92.

1954a. Production of repeated gonadal, fat and moult cycles within one year in the Junco and White-crowned Sparrow by manipulation of day length. *J. exp. Zool.* 125:353–76.

1954b. Weight and fat deposition in relation to spring migration in transient White-throated Sparrows. *Auk* 71:413–34.

1954c. Body weight and fat deposition in captive White-throated Sparrows in relation to the mechanics of migration. *Wilson Bull.* 66:112–18.

1958. Regulation of refractory period in the photoperiodic responses of the White-throated Sparrow. *J. exp. Zool.* 139:349–79.

1959a. Ecologic and physiologic factors in the regulation and spring migration and reproductive cycles in birds. *In* Comparative Endocrinology. New York (J. Wiley & Sons) pp. 38–70.

1959b. Rôle of light and darkness in regulation of refractory period in gonadal and fat cycles of migratory birds. *Physiol. Zool.* 32:160–76.

1960. Rôle of light and darkness in the regulation of the annual stimulus for spring migration and reproductive cycles. *Proc. 12th International Ornithological Congress* (Helsinki, 1958) pp. 758–89.

——, and David P. Winchester

1960. Rôle of darknes in the photoperiodic responses of migratory birds. *Physiol. Zool.* 33:179–89.

Woodbury, Angus M.

1941. Animal migration—periodic response theory *Auk.* 58:463–505.

Wuczeticz, V. N.

1939. (Editor.) [Seasonal distribution and migrations of Ducks (*Anatinae*) as shown by banding results in USSR. Gadwall (*Anas strepera*) Shoveler (*Spatula clypeata*)—Wigeons (*Mareca penelope*).] *Trudy Byuro Kolts.* pp. 1–101. (In Russian.)

1941. (Editor.) [Seasonal distribution and migrations of Ducks (*Anatinae*) as shown by banding results in USSR. Teal (*Querquedula crecca*)—Garganey (*Querquedula querquedula*).] *Trudy Byuro Kolts.* pp. 1–87. (In Russian.)

——, and A. A. Tugarinov

1937a. (Editor.) [Seasonal distribution and migrations of Ducks (*Anatinae*) as shown by banding results in USSR. Mallards (*Anas platyrhynchos*).] *Trudy Byuro Kolts.* pp. 1–73. (In Russian.)

1937b. (Editor.) [Seasonal distribution and migrations of Ducks (*Anatinae*) as shown by banding results in USSR. Pintail *Dafila acuta* L.).] *Trudy Byuro Kolts.* pp. 1–57. (In Russian.)

WYNNE-EDWARDS, Vero Copner
1935. On the habits and distribution of birds on the North Atlantic. *Proc. Boston Soc. nat. Hist.* 40:233–346.
1948. Yeagley's theory of bird navigation. *Ibis* 90:606–11.

YAPP, W. B.
1956. Two physiological considerations in bird migration. *Wilson Bull.* 68:312–19.

YEAGLEY, Henry L.
1947. A preliminary study of a physical basis of bird navigation. *J. Appl. Phys.* 18:1035–63.
1951. A preliminary study of a physical basis of bird navigation. Part II. *J. Appl. Phys.* 22:746–60.

ZIMMER, John T.
1938. Notes on migrations of South American birds. *Auk* 55:405–10.

ZINK, Gerhard
1958. Vom Zug des Grossen Rohrdommel (*Botaurus stellaris*) nach den Ringfunden. *Vogelwarte* 19:243–7.

Index of Birds

Acanthis,
cannabina, 227
flammea rostrata, 246, 264
Acanthiza pusilla, 147
Accipiter,
gentilis atricapillus, 276, 322
nisus, 28, 219, 224
striatus, 258
virgatus, 232
Acrocephalus australis, 146
Aeronautes saxatilis, 107
Agelaius phoeniceus, 122, 202
Aix sponsa, 320
Alauda arvensis, 29, 218, 227, 259
Albatrosses, 145, 171, 195, 197
Black-browed, 198
Laysan, 324, 326
Royal, 196
Wandering, 195, 196, 198
Alca torda, 28, 141, 219
Ammomanes,
cinctura, XIV
deserti hijazensis, 380
Anarhynchus frontalis, 149
Anatidae, 253, 259
Anas,
acuta, 27, 90, 129, 131, 219, 225, 284
clypeata, 90
crecca, 28, 43
discors, 202, 332
gibberifrons, 147
penelope, 45, 90
platyrhynchos, 28, 45, 129, 219, 246, 284, 320, 363, 364
rubripes, 246
strepera, 90, 284
superciliosa, 147
Anastomus lamelligerus, 159
Anhinga anhinga, 161
Anser, 219, 224
albifrons, 27
anser, 27, 45
brachyrhynchus, 26, 28
Anseranas semipalmata, 148
Anthochaera caruncula, 147
Anthus,
campestris, 96
cervinus, 224
novaeselandiae, 149
pratensis, 224, 259
Aptenodytes forsteri, 199
Apus,
apus, 18, 68, 218, 224, 235, 278, 325
caffer, 143
horus, 143
melba, 325
pacificus, 144
pallidus, 69
Archilochus,
alexandri, 103
colubris, 102, 218, 297
Ardea,
cinerea, 28, 47, 49, 204
herodias, 139
purpurea, 47
Ardeola,
idae, 165
ralloides, 50
Arenaria interpres, 149, 163, 222, 377
Artamus,

personatus, 146
superciliosus, 146
Asio flammeus, 258
Auk, 171, 283
Aythya,
affinis, 127, 246, 359
americana, 127, 131
ferina, 28, 90
marila, 127
nyroca, 90
valisineria, 127, 134

Bartramia longicauda, 202
Basileuterus belli, 257
Bee-eater, 96ff, 167, 253, 259, 375, 379, 386
Carmine, 160
Madagascar, 165
Bishop, orange, 312
Bittern, 258
European, 50
Little, 50, 258
Blackbird, 28, 76, 292, 293, 317, 318,
Red-winged, 122, 202, 259
Blackcap, 79, 81, 252, 293, 366, 367, 368, 369, 379
Bluebird, Eastern, 109, 253
Bluethroat, 216
Bobolink, 122, 124, 138, 139, 371
Bombycillidae, 270
Bombycilla,
cedrorum, 274
garrulus, 269, 270, 272
g. pallidiceps, 273
Bonasa umbellus, 97, 276, 281
Botaurus stellaris, 50, 258
Brambling, 227, 240, 259, 264, 297
Branta, 200
bernicla hrota, 127, 258
canadensis minima, 132, 239
Bubulcus ibis, 204
Bucephala clangula, 45
Budgerigar, 147
Bulbul,
Black-capped, 312
Yellow-streaked, 312
Bullfinch, 29
Bunting,
Black-headed, 221
Indigo, 119
Lazuli, 119
Painted, 119
Reed, 29, 252
Bustard, 93
Butastur rufipennis, 157
Buteo,
auguralis, 158
buteo, 28, 61, 257
b. vulpinus, 61
jamaicensis, 258
lagopus, 276
p. platypterus, 138, 257
Buzzard, 28, 208
Common, 61, 62, 257
Honey, 63, 257
Red-necked, 158

Cacomantis variolosus, 146
Calcarius lapponicus, 246
Calendrella cinerea brachydactyla, 380
Calidris,
bairdi, 202
canutus, 149, 378
Calothorax lucifer, 251
Calypte anna, 103
Calyptorhynchus baudini, 147
Camptostoma i. imberbe, 250
Capella,
gallinago, 28, 91
media, 91
paraguaiae magellanica, 141
Capercaillie, 269
Caprimulgus,
carolinensis, 128
europaeus, 94, 280
inornatus, 156, 158
rufigena, 143
Cardinal, 371
Carduelis,

cannabina, 29, 224
carduelis, 76
flammea, XIII
Carpodacus,
p. californicus, 120
p. purpureus, 119, 120, 264
Catharacta,
maccormicki, 193
skua lönnbergi, 144
s. skua, 175
Catoptrophorus semi-palmatus, 139, 219
Cecropis,
cucullata, 143
semirufa, 143
Chaetura pelagica, 107
Chaffinch, 29, 77, 78, 209, 210, 211, 218, 225, 226, 227, 228, 229, 230, 239, 240, 252, 259, 319, 331, 346, 362
Chaimarrornis leucocephalus, 166
Chalcites,
basalis, 146, 148
lucidus harterti, 151
l. layardi, 151
l. lucidus, 151, 152
l. plagosus, 146, 151, 152
Charadriidae, 375
Charadrius,
bicinctus, 150
hiaticula, 29, 163, 219, 382, 384
leschenaulti, 163
mongolus, 163
vociferus, 202, 219
Chen,
hyperborea, 132
rossii, 132
Chickadee,
Black-capped, 264, 317
Boreal, 264
Mexican, 257
Chicken, Greater Prairie, 252
Chiff-chaff, 80, 96, 104, 246
Chloephaga,
picta, 141
poliocephala, 141
rubidiceps, 141
Chordeiles,
acutipennis, 280
minor gundlachi, 169
Chrysococcyx caprius, 144
Ciconia,
ciconia, 50, 52, 58, 224, 324
c. asiatica, 51, 58
c. boyciana, 51, 58
nigra, 58
Cinclodes oustaleti, 142
Cinclorhamphus,
cruralis, 146
mathewsi, 146
Cinnyricinclus leucogaster, 144
Circaetus gallicus, 64
Circus,
aeruginosus, 64
approximans, 145
cyaneus, 28
Clamator,
glandarius, 144
jacobinus, 144, 157
levaillantii, 144
Clangula hyemalis, 219
Coccyzus,
americanus, 102, 128, 138, 202, 245
erythrophthalmus, 102, 128, 202
Cockatiel, 147
Cockatoo, White-tailed black, 147
Colius striatus mombassicus, 312
Columba,
fasciata, 101
oenas, 28
palumbus, 28, 224
Contopus,
pertinax, 104
virens, 105
Coot, 93, 326
American, 200
European, 28
Coracias,
abyssinica, 157
garrulus, 84
Coracina lineata, 146

Cormorant, 27, 171, 317
Reed, 161
Corncrake, 144, 259
Corvidae, 253
Corvus,
brachyrhynchos, 288, 329
cornix, 28, 75, 327, 328, 329, 385
corone, 75
coronoides, 147
frugilegus, 28, 73, 74, 217, 218, 224
monedula, 28, 75, 218, 224
Cosmetornis vexillarius, 159, 160
Coturnix coturnix, 219, 259
Cowbird, 122, 259, 317, 325, 371
Brown-headed, 122
Cranes, 58, 208, 214, 219, 224, 225, 253, 259, 260, 283, 360
Whooping, 135
Courol, Kirombo, 163
Crake, Malay banded, 144
Creatophora cinerea, 264
Crex crex, 144, 259
Crocethia alba, 149, 163, 377
Crossbill,
Parrot, 264
Red, 264, 265, 386
White-winged, 264
Crow, 73, 288
American, 329
Carrion, 73, 75
European, 359
Hooded, 28, 75, 216, 225, 233, 292, 327, 328, 329, 330, 347, 385
Pied, 163
Cuckoo, 29, 233, 252, 253, 258, 282
African, 157
Black, 143
Black-billed, 102, 128, 202, 371
Bronze, 151
Brush, 146
Channel-bill, 146
Didric, 144
European, 375
Golden bronze, 146
Great spotted, 143
Jacobin, 144
Lesser, 166
Long-tailed, 152, 201
Madagascar, 164
Narrow-billed bronze, 146
Pallid, 145
Pied, 157
Red-chested, 143
Shining, 201
Striped crested, 144
Yellow-billed, 102, 128, 138, 245
Cuckoo-shrike, barred, 146
Cuculus,
cafer, 143
canorus, 29
c. gularis, 158
pallidus, 145
p. poliocephalus, 165, 166
poliocephalus rochii, 164
solitarius, 143
varius, 166
Curlew, 28, 224, 249, 250, 317
Bristle-thighed, 203, 205
Eskimo, 99
Slender-billed, 88
Cursorius cursor, XIV
Cygnus,
bewickii, 219
cygnus, 45, 219
olor, 372
Cypseloides niger, 69

Daption capensis, 193
Darter, 161
Delichon urbica, 29, 65, 218, 234, 284, 325
Dendrocolaptidae, 257
Dendrocopus,
major, 28, 263
villosus, 252, 318
Dendrocygna javanica, 166
Dendroica,
coronata, XV, 115, 116, 129
pensylvanica, 136
petechia, 117, 138, 238
pinus, 115

striata, 117, 118, 138, 245
tigrina, 118
Dickcissel, 119
Dicrurus,
hottentotus, 375
leucophaeus, 375
Diomedea,
epomophora, 196
exulans, 195
immutabilis, 324, 326
melanophrys, 198
Diplootocus moussieri, 95
Diver, 283
Dolichonyx oryzivorus, 122, 123, 138, 297
Dollar-bird, 167
Dotterel, 219
Double-banded, 150
Doves, 258
Mourning, 101, 302, 371
Stock, 28
Turtle, 28, 219
Violet-eared, 168
Dovekie, 183, 201
Dowitcher, Short-billed, 202
Drongo, 167, 375
Ducks, 260, 262, 374, 375, 388
Australian black, 147
Baldpate, 131, 135
Brant, 127
Canvasback, 124, 127, 134
Eider, 28, 200, 212, 214, 225
Ferruginous, 90
Golden eye, 45
Indian whistling, 166
Mallard, 28, 45, 93, 129, 135, 219, 246, 284, 320, 363, 364
Old Squaw, 219
Redhead, 124, 127, 131
Scaup, Greater, 127, 359
Lesser, 127, 135, 246
Tufted, 27, 93, 284
Wood, 320
Dunlin, 259
Dunnock, 29
EAGLES, 257
Bald, 47
Short-toed, 64, 208
Ectopistes migratorius, 101
Edoliisoma tenuirostre, 146
Egret,
Cattle, 204
Little, 50
Egretta,
alba, 50
garzetta, 50
Elaenia albiceps chilensis, 142
Emberiza,
citrinella, 29
melanocephala, 221
schoeniclus, 29
Empidonax,
difficilis, 104, 251
flaviventris, 104
traillii brewsteri, 138
t. traillii, 138
Empidonomus,
varius rufinus, 167
v. varius, 167
Eopsaltria griseogularis, 147
Ereneutes pusillus, 139
Ergasticus ruber, 257
Erithacus rubecula, 29, 77, 244, 254, 289, 294, 300
Erolia,
acuminata, 149, 205
alpina, 259
fuscicollis, 202
maculata, 149
melanotos, 202
minuta, 163, 259
ruficollis, 149
testacea, 149, 163
Eudromias morinellus, 219
Eudynamys orientalis, 146
Eudyptes sclateri, 149
Eudyptula,
albosignata, 149
minor, 149
Euplectes franciscana, 312

Eurystomus,
glaucurus, 163
orientalis, 146

Falco,
amurensis, 94
columbarius, 28, 246
concolor, 165
naumanni, 63, 94
perconfusus, 375
peregrinus, 18, 219, 325, 375, 379
peregrinus anatum, 138, 325
rupicola, 375
sparverius, 258
subbuteo, 64
tinnunculus, 28, 63, 375
vespertinus, 64
Falcon,
African peregrine, 375
Peregrine, 375
Red-footed, 64
Sooty, 165
Fantail, Grey, 147
Ficedula hypoleuca, 80, 81
Fieldfare, 227, 372
Finches, 273
Eastern Purple, 119, 264
Florida caerula, 47
Flycatcher,
Ash-throated, 250
Beardless, 250
Coues's, 104
Fork-tailed, 142
Leaden, 146
Little, 138
Paradise, 143
Pied, 80, 81
Red-breasted, 88, 94
Rufous fantail, 146
Satin, 146
Spotted, 29, 81, 255, 258
Traill's, 138
Tyrant, 375
Varied, 167
Vermilion, 104
Western, 104, 250
Yellow-bellied, 104
Fratercula arctica, 29, 41
Fringillidae, 253, 310
Fringilla,
coelebs, 29, 77, 78, 211, 218, 226, 227, 230, 252, 331, 362
montifringilla, 227, 264, 297
Fulica,
americana, 200
atra, 28, 326
Fulmar, 29, 195, 196, 198
Fulmarus glacialis, 29, 195

GADWALL, 90, 284
Gannet, 28, 41, 42, 171, 212, 253, 290, 317, 324, 330, 343, 344
Australasian, 150, 388
Cape, 172
Garganey, 93
Garrulus glandarius, 28, 263
Gavia arctica, 46, 215
Gerygone olivacea, 146
Godwit,
Bar-tailed, 149, 203, 205, 224
Black-tailed, 225
Goldfinch,
American, 120
European, 76
Goose, 219, 224, 251, 258, 260, 283, 299, 359, 360, 374
Ashy-headed, 141
Bean, 93
Blue, 222, 223
Brant, 200, 258
Cackling Canada, 132
Canada, 127, 129, 222, 223, 238, 239
Emperor, 133
Grey Lag, 27, 45
Pied, 148
Pink-fronted, 26, 28
Ross's, 132, 208
Ruddy-headed, 141
Snow, 132
South American sheld, 141

Upland, 141
White-fronted, 27, 93
Goshawk,
American, 276
European, 322
Grackles, 259
Bronzed, 121
Purple, 122
Grantiella picta, 147
Graucalus cinereus, 163
Grebes, 283
Great Crested, 200
Red-necked, 200
Greenshank, 206, 219, 250, 259
Grosbeaks,
Black-headed, 119
Blue, 119
Evening, 124, 264
Pine, 264
Rose-breasted, 119, 120
Ground-tyrant, Smoke-fronted, 142
Grouse, 318
Black, 269
Ruffed, 97, 276, 281
Willow, 269
Grus,
americana, 135
grus, 58, 94, 219, 224
Guillemot, 28, 41, 171
Guiraca caerulea, 119
Gulls,
Black-headed, XV, 28, 38, 39, 40, 69, 70, 88, 225, 317, 326, 351, 383
Common, 28, 171, 208, 258, 359
Great black-backed, 28, 325
Herring, 28, 40, 128, 322, 325, 340, 362, 372
Laughing, 128, 139, 171
Lesser black-backed, 28, 40, 213, 322, 325, 340, 362
Mediterranean, 40
Silver, 171
Slender-billed, 41
Gyrfalcon, 276
Haematopus,
ostralegus, 28
o. finschi, 150
Halcyon,
coromanda, 375
pileata, 375
sancta, 146, 148
Haliaeëtus l. leucocephalus, 47
Haloboena coerulea, 193
Harrier,
Hen, 28
Marsh, 64
Swamp, 145
Hawks, 219
Broad-winged, 138, 257
Duck, 138
Grasshopper, 157
Japanese Sparrow, 232
Red-tailed, 258
Rough-legged, 276
Sharp-shinned, 258
Sparrow, 28, 219, 224, 258
Hawk-cuckoo, common, 166
Herons, 28
Black-crowned night, 20, 47
Common, 47, 48, 49, 181, 204, 252, 253, 258, 317
Great blue, 139
Great white, 50
Little blue, 47
Madagascar Squacco, 165
Night, 35, 47, 50
Purple, 47
Squacco, 50
White-necked, 148
Hesperiphona vespertina, 124, 264
Heteroscelus,
brevipes, 203, 205
incanus, 203, 205
Himantopus himantopus leucocephalus, 150
Hippolais pallidus, 290
Hirundapus caudacutus, 69, 144, 149, 201
Hirundo,
albigularis, 143

dimidiata, 143
neoxena, 145
rustica, 29, 65, 67, 217, 218, 224, 233, 236, 284, 323, 325
r. erythrogaster, 107, 138
Hobby, 64
Honey-eaters,
Painted, 147
Scarlet, 146
White-naped, 146
Yellow-faced, 146
Hoopoe, 375
Humming-birds, XIII, 201, 220, 258, 279, 375
Anna's, 103
Black-chinned, 103
Calliope, 103
Ruby-throated, 102, 103, 218, 252, 297
Rufous, 103
Hydrobates pelagicus, 324
Hylochelidon nigricans, 145, 147
Hylocichla,
fuscescens, 109
guttata, 111
minima, 109, 138, 377
mustelina, 111
m. bicknelli, 109
ustulata, 111, 202
u. swainsoni, 111
Hypolais,
icterina, 80
polyglotta, 80

IBISES, 161
Black-faced, 141
Wood, 168
Icteridae, 98, 253, 259, 375
Icterus.
galbula, 122
spurius, 122
Iridoprocne bicolor, 105
Ixobrychus minutus, 50, 258

JACKDAWS, 28, 75, 218, 224, 259, 261, 302

Jaegers, 279
Long-tailed, 174
Parasitic, 149, 175
Pomarine, 174
Jays, 28, 263, 303
Junco,
hyemalis, 121, 286, 297, 311
montanus, 305
oreganus, 121, 297, 305, 306, 310
pinosus, 305
thurberi, 305
Juncos,
Slate-coloured, 121, 286, 287, 288, 291, 297, 305, 307, 311
Jynx torquilla, 323, 325

KESTRELS, 28, 63, 375
Lesser, 63
Killdeer, 202, 219
Kingbirds,
Arkansas or western, 105
Eastern, 105, 138
Grey, 169
Kingfishers, 46
Black-capped, 375
Ruddy, 375
Sacred, 146
Kites, 64, 163, 225, 261
Black, 64, 262
Kittiwakes, 29, 38, 172, 173, 179, 184, 185, 186
Knots, 149, 378
Koel, 146

Lagopus,
lagopus, 269
mutus, XVI
scoticus, 318
Lamprocolius splendidus, 162
Lanius,
borealis, 276
collurio, 85, 86, 95, 96, 237, 238, 290, 325, 326, 355, 376
cristatus, 95
minor, 96, 290, 376
senator, 250

Lapwings, 29, 217, 219, 223, 224, 232, 253, 303, 317, 318
Larks, 240
  Wood, 227, 232
Larus,
  argentatus, 28, 40, 322, 325, 326, 372
  atricilla, 128, 139, 171
  canus, 28
  fuscus, 28, 40, 213, 322, 325, 340
  f. graellsi, 40
  genei, 41
  marinus, 28, 325
  melanocephalus, 40
  novaehollandiae, 171
  ridibundus, 28, 38, 39, 326
Legatus, 168
Leptolophus hollandicus, 147
Leptosomus discolor, 163
Limicoles, 253
Limnocryptes minima, 91
Limnodromus griseus, 202
Limosa,
  lapponica, 163, 203
  l. baueri, 149, 205
  l. limosa, 225
Linnets, 29, 224, 227
Locustella fluviatilis, 96
Lophophorus impeyanus, 318
Longspur, Lapland, 246
Loon, Arctic or Black-throated diver, 46, 215
Loxia,
  curvirostra, 264, 266
  leucoptera, 264
  pityopsittacus, 264
Luscinia,
  luscinia, 92
  svecica, 216
Lyrurus tetrix, 269

Macrodipteryx longipennis, 156, 157, 158
Macronectes giganteus, 193, 194
Magpie, 28, 261
Manakins, 169, 379
Mareca,
  americana, 131, 202
  penelope, 27, 284
Martins, 219
  African river, 162
  Crag, 68
  House, 29, 65, 66, 67, 68, 218, 233, 234, 235, 284, 325
  Purple, 10, 106, 218, 325
  Sand or Bank Swallow, 66, 68
  Southern brown-chested, 142
Meadow-larks,
  Eastern, 122, 202, 371
  Western, 355
Megadyptes antipodes, 149
Melanitta,
  deglandi, 124, 133, 359
  perspicillata, 133
Meliphaga chrysops, 146
Melithreptus lunatus, 146
Melopsittacus undulatus, 147
Melospiza melodia, 121, 218, 252, 310, 317, 318
Merlins, 28
  Iceland, 246
Merops,
  nubicoides, 160, 161
  nubicus, 160, 161
  ornatus, 145, 148
  s. persicus, 165
  s. superciliosus, 165
Mockingbirds, 252, 317, 318, 371
Milvus,
  migrans, 64, 225
  milvus, 64, 262
Mimidae, 129
Mimus polyglottos, 252, 317, 318
Minivet, 375
Mniotilta varia, 115, 116, 202
Molothrus ater, 122, 317, 325
Monal, Himalayan, 318
Monticola,
  saxatilis, 94
  solitarius, 95
Morus,
  bassanus, 28, 41, 42, 150, 324, 343

capensis, 172
serrator, 150, 388
Motacilla,
alba, 83, 84, 96
cinerea, XV
flava, 29, 93, 144, 218, 224, 227, 232, 290, 314, 315, 385
f. alascensis, 377
beema, 385
cinereocapilla, 385
flavissima, 385
feldegg, 385
leucocephala, 385
thunbergi, 315, 385
tschutschensis (— *alascensis*), 110
Mousebird, speckled, 312
Murres, 200
Muscicapidae, 253
Muscicapa,
parva, 88
striata, 29, 81, 258
Muscisaxicola macloviana mentalis, 142
Muscivora t. tyrannus, 142
Myadestes townsendi, 108
Mycteria americana, 168
Myiagra,
cyanoleuca, 146
rubicula, 146
Myarchus cinerascens, 250
Myioborus miniatus, 257
Myodynastes, 168
Myzomela sanguinolenta, 146

Neophron percnopterus, 64
Netta rufina, 90
Nighthawks,
Common, 169
Trilling, 280
Nightingales, 92, 289
Nightingale-thrushes, 92
Nightjars,
European, 280
Pennant-wing, 159, 160
Plain, 156, 158, 258
Rufous-cheeked, 143
Standard-wing, 156, 157, 158
Notophoyx pacifica, 148
Nucifraga,
caryocatactes macrorhynchus, 265, 267
columbiana, 267
Numenius,
arquata, 28, 163, 249
borealis, 99
phaeopus, 163, 219
tahitiensis, 203, 205
tenuirostris, 88
Nutcrackers,
Clark's, 267
Siberian, 265
Nyctea scandiaca, 274, 275
Nycticorax,
nycticorax, 35, 47, 50
n. hoactli, 20, 47

Oceanites,
oceanicus, 144, 178, 181, 182
o. wilsoni, 182
Oceanodroma leucorrhoa, 182, 183, 186, 324
Oenanthe,
leucorhoa, 79, 383
oenanthe, 29, 79, 94, 109, 218, 221, 376
schiöleri, 79
Oidemia nigra, 258
Open-bill, 159
Oporornis agilis, 118
Orioles, 215, 258, 375, 376, 379
Baltimore, 122, 232
Black-naped, 379, 380
Golden, 83, 85, 221, 380
Indian black-headed, 379, 380
Orchard, 122
Oriolus,
chinensis, 379, 380
oriolus, 83, 85, 379
xanthornus, 379, 380
Ospreys, 62, 138, 139, 215
Otus scops, 63, 258

Ouzel, black, 381
Ovenbird, 116, 232
Owls,
  Barn, 28
  Hawk, 276
  Little, 302
  Scops, 63, 258
  Short-eared, 258
  Snowy, 274, 275, 276
  Tawny, 47
Oystercatchers,
  European, 28, 249
  South Island, 150

Pachycephala,
  pectoralis, 147, 312
  rufiventris, 145
Pandion,
  haliaetus, 62
  h. carolinensis, 138, 139
Parakeets, 167
Partridges, 261
Parulidae, 238, 253
Parus,
  ater, 264
  atricapillus, 264, 317
  caeruleus, 29, 322
  hudsonicus, 264
  major, 29, 76, 322
  sclateri, 257
Passer,
  domesticus, 29, 297, 300
  montanus, 227
Passerculus,
  princeps, 209
  sandwichensis, 209
Passerella,
  iliaca, 121, 296, 306, 310, 381, 382
  i. annectens, 382
    fuliginosa, 382
    insularis, 382
    sinuosa, 382
    townsendi, 382
    unalaschcensis, 382
Passerina,
  amoena, 119
  ciris, 119
  cyanea, 119
Passerines, 202, 209, 215, 220, 223, 225, 227, 232, 236, 259, 264, 283, 295
Pastor roseus, 148, 264, 276
Pelagodroma marina, 34, 192
Pelicans, 253, 260
Penguins, 22, 199
  Emperor, 199, 301
  Erect-crested, 149
  Gentoo, 199
Pernis apivorus, 63, 64, 257
Pericrocotus,
  divaricatus, 375
  ethologus, 375
Petrels,
  Blue, 193
  Cape, 193
  Giant, 145, 193, 194, 195
  Leach's, 182, 183, 186, 201, 324
  Storm, 324
  White-faced storm, 192
  Wilson's storm, 144, 172, 178, 181, 182, 183, 185, 187, 189, 191, 200, 201, 247
Petrochelidon,
  pyrrhonota, 106
  pyrrhonata, 107, 130
  spilodera, 143
Petroica,
  multicolor, 146
  phoenicea, 146
Pewee, Eastern wood, 105
Phaeoprogne tapera fusca, 142
Phalacrocorax,
  africanus, 161
  aristotelis, 28
Phalaenoptilus nuttallii, 279
Phalaropes,
  Northern, 174
  Red, 174, 186
Phalaropus fulicarius, 186
Pheasants, 261

Pheucticus,
ludovicianus, 119, 120
melanocephalus, 119
Philacte canagica, 133
Phoebes,
Black, 104
Eastern, 104
Say's, 104
Phoenicurus,
ochruros gibraltariensis, 82
phoenicurus, 82, 83, 94, 236, 289
Phyllastrephus flavostriatus tenuirostris, 312
Phylloscopus, 257
borealis, 88
collybita, 80, 96, 246
kennicotti, 111, 377
sibilatrix, 222
trochiloides, 87, 372
trochilus, 29, 80, 94, 235, 237, 245, 290
Pica pica, 28
Picoides,
arcticus, 264
tridactylos, 264
Pigeons, 215, 302
Band-tailed, 101
Carrier, 327, 332, 335, 337, 338, 345, 346, 347, 351, 354, 356, 359
Domestic, 340
Green, 166
Passenger, 101
Wood, 28, 224
Pinicola enucleator, 264
Pintail, 27, 90, 129, 131, 219, 225, 284
Pipilo erythrophthalmus, 120
Pipits,
Meadow, 29, 209, 224, 227, 240, 259
New Zealand, 149
Red-throated, 218, 224
Tawny, 96
Pipridae, 379
Piranga,
ludoviciana, 111, 112, 132
olivacea, 112, 114, 297
rubra, 138
r. cooperi, 115
r. rubra, 113
Pittas,
Blue-winged, 166
Fairy, 379
Pitta,
brachyura, 375, 379
moluccensis, 166
Plautus alle, 183
Plovers, 260
American golden, 99, 100, 101, 125, 220
Black-bellied, 139
Golden, 204, 205
Pacific golden, 101, 133, 149, 260
Ringed, 29, 219, 382, 384
Upland, 202
Wrybill, 149
Pluvialis,
dominica dominica, 99, 100
d. fulva, 101, 133, 149
Pochards, 28, 90
Red-crested, 90
Podiceps,
cristatus, 200
griseigena, 200
Poor-wills,
North American, 279, 280, 281
Nuttall's, 97
Prairie chicken, 318
Procellariiformes, 182, 185, 187, 190, 193, 198, 199, 205, 362
Procellaria tenuirostris, 191
Progne subis, 106, 138, 218, 325
Prosthemadera novaezelandiae, 149
Prunella modularis, 29
Pseudochelidon eurystomina, 162
Ptarmigans, 281
Pteroclididae, 268
Puffins, 29, 41
Puffinus,
brevicaudus, 191

bulleri, 192
carneipes, 191
gavia, 150
gravis, 187, 188, 283
griseus, 192
puffinus, 29, 187, 192, 219, 326, 352
tenuirostris, 34, 189, 190, 283, 314
Pycnonotus barbatus micrus, 312
Pygochelidon cyanoleuca patagonica, 142
Pygoscelis papua, 20, 199
Pyrocephalus rubinus, 104
Pyrrhula pyrrhula, 29

QUAILS, 202, 219, 259, 283, 375
Quiscalus,
quiscula stonei, 122
q. versicolor, 121

RAILS, 283
Northern clapper, 128
Rainbow-bird, 145
Rallidae, 259
Rallina fasciata, 144
Rallus longirostris crepitans, 128
Raptores, 208, 230, 257, 322
Raven, Australian, 147
Razorbill, 28, 41, 219
Redpoll, Greenland, 246, 264
Redshanks, 28
Spotted, 259
Redstarts, 232, 236, 252, 289
American, 117, 125, 209
Black, 82
Slate-throated, 257
White-capped water, 166
Redwing, 227, 243, 244, 245, 293
Reed-warbler, Australian, 146
Rhipidura,
fuliginosa, 147
rufifrons, 146
Rhodopis vesper atacamensis, 167
Riparia riparia, 10, 29, 66, 68, 138
Rissa,
tridactyla, 29, 38, 172
t. pollicaris, 173

Robins,
American, 108, 109, 110, 129, 202, 218, 223, 238, 253, 273
European, 29, 77, 244, 254, 255, 289, 294, 295, 299, 300, 301, 303, 317, 319
Western yellow, 147
Rollers, 375, 376
Abyssinian, 157
Eastern broad-billed, 146
European, 84, 220, 222
Madagascar broad-billed, 163
Rook, 28, 73, 74, 217, 218, 224, 259, 260, 261

SANDERLING, 149, 377
Sandgrouse, Pallas's, 268, 386
Sandpipers,
Baird's, 202
Buff-breasted, 202
Common, 206, 224, 258, 260
Curlew, 149
Pectoral, 149, 202, 258
Rufous-necked, 149
Semi-palmated, 139
Sharp-tailed, 149, 205
Solitary, 202
White-rumped, 202
Wood, 285
Saxicola rubetra, 92
Sayornis,
nigricans, 104
phoebe, 19, 104
saya, 104
Scolopax rusticola, 28, 240, 241
Scoters, 258, 359
Surf, 133
White-winged, 124, 133
Scythrops novae-hollandiae, 146
Seiurus,
aurocapillus, 116
noveboracensis, XV, 202
Selasphorus,
platycercus, 250
rufus, 103, 250
Serin, 371

Serinus serinus, 371
Setophaga ruticilla, 117, 125, 209
Shag, 28
Shearwaters, 187, 198
  Buller's, 192
  Flesh-footed, 191
  Fluttering, 150
  Greater, 183, 187, 188, 189, 192, 200, 247, 283
  Manx, 29, 172, 187, 192, 219, 324, 326, 327, 340, 352, 361
  Short-tailed, 189, 190, 191, 283, 314
  Sooty, 192
Shelduck, 284, 285
Shoveler, 27, 90, 93
Shrikes,
  Brown, 232
  Cuckoo, 163
  Lesser Grey, 96, 290, 376
  Northern, 276
  Red-backed, 85, 86, 96, 215, 221, 222, 237, 238, 252, 253, 258, 283, 290, 325, 326, 355, 376, 383
  Woodchat, 250, 258
Sialia sialis sialis, 109
Skuas, 172, 276
  Great, 175
  Pomarine, 290
  Southern, 144
  South Polar, 193
Skylark, 29, 218, 227, 252, 259
Snipes, 28, 232
  Chilean lesser seed, 141
  European, 91
  Great, 91
  Jack, 91
  Magellanic, 141
Somateria, 200, 225
  mollissima, 28, 214
Song-larks,
  Brown, 146
  Rufous, 146
Sparrows, 261, 292
  Chipping, 218
  Fox, 121, 296, 306, 310, 381, 382, 383
  Golden-crowned, 121, 224, 296, 297, 306, 311
  Harris's, 121, 209
  House [or English], 29, 297, 299, 300, 301, 302, 311
  Ipswich, 209
  Puget Sound white-crowned, 306
  Savannah, 209
  Song, 121, 218, 252, 310, 317, 318
  Tree, 227, 296, 299, 301, 306
  White-crowned, 121, 296, 297, 305, 310, 311
  White-throated, 121, 297
Spatula clypeata, 27, 284
Sphenorynchus abdimi, 158, 159
Spinus tristis, 120
Spiza americana, 119
Spizella,
  arborea, 296, 306
  passerina, 218
Squatarola squatarola, 139, 163
Starlings, 28, 47, 69, 70, 72, 75, 210, 213, 218, 224, 225, 227, 232, 239, 253, 257, 290, 317, 323, 325, 330, 331, 333, 345, 347, 348, 349, 350, 351, 352, 353, 356, 361, 383
  Plum-colored, 144
  Rosy, 148, 276
  Splendid, 162
  Wattled, 264
Steganura, 312
Stelgidopteryx ruficollis, 325
Stellula calliope, 103
Stercorarius,
  longicaudus, 174
  parasiticus, 149
  pomarinus, 174
Sterna,
  balaenarum, 172
  fuscata, XIV
  hirundo, 29, 179, 325, 329, 388
  h. longipennis, 180
  macrura, 175

paradisaea, 29, 175, 176, 325
striata, 150, 151
Stilt, pied, 150
Stiltia isabella, 148
Stint, little, 259
Storks, 90, 161, 208, 214, 215, 216, 224, 230, 233, 259, 261, 290, 292, 321, 360, 361
Abdim's, 158, 159
Black, 54, 58, 258
European white, 50, 52, 220, 253, 324, 386
North African, 55
Strepera,
fuliginosa, 146
graculina, 146
Streptopelia turtur, 28, 219
Strigiformes, 276
Strix aluco, 47
Sturnella,
magna, 122, 202
neglecta, 355
Sturnus vulgaris, 28, 69, 70, 213, 218, 224, 227, 323, 325, 330, 331, 333, 348
Surnia ulula, 276
Swallows, 215, 217, 218, 219, 224, 233, 234, 235, 236, 251, 253, 254, 257, 259, 261, 281, 284, 323, 325, 379, 386
Bank or Sand martin, 10, 29
Barn, 65, 66, 68, 96, 107, 129, 138
Cliff, 106, 107, 130, 143, 232
European, 107, 252
Larger striped, 143
Northern cliff, 232
Patagonian, 142
Pearl-breasted, 143
Red-breasted, 143
Rough-winged, 325
Tree, 105, 106, 107
Violet-green, 106
Welcome, 145
White-throated, 143
Wood, 146
Swans, 374
Bewick's, 219
Mute, 372
Whooper, 45, 219
Swifts, 29, 68, 69, 218, 224, 232, 233, 234, 235, 251, 253, 254, 282, 283, 316, 325
Alpine, 325
American black, 69
Black, 69, 278, 279, 281
Chimney, 10, 107
Fork-tailed, 144
Horus, 143
Pallid, 69
Spine-tailed, 69, 144, 149, 201
White-rumped, 143
White-throated, 107
Sylvia, 257
atricapilla, 79, 81, 366, 367, 369, 370
borin, 29, 80, 81, 290, 366, 367, 370
cantillans, 80
communis, 29, 80, 254, 289, 294, 296, 298, 314, 370
conspicillata, 95
curruca, 366, 369
deserticola, 95
melanocephala, 96
nisoria, 355
Sylviidae, 25, 253, 289, 302, 375
Syrrhaptes paradoxus, 268

Tachycineta thalassina, 106
Tadorna tadorna, 284
Tanagers, 98, 258, 375
Cooper's summer, 115
Eastern summer, 113
Scarlet, 112, 114
Summer, 138
Western, 111, 112, 132
Tattlers,
American wandering, 203, 205
Asiatic wandering, 203
Teal, 28, 43, 45, 69, 70, 93
Blue-winged, 202, 332
Grey, 147

Terns,
  Arctic, 29, 172, 175, 176, 177, 178, 179, 180, 183, 247, 325, 340, 378, 379
  Asiatic common, 180
  Common, 29, 179, 180, 258, 325, 329, 388
  Damara, 172
  Sandwich, 29, 180, 181
  White-fronted, 150, 151
Terpsiphone viridis, 143
Tetraonidae, 269
Tetrao urogallus, 269
Thalasseus sandvicensis, 29, 180
Theristicus,
  caudatus branickii, 141
  c. melanopis, 141
Thinocorus r. rumicivorus, 141
Thornbill, brown, 147
Thrushes, 224, 240, 255, 316
  Bicknell's, 109
  Grey-cheeked, 109, 138, 222
  Hermit, 111
  Mistle, 28
  Olive-backed, 111
  Pallid, 232
  Rock, 252
  Russet-backed, 111
  Song, 77, 79, 251, 317, 318, 381
  Swainson's, 202
  Water, 114, 202
  Wood, 111
Timaliidae, 379
Tits, 75, 256
  Blue, 29, 322
  Coal, 264
  European, XV
  Great, 29, 76, 322
Totanus,
  erythropus, 259
  flavipes, 99, 202
  hypoleucos, 163
  melanoleuca, 99
  nebularia, 163, 206, 219, 259
  ochropus, 163
  totanus, 28
Towhee, rufous-sided, 120
  Tree-martin, 145, 147
Townsend's solitaire, 108
Trillers,
  Jardine, 146
  White-winged, 146
Tringa,
  glareola, 285
  hypoleucos, 206, 258, 386
  melanoleucus, 202
  solitaria, 202
Trochilidae, 98, 167, 375
Troglodytes aedon, 302
Tryngites subruficollis, 202
Tui, 149
Turdidae, 253, 302
Turdus,
  merula, 28, 76
  m. migratorius, 108, 109, 110, 129, 202, 218, 224
  musicus, 227, 243, 244
  m. coburni 243, 244, 245
  obscurus, 232
  philomelos, 77, 79, 381
  pilaris, 227, 372
  serranus, 381
  viscivorus, 28
Turnstone, 149, 222, 377
Turtledove, 253
Tympanuchus cupido, 252, 318
Tyrannidae, 253, 257, 375
Tyrannus,
  dominicensis, 169
  tyrannus, 105, 138
  verticalis, 105
Tyto alba, 28

Uria, 41, 200
  aalge, 28
Urodynamis taitensis, 152, 153
Vanellus vanellus, 29, 217, 219, 224
Veery, 109, 129
Vireo,
  altiloquus, 169
  flavoviridis, 168
  olivaceus, 137

virescens, 168
Vireos, 238, 253
Black-whiskered, 169
Red-eyed, 137, 168
Yellow-green, 168
Vultures, 224, 261
Egyptian, 64

WAGTAILS,
Blue-headed, 385
Pied, 83
Pied white, 29
White, 83, 84, 96, 317
Yellow, 29, 93, 110, 144, 218, 224, 227, 232, 290, 314, 377
Warblers, 223, 259
Arctic, 88, 94, 111, 377
Barred, 355
Black-and-white, 115, 116, 202
Blackpoll, 107, 117, 118, 138, 245
Cape May, 118
Chestnut-sided, 136
Connecticut, 118
Garden, 29, 80, 81, 290, 293, 366, 367, 368, 370
Golden-browed, 257
Greenish, 87, 94, 372
Icterine, 80, 255
Leaf, 29, 80, 255
Melodious, 80
Myrtle, 115, 116, 129
Olivaceous, 290
Pine, 115
Red, 257
River, 96
Sardinian, 96
Subalpine, 80
White-throated, 146
Willow, 80, 232, 235, 236, 237, 245, 290
Wood, 129, 222, 238
Yellow, 117, 138, 238
Wattle-bird, red, 147
Waxwings,
Bohemian, 263, 269, 270, 271, 272, 273, 276
Cedar, 274
Wheatear, 29, 79, 94, 109, 218, 221, 376, 377, 378, 383
Whimbrel, 219
Whinchat, 92
Whistlers,
Golden, 147, 312
Rufous, 145
Whitethroats, 29, 80, 254, 255, 289, 293, 294, 295, 296, 298, 314, 370
Lesser, 366, 368, 369
Whydah, paradise, 312
Widow-bird, 169
Widow, chuck-will's, 128
Wigeon, 27, 44, 45, 93, 202, 284
Willet, 139, 219
Woodcock, European, 28, 232, 240, 241, 317, 318
Woodpeckers,
Great spotted, 28, 263
Hairy, 252, 318
Wren, house, 302
Wryneck, 283, 323, 325

Xenus cinereus, 163

YELLOWHAMMER, 29, 299, 301
Yellowlegs,
Greater, 99, 202
Lesser, 99, 202

Zenaida auriculata stenura, 168
Zenaidura macroura, 101, 302
Zonotrichia,
albicollis, 121, 297
atricapilla [= *coronata*], 121, 224, 296, 297, 306, 311
leucophrys, 121, 296, 297, 310, 311
l. nuttalli, 297
l. pugetensis, 296, 306
querula, 121, 209
Zosterops,
erythropleura, 375
japonica, 375

Geographical Index

ABYSSINIA, 45, 58, 64, 65, 221
Addis Ababa, 58
Adélie Land, 22
Adriatic, 241
Ægean Sea, 84
Africa, 37, 38, 42, 45, 47, 48, 50, 56, 57, 58, 61, 62, 63, 64, 65, 66, 68, 77, 80, 81, 83, 87, 89, 90, 91, 92, 93, 95, 96, 136, 140, 156, 158, 159, 163, 165, 169, 176, 177, 179, 216, 253, 312, 376, 377, 383
Africa, Central, 54, 64, 66, 77, 158, 314
Africa, East, 40, 51, 55, 56, 57, 66, 79, 80, 81, 83, 84, 89, 96, 110, 158, 160, 163, 164, 165, 166, 168, 213, 290
Africa, North, 41, 48, 50, 51, 54, 55, 58, 60, 61, 69, 70, 73, 77, 79, 80, 82, 83, 84, 87, 89, 90, 204, 214, 258, 270, 276
Africa, South, 35, 54, 63, 64, 66, 77, 80, 84, 85, 89, 140, 143, 144, 165, 172, 176, 177, 180, 186, 205, 218, 264, 284, 292, 377, 378, 379, 383, 386
Africa, Southwest, 179, 370
Africa, West, 40, 51, 57, 64, 66, 68, 79, 80, 84, 96, 143, 157, 172, 174, 176, 179, 186, 253, 322, 383
Ahaggar, 55, 56, 57, 91
Aiguillon Bay, 88
Ait-Baha, 56
Aland, 250
Alaska, 94, 99, 101, 102, 103, 104, 105, 107, 108, 109, 110, 111, 117, 121, 128, 131, 132, 133, 205, 220, 273, 376, 377, 381
Alberta, 112, 249
Aleutian Islands, 173, 189, 205
Alexandria, 60
Algeria, 38, 55, 56, 64, 77, 91
Alps, 88, 98, 215, 264, 281, 376
Alsace, 51, 54
Altai Range, 276
Amani, 312
Amazon, 106, 139, 142, 167, 168, 169
America, Central, 98, 99, 101, 102, 104, 107, 109, 111, 114, 115, 116, 117, 119, 122, 124, 126, 135, 136, 137, 142, 167, 168, 209, 214, 242, 274, 377
America, Latin, 156
America, North, 34, 35, 45, 72, 88, 97, 98, 100, 101, 102, 103, 105, 106, 107, 108, 109, 111, 115, 116, 121, 126, 132, 133, 134, 135, 136, 138, 139, 168, 173, 174, 175, 176, 177, 183, 190, 200, 207, 209, 222, 237, 239, 247, 252, 274, 318, 335, 371, 372, 374, 377
America, South, 98, 99, 100, 102, 105, 106, 107, 109, 111, 113, 117, 118, 119, 123, 124, 128, 136, 139, 140, 141, 142, 167, 168, 169, 172, 174, 177, 183, 185, 186, 192, 196, 214, 280, 292, 297, 375, 381
Amsterdam Island, 177, 185
Andalucia, 58, 60
Andes, 138, 139, 142, 168, 224

Angola, 64, 159, 161
Antarctic, 35, 144, 149, 175, 182, 193, 194, 195, 196, 197
Antilles, 117, 169
Antipodes Islands, 149
Antwerp, 198
Appalachians, 98
Arabia, 58, 66, 88, 218
Arabian Sea, 185
Archangelsk, 44
Arctic Ocean, 97, 189, 269
Argentina, 100, 103, 107, 111, 123, 138, 141, 142, 167, 174, 177, 204, 376
Arizona, 104, 111
Arkansas, 115, 131
Asia, 37, 43, 45, 47, 50, 51, 58, 61, 69, 87, 89, 90, 92, 93, 94, 95, 101, 109, 111, 144, 148, 156, 175, 215, 232, 264, 268, 284, 377, 383
Asia, East, 166
Asia Minor, 60, 61, 62, 64, 83, 85, 90, 221, 376
Asia, South-east, 166
Assam, 58
Atacama, 142
Athabaska Lake, 132
Athens, 323
Atlantic, 87, 88, 102, 111, 119, 126, 127, 128, 133, 139, 171, 172, 173, 174, 175, 177, 178, 179, 180, 181, 182, 183, 185, 186, 187, 188, 189, 192, 195, 198, 199, 200, 201, 204, 205, 214, 247, 284, 326
Australia, 34, 50, 69, 95, 133, 140, 144, 145, 146, 147, 148, 149, 150, 151, 152, 153, 156, 171, 175, 178, 179, 180, 186, 189, 190, 191, 192, 205, 206, 264, 377, 378
Austria, 73, 74, 323
Azores, 49, 183, 187, 192, 204, 245

Babel Island, 191
Baffin Island, 195
Bahamas, 107, 116, 119, 169
Balaton (Hungary), 41
Balearics, 70, 77
Bali, 145
Balkan Peninsula, 48
Baltic, 32, 40, 41, 43, 45, 46, 61, 62, 72, 73, 83, 88, 89, 213, 285, 328, 331, 371
Baltimore, 317
Baluchistan, 45, 218
Banks Island, 151
Barbary Coast, XIV, 80
Basel, 331, 333
Bass Strait, 189
Bay of Biscay, 187, 192, 340
Bay of Whales (Antarctica), 200
Belfort Gap, 74
Belgium, 35, 47, 48, 59, 61, 67, 70, 71, 73, 74, 76, 77, 331
Benguella Current, 172
Bering Strait, 94, 189, 205
Berkeley (California), 305, 307
Berlin, 38, 39, 323, 324, 326
Bermuda, 99, 100, 101, 125, 128, 192, 377
Berne, 326
Bismarck Archipelago, 152, 153, 201
Black Sea, 33, 40, 41, 46, 54, 60, 93
Bohemia, 74
Bolivia, 105, 113, 114, 123
Bombay, XV
Bonaventure Island (Gaspé Peninsula), 343, 344
Bonin Islands, 205
Borku, 55
Borneo, 146, 232
Bosphorus, 51, 53, 54, 60, 61, 90, 208, 257, 260, 262
Boston (Massachusetts), 326
Bounty Island, 149
Brandenburg, 216
Brazil, 99, 101, 107, 109, 114, 117, 118, 123, 138, 139, 142, 167, 171, 186
Bremen, 368

British Columbia, 101, 103, 105, 108, 109, 112, 122, 132, 279
British Guiana, 138
British Isles, 43, 48, 53, 69, 75, 77, 83, 88, 173, 174, 186, 187, 192, 195, 223, 237, 240, 242, 245, 270, 318
Brittany, 33, 48, 75, 192
Brunswick (Germany), 58
Buenos Aires, 142, 174, 195
Bukhara, 51
Burgundy, 59
Burma, 45, 58, 166

CAIRO, 220
California, 98, 101, 103, 104, 105, 106, 111, 112, 118, 121, 132, 133, 135, 171, 173, 190, 208, 224, 232, 267, 273, 280, 381, 382
Calvados (France), 181
Camargue, 33, 38, 47, 50, 59, 285
Cameroons, 54, 65, 156, 157
Campbell Island, 196
Canada, 35, 72, 97, 98, 99, 102, 103, 105, 107, 109, 111, 113, 115, 117, 118, 119, 120, 121, 122, 123, 124, 125, 126, 127, 135, 173, 208, 219, 273, 274, 276, 186, 316, 343
Canaries Current, 174
Cannes, 281
Cap Bon, 33, 90
Cap Breton, 221
Cape Charles, 211
Cape Cod, 211, 388
Cape Frio (Brazil), 193
Cape Horn, 192, 195, 196
Cape Lopez, 172
Cape May, 128, 211
Cape of Good Hope, 54, 81, 94, 175, 179
Cape Province, 66, 80
Cape San Antonio, 192
Cape Verde Islands, 49, 173, 174, 341
Caracas, XV
Caribbean, 141, 214
Caribou (Maine), 344
Caroline Islands, 153, 205
Caspian Sea, 41, 93, 165
Castilla, 59
Caucasus, 61, 341
Celebes, 145
Central Palearctic, 92
Ceylon, 45, 58, 165, 166, 379
Chaco, 139
Chad, 55, 56, 57, 65
Chagos Islands, 206
Champagne, 59
Chesapeake Bay, 126, 135
Chile, 99, 107, 117, 138, 141, 142, 167, 174, 175, 177, 192
China, 58, 92, 144, 165, 166, 167, 268, 375, 379
Christianshab district, 177
Churchill, 275
Cirque de Gavarnie (Pyrenees), 215
Clairmarais, 48, 49
Colombia, 102, 105, 107, 113, 118, 119, 122, 138, 142, 167, 169
Colorado, 273
Columbia River, 132
Comoro Islands, 163
Congo, 40, 54, 66, 68, 85, 143, 156, 157, 158, 160, 161, 162, 163, 164, 165, 314
Connecticut, 329
Cordoba, 141
Costa Rica, 105, 106, 111, 113, 136, 168
Cotentin, 88
Crete, 53
Crimea, 66, 234
Croisic, 341
Cuba, 102, 105, 117, 124, 128, 129, 130, 136, 169, 377
Czechoslovakia, 35, 66, 67

DALMATIA, 221
Damaraland, 159
Danube, 41
Dardanelles, 62

Dchang, 54
Deccan, 58, 221
Dehra Dun, 224
Delaware (Bay), 126, 128
Denmark, 40, 41, 43, 53, 58, 67, 75, 78, 212, 229, 242, 331
Denver, 273
Derbyshire (Great Britain), 198
Devon Island, 195
Dieppe, 198
Dnieper, 41
Dobruja, 54, 60
Dominican Republic, 109
Doñana (Huelva, Spain), 204
Doubs, 59
Draa, 77
Drave, 241
Durban Harbour, 177
Dutch Lesser Antilles, 245

Eastern Cape Province (South Africa), 176
Eastern Egg Rock (Maine), 176
Ecuador, 102, 105, 109, 113, 115, 117, 119, 138, 180, 193
Edmonton (Alberta), 286, 288
Egypt, 41, 54, 60, 64, 66, 77, 80, 81, 82, 83, 84, 85, 221, 252, 258, 341, 385
Elbe, 75, 229
Elburz, 93
Ellesmere, 195
Ellice (Islands), 153
El Tabo (Santiago, Chile), 196
England, 25, 33, 36, 46, 48, 53, 62, 66, 71, 73, 74, 77, 89, 194, 216, 217, 228, 229, 242, 244, 246, 266, 267, 276, 290, 317, 318, 320, 326, 331, 340, 341
English Channel, 41, 53, 187
Ennedi, 55
Entebbe (Uganda), 314
Erie, Lake, 240
Eritrea, 165
Esbo, 250
Essen (Germany), 321, 328
Estremadura, 58
Ethiopia, 87, 96
Eurasia, 95, 174
Europe, 33, 35, 36, 38, 40, 42, 43, 44, 45, 46, 47, 48, 49, 50, 52, 58, 61, 62, 63, 64, 65, 66, 68, 69, 70, 71, 72, 73, 75, 77, 79, 80, 81, 82, 83, 84, 85, 87, 88, 89, 91, 93, 94, 96, 97, 115, 128, 173, 177, 179, 183, 184, 186, 187, 202, 204, 208, 210, 213, 220, 221, 241, 242, 243, 245, 246, 251, 253, 257, 264, 266, 268, 270, 271, 274, 276, 284, 285, 290, 293, 314, 315, 317, 326, 370, 372, 373, 374, 376, 377, 382
Everest, Mt., 225

FAIR ISLE, 31, 242, 243, 244, 245
Falkland Islands, 22, 180, 187, 194, 199
Far Eastern Palearctic, 92
Faroes, 175, 187, 192
Fiji Islands, 153, 205
Finistère, 33, 187
Finland, 59, 60, 70, 83, 88, 224, 241, 249, 264, 265, 270, 271, 272, 320, 328, 372
Fish Point (Lake Huron), 211
Flensburg, 328, 329
Flinders Island (Tasmania), 191
Florida, 47, 102, 107, 109, 111, 113, 117, 118, 119, 124, 128, 129, 130, 131, 136, 169, 180, 210, 297
Formosa, 201, 379
Franconia, 73, 74
France, 33, 40, 43, 44, 45, 46, 47, 48, 51, 55, 59, 61, 62, 63, 64, 68, 70, 71, 73, 74, 75, 76, 77, 79, 80, 81, 82, 83, 89, 90, 173, 176, 181, 184, 186, 204, 208, 214, 218, 219, 224, 242, 266, 268, 270, 276, 281, 317, 322, 331
Frankfurt-on-Main, 328
Freemantle, 179, 180, 194
Frisian Islands, 211

GABON, 54, 96, 162, 172
Galicia, 60
Gambia, 50, 66, 182
Garonne, 77
Gascoyne River, 145
Gaspé Peninsula, 13, 316
Geneva, 39, 331, 333
Georgia, 209
Germany, 43, 46, 47, 48, 51, 58, 59, 61, 62, 63, 67, 69, 70, 71, 73, 75, 76, 77, 78, 79, 82, 83, 88, 218, 219, 222, 224, 227, 229, 241, 242, 267, 276, 281, 320, 321, 322, 331, 356, 367
Ghana, 35, 66
Gibraltar, Straits of, 51, 53, 55, 61, 90, 253
Gold Coast, 40
Gran Chaco, 100
Grand Banks of Newfoundland, 195
Great Britain, 32, 40, 41, 42, 44, 45, 48, 62, 66, 67, 69, 70, 83, 184, 186, 202, 220, 234, 241, 243, 245, 246, 268, 284, 290, 318, 322
Great Lakes, 124, 126, 128, 211, 238, 247
Great Plains, 101, 104, 131, 247, 248
Great Slave Lake, 132
Great Smoky Mountains, 115
Greater Antilles, 116, 117, 119, 169
Greater Sunda Islands, 166
Greece, 45, 64, 81, 82, 84, 85, 264
Greenland, 79, 88, 173, 177, 186, 187, 192, 242, 245, 281, 283, 284, 372, 376, 377
Grenada, 169
Grenadines, 169
Griqualand, 220
Guatemala, 101, 102, 105, 106, 111, 114, 119, 125, 135, 136
Guerrero, 103
Guiana, 117, 119, 142, 167
Guiana, British, 138
Guinea, 157, 158
Guir, 55
Gulf Coast, 113, 122, 129, 130, 131, 132, 135, 201, 297
Gulf of Campeche, 131
Gulf of Gascony, 41
Gulf of Genoa, 41
Gulf of Mexico, 97, 99, 102, 106, 107, 113, 117, 124, 125, 126, 129, 174, 201, 208, 220, 247, 297
Gulf of St. Lawrence, 127
Gulf States, 97, 98, 104, 105, 106, 109, 111, 115, 116, 117, 119, 129, 131, 133, 135, 208
Gulf Stream, 183

HAGUE, 330, 333
Haiti, 109, 128
Hamburg, 251, 257
Hawaiian Islands, 101, 205, 220
Hawk Mountain Sanctuary, 219, 247, 257
Heard Island, 177, 195
Hebrides, 246
Heligoland, 24, 29, 31, 64, 216, 222, 227, 228, 252, 284, 359
Hemisphere, northern, 158, 159, 160, 165, 291, 358, 374, 386
Hemisphere, southern, 140, 160, 182, 193, 194, 291, 378
Henderson Island, 205
Himalayas, 92, 166, 215, 225
Hispaniola, 109, 119
Holland, 43, 47, 48, 51, 54, 59, 71, 73, 210, 224, 228, 252, 319, 345, 346
Honduras, 113
Hudson Bay, 127
Humboldt (or Peruvian) Current, 172, 186, 193
Hungary, 58, 60, 66, 67, 240, 241, 270, 271

IBERIAN PENINSULA, 41, 44, 48, 55, 70, 77, 81, 83, 264, 322, 331
Iceland, 26, 43, 44, 79, 88, 173, 175, 186, 187, 195, 242, 243, 244,

245, 270, 372
Idaho, 108
Ifrane, 54
Ikamint, 177
Illinois, 104
Illinois River Valley, 363
India, 45, 58, 89, 90, 93, 95, 165, 166, 180, 201, 205, 215, 225, 378, 379
Indian Ocean, 150, 177, 178, 179, 192
Indochina, 93, 165, 166, 167
Indonesia, 145
Ionian Sea, 90
Iowa, 134
Iran, 93
Iraq, 45, 219, 224
Ireland, 53, 69, 70, 187, 192, 218, 219, 228, 276, 326, 331
Irharhar, 55
Irish Sea, 187
Isle of May, 31
Israel, 224
Istambul, 262
Isthmus of Panama, 174
Istria, 221
Italy, 35, 38, 39, 40, 41, 44, 45, 49, 50, 53, 60, 63, 64, 70, 73, 76, 77, 79, 80, 81, 84
Ituri, 162
Ivory Coast, 66

JALISCO, 103
Jamaica, 123, 124, 173
James Bay, 97, 222, 248
Japan, 35, 51, 58, 93, 144, 173, 178, 191, 201
Java, 146
Jjebel Tichka, 57
Jordan Valley, 224
Jura, 47, 74
Jutland, 58

KAMCHATKA, 189, 191
Kandalaksha, 33, 178
Kansas, 121, 135
Kasai, 163
Katanga, 66
Kearney (Nebraska), 335
Kentucky, 122
Kenya, 45, 54, 66, 80, 83, 84, 156, 165, 218, 220, 221, 224, 385
Kerguelen Island, 185, 193, 195, 199, 206
Kermedec Islands, 153
Keweenaw Point (Lake Superior), 211
Kharlov Island, 173
Khumbu Glacier, 225
Korea, 51, 58
Kurische Nehrung, 211, 212, 228
Kurisches Haff, 212

LABRADOR, 97, 99, 100, 124, 125, 176, 192
Ladoga, Lake, 38
Lake Chad, 54
Lake Fitri, 54
Lake Nyassa, 40
Lake Victoria, 40
Landes, 88
Laos, 166
Lapland, 58, 173
La Rochelle (France), 176
Latvia, 70
Laurel (Maryland), 34
Lech, 51
Leger Brook (New Brunswick), 47
Leiden, 32, 51
Lena River, 205
Leningrad, 31
Lesser Antilles, 99, 101, 115, 125, 128, 169
Libya, 81, 214
Lima, 55, 142
Lithuania, 54
Little Sunda Islands, 148, 152
Loire, 47, 70, 204
Lombok, 152
London, 323
Long Island, 100, 105
Lord Howe Island, 152
Lorraine, 47, 59, 208

Louisiana, 99, 117, 222, 248
Lower California, 111
Lucerne, 326
Lugano, 326
Lunsjäholm, 250
Lyon, 325

MACHIAS SEAL ISLAND, 176
Mackenzie, 104, 128, 131, 134
Macquarie Island, 194, 199
Madagascar, 47, 163, 164, 165, 179, 201, 206, 377
Madeira, 175, 192
Madrid, 323
Maine, 111, 116, 117, 122, 124, 176, 329
Malay Peninsula, 109, 144, 146
Malaya, 93, 148, 166, 201
Malaysia, 93, 95, 101, 144, 232, 375
Malta, 53
Manchuria, 94, 375
Manitoba, 103
Marburg, 51
Margate, 176
Marquesas, 153
Marseilles, 326
Martinique, 169
Massachusetts, 115, 117, 124, 186
Massif Central, 264
Matto Grosso, 139
Mauritania, 42, 49, 57, 91
Mediterranean, 38, 40, 41, 50, 53, 59, 60, 61, 62, 63, 64, 66, 68, 73, 77, 79, 80, 81, 85, 86, 87, 88, 89, 90, 97, 130, 136, 201, 202, 208, 213, 214, 219, 244, 268, 285, 326, 371, 375
Melanesia, 101
Melbourne, 34
Memphis (Tennessee), 131
Mendoza, 141
Mesopotamia, 41, 58, 61
Mexico, 72, 102, 103, 106, 107, 108, 109, 111, 113, 115, 116, 117, 119, 129, 130, 134, 136, 142, 168, 171, 180, 257, 279, 293
Mexico, Gulf of, 129, 130, 238
Michigan, 122, 124
Michoacan, 103, 114
Micronesia, 101, 205
Midway Island, 326
Minden, 51
Minnesota, 122
Mississippi, 115, 126, 133
Mississippi Valley, 72, 99, 100, 119, 124, 129, 131
Missouri, 129
Mongolia, 92
Montana, 108, 131, 132, 273
Montserrat (Lesser Antilles), 204
Morocco, 42, 48, 51, 54, 55, 56, 63, 66, 79, 84, 285
Mozambique Channel, 163
Müritz, 59
Murmansk, 33, 173, 179
Myslowice, 240

NAPO RIVER, 168
Natal, 80, 176, 177, 220
Near East, 81, 85, 208, 260
Nebraska, 336
Netherlands, 25, 32, 35, 44, 46, 50, 51, 61, 67, 77, 210, 211, 230, 331, 333, 362
New England, 274, 275
Neusiedler (Austria), 41
Neustadt, 56
Nevada, 104
New Amsterdam, 205
New Brunswick, 101, 102, 122, 176
New Caledonia, 151, 152
Newfoundland, 173, 186, 187, 201, 279
New Guinea, 144, 145, 146, 148, 152, 186
New Hampshire, 104, 117
New Hebrides, 152, 312
New Jersey, 127, 135
New Mexico, 111, 131, 273
New South Wales, 145, 146
New York City, 72
New York State, 117, 274

New Zealand, 35, 101, 133, 140, 148, 149, 150, 151, 152, 153, 174, 178, 192, 201, 205, 220, 377, 378
Niari River, 162
Nicaragua, 142
Niger, 48, 57, 68, 176
Nigeria, 35, 63, 66, 143, 160, 176
Nile, 40, 54, 91, 213, 214
Norfolk, 53, 152, 153, 181
Normandy, 47, 48, 186
North Carolina, 105, 121, 122, 127, 356
North Dakota, 135, 248
Northern Territory, 147
North Sea, 45, 88, 89, 216, 219, 224, 227, 242, 244, 245, 246, 284
Norway, 41, 229, 268
Nova Scotia, 104, 107, 125, 209
Nyanga River, 162

OCEANIA, 133, 153, 154, 201, 205
Ohio, 101, 104, 109, 129
Oka, 33
Oklahoma, 135
Oland, 32, 250, 285, 328
Ontario, 109, 371
Orbigo Valley, 73
Oregon, 112, 132, 200
Orinoco, 168
Orkney Island, 175, 192
Orlov Island, 40, 41
Osnabrück, 51
Ottawa, 34
Ottenby, 32, 285
Ouessant, 33, 88

PACIFIC, 35, 126, 133, 135, 139, 154, 167, 171, 172, 174, 175, 177, 178, 180, 186, 189, 190, 191, 192, 205, 284, 326, 383
Pahlevi, 93
Palau, 201
Palestine, 51, 54, 218, 219
Panama, 102, 104, 105, 111, 114, 119, 135, 136, 139, 142, 274
Paraguay, 167
Paris, 186, 218
Pas-de-Calais, 47
Patache, Chile, 195
Patagonia, 97, 140, 142, 174, 375, 376, 378
Pemba Island, 165
Pennsylvania, 126, 257, 336
Pennsylvania State College, 335
Perry River, 132
Persia, 58, 77
Persian Gulf, 41, 385
Peru, 99, 102, 105, 109, 111, 113, 117, 138, 141, 142, 167, 171, 174, 193
Philippines, 45, 326
Poland, 35, 44, 54, 66, 67, 73, 74, 88, 89, 267, 331
Polynesia, 101, 153, 205
Pomerania, 71
Port of Spain (Trinidad), 204
Port Shepstone, 176
Portugal, 35, 48, 60, 174, 317, 341
Portuguese East Africa, 161
Prussia, 46, 48, 58, 71, 83, 321
Puerto Rico, 128
Pyrenees, 59, 88, 98, 208

QUEENSLAND, 145

RADOLFZELL, 30, 31
Rajputana, 58
Red Sea, 40, 53, 156, 158, 160, 185
Renell Island, 151
Rhine, 41
Rhodesia, 66
Rhône, 38, 47, 59, 77
Rio de Janeiro, 192
Rio Negro (Buenos Aires), 141
Rocky Mountains, 98, 103, 111, 131, 132
Romania, 54
Ross Archipelago, 200
Rossitten, 30, 31, 39, 54, 211, 212, 328, 329

Russia, 32, 38, 41, 43, 44, 46, 51, 60, 73, 75, 88, 89, 173, 215, 233, 234, 244, 266, 268, 284
Ryazan, 33
Rybatschi, 31, 211, 212, 328

SACRAMENTO, 132, 133
Sahara, 55, 56, 57, 64, 68, 77, 80, 81, 84, 87, 90, 91, 95, 96, 97, 136, 158, 159, 375, 377
Sahel, 96
Sable Island, 209
St. Flavié (Pictou), 344
Saint Kilda, 32
St. Lawrence, 247
St. Nazaire, 176
St. Lucia, 119
Saint Paul Rocks, 182
Salonica, 221, 324
Salvador, 105, 136
Samoa, 153
San Joaquin, 132, 133
San Juan Capistrano, 232
Sand Point (Lake Huron), 211
Santa Barbara, 101
Santa Cruz, 151, 205
Santa Fé, 141, 142
Saône, 47
Saoura, 55, 57
Sardinia, 50
Sargasso Sea, 173, 175
Saskatchewan, 103, 135
Saxony, 38, 70, 216
Scandinavia, 32, 43, 58, 59, 61, 62, 67, 73, 75, 83, 89, 173, 210, 220, 243, 244, 245, 252, 264, 270, 271, 276, 315, 316, 372
Schleswig, 38, 58, 71, 371
Schonen, 59
Schweinfurt, 51
Scotland, 31, 181, 187, 216
Sea of Oman, 41
Séfrou, 54
Sempach, 32
Senegal, XVI, 35, 40, 41, 42, 64, 80, 156, 158, 160
Senegambia, 45, 179
Sevilla, 56
Sfax, 50
Shetlands, 31, 175, 192, 193, 242
Siam, 166
Siberia, 45, 69, 73, 85, 88, 92, 93, 95, 96, 101, 109, 173, 210, 205, 225, 240, 268, 270, 375, 376, 379
Sicily, 60
Sierra Leone, 40, 79, 159
Sierra Nevada, 280
Signy Island (South Orkneys), 194
Sikkim, 284
Silesia, 38, 70, 73, 74
Sinai, 54, 64, 221
Skagerak, 244
Skane, 257
Skokholm, 32, 172, 187, 192, 221, 326, 327, 340, 361
Slimbridge, 32
Smith Point, 246
Society Islands, 153
Sologne, 59
Solomons, 144, 146, 152, 153, 201, 205
Somaliland, 45
Somme Bay, 88
South Carolina, 121
South Dakota, 111, 135
South Georgia, 193, 199
South Pole, 140, 193, 198
South Sea, 93
Spain, 35, 38, 40, 44, 48, 50, 51, 55, 58, 59, 61, 63, 73, 76, 77, 79, 81, 82, 84, 89, 185, 317, 341
Spitzbergen, 195, 281
Spurn Head, 32
Strait of Magellan, 180
Strasbourg, 59
Sudan, 157, 219
Sudan, Anglo-Egyptian, 45, 54, 58, 83, 96, 220
Sudan, French, 156
Suez, Gulf of, 53, 54, 230
Suffolk, 53
Sumatra, 146

Sumbawa, 146
Sunda Islands, 146
Surinam, 139
Sussex, 48, 53
Sweden, 32, 48, 58, 82, 180, 209, 212, 214, 250, 272, 316, 328, 372, 383
Switzerland, 32, 41, 62, 71, 73, 82, 255, 281, 330
Syria, 54, 82, 85, 224, 376

TADEMAIT, 57
Tahiti, 205
Tamanrasset, 55
Tamaulipas, 104
Tampa, 47
Tanezrouft, 57
Tanganyika, 63, 64, 79, 84, 143, 158, 159, 161, 163, 165, 219, 312
Tanoura (Shikoku Island, Japan), 191
Tarragona, 221
Tasman Sea, 150
Tasmania, 69, 101, 140, 145, 146, 150, 151, 152, 189, 191, 201
Texas, 99, 102, 103, 111, 113, 121, 130, 131, 135, 201, 250
Thomasville, XV
Tibet, 284
Tierra del Fuego, 142
Tizi-n-Test, 57
Togo, 64, 157
Tokyo, 35
Tombouctou, 50, 68
Tomsk, ʒ67, 269
Tonga, 153, 205
Toubkal, 57
Tour de Valat, 33
Tranninh, 166
Transcaucasia, 41
Transvaal, 159, 220, 221
Trinidad, 204
Tripolitania, 84
Tristan da Cunha, 187, 188, 192, 205, 206
Tropic of Cancer, 173, 182
Tropic of Capricorn, 196
Tuamotus, 153, 201
Tunisia, 33, 40, 41, 55, 60, 61, 77, 84, 90
Turkestan, 51, 58, 69, 276
Turkey, 51, 54, 82
Turnevik Bay, 176
Tuskar R. K., 224

UBANGI, 162
Ubangi-Shari, 48, 54
Uele, 163
Uganda, 54, 160, 165
Ukraine, 60, 73, 74, 267
Ungava, 127
United Kingdom, 218, 219, 224
Uruguay, 141
Upemba, 68
Uppland, 180
Uruguay, 99
U.S.A., 33, 35, 47, 72, 102, 105, 109, 113, 115, 117, 118, 119, 120, 121, 122, 134, 171, 182, 201, 204, 211, 218, 219, 242, 247, 255, 276, 279, 280, 286, 316, 320, 326, 330, 332, 336, 359
U.S.S.R., 66, 178
Ussuri, 51, 58
Utah, 104

VALDIVIA, 142
Vancouver, 112
Varanger, 235
Vendée, 48, 59
Venezuela, 102, 109, 116, 117, 118, 119, 122, 142, 167, 169, 245
Venice, 323, 326, 327
Veracruz, 109, 136
Versailles, 33
Viborg, 54
Victoria, 140, 145, 147
Virginia, 115, 122, 127, 128
Vlieland (Netherlands), 213
Volga, 284
Volga Delta, 33

Vosges Mountains, 74

Wales, 326
Washington, 112
Washington (D.C.), 34
Weddell Sea, 177
Weser, 51
West Indies, 49, 98, 99, 100, 107, 115, 117, 118, 119, 126, 128, 168, 169, 204
White Nile, 60, 61
White Sea, 178
Wilderness, 176
Willamette River, 132
Windward Islands, 100
Wrangel Island, 190

Yarkand, 51, 58
Yenissei, 92
Yucatan, 114, 117, 129, 130, 131
Yugoslavia, 60
Yukon River, 132
Yukon Territory, 249

Zacatecas, 103
Zambesi, 165
Zousfara, 55
Zürich, 15, 16, 331, 333

Biographical Index

ABDULALI, 90
Adanson, 9
Agricola, G., 5
Aldrich, John W., 34, 135
Aldrovandi, Ulysses, 6
Alexander, 202
Ali, XV
Allen, A. A., 205
Anacreon, 2
Anderson, 200
Angot, 195, 196
Arnhem, 23
Aristophanes, 2
Aristotle, 2
Audubon, J. J., 10, 19, 104, 182
Austin, 20, 175, 176, 388

BAGG, 246
Baird, 18, 138
Baker, 312
Baldwin, 278, 296
Ball, 13, 316
Bannerman, 156
Barnwell, F. H., 359
Bartholomew, 280
Bartsch, Paul, 20, 33
Batrawi, 290, 292
Baughman, 7
Baxter, 242
Beebe, 245
Beecher, 338
Bellrose, 247, 248, 332, 363, 364, 366
Belon, Pierre, 6, 202
Benedict, 302
Bennett, M. F., 359
Benoit, 304, 309
Bent, XV, 98, 232
Berndt, 263
Bernis, 55, 56, 57, 60
Bissonnette, 310, 311
Blanchard, 296
Bodenstein, 46
Bogert, 153
Böhringer, 90
Bonaparte, 182
Bon Saint Come, 169
Bond, 119
Bonham, 15
Bont, de, 66, 297
Bouet, 55, 56
Bourdelle, E., 33
Bourlière, 301
Boyd, 186
Brackbill, 317
Brett, W. J., 359
Brickenstein-Stockhammer, 29, 81
Broekhuysen, 284
Broley, 47
Broun, 219, 258, 312, 359
Buffon, 9
Bullis, 130
Bullock, 99, 138
Bullough, 290
Burckhardt, 281
Burr, 61
Busnel, 359
Butterfield, 245

CADE, 258
Carrick, 171, 193, 194
Casamajor, 332, 335
Caub, Johann Wonnecke von, 4

Cendron, J., 23
Chapin, J. P., XIV, 63, 91, 92, 156, 157, 158, 159, 160, 161, 162, 163, 164
Chapman, F. M., 138
Chappellier, A., 33
Claparède, 341
Clarke, Eagle, 242
Cochran, 13
Connell, 297
Cooch, 222
Cook, Captain, 205
Cooke, W. W., 98, 129, 237, 240
Coombes, 284
Cornwallis, 246
Creutz, 81, 322
Crocker, 238
Crozier, 339
Culbertson, 279
Curry-Lindahl, 258, 304, 314
Cuvier, Georges, 9

DACHY, 325
Dancker, 263
Dare, 345
Darwin, Charles, 386
David, Beaulieu, 166
Davis, T. A. M., 137, 138, 246, 267, 276
Deelder, 78, 207, 210, 211, 225, 226, 228, 252
Delacour, J., 163, 166
Dementiev, 173
Dennis, 246
Dennler de la Tour, 138, 139, 142
Desselberger, 290
Devlin, 247
Dickey, 136
Dircksen, 325
Dixon, 196, 197, 198
Dobben, 210, 211, 213
Domm, 312
Donker, 45
Donovan, E., 132
Dorst, 185
Douaud, 157
Dove, H. Stuart, 69
Downes, 193
Drost, 29, 64, 65, 76, 80, 81, 84, 216, 227, 240, 359, 363
Dunnet, 178, 180
Dutertre, Jean Baptiste, 6

EDELSTAM, 250
Eichler, 77, 79
Eisenmann, E., 139, 142
Eklund, 193
Elgood, 156
Eliasson, 245
Elliot, 105
Elliott, H. F. I., 205
Ellis, 316
Erard, 41
Eyster, 289, 297

FALLA, 149, 192
Farner, 289, 297
Favaloro, 180
Fisher, James, 26, 31, 32, 115, 177, 195, 198
Fitter, 202
Flinders, 189
Fog, 280
Forbush, 175
Formosov, 265, 267
Forster, 229, 231
Fox, 325
Fragnière, 325
Franzisket, 260, 261
Frederick II of Hohenstaufen, 4
Friedmann, 65
Frisch, von, 350, 354
Frith, 147

GAIN, L., 20
Gätke, Heinrich, 31, 216, 223
Gavin, A., 132
Géroudet, 225
Gesner, Conrad, 5
Giban, 73, 74
Gladstone, R., 8
Glover, 148

Gmelin, 8
Goethe, F., 31
Goldsmith, 329
Gould, 191, 279
Graber, 13
Grant, 165
Greenway, 99
Griffin, 17, 323, 324, 325, 326, 327, 329, 330, 332, 337, 338, 339, 340, 341, 342, 343, 344, 345, 346, 347, 351, 357, 362
Griscom, L., 117, 119, 135
Grittner, 76
Groebbels, 295, 302
Groskin, 10
Gross, 128, 274, 275
Grote, 65, 269
Gudmundsson, 373
Gunn, 238
Gurtchich, 50
Gwynn, 193

HAARTMAN, 248
Hamilton, 258
Harper, 15
Harrison, H. G., 229
Harrison, 217, 232, 312
Haverschmidt, 51, 139
Hawksley, 176
Heim de Balsac, H. and T., XIV, 95
Heim de Balsac, 56, 66, 69, 80
Heinemann, 350
Heinroth, 252, 345
Hemmingesen, 58, 383
Hempel, 79, 82, 83
Henning, 233
Hillary, Sir Edmund, 193
Hindwood, 146, 150, 153
Hitchcock, 180, 193, 194, 327
Hobbs, 145
Hochbaum, 247
Hock, 324, 327, 343, 344
Hodge, 342, 343
Hoffmann, L., 33, 285, 356
Homer, 2
Howard, 193
Howell, 280
Hudson, 141
Hugues, 278
Hunter, John, 9

ISAKOV, 388
Ising, 334, 338

JANY, 95
Jeremiah, 1
Jespersen, 56, 172, 175
Johnston, 297
Jouanin, 184, 186, 205

KALELA, 372
Keast, A., 146
Kemper, XVIII
Kendeigh, 278, 296, 302
Kenyon, 324, 326
Kessell, 72
Kipp, 379, 380
Klein, J. T., 8
Knabe, 48
Knorr, 359
Koch, 227, 233
Koskimies, 69, 278
Kramer, VIII, IX, 327, 347, 348, 349, 350, 351, 352, 353, 354, 255, 356, 357, 358, 359, 361, 362, 363, 366, 367
Kratzig, 71, 72
Küchler, 299, 300, 301
Kühk, R., 30, 281
Kullenberg, 57, 91, 175, 176
Kuroda, 35, 189, 191

LACK, 15, 201, 209, 215, 223, 239, 317, 318, 319, 324, 326, 327
Laenen, 96
Lavauden, 163
Lebret, 43
Le Grelle, 50
Lewis, 127, 240
Libbert, 59, 60
Liche, 324
Lincoln, F. C., 98, 102, 106, 107,

111, 112, 113, 114, 116, 118, 120, 123, 125, 126, 128, 133, 137, 139, 176, 209, 222, 237, 239, 273
Linnaeus, 8, 9, 252
Linsdale, 296, 297
Lockley, R. M., 32, 172, 177, 187, 192, 324, 326, 327, 340
Loetscher, 136
Lorenz, 225, 281
Lowery, IX, 13, 14, 15, 129, 130, 131, 241, 247, 255, 363, 367

MacCabe, 320
McCartan, 184
McGee, 124
MacGill, 146
Mackintosh, 229
Mackworth-Praed, 165
Maclatchy, 65
Makking, 210
Malbrant, 54, 65
Marshall, 147, 190, 280, 283, 290, 310, 312, 314
Mascher, 316
Matthews, 322, 323, 324, 325, 326, 327, 340, 347, 351, 352, 356, 357, 358, 361, 362
Mayaud, 40, 61, 64, 80
Meinertzhagen, 217, 218, 223, 224, 225, 283, 284, 380, 385
Meise, 338
Menner, 339
Mennig, 281
Merkel, 254, 255, 256, 289, 294, 295, 296, 298, 299, 301
Mewalt, 289, 297
Middendorf, 233
Mildenberger, 217
Miller, A. H., 280, 311
Miner, Jack, 19
Miskimen, 246
Misonne, 93
Montgomery, H. H., 191, 350
Moreau, 87, 91, 93, 214, 252, 291, 311
Morley, 318
Morris, 297
Mortensen, H. C. C., 18, 20
Morton, Charles, 8
Murphy, R. C., 55, 175, 182, 183, 189, 199, 201
Murray, 171

Natorp, 240
Naumann, 289, 294
Newman, 13, 129, 225, 242
Nice, 121, 296, 317, 318
Niethammer, 96, 380
Nisbet, 316

Odum, 297
Olaus Magnus, 5, 281
Oliver, 150
Olsson, 47
Orgel, 338
Otterlind, 372
Oviedo, 7

Palmgren, 254, 256, 289, 293
Panouse, 54, 55, 56
Papi, 354
Pardi, 354
Paulian, 177, 185, 205, 206
Pearson, 279
Peiponen, XIII
Percy, Lord William, 20
Perdeck, 330, 331, 333
Petersen, 280
Peterson, R. T., 115
Philippi, 99, 138
Pinchon, 169
Platt, 345
Pliny, 3
Pontopiddan, 8
Pratt, 351, 356
Prévost, J., 23, 301
Prill, 200
Puchalski, 324
Pumphrey, 338, 339
Putzig, 303, 320
Pynnönen, 213

RABAUD, 341
Rand, 163, 165
Rautenberg, 297
Raynor, 246, 316
Reetz, 82, 83
Reinikainen, 264, 266
Reitz, XVIII
Rendahl, 82
Rice, 324, 326
Riddle, 302
Riley, 311
Rintoul, 242
Roberts, Austin, 54
Roberts, Brian, 144, 172, 178, 182
Robertson, 146
Rollo, 312
Rougeot, 162, 172
Rousselot, 57
Roux, F., XVI
Rowan, 285, 286, 289, 291, 292, 305, 306, 307, 310, 311, 329, 347
Rudebeck, 88, 89
Rüppell, 36, 253, 322, 323, 324, 325, 326, 327, 329, 330, 331, 347, 361
Rydzewski, 18, 36, 47

SABINEVSKII, 41
Saint Paul, 351, 355, 356
Salomonsen, 373, 382, 383, 384, 385
Santschi, 354
Sapin-Jaloustre, 23, 199
Sauer, VIII, IX, 314, 366, 367, 368, 369, 370
Schäffer, E., 284
Schenk, 240, 241
Schevareva, 40
Schierer, 51
Schifferli, 325, 326
Schildmacher, 289, 290
Schilling, 80
Schmidthoffen, Tschusi von, 268
Scholander, 128, 169
Schott, 184
Schuster, 233
Schüz, 39, 40, 46, 51, 53, 65, 70, 71, 84, 93, 212, 321, 361
Schwartz, P., XV
Schweppenburg, Geyr von, 207, 208, 209
Scott, Peter, 25, 31, 32
Sedgwick, 147
Seebohm, 285
Seilkopf, 251
Semenov, 41
Serle, 66
Serventy, 144, 147, 148, 189, 190, 191, 283, 314, 388
Shank, 311
Sharland, 145
Shelford, 274, 275
Sibson, 148
Siebenaler, 130
Sieh, 247, 248
Siivonen, 270, 272, 293
Simmons, 258
Skinner, 340
Skovgaard, 53
Skutch, 105, 114, 136
Sladen, 21, 22
Sliwinsky, 233, 234, 235
Smith, 302, 338
Snellman, 250
Snyder, 372
Soresen, 196
Southern, 66, 234, 237, 238, 325
Spaepen, 325
Spallanzani, 9
Speirs, 110
Spencer, 27
Spruce, 168
Sprunt, 117, 119
Stanford, 186
Stanislaus, 80
Stein, 150
Steinbacher, G., 290
Stevenson, 130
Stewart, D., 200
Stewart, R. E., 128
Stewart, Geis and Evans, 134
Stickney, 203, 205
Stonehouse, 193
Storer, 217, 260

Storr, 175, 176
Stresemann, 84, 85, 96, 148, 205, 220, 221, 222, 284
Sudilovskaia, 268
Sumner, 296, 297
Sutter, Ernst, VIII, 15, 16, 255, 363
Svärdson, 209, 212, 214, 277
Swarth, 381, 382

Taverner, P. A., 33
Temminck, 191
Thauzies, 332, 359
Thienemann, Joh., 30
Thomson, 12, 32, 41, 42, 44, 62, 221, 253, 320
Thouless, 356
Ticehurst, 48
Tickell, 22
Tinbergen, 77, 78, 210, 225, 226, 228, 230, 345
Tugarinow, 284

Udvardy, M. D. F., 69

Välikangas, 320, 321, 372
Valverde, 59, 73
Van Rossem, 136
Van Sanden, 261
Verheyen, 50, 54, 65, 68, 85, 86, 261
Vestergren, 82
Viguier, 332
Vleugel, 228, 346, 362
Vogt, 183
Voous, 245

Wagner, 6, 257, 289, 293, 297
Wallace, 138, 282, 385
Warga, 270
Waterhouse, 75
Weaver, 120
Wegener, 377, 378
Weigold, Hugo, 31, 39, 70, 252
Westernhagen, 229, 257
Wetmore, A., 98, 141
Wheeler, 171
Wichert, 51
Wilk, 311
Wilkinson, 322, 347
Williams, 130, 131, 250, 267, 314
Williamson, 202, 209, 242, 243, 244, 245, 246, 383
Willughby, 8
Wimsatt, 325
Witherby, H. F., 32
Wodzicki, 150, 324
Wojtusiak, 363
Wolf, 339
Wolfson, 297, 304, 306, 307, 308, 309, 310, 311, 315, 316, 377, 378
Wuczeticz, 284
Wynne-Edwards, 174, 175, 188, 336, 337

Yeagley, IX, 332, 334, 335, 336, 337, 338, 339
Young, 65, 177

Zedlitz, 295
Zimmer, J. T., 141, 167, 168